D1591813

The Raymond and Frances Bushell Collection of

Netsuke

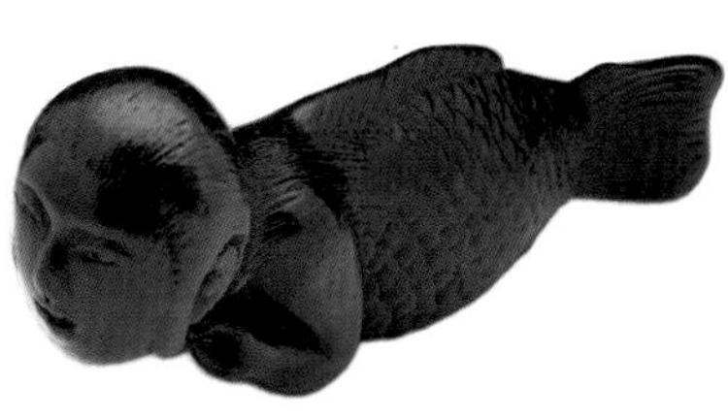

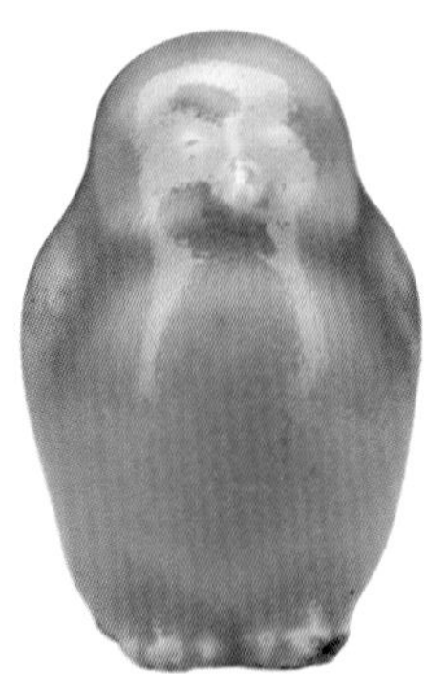

The Raymond and Frances Bushell Collection of

Netsuke

A Legacy
at the Los Angeles County Museum of Art

Acknowledgments by Frances Bushell

Hollis Goodall
with
Virginia G. Atchley
Neil K. Davey
Christine Drosse
Sebastian Izzard
Odile Madden
Robert T. Singer

Art Media Resources
CHICAGO, ILLINOIS

All photographs of netsuke in this book are by the Photographic Services Department of the Los Angeles County Museum of Art and are copyright © 2003 by Museum Associates/LACMA. Additional photographs and illustrations for Odile Madden's essay (pp. 76–91) were provided courtesy of the individuals and institutions credited below:

Diagram reproduced courtesy of Art Media Resources, Inc.: fig. 3.
Photographs by Adam Avila: figs. 8a, 8b, 9a, 10, 11a, 19 (detail), 26.
Photographs by Odile Madden: figs. 4a, 5a, 5b, 6a, 17, 20, 22, 25a.
Photograph by and reproduced courtesy of Dr. Jeheskel Shoshani: fig. 2.
Drawing by Jill Ball reproduced courtesy of UCLA Fowler Museum of Cultural History: fig. 1.

Most photographs are reproduced courtesy of the creators and lenders of the material depicted. For certain artwork and documentary photographs, we have been unable to trace copyright holders. We would appreciate notification of additional credits for acknowledgment in future editions.

JACKET FRONT AND BACK: *Dancing Fox* (CAT. 239)
FRONT FLAP: *Moon-Shaped Rabbit* (CAT. 286); *Woman Blackening Teeth* (CAT. 622)
BACK FLAP: *Demon with Spiked Club* (CAT. 135)
SPINE: *Fox Disguised As Priest* (CAT. 241)
PAGE 1: *Kappa and Clam* (CAT. 252)
PAGE 2: (TOP ROW, LEFT TO RIGHT) *Chinese Lion Mask* (CAT. 765); *Mermaid* (CAT. 218); *Raconteur* (CAT. 587); *Gourd* (CAT. 715); *Camellia* (CAT. 483); *Toy Dog* (CAT. 729); *Shōjō the Sea Sprite in Sake Bowl* (CAT. 260); *Snail on Well Bucket* (CAT. 459); *Fukurokuju: God of Wisdom* (CAT. 166)
PAGE 3: (TOP ROW, LEFT TO RIGHT) *Plover* (CAT. 382); *Female Daruma Doll* (CAT. 603); *Standing Doll* (CAT. 735); *Entertainers* (CAT. 589); *Tea Bowl and Whisk* (CAT. 706); *Suisai* (CAT. 259); *Bat on Roof Tile* (CAT. 366); *"No Evil" Monkey* (CAT. 561); *Owl* (CAT. 378)
PAGE 4: *Inrō, ojime, and netsuke* (CAT. 832)
PAGE 5: *Zodiac Animals* (CAT. 345)
PAGE 7: *Cicada* (CAT. 472)

Published by
Art Media Resources, Inc.
Chicago, Illinois
www.artmediaresources.com
and
Los Angeles County Museum of Art
5905 Wilshire Boulevard
Los Angeles, California 90036

EDITED BY Jennifer Boynton
DESIGN BY Sandy Bell Design
CARTOGRAPHY BY David Fuller, DLF Group, Santa Barbara, California
TYPESETTING BY G & S Typesetters, Inc., Austin, Texas
PRODUCTION BY The Actualizers, New York, New York
PRINTED BY Arti Grafiche Amilcare Pizzi S.pA., Milan, Italy

LIBRARY OF CONGRESS CATALOGING-IN-PUBLICATION DATA

The Raymond and Frances Bushell collection of netsuke : a legacy at the Los Angeles County Museum of Art / acknowledgments, Frances Bushell ; Hollis Goodall ... [et al.].
p. cm.
Includes bibliographic references and index.
ISBN 1-58886-034-5 (hardcover) — ISBN 1-58886-035-3 (softcover)
1. Netsukes—Catalogs. 2. Bushell, Raymond—Art collections—Catalogs. 3. Bushell, Frances—Art collections—Catalogs. 4. Netsukes—Private collections—California—Los Angeles—Catalogs. 5. Los Angeles County Museum of Art—Catalogs. I. Goodall, Hollis. II. Los Angeles County Museum of Art.

NK6050.R39 2003
736'.68'07479494—DC21

2003041931

I would like to dedicate this scholarly book to the memory of my dear husband, Raymond; it was made possible through the efforts of Robert Singer and the book's knowledgeable staff, to whom I am deeply grateful.
—Frances Bushell

Contents

Frances Bushell

MY PART IN RAYMOND'S LIFE comes very late, when he was forty-two. We met through a Japanese priest with whom Ray happened to start a conversation on the platform of a tram going to Kyoto. This was a few days after landing his boat at Wakayama. Ray of course wanted to see the famous city of Kyoto, which had been spared bombing. The priest told Ray that he knew a Japanese girl, born in the United States, who spoke English. And who worked in the U.S. army personnel section. Naturally Ray was curious and peeked into my office. In those days, Ray kept a sort of off-and-on diary. Much later, when we were dating, I peeked into his diary. His comment upon having seen me was that I had "possibilities." Eventually, in 1952, we were married, and I consider myself the luckiest and happiest girl ever; that is, until 1998, when Ray passed away. Now I only have his urn, which I keep in his study, where I can greet him every morning and say goodnight every night.

Acknowledgments

As we were getting to know each other, I discovered Ray's deep fascination with Japanese art, particularly with netsuke. I had a few netsuke of my own, so I understood his interest in this miniature art form.

I am very excited, pleased, and thrilled that our gift to the Los Angeles County Museum of Art of more than eight hundred netsuke is featured in its own catalogue. This scholarly book begins with my admiration for and deep gratitude to my longtime friend from the Tokyo days, Robert T. Singer, LACMA's curator of Japanese art. Thanks to his encouragement, this book for me is a dream come true. My deep gratitude extends to a true scholar, Hollis Goodall, LACMA's associate curator of Japanese art. I would like to emphasize that, in my opinion, Hollis knows the netsuke better than Raymond, because for years she has organized the netsuke exhibitions at the museum, which are changed every few months!

ŌHARA MITSUHIRO
(Japan, 1810–1875)
Gingko Nut
ivory with sumi
AC1998.249.305
CAT. 720

I thank Jeffrey Moy, who has nurtured this project from the beginning. Everyone should have someone like Jeffrey in his or her life—a true friend and advisor. I thank Jeffrey for his wise counsel and integrity.

I would like to thank those who contributed essays to the catalogue. Hollis Goodall, in addition to her section introductions and hundreds of object descriptions, wrote extensively on the vast topic of netsuke in the Edo period. Virginia Atchley, past president of the International Netsuke Society and author of several articles about netsuke and inrō, provided the introduction to netsuke as well as object descriptions. Neil K. Davey, of Sotheby's London, wrote about Raymond's favorite netsuke and his lifelong involvement in the field. Neil also made several trips to Los Angeles from London to review the collection, and his connoisseurship was an invaluable asset to this project. Sebastian Izzard, who is very knowledgeable about Japanese art—especially netsuke, paintings, and *ukiyo-e*—discussed the wealth of netsuke by later carvers in the Bushell collection. Conservator Odile Madden's essay on the techniques used to fabricate ivory netsuke fills a void in netsuke scholarship. Robert T. Singer recounted the history of our long and successful relationship with LACMA, to which this catalogue is a splendid tribute.

I would also like to thank the following people for their long hours of assistance: Adam Avila, conservation photographer at LACMA, who shot the wonderful details of the netsuke for Odile's essay; Christine Drosse, curatorial administrator in LACMA's Department of Japanese Art, who wrote many object descriptions, compiled the artist signature section, and performed innumerable other tasks with consummate thoroughness, focus, and attention to detail; Tom Harper; Robert Haynes, who provided invaluable assistance with metalwork netsuke; Rika Hiro, research assistant in LACMA's Department of Costume and Textiles, who patiently researched and compiled the Japanese names of netsuke artists in the signature section; Robert Hori, board and donor relations director of Los Angeles's Japanese American Cultural and Community Center, who spent many hours reading seals and inscriptions; Makiko Komada, with the Netsuke Kenkyūkai in Japan, who provided biographical information on carvers and translations of inscriptions; Paul Moss, proprietor of Sydney L. Moss Ltd., London, who reviewed text in its nascent stages and made invaluable comments; LACMA photographer Steve Oliver, who took such exquisite photographs of the netsuke and their signatures and seals; Doreen Simmons, television sumo commentator, who reviewed the sumo netsuke; and Yasuhiro Yoshida, Oriental Art Taihaku, Kyoto, who also spent a great amount of time deciphering seals and inscriptions.

This magnificent book is due primarily to the Herculean efforts and immense talents of two people: editor Jennifer Boynton and designer Sandy Bell. Jennifer Boynton has skillfully organized and edited a vast amount of material, and Sandy Bell has designed the most beautiful book on netsuke ever.

Robert T. Singer

Raymond Bushell collected netsuke for more than fifty years; in his own words, it was his "private addiction and monomania." He was both the leading collector and leading scholar of netsuke, with many books, countless articles, and a long-running journal column to his credit. He supported modern carvers financially to help them resume their work after the war; he encouraged and instructed younger collectors; and he worked unceasingly to bring netsuke to a broader audience.

I once asked Raymond how many netsuke he had owned over the years, and he replied, "Over ten thousand." In the late 1970s, he decided to give a group of about 650 netsuke to a museum, either in Japan or the United States, to be known as the Raymond and Frances Bushell Collection of Netsuke. In his expert opinion, this group was comprehensive in both breadth and depth: it contained examples of every period, school, artist, subject matter, and material, and each netsuke was a masterpiece of its kind.

Raymond wrote two articles discussing his attempts to arrange the donation of this incomparable collection. Reading them, one gets a wonderful sense of his cautious, careful, and eminently judicious character. His background as a lawyer stood him in good stead, and his every action was logical and reasoned. Raymond knew exactly what he wanted to donate—a permanent gift that could not be broken up and sold, which would be on view to the public throughout the year—and he was prepared to work with any eligible candidate. He relates that the major Japanese museums showed little interest when he insisted on a permanent exhibition of a rotating selection of the collection. In Japan at that time, netsuke were still considered a "minor decorative art," much as *ukiyo-e* had been until their discovery by Europeans in the late 1800s.

Raymond and Frances Bushell and the Los Angeles County Museum of Art

Raymond goes on to describe pilgrimages to several American museums, including the Brooklyn Museum of Art, the Freer Gallery of Art, and the Metropolitan Museum of Art. The stumbling block at these museums, however, was their reluctance to consider a permanent gift, with no possibility of future deaccession.

Raymond was introduced to the Los Angeles County Museum of Art (LACMA) through the kind offices of scholar Julia Meech. Raymond's initial discussions were held with LACMA's George Kuwayama, then senior curator of Far Eastern art, who organized an exhibition of Raymond's netsuke in 1984. That exhibition, one of the most popular in the museum's history, not only convinced Raymond that Los Angeles appreciated his collection but also convinced the museum that it should do all it could to secure this treasure. Negotiations were conducted by LACMA's director at that time, Earl A. ("Rusty") Powell III, in close collaboration with George Kuwayama.

In early 1988, I was brought to LACMA by Rusty Powell to be the founding curator of the Pavilion for Japanese Art, and I was soon introduced to Raymond and his wife, Frances. Negotiations for the collection continued, and I became part of them. It is true that museums are often loath to accept a permanent donation and the restrictions such a gift entails, but I argued that Raymond's collection, already a distillation of the finest netsuke collection ever formed, certainly warranted acceptance. The beauty of such a gift is that all the work has been done: in this case, the world's leading expert on netsuke had spent fifty years honing his collection. While others at the museum were concerned about what Raymond called his "policy of gradualism"—the netsuke were donated in increments over time—he and I had developed such a relationship of mutual trust that I counseled patience.

FIG. 1
Kaigyokusai Masatsugu
(Japan, 1813–1892)
Floating Crane
ivory with staining, sumi, inlays
M.91.250.339
CAT. 370

In the end, any worries proved groundless. Because the collection had not yet been formally given in full, Raymond continued to search for the perfect "missing" netsuke to add to it. He would bring near-priceless netsuke to LACMA in little plastic baggies placed inside brown paper lunch bags . . . to the horror of the museum's security and conservation staffs. I will never forget the day he met with Rusty and me, casually placing on the table one of the jewels of the collection, Kaigyokusai Masatsugu's legendary *Floating Crane* (FIG. 1). He had pursued this piece for decades. Long held by several generations of a Kyoto family, it had come up at auction, where it was the subject of a bidding war. As Raymond said to us that day, "I had to obtain it because of its quality and importance to the collection."

In the last year of his life, I made numerous visits to the Bushells' San Francisco home, where Raymond and I would make countless lists to refine the final gift. After Raymond's death in January 1998, Frances and I continued to work together, and the gift was completed in 1998, bringing the total number of netsuke close to 850. In the mid-1990s, Raymond wrote: "I am terribly pleased with LACMA. . . . If LACMA is beholden to me for a generous donation, my wife and I are beholden to LACMA for its accommodation and cooperation. Were we given a second chance to choose a home for our netsuke, we could not make a better choice."

I was honored to know Raymond Bushell and to work with him. His connoisseurship, his integrity, and his generosity are an inspiration. Raymond and Frances have left an enduring legacy to the museum and to the people of Los Angeles.

Neil K. Davey

Raymond Bushell: A Life in Netsuke

Raymond Bushell was born in 1910, in New York. After completing his undergraduate education, he studied law at the University of Virginia and went on to become a highly successful international lawyer.

In September 1945, he traveled to Japan as captain of an air-sea rescue boat in the American armed forces. To make use of his training in law, he was drafted to work as a legal assistance officer with the occupation forces in Kyoto. He became immediately enamored with the country, its people, and especially with its arts. He decided to stay, setting up home in Tokyo in 1948, where he entered into a partnership with Shin Asahina as a lawyer of repute in the Marunouchi district of that city.

Soon after he landed, he met the lovely Frances Numano, who was later to become his wife (FIG. 1). Raymond and Frances began collecting in earnest, and it is in his role as collector and author that Raymond is perhaps best known and remembered. From the time he arrived in Japan, Raymond combined his work in law with the intensive study of art, particularly the miniature arts of Japan, and thus began the enormous collection that he later used as illustrative examples in his eight books covering various aspects of netsuke, inrō, and lacquer. It is not known exactly how large the collection eventually became, but conservative estimates enumerate more than fifty-five hundred total netsuke, as well as inrō, pipe cases, sword fittings, Chinese snuff bottles, and jade carvings. There is no doubt that many more found their way into his hands and were subsequently replaced by better examples or simply sold to fund new acquisitions.

His collection started with one netsuke, purchased in the New Osaka Hotel gift shop shortly after he arrived in Japan in 1945. From that time onward, he studied netsuke with great zeal, visiting the few extant dealers and collectors in Japan and corresponding with others around the world. Raymond was a prodigious writer of letters and exchanged correspondence with many of the great collectors of the third quarter of the twentieth century, including Frederick Meinertzhagen, William Winkworth, Julius Katchen, Avery Brundage, U. A. Casal, Joseph Seo, M. T. Hindson, Cornelius Roosevelt, and V. F. Weber.

This group of friends served a dual purpose for the developing collector. Firstly, they all helped to increase each other's knowledge of netsuke and, secondly, they discovered where the great netsuke of the world were situated. In 1963, Raymond wrote to one friend that he was trying to learn the names and addresses of netsuke collectors throughout the world. Having eventually acquired the names of these people, he would write to them and find out their particular interests. When he needed to weed out pieces from his collection, Raymond would get in touch again, advising them of particular netsuke in which he already knew that they would have an interest.

RAYMOND BUSHELL, THE AUTHOR

Having studied the subject of netsuke in great depth, Raymond decided that he wished to share his knowledge with existing and future collectors. His first book, published in 1961, was *The Netsuke Handbook of Ueda Reikichi*, adapted from two of Ueda's books, *Netsuke no kenkyū* and *Shūbi no netsuke*, and profusely illustrated with netsuke from Raymond's own collection. He followed this with two small books for beginners, *The Wonderful World of Netsuke* (1964) and *An Introduction to Netsuke* (1971). Having completed those, he apparently felt compelled to continue to write books on netsuke, but only if he had something new to say that had not hitherto been published. Thus, he continued with *Collectors' Netsuke* (1971); *Netsuke Familiar and Unfamiliar* (1975); *The Inrō Handbook* (1979); *The Art of Netsuke Carving* by Masatoshi, as told to Raymond Bushell; and *Netsuke Masks*, completed in 1985. All of these books dealt with different aspects of the subject, each treated in a new and, in some cases, deeply personal manner. During this time, he also wrote numerous scholarly articles for several international journals, including *Arts of Asia*, the *Journal of the International Netsuke Collectors Society*, and the *Netsuke Kenkyūkai Study Journal* (later, the *International Netsuke Society Journal*); for the latter two publications, he regularly wrote a column called "Questions and Answers," in which he replied to queries sent in by collectors from around the world. In all, he adroitly fielded questions in more than ninety columns. His articles were meticulously written, and an editor's delight. There is hardly a punctuation mark out of place or a grammatical error in any of his books or articles, all of which were composed in a flowing manner, with not a hint of the legalese to which he would have been accustomed in his work.

FIG. 1
Raymond Bushell and his devoted wife, Frances, at their home in San Francisco. Photograph courtesy Frances Bushell.

Perhaps the most cogent illustration of the seriousness with which he viewed netsuke can be seen in *Netsuke Familiar and Unfamiliar*. This remarkable work divided netsuke into forty-five categories covering a wide range of subjects—including rare artists, materials, treatment of particular themes, seals, and religions—and it gives us the greatest insight into the author's mind, which appeared capable of absorbing every imaginable aspect of the genre.

Raymond was also completely unafraid to speak (or write) his mind. *Netsuke Familiar and Unfamiliar* bears a long introduction, entitled "Principles for Collecting," which incorporates his personal thoughts and ideas. In this, he ventured boldly into the financial realm of netsuke, discussing historical collections and their sales, and the justification for prices attained at auction or demanded by dealers. He wrote about fads and trends in collecting and about assessing netsuke, and he proffered views on learning about netsuke, giving invaluable advice on a wide range of topics to assist both new and experienced collectors.

RAYMOND BUSHELL, THE COLLECTOR

When looking over the huge number of netsuke that Raymond acquired—through illustrations in his books and catalogues of exhibitions, those that have been sold at auction and those that are illustrated in these pages—it is difficult to discern a pattern to his collecting, and perhaps there is none. Obviously, he was partial to some styles and individual artists, but there are also many netsuke that one might best describe as "quirky." Although the collection incorporates a large number of standard types (FIGS. 2 and 3), it also contains many rarities: subjects that were hitherto unrecorded in the genre (FIGS. 4 and 5); artists who produced comparatively few works (FIG. 6); or materials that were hardly ever used, such as glass.

FIG. 2
Ōhara Mitsuhiro
(Japan, 1810–1875)
Gourd-Shaped Sake Cup
ivory with light staining, sumi
AC1998.249.81
CAT. 713

FIG. 3
Hokkyō Sessai (Japan, 1820–1879)
Snake
wood with inlays
AC1998.249.41
CAT. 310

FIG. 4, FRONT AND SIDES
Mermaid and Monkey
Japan, late 19th–early 20th century
wood with inlays
AC1998.249.73
CAT. 220

A few years ago, Raymond was asked to select his favorite netsuke from those he had given to the Los Angeles County Museum of Art (LACMA). He subsequently produced a list of 150 netsuke from which one can glean no further insight into his taste. (All the netsuke used to illustrate this essay are from this list of Raymond's favorites.) Included are worn, old netsuke by artists such as Tanaka Minkō of Tsu (FIG. 7) and followers of

FIG. 5
Decapitated Woman's Head
Japan, 19th century
boxwood with inlays
AC1998.249.123
CAT. 689

FIG. 6
KOKEISAI SANSHŌ
(Japan, 1871–1936)
Entertainer Playing Turtle
boxwood, ivory with staining, sumi
AC1998.249.234
CAT. 590

FIG. 7
Tanaka Minkō (Japan, 1735–1816)
Foreign Drum Master
wood with inlays
AC1998.249.65
CAT. 42

Yoshimura Shūzan of Osaka (FIG. 8); supreme examples by artists from the major netsuke-producing centers, such as Ryūsai of Edo (FIG. 9); as well as fine examples by the myriad anonymous carvers who worked in the seventeenth and early eighteenth centuries (FIGS. 10, 11, and 12). These show a marked contrast to the highly sophisticated and delicate works (FIG. 13) produced in the Meiji period (1868–1912) and beyond. He never forgot netsuke that he had failed to acquire in his early days of collecting, due presumably to lack of ready funds, and if these netsuke appeared on the market in subsequent years, he did not hesitate to bid highly. One such example is the study of a floating crane by Kaigyokusai (CAT. 370, illustrated on p. 13). Raymond was unable to buy this when it was sold in Japan in the early 1950s to the renowned collector-dealer Imai Kenzō of Kyoto. However, when it appeared at auction in 1990, Raymond purchased it for a considerably higher price and immediately reserved it to be added to the donation to LACMA.

FIG. 8, FRONT AND BACK
After Yoshimura Shūzan
(Japan, late 18th–19th century)
Demon
soft wood with pigments
M.87.263.89
CAT. 137

9

9 BACK

10

FIG. 9, FRONT AND BACK
Ryūsai (Japan, active late 18th century)
Foreign Archer with Monkey
wood with inlays
M.91.250.30
CAT. 43

FIG. 10
Heavenly Spirit: Karyōbinga
Japan, 18th century
ivory with dark staining, sumi
AC1998.249.110
CAT. 160

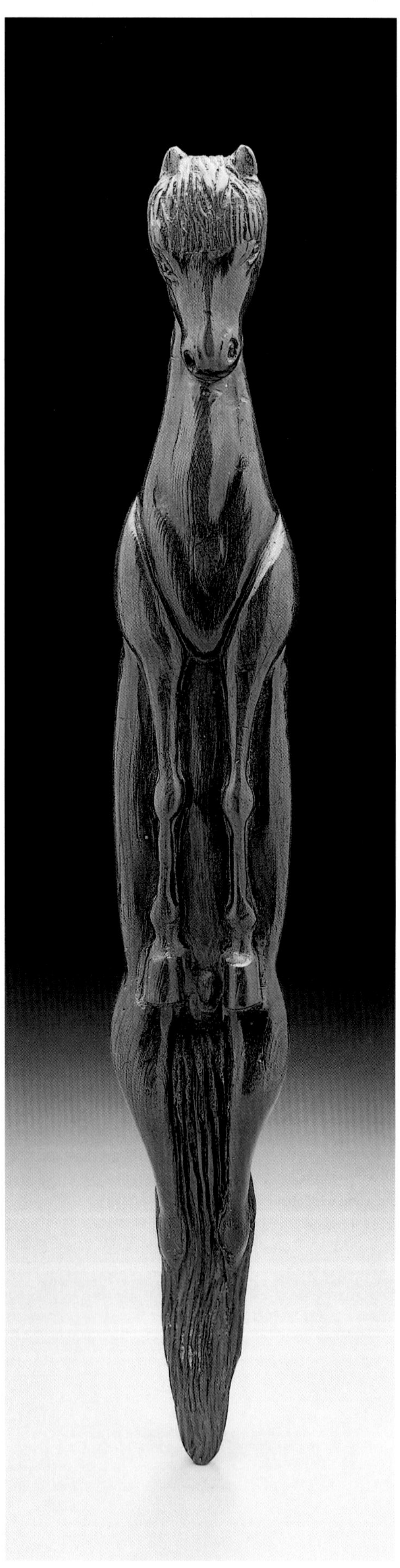

FIG. 11
Vertical Horse
Japan, 18th century
wood with inlays; sashi type
AC1998.249.67
CAT. 311

FIG. 12
Seiōbo: Queen Mother of the West
Japan, 18th century
ivory with staining, sumi, inlays
M.91.250.11
CAT. 56

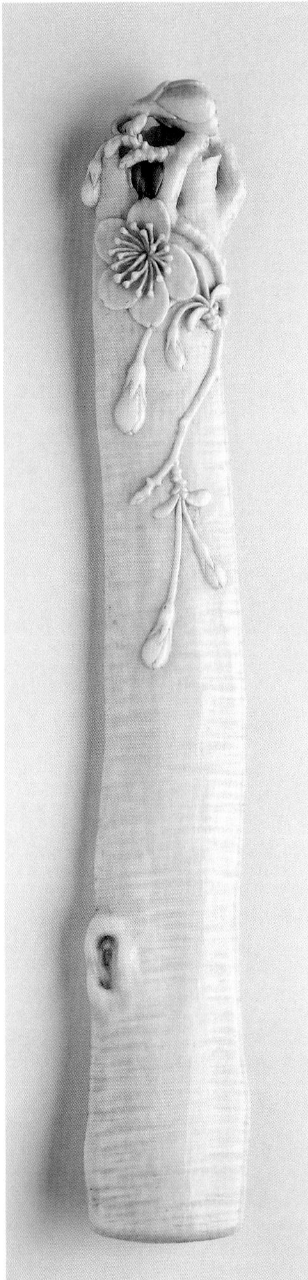

13

Raymond, having an eye for quality in carving, was much taken with the netsuke produced by what came to be known as the Sō School and became acquainted with the last member of that group, Ōuchi Sōsui (FIG. 14), and with Shōko (Nishino Shōtarō). He made an arrangement with them in which he would act as a patron or sponsor, contracting to buy a certain number of their netsuke for agreed sums. This worked to great advantage for all parties, in that Sōsui and Shōko had a ready market for their netsuke while Raymond was able to build a fine collection of their works, along with netsuke from other members of the school. Later, he befriended the fine artist Kūya (Nakamura Shinzō) and his son Masatoshi (Nakamura Tokisada) and eventually initiated a similar arrangement with Masatoshi (FIG. 15).

In the early 1990s, a slightly acrimonious debate about the pros and cons of donating netsuke to museums appeared in the pages of the *Netsuke Kenkyūkai Study Journal*, and it continued for about a year. The final word, with good reason, was left to Raymond Bushell. He wrote a long article in the winter 1993 issue of the *Journal* stating his reasons for selling during his lifetime and for leaving part of his collection to a museum, in particular to the Los Angeles County Museum of Art. He said that he initially chose that museum because George Kuwayama, then senior curator of Far Eastern art, was open to his requirement that the donated pieces be on permanent display, on a rotating basis, with the exhibit changing every four months. Although this has entailed additional work for the museum's staff, we can be grateful to them for agreeing to his request. However, our gratitude is directed more to Raymond and Frances for their great gift, which allows us as well as future students to learn from and enjoy the netsuke displayed.

15

14

FIG. 13
Sōko (Morita Kisaburō)
(Japan, 1879–1943)
Plum Branch and Blossoms
ivory with staining, lacquer inlay;
sashi type
M.91.250.79
CAT. 485

FIG. 14
Ōuchi Sōsui (Japan, 1911–1972)
Chinese Lion Dance
wood
AC1998.249.98
CAT. 597

FIG. 15
Masatoshi (Nakamura
Tokisada) (Japan, 1915–2001)
Sea Cow and Young
December 1964
boxwood with inlays
M.91.250.97
CAT. 433

Virginia G. Atchley

Netsuke and Inrō: An Introduction

FIG. 1
Inrō, ojime, and netsuke
Japan, late 18th–early 19th century
inrō, saya type: lacquer, metal flecks
ojime: coral
netsuke, manjū type: ivory
AC1998.249.325
CAT. 831

WHAT IS A NETSUKE? Basically a netsuke (*ne-tsuke*; literally, "root attachment" and pronounced "nets-keh") is a Japanese toggle used to support an object that is attached to it, such as an inrō (FIG. 1). Because Japanese clothing had no pockets, small items were carried by tucking them inside the wide sash (*obi*) of the woman's kimono, by suspending them from the narrow obi of the man's kimono, or by placing them in the kimono's large sleeves. Netsuke developed out of necessity: men had to carry things as they went about their daily affairs. The objects carried, called *sagemono* ("hanging objects"), were suspended from braided silk cords. The cords ran under the obi and were attached and knotted to the netsuke, which rested atop the obi, holding the sagemono securely in place.

Men carried many items in this fashion—purses, smoking utensils, and writing cases—but one of the most widely used and the most beautiful and varied was the inrō, a nest of boxes, cleverly fitted together, for holding medicines and seals (FIG. 2). A sliding bead, the *ojime*, was threaded through the cords between the netsuke and the inrō to allow the wearer to open or close the boxes.

Toggles were used in many countries, wherever a belt or sash was an integral part of the costume, but the Japanese netsuke is unique because it developed from a simple utilitarian article into a sophisticated art form. Craftsmanship, carving skill, and original design were important to the Japanese, who have always seemed instinctively to desire that their objects be beautiful as well as useful. Individuals selected their netsuke based on subject and suitability of material, as well as artistic considerations such as form, balance, composition, and carving.

Netsuke are classified into a few main types called *manjū, ryūsa, kagamibuta, sashi*, and *katabori*. The manjū is round and flat, like the rice cake of the same name, and decorated with etching or relief carving on the surface. It was either a solid piece or made from two sections that fitted together with the attachment of the cord through a metal ring (FIGS. 3

FIG. 2
A man wearing traditional Japanese costume. The inrō is suspended from braided cords that run under the obi. The netsuke is attached to the cords and rests on top of the obi, holding the inrō in place.

3

4

FIG. 3
Shunkōsai Chōgetsu
(Japan, 1826–1892)
Tadamori and the Oil Thief
ivory with staining, sumi; manjū type
M.87.263.21
CAT. 526

FIG. 4
Kaigyokusai Masatsugu
(Japan, 1813–1892)
Raijin: God of Thunder
ivory with staining; manjū type
M.87.263.34
CAT. 139

FIG. 5
Ryūkō (Japan, active mid-19th century)
Confronting Dragons
ivory with staining, sumi; ryūsa type
M.87.263.39
CAT. 304

FIG. 6
Ozawa Shūraku
(Japan, 1830–after 1878)
Hitomaro: The Classic Poet
mixed-metal disk, ivory bowl; kagamibuta type
M.91.250.69
CAT. 550

FIG. 7
Unicorn
Japan, 19th century
wood; sashi type
M.91.250.299
CAT. 257

5

and 4). The ryūsa netsuke—actually a variety of manjū—is hollowed out with deeply carved openwork (FIG. 5). The kagamibuta (literally, "mirror lid"), also usually round in shape, has two parts: a decorated lid, or disk, typically metal, and a bowl of ivory or wood, which sometimes was also elaborately carved (FIG. 6). The sashi netsuke, long and often with cord holes at one end, was worn thrust inside the obi (FIG. 7). The most interesting and certainly the most popular netsuke forms were the katabori or figural netsuke, especially of people and animals, which were carved on all sides, including the bottom (FIGS. 8, 9, and 10).

Although many materials were used to make netsuke, including horn, bone, metal, lacquer, black coral, ceramic, porcelain, mother-of-pearl, tortoiseshell, amber, hard stones, glass, and nuts, 80 percent or more were made from ivory and wood. Japan has a great variety of woods and, although only elephant tusk is considered true ivory, other ivory-like materials include boar tusk, narwhal tusk, and teeth from large mammals. Stag antler was the third most commonly used material.

The average netsuke is approximately one and one-half to two inches on a side. Sizes range from fairly large netsuke to small, delicately carved netsuke. Subjects for netsuke were taken from all spheres of life and lore, and the same subjects could be depicted in myriad ways.

6

7

8

9

10

FIG. 8
Dancing Fox
Japan, 18th century
ivory with dark staining, sumi
AC1998.249.69
CAT. 239

FIG. 9
Chinese Lion Guarding the Jewel of the Buddha
Japan, 18th century
ivory with staining, sumi, inlays
AC1998.249.224
CAT. 199

FIG. 10
Chingendō Hidemasa
(Japan, active early 19th century)
Tadamori and the Oil Thief
ivory with staining, sumi, inlays
M.91.250.38
CAT. 524

FIG. 11
Suzuki Tōkoku
(Japan, 1846–1913)
Cleaning Daruma's Ears
wood with inlays
M.91.250.241
CAT. 122

FIG. 12
Ittan (Japan, circa 1820–1877)
Frustrated Rat Catcher
wood
M.91.250.166
CAT. 613

Some netsuke were boldly simple in design, while others were minutely detailed. They are signed or unsigned in about equal proportion.

Two special qualities of netsuke must be mentioned. The first is the humor they portray. The Japanese have a broad sense of the comic, which the netsuke carver loved to depict (FIGS. 11 and 12). Again and again, he slyly pokes fun at humans and gods, such as the venerable characters of Daruma, Hotei, and Shōki (the demon queller). The humor is pervasive and charming, and often it is downright funny. Rarely, if ever, is it mean-spirited. The second quality, something the artist did not control, is what the Japanese call *aji*: the smoothness, the lustrous patina, the *feel* that results from generations of handling and wear. This is a tactile quality without which, to many collectors, a netsuke is somehow not quite complete (FIG. 13).

The history of netsuke roughly coincides with the dates of the Tokugawa regime (the Edo period; 1615–1868), from the beginning of the seventeenth century, into the Meiji era (1868–1912). Netsuke at first may have been natural objects (for example, a shell, a gourd, or a stone) carefully selected. The earliest netsuke that were created as art as well as functional objects display more attention to design rather than to technical virtuosity, and they are mostly unsigned. The designs were bold and imaginative, and the subjects were taken from the Chinese, for example, the *shishi* (Chinese lion), the Daoist immortals called *sennin* by the Japanese (FIG. 14), mythological creatures such as dragons, and historical characters like the Han generals.

Groups of netsuke carvers, sometimes called schools, developed in different regions of Japan, notably in Osaka, Kyoto, Nagoya, Iwami, and later, Edo (now Tokyo), and each school had its outstanding artists, its favorite subjects, and its particular style of carving. As smoking became nearly universal for all classes of society, the demand for netsuke to support tobacco pouches and pipe sets grew so great that by the late eighteenth century hundreds of carvers were working full time, creating more and more netsuke of fine workmanship. This period, roughly from 1780 to the middle of the 1850s and known as the "golden age of netsuke," produced many of the netsuke that have so delighted Western collectors.

Netsuke are often called miniature sculpture, as the katabori netsuke surely are. But while sculpture in general is a free art form, the *netsukeshi*, as the carvers are called, had to create and then carve under limitations imposed by how the netsuke were to be used. A netsuke had to be small or slender enough to pass between the obi and the kimono, strong enough to support the weight of the object to which it was attached, sufficiently durable to withstand the rubbing of daily wear, and smooth enough that its parts would neither break off nor tear through the fabric of the kimono and obi. Also, because a netsuke was expected to be handled and admired, it had to be finished in the round, and the carver had to keep in mind the effect his netsuke would give when worn. Lastly, and by no means least, the netsuke required a hole, called *himotōshi* (FIG. 15), through which the cords attached to the sagemono could pass and be knotted. Himotōshi had to be placed so that the hole openings did not mar the design and so that the netsuke would hang naturally, with the face or best side visible, while being comfortable for the wearer. Sometimes the carver could use a natural opening in the design, such as the crook of an elbow or the space between a seated animal's leg and body, for the cords to pass through, but in most cases it was necessary to carve himotōshi.

To offset these design restrictions, the netsuke carver had one glorious freedom. Unfettered either by academic canons or bonds of tradition, he was free to choose his subject, his material, his design, and his style. He had to please only himself and his patron. His ingenuity, imagination, and originality, in addition to the sense of humor already mentioned, give his art its

FIG. 13
Baku: Monster That Eats Nightmares
Japan, 18th century
ivory with staining, sumi
M.91.250.270
CAT. 216

FIG. 14
Daoist with Gourd
Japan, 18th century
ivory with staining, sumi
M.91.250.298
CAT. 65

FIG. 15, FRONT AND BACK
Chinese Boy with Puppy
Japan, mid-19th century
wood
M.91.250.131
CAT. 176

FIG. 16
Hara Yōyūsai (Japan, 1772–1845)
Inrō, ojime, and netsuke
inrō: lacquer, mixed metals
ojime: coral
netsuke: wood, horn and ivory inlays
AC1998.249.307
CAT. 829

distinction. As a result, all aspects of Japanese life can be found in netsuke. One cannot be a serious collector without learning much about Japan and its people: its history, legends, myths, demonology, gods, fairy tales, and folktales; its culture (drama, dance, music) and occupations; its customs and daily life; and its flora and fauna, including imaginary as well as real animals.

One of the earliest collectors of netsuke wrote:

> No objects of art found in Japan are more essentially Japanese whether their range of fanciful motives be considered, or the extraordinary dexterity of their carvers, or their originality. It is scarcely possible to possess too many netsuke. The range of conception is so large, the motives display such a wealth of fancy, realistic, conventional, grave, humorous, and grotesque, that the collector perpetually finds some new source of admiration, instruction, or amusement.[1]

Inrō encompass an endless variety of subject matter and techniques. Of the many forms taken by Japanese lacquer, the inrō is one of the loveliest. It exemplifies the hundreds of techniques devised by Japanese lacquerers over the centuries, through the careful preparation of the basic frame and the numerous coats of prime and base lacquers, to the last exquisite detail of the artist's design. The Japanese inrō may well be the finest miniature lacquer ever produced, a utilitarian object of extreme beauty that was highly prized by the Japanese (FIG. 16).

With the opening of Japan in 1868 and the accompanying swift westernization of styles of living and dress during the Meiji era, the use of netsuke inevitably declined. Some artists in the Tokyo area, notably the famous Sō School (FIGS. 17 and 18), continued to produce meticulously carved netsuke for use by wealthy Japanese, but in general netsuke were no longer needed. At this time of vast change for Japan, Westerners discovered and fell in love with these small objects, and the making of netsuke for collectors rather than for users continued to furnish a livelihood for some carvers into the twentieth century. Today, as a result of an increasing and widespread interest in netsuke as highly desirable collectors' items, several contemporary carvers, in Japan as well as in many other countries, are now making netsuke of excellent quality, showing that the old skills in miniature carving have not been lost.

FIG. 18
Ōuchi Gyokusō
(Japan, 1879–1944)
Genroku-Era Urban Sophisticate
wood
AC1998.249.79
CAT. 666

FIG. 17
Sōko (Morita Kisaburō)
(Japan, 1879–1943)
Windblown Peony
wood
M.91.250.78
CAT. 484

1 F. (Frank) Brinkley, *Japan: Its History, Arts, and Literature*, vol. 7 (London: J. B. Millet Co., 1902), pp. 176–77.

Hollis Goodall

FIG. 1
Seal Carved As Southeast Asian–Style Lion
Japan, 17th century
ivory with dark staining, red seal pigment
M.91.250.201
CAT. 691

NETSUKE ARE ARCHETYPAL as functional objects that evolved into an art form adopted by the Japanese from China and initially utilized as talismans and as a potent form of communication through rebus and symbolic association. Like many of the artistic genres in Japan that were taken from Chinese models during the two countries' long association, netsuke diverged from their original uses and style and evolved into an elevated form of aesthetic expression. In his introduction to *The Gō Collection of Netsuke* catalogue for the Tokyo National Museum, curator Arakawa Hirokazu relates what is presently understood of the early history of inrō, describing their introduction to Japan as larger layered boxes for carrying Chinese-style herbal medicines.[1] Looking further into the function of Chinese toggles that acted as counterweights for medicine boxes, or for objects such as flint pouches or money purses, one finds what is clearly the forerunner of the netsuke. There was also considerable interest in Daoism sparked by literature imported to Japan in the early seventeenth century, and the idea that the precursors of netsuke and inrō gained a foothold in Japan at this moment is only logical once their early medicinal and talismanic functions are understood.

Netsuke of the Edo Period (1615–1868)

The Chinese toggle had numerous applications—particularly those of counterweight and medicinal, protective agent—and these were mirrored in early netsuke in Japan. Some toggles were made from roots that had been adapted for use as simple counterweights, or sculpted so that they could also act as curative amulets and as tactile, decorative accessories. These toggles were believed to contain the potent restorative power of the source plant from which they were created.[2] The Japanese word *netsuke* means "root attachment" and derives from the root type of toggle.

Several common styles of toggles, as well as their tactile quality and function, were transferred to netsuke. *Katabori*, *manjū*, and *kagamibuta* netsuke all have precedents among Chinese toggles,[3] and each matured into highly sophisticated art forms in Japan, eventually leaving behind their Chinese folk sources. One type of netsuke that was consciously anachronistic, however, and made specifically to refer to the Chinese toggle style, was the carved figure on a stand (FIG. 1). In netsuke, the plinth itself could be carved as a seal (FIG. 2); or, in some later examples, figures on a plinth could be grouped in tableau to tell a story (FIG. 3).

Japan had had sporadic contact with China throughout the fifteenth and sixteenth centuries in areas of trade and diplomatic exchange. In the 1590s, Toyotomi Hideyoshi (1536–1598), military leader of Japan until his death, led two unsuccessful invasions of the Korean Peninsula. Hideyoshi's rule was followed by the more peaceful Tokugawa shogunate (1615–1868), whose leaders were anxious to learn of developments in China since the founding of the Ming dynasty in 1368, especially in the study of Confucianism, in order to emulate them.[4]

FIG. 2
Seal Carved As Kirin
Japan, 18th century
ivory with staining, sumi, red pigment, inlays
M.87.263.5
CAT. 692

FIG. 3
ONO RYŌMIN
(Japan, active late 19th century)
Kōsekikō and Chōryō
ivory with staining, sumi, inlays
AC1998.249.88
CAT. 510

The seventeenth century became an extremely fruitful period of cultural exchange between the two countries. Japan's reawakened interest in Chinese and Korean culture coincided with a surge in the publication of woodblock-printed books during the reign of China's Wanli Emperor Shenzong (r. 1573–1620). In the study of netsuke, the most important of these are books about Daoist immortals, especially the *Liexuan quanchuan* (J., *Yūshō ressen zenden*; Complete illustrated lives of immortals), imported in 1602 and reprinted in Japan in 1650, and the *Shifo qizong* (J., *Senbutsu kishō*; Miracles of immortals and Buddhist figures), imported after 1602.[5] Both of these texts had a pivotal role in Japan disseminating and clarifying information about Daoist immortals and their identities and practices. Netsuke artists would refer to such books for iconographic details, including appearance and attributes; occasionally, carvers adopted the pictorial qualities as well.

FIG. 4, TOP AND BOTTOM
Fossilized Insects
Japan, 19th century
cloisonné with gold wire on silver ground, amber
M.91.250.259
CAT. 463

NETSUKE MATERIALS

Common materials for seventeenth- and eighteenth-century netsuke frequently find their sources in Chinese toggles. Gourds, often seen being used as netsuke in seventeenth-century Japanese painting, were first used in China as good luck and longevity amulets.[6] The gourd, a metaphor for medicinal power, was employed as the shop sign of the Chinese apothecary; because it was filled with seeds, it also represented fertility. Elderly countrymen often used gourds as canteens, which fostered their symbolic association to longevity. In Daoist lore, entire worlds could be contained within a gourd, and it could house an immortal or his animal familiar. As toggles, gourds would sometimes be fitted with metal caps, an ivory hand, and a metal attachment ring to embody the idea of the unification of the vegetable, animal, and mineral worlds.[7]

Boxwood (*tsuge*) is extolled by modern netsuke and mask carvers for its very fine grain and relative level of hardness, which make it perfect for carving detail. Slow growing and therefore expensive as a raw material, boxwood did not come into use purely because of its availability in Japan; rather, it arrived from southern and western China complete with auspicious and medicinal overtones and functions. As an evergreen, boxwood was considered by Chinese Daoists to be filled with *yang* (positive male energy) because it remained green through adverse, wintry weather. It was believed that boxwood held the magical potential for sharing its powers of longevity and perseverance.[8] Boxwood leaves were an herbal remedy, and ashes from the wood were used to reduce fever.[9] Cypress, favored by some early netsuke carvers, was, like boxwood, credited in China with the power to confer longevity. Pinesap was a standard ingredient in longevity elixirs,[10] and in Japan, the pine tree was traditionally a resting place for *kami*, or Shinto gods.[11] Amber (as fossilized pinesap) contained the longevity powers of the pine tree and could be used as a long-life amulet (FIG. 4).[12]

Daoists believed that fruitwood, another common netsuke material, had many magical powers; in China, it was called the "wood of the immortals" (*xianmu*).[13] Not only did Daoists associate life-preserving properties with fruitwood, they also believed that it helped deflect demons and avert evil. The most powerful tree was the peach tree in the garden of the Queen Mother of the West (Ch., Xiwangmu; J., Seiōbo), which every three thousand years sprouted peaches that would grant immortality when eaten. Scented trees such as camphor and sandalwood were also said to share the fruit trees' function[14] of driving off demons, although in Japan these perfumed woods were used more for Buddhist images than for netsuke carving.

Elephant ivory, one of the most popular materials for netsuke, was imported in tusk form from South and Southeast Asia to China for carving images. The triangular tips of the tusks were often purchased by toggle makers, and many Chinese toggles as well as early Japanese netsuke reflect this triangular shape (FIG. 5). Ivory dust was utilized in medicine, and amulets made from ivory were thought to contain its curative powers. Raw ivory dust was a diuretic when added to water; burned ivory was an anti-diuretic when diluted; and ivory chips were ingested to fight symptoms of epilepsy, osteomyelitis, and smallpox.[15] Mammoth, walrus, and narwhal tusks, all brought from Siberia into China, were used to detect poison and to stop bleeding.[16] The ready availability of walrus tooth and narwhal tusks from Siberian traders meant that they were less valued as a luxury item than elephant ivory. Hornbill and ox bones were also used in elixirs, toggles, and netsuke for their medicinal value.[17]

Stag antler has long been one of the favored materials for netsuke carvers, supposedly for its availability (FIG. 6). However, deer often ingest shed antlers (which provide calcium), and stag antler may not have been as widely available as previously thought. Like the materials described above, stag antler in China was perceived to have additional talismanic powers, and this concept was transferred to Japan with the information on Daoist practice. According to Chinese folk belief, deer were the only animals capable of rooting out and eating *lingzhi* (J., *reishi*), the fungus of immortality. Antler, therefore, should contain some of the elixir of long life and, by wearing antler, one would receive its properties of longevity.

Since prehistoric times in Japan, deer were the sacred messengers of the Shinto Kasuga deities. Among the Mongols, antler was thought to stimulate sexual rejuvenation; however, phallic netsuke carved from antler are not common, and this belief was evidently not transferred to Japan.[18]

Water buffalo horn and rhinoceros horn, both seen in nineteenth-century netsuke, had broad applications in Daoist medicine (FIG. 7). Water buffalo horn could be used as a remedy for headache, fever, or baldness, while rhinoceros horn could detect poison or be used as an aphrodisiac. Chinese courtiers drank beverages served in rhinoceros-horn cups to protect themselves from poisoning.[19]

By the nineteenth century, the numerous types of new media used for netsuke in Japan, including lacquer, glass, ceramic, and metal, perhaps indicate that more importance was then given to the aesthetic quality of materials rather than to their prophylactic powers.

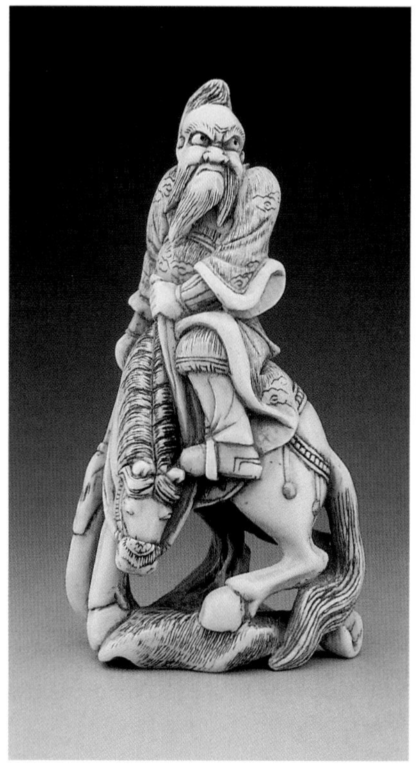

FIG. 5
Kan'u Mounted
Japan, 18th century
ivory with staining, sumi, gold-colored powder pigment
M.87.263.6
CAT. 497

FIG. 6
FUKUMOTO HŌMIN (Japan, active mid- to late 19th century)
Kappa Mask
stag antler with hide, inlays
M.91.250.215
CAT. 780

FIG. 7
Chinese Lion
Japan, late 18th–early 19th century
rhinoceros horn
AC1998.249.124
CAT. 201

FIG. 8
From *Yūshō ressen zenden* (Complete illustrated lives of immortals)
Wang Shizhen, ed.
Kyoto, 1650
woodblock illustrated book
The British Library
16087.b.20

NETSUKE SUBJECTS

Netsuke themes were also originally imported from China and were altered in the transference. Subjects slowly turned from those either Daoist or otherwise propitiatory in nature to subjects specifically of interest to the Japanese wearer and his group. One exception, from *Ryokō yōjin shū* (Precautions for travelers), a nineteenth-century text by Yasumi Roan, was the suggestion that travelers carry an emblem of a *hakutaku* (a mythical Chinese beast that was capable of human speech and had multiple eyes) to avert evil during their journey.[20]

Eventually, both inrō and netsuke developed an identity separate from their source, and would take on new functions and meanings. Joe Earle, curator of the exhibition *Netsuke: Fantasy and Reality in Japanese Miniature Sculpture* (2001) for the Museum of Fine Arts, Boston, and author of its accompanying catalogue, describes how the *Yūshō ressen zenden* (Complete illustrated lives of immortals), a compendium of 497 immortals and perfected beings, was used as source material by early carvers of netsuke (FIG. 8).[21] Within the complex web of Chinese good-luck symbolism, images of immortals, when worn as talismans, were thought to confer longevity upon the wearer. Longevity was one of six main categories of good luck especially yearned for by Chinese of all classes. The others were wealth; fertility, in terms of heirs as well as crops and herds; raising one's station in life through success on examinations; happiness and marital bliss; and aversion of evil. In Japan, with the rigid stratification of Edo-period society into four classes (samurai, farmers, artisans, and merchants, in descending order), members of Japanese society could not hope to raise their station. This meant also that wealth, although it would provide a level of comfort, could not be displayed in ways that were considered to be either above or below one's station in society, and could not boost one into a higher class. Therefore, especially early netsuke tended to reflect a longing for great age, numerous heirs, happiness, and aversion of evil.

Many of the Chinese symbols for luck are based on linguistic homophones that do not necessarily transfer to Japanese. As a result, when early Japanese netsuke carvers chose designs from extant toggles or from illustrated books, they generally disregarded designs that made no sense to them, selected others possibly for their decorative value, and placed greatest emphasis on figures whose efficacy in amulet form would be understood by a Japanese buyer. Zodiacal animals, a lesser theme in Chinese toggles, were one of the most popular subjects in Japanese netsuke, each animal immediately recognizable as representing one year in a cycle of twelve, a time of day, a direction, or a virtue. For example, because a snake shed its skin, it represented the virtue of rebirth and regeneration in addition to its zodiacal symbolism. A dog protected its master, and its image was used to repel demons. Another symbol taken from the Chinese was the combination of a monkey and a wasp (FIG. 9). In

Chinese, these words—*ma shang feng hou* (literally, "wasp riding monkey's back")—can be interpreted by homophone as "May you quickly become a marquis." The marquis rank, along with four others, was created in Japan in 1884. Although the titles were hereditary, they could also be conferred on those from nonaristocratic backgrounds as a reward for distinguished service to the nation.

FIG. 9
Masanao II (Miyake)
(Japan, 1848–1922)
Monkeys and Wasp
wood with inlays
AC1998.249.27
CAT. 331

THE KAMIGATA AND NARA REGIONS

Chinese figures commonly recognized by the Japanese—for example, Shōki (the demon queller) or one of the "Eight Immortals" group—important sources for most carvers, were not necessarily a thematic priority for Yoshimura Shūzan (d. 1776), the first carver listed among the netsuke sculptors in Inaba Tsūryū's *Sōken kishō*. Being first a painter and second a carver of netsuke, he found his sources in pictorial imagery rather than in imported toggles. He also seemed to feel free to choose from any of the 497 images in the *Yūshō ressen zenden* (Complete illustrated lives of immortals).

Shūzan lived in a time—from the mid- to the late eighteenth century—when the exotic was especially prized in Japan. Since at least 1615, the Tokugawa shogunate had been utilizing a Chinese-based vocabulary in their architecture and painted decor as a way of lending credence to their own authority, based on respect for the richness of Chinese tradition.[22] Combinations of the exotic and heroic were used specifically to impress and daunt the visitors to the shogunal environs. This, combined with the insularity of a nation that was isolated and restrained from foreign contact, sparked a broad fashion for imported, and especially Chinese, goods. Art historian Timon Screech remarks that imported "Nagasaki" cloth was "feeding a fashion frenzy in Edo" (now Tokyo) in the 1790s.[23] Worldliness, represented in part by interest in cultures outside Japan, was one of the hallmarks of the sophisticated aesthete in Edo.

Unlike the Chinese Confucian paragons, whose lofty qualities made them the subject of art for the samurai,[24] Daoist immortals were accessible to a wider audience. Theoretically, anyone could become a perfected human being by following a strict diet of sacred herbs and fungus, practicing specific rituals and exercises, and meditating.[25] The aesthetic result was that Daoist immortals, although ancient and otherworldly, were depicted complete with human foibles.[26] This made them a very popular subject, and probably mostly among members of the literati movement in Kyoto and Osaka. They admired the Chinese scholar-gentleman concept of self-improvement through education, travel, and artistic practice, all of which often involved leaving society, as the Daoists did. In a society as rigidly stratified as that of Edo-period Japan, Daoist immortals served as a reminder that social

FIG. 10
Yoshimura Shūzan
(Japan, died 1776), illustrator
From *Wakan meihitsu gaei* (Glories of Japanese and Chinese painting)
1750; later edition 1807
woodblock printed illustrated book; ink on paper
9 7/8 x 7 1/8 in. (25.2 x 18 cm)
source unknown, 2000; Museum of Fine Arts, Boston
2000.1044.1-6

climbing need not be as worthy an ambition as self-perfection. With educated, Chinese-oriented literati[27] as his customers, Shūzan would have felt encouraged to sculpt obscure immortals and arcane Chinese subjects.

As Shūzan's painting[28] and one of his illustrated books, *Wakan meihitsu gaei* (Glories of Japanese and Chinese painting; FIG. 10), in the Museum of Fine Arts, Boston, reveal about his pictorial images, he specialized in Chinese themes and preferred his figures posed either three-quarters or frontally, often dressed in extremely elaborate and fantastic garb. His netsuke and those of his immediate followers retain these qualities, and indeed seem to have been conceived as figures that have stepped off a page rather than being truly planned in the round (FIGS. 11 and 12). Conversely, twists of the torso, a turned head, an open-mouthed scream, or a piercing gaze give these small carvings tremendous internal energy. Shūzan also surpasses other carvers in the elaboration of his costuming, which, combined

11

12

FIG. 11
After Yoshimura Shūzan
(Japan, late 18th–19th century)
Rakan: Buddhist Disciple of Exceptional Merit
late 18th century
cypress wood with pigments
M.90.186.11
CAT. 84

FIG. 12
Attributed to Yoshimura Shūzan (Japan, died 1776)
Ryūjin: Ruler of Seas and Tides
wood with pigments
M.91.250.9
CAT. 515

with central Asian hirsute features, makes his figures so foreign to the Japanese as to be outlandish. The painted surfaces and carved details of Shūzan's netsuke removed them from the realm of the practical and the tactile, although aesthetically they are in a class of their own.

FIG. 13
MASANAO (Japan, active before 1781)
Household Dog on Embroidered Zabuton
ivory with staining, sumi, inlays
AC1998.249.304
CAT. 336

Other carvers in Osaka and Kyoto seem to have turned immediately from Shūzan's painterly style to a manner based on sculpting. Carvers of this region who signed their work, such as Masanao (active before 1781), tended toward a more elegant and tactile treatment of surface, and a truly sculptural approach to the figure (FIG. 13). Many of the carpenters who worked on temples and shrines across the country—most notably the overwrought transom carvings fashionable in the early Edo era in Nagoya and Nikkō—came from the area including Kyoto, Nara, and Osaka (also known as the Kamigata region).[29] Kamigata was and remains a center for doll making and icon carving, meaning that many of the carvers in this district who began to create netsuke may have had opportunities for training in the plastic arts, not just the graphic arts. Carvers of katabori and sashi, starting in the late eighteenth century, brought about an evolution in design, away from the frontal style of early netsuke. In contrast with the three-dimensional aspects of katabori, the front surfaces of manjū and kagamibuta continued to require graphic pictorial treatment that was easily sourced from illustrated books.

FIG. 14
Fox Disguised As Priest
Japan, 18th century
ivory with staining, sumi
M.87.263.7
CAT. 241

Looking at unsigned netsuke attributed to the early to mid-eighteenth century, one can see the first mature evolutionary phase of true (that is, non–Chinese toggle type) netsuke.[30] It is immediately evident that the subjects, even of these relatively early netsuke, differ widely from the common motifs of paintings, prints, many lacquers, and textiles (FIGS. 14 and 15). In his essay on woodblock-printed books as disseminators of artistic themes,[31] Earle

FIG. 15
KANKŌ (Japan, active 18th century)
Baku: Monster That Eats Nightmares
ivory with staining, sumi, inlays
AC1998.249.154
CAT. 213

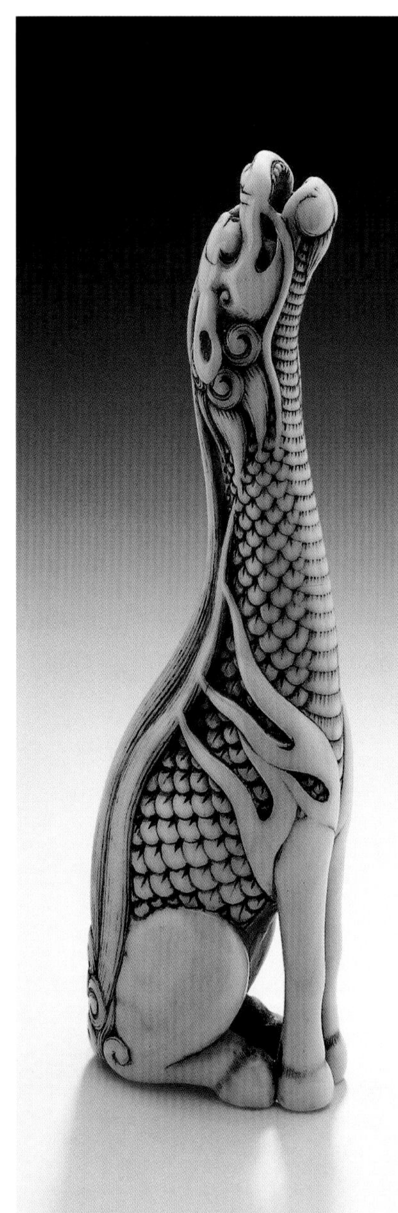

points out that many subjects that were interpreted in netsuke—Chinese and Japanese legends; mythological and real animals (FIG. 16); imaginary and actual foreigners (FIG. 17); and objects of interest, of auspicious meaning, and of desire—were first relayed in the seventeenth and early eighteenth centuries through print. Traditional painting themes, however, such as the passage of the seasons, annual celebrations, scholarly Chinese-gentlemen recluses, Japanese peasantry at work, and popular beauties—in fact, hundreds of the subjects presented in books by prolific Kano School[32] artist Tachibana Morikuni (1679–1748), as an example—infrequently met the carver's knife. In the eighteenth century, themes such as auspicious zodiacal and mythological animals (FIG. 18); objects of curiosity such as strange-looking foreigners (FIG. 19) and odd Japanese characters; the gods of good luck (FIG. 20);[33] and, of course, Daoist immortals seemed to overtake the competition (FIGS. 21 and 22). Chinese ivory carvers of the Ming (1368–1644) and Qing (1644–1911) dynasties had favored gods, immortals, and Buddhist worthies. This is one indication that netsuke artists were looking to imported ivories and toggles as well as to each other and to woodblock-printed books for ideas, rather than casting a wide net through other media, such as painting, lacquer, and ceramics.

FIG. 17
Mongolian Archer
Japan, 18th century
wood
M.91.250.107
CAT. 15

FIG. 16
ATTRIBUTED TO TOMOTADA
(Japan, active before 1781)
Kirin
ivory with staining, sumi
AC1998.249.64
CAT. 191

FIG. 18, FRONT AND SIDE
TOMOTADA
(Japan, active before 1781)
Tiger and Cub
ivory with staining, sumi, inlays
M.90.186.9
CAT. 272

FIG. 20
Fukurokuju: God of Wisdom
Japan, 18th century
ivory with staining, sumi
M.91.250.174
CAT. 166

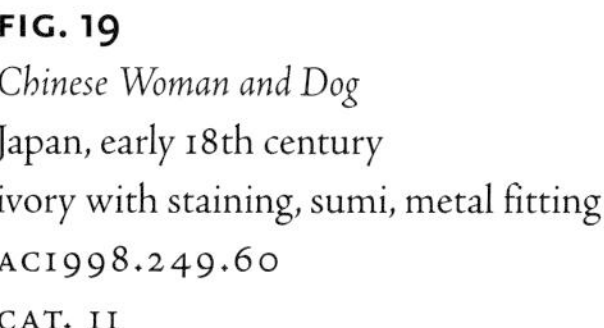

FIG. 19
Chinese Woman and Dog
Japan, early 18th century
ivory with staining, sumi, metal fitting
AC1998.249.60
CAT. 11

FIG. 21
Figure on Baku
Japan, 18th century
wood
AC1998.249.113
CAT. 70

FIG. 22
Daoist Immortal
Japan, 18th century
boxwood
M.91.250.100
CAT. 67

FIG. 23
Kan'u: Chinese God of War
Japan, early 19th century
stag antler with staining, sumi
M.87.263.15
CAT. 499

As mentioned previously, Daoist immortals were a subject that found its source in the Daoist principles transferred to Japan from China, along with inrō, toggles, and sculpted ivories. Chinese legendary heroes (FIG. 23) as a theme also crossed the ocean, both as toggles and in Chinese illustrated books, as did imaginary foreigners like Ashinaga and Tenaga (FIGS. 24 and 25), the symbiotic long-armed, long-legged people, and the Senkyō (FIG. 26), who carry each other by a pole inserted through a hole in the belly. *Rakan* (Skt., *arhat*), the most worthy five hundred disciples of the Buddha who all received enlightenment during the Buddha's sermon at Vulture Peak, became a symbol of escapism and reclusion in Chinese art (FIG. 27). Rakan netsuke had a function similar to that of eremitic Daoists. In the case of rakan netsuke, they were thought to confer the possibility of enlightenment on the wearer, while, like immortals, reminding him of the ideal of a quiet, apolitical life of learned, religious seclusion. With many foreigners (that is, non-Chinese) among Daoists and rakan, they became objects of gentle derision in netsuke, with their features and costumes exaggerated to the point of becoming bizarre.

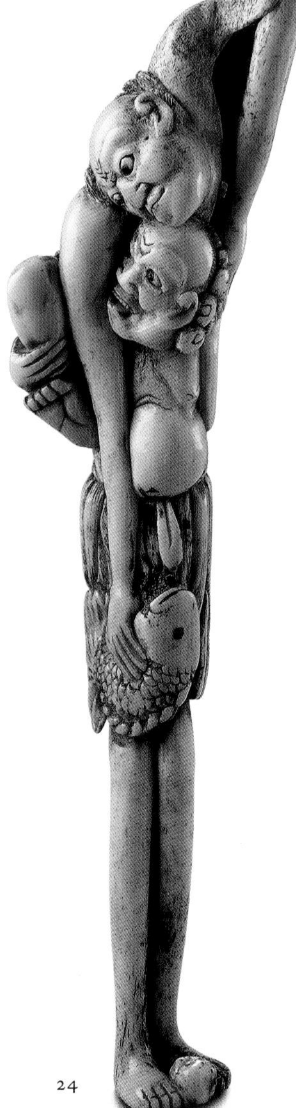

24

25

FIG. 24
Ashinaga and Tenaga
Japan, 18th century
stag antler with inlays
M.91.250.111
CAT. 31

FIG. 25
Ashinaga and Tenaga
Japan, 18th century
ivory with staining, sumi
M.91.250.113
CAT. 32

Some of the strangest foreigners among netsuke subjects were those with their feet actually upon Japanese soil; that is, the Dutchmen who retained the right to trade with Japan through the period of national seclusion (1639–1854).[34] The Dutch, in Japan since 1609, were the first northern Europeans with whom the Japanese had ongoing contact. Dutchmen tended to have light-colored hair that the Japanese generalized as "red," giving the Dutch the epithet "red hair" (*kōmō*). To the Japanese, the Dutch were also ridiculously tall, and had popping eyes of strange color, and beaked noses. They possessed weird habits, such as hunting and eating meat (FIG. 28) and becoming emotionally attached to their pets (FIG. 29). And they brought as their servants even stranger-looking black-skinned south Asian people (FIG. 30). A delegation from the Dutch East India Company—consisting of the captain in charge of affairs, the doctor, and a few in the upper echelon of the company required to live on the artificial island of Dejima near Nagasaki—regularly traveled to Edo to visit the shogun. For those who lived along the route, it was a bit like the circus coming to town as the delegation made its way on the three-month trek back and forth from Edo to Dejima. Artists who observed the procession on the highway, those allowed to document the lives of the Dutch in Dejima, and the few, including Hokusai, who saw the Dutch in their quarters at the Nagasaki-ya in Edo were able to make first-hand drawings.[35] The Dutch represented in eighteenth-century netsuke appear to be conflated from some of these sketches, from stories published in illustrated books, and possibly from imported Dutch books.

In addition to odd European physical features, carvers were fascinated by details of costume such as high-buttoned boots, knee-length button-down coats, ruffled collars and cuffs,

FIG. 26
RYŌSAI (Japan, active 19th century)
Senkyō
wood
M.91.250.64
CAT. 36

FIG. 27
FOLLOWER OF YOSHIMURA SHŪZAN (Japan, late 18th century)
Handaka Sonja: Disciple of the Buddha with Dragon
soft wood with pigments
M.87.263.90
CAT. 85

FIG. 28, FRONT AND BACK
Dutchman with Deer Carcass
Japan, 18th century
ivory with staining, sumi
AC1998.249.61
CAT. 2

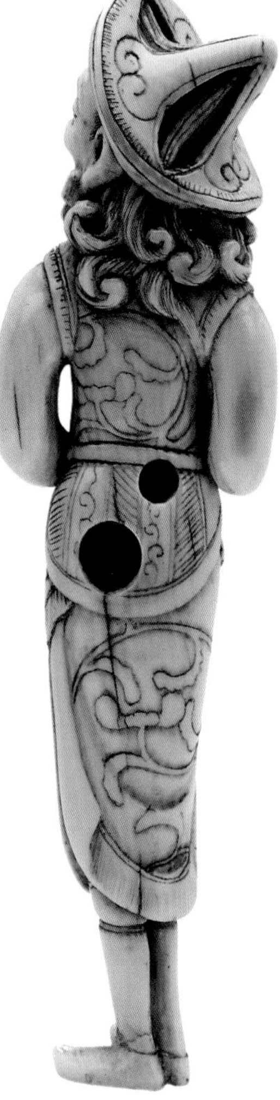

FIG. 29, FRONT AND BACK
Dutchman Holding Dog
Japan, 18th century
ivory with staining, sumi
AC1998.249.66
CAT. 4

and broad-brimmed hats. The carvers were also inventive (FIG. 31), fancifully embellishing on fact. Dutch were often shown in coats patterned with waves, perhaps indicating that they came from across the seas,[36] with ringlets of hair (strange to the preponderantly straight-haired Japanese) and curling beards (yet more strange). Their facial expressions are sometimes quite risible. Westerners have never had the behavioral trait of the Japanese of keeping their thoughts and reactions to themselves, and this tendency to emote would have seemed odd. Sailors in the eighteenth and nineteenth century, who traditionally have been known as a rowdy bunch of men, may have especially lacked restraint.

30

31

FIG. 30
South Seas Islander
Japan, 18th century
wood
AC1998.249.291
CAT. 26

FIG. 31
Dutchman
Japan, 18th century
wood
M.87.263.115
CAT. 7

FIG. 32
Dutchman Holding Dog
Japan, 18th century
ivory with staining, sumi, inlays
M.87.263.1
CAT. 3

Scanning a variety of eighteenth-century netsuke from different areas throughout Japan that depict Dutchmen, one is struck first by the frontal pose (FIG. 32) that reflects the aesthetic seen in book illustrations of the same period. In the mid-eighteenth century, book illustrators and carvers would pose figures in a head-on fashion, or from a 45 degree angle (FIG. 33). Dynamic movement, especially within the netsuke, was often confined to a twist in the torso, perhaps finishing with the head turned in the opposite direction. The frontal aspect is seen also in Chinese ivory sculptures, some of whose typical poses were drawn from theatrical formula. Western drawing mannerisms of perspective and of depicting a figure as a volume in space did not affect Japanese artists until the last quarter of the eighteenth century, when it stimulated a watershed in all of the arts.

FIG. 33
TACHIBANA MORIKUNI
(Japan, 1679–1748), illustrator
From *Ehon kojidan* (A treasury of historical events); 1714
woodblock printed illustrated book; ink on paper
$8\,^{7}/_{8}$ x $6\,^{1}/_{4}$ in. (22.4 x 16 cm)
source unknown, 2000; Museum of Fine Arts, Boston
2000.1048.1-9

THE EFFECTS OF WESTERN SCIENCES

In 1774, the Edo doctor Sugita Genpaku (1733–1817) and his colleague Maeno Ryōtaku (1723–1803), with the help of the Akita fief artist Odano Naotake (1749–1780) and a group of fief doctors, translated, illustrated, and published *Anatomische tabellen* (J., *Kaitai shinsho*; New anatomical atlas), a book on anatomy by Johann Kulmus, originally published in German in 1725.[37] Before Sugita published this reference, Japanese medicine had been practiced in the ancient Chinese manner; that is, the body of the patient was not subjected to invasive tests. A diagnosis was performed by referring to texts, rather than by empirical observation, and was based on antiquated ideas of what was assumed to be inside the human body. There was a wave of interest in empirical science stimulated by the Japanese government allowing European books to be imported in the eighteenth century, and Sugita made it his mission to update Japanese medical practice to reflect European discoveries. Sugita had also attended an autopsy and watched with other interested parties, artists included, as ancient medical texts were debunked in the operating room.

The Kyoto painter Maruyama Ōkyo (1733–1795) attended a similar autopsy. Ōkyo was not, perhaps, the first artist to do so, but he was definitely the most successful to take to heart Western scientific principles of empiricism. Ōkyo was stimulated by the experience of the autopsy, and by numerous new encyclopedia publications that described and illustrated in much greater detail than ever before the plant, animal, and aquatic species, as well as sites in Japan. He chose not to copy Western style slavishly, but made it palatable to Japanese taste by incorporating carefully observed volumetric form within a native-style decorative format (FIG. 34). Ōkyo's atelier, called the Maruyama School, and an associated atelier run by Goshun (1752–1811), his colleague later in life, translated the new principles imported from the West into paintings of Chinese nobles and exemplars of Confucian virtue, ani-

FIG. 34
Maruyama Ōkyo
(Japan, 1733–1795)
Puppies among Bamboo in the Snow
six-panel screen; ink and light color on paper
64 x 140 in. (162.6 x 355.6 cm)
Los Angeles County Museum of Art
Mr. and Mrs. Allan C. Balch Fund
M.58.9.1-.2

mals, landscape, and in the case of Goshun's followers of the Shijō School, the average Japanese citizen. The Maruyama-Shijō School style affected all painting in Japan by the mid-nineteenth century and became the basis for Kyoto-style *nihonga* (Japanese-style painting) in the twentieth century. Every school of painting, except the most academic Kano and Tosa Schools, evolved a naturalistic bent—in adaptation of Maruyama-Shijō style and in recognition of all of the encyclopedia publications—that became the hallmark of a national manner of painting.

This evolution is notable in netsuke as well as in the graphic arts, which carried motifs across the different artistic genres. The most obvious change in terms of graphics, if one compares book illustrations by Morikuni, who was active in the mid-eighteenth century, with those of mid-nineteenth-century artist Katsushika Isai (1821–1880), is that human or animal figures are no longer planar forms bound to their place in a picture by their modulated outlines, but figures conceived as volumes twisting in space (FIGS. 35 and 36). Morikuni essentially presented a broad spectrum of classical themes, while Hokusai's student Isai had become part of the empiricism movement, drawing and studying what he could directly observe. Hokusai had thoroughly studied the parade of life in Edo in his series of *manga*, and the subject matter and treatment of figures fostered by his school would inspire netsuke carvers, especially in the new capital.

FIG. 35
Tachibana Morikuni
(Japan, 1679–1748), illustrator
From *Ehon tsūhōshi* (A treasury of instructional illustrations); 1729
woodblock printed illustrated book; ink on paper
8 7/8 x 6 1/4 in. (22.5 x 16 cm)
source unknown, 2000; Museum of Fine Arts, Boston
2000.1046.1-10

Netsuke evolved in tandem, from figures posed frontally or in defining profile and dependent upon size, weight, and rhythmically modeled surface treatment for visual impact, to dynamic forms that occupied three-dimensional space, reacting to that space with multidirectional movement. Their surface treatment was also tighter and more detailed. Naturalistic surface treatment was a priority for Ōkyo, and it became so for netsuke carvers from his time on. Ōkyo instructed his pupils to work empirically, and he had two methods of particular relevance to netsuke carvers. He encouraged the use of optical devices imported from northern Europe, including the hand-held telescope to view animals in their natural surroundings, and magnifying glasses or microscopes to view insects. He also suggested looking at subjects in a mirror to clarify one's viewpoint.[38] Additionally, he devised a method of treating human or animal figures by first studying their skeletal structure. For drawing humans, he recommended that they be portrayed first unclothed to understand their pose, and then shown with clothing.

FIG. 36
Katsushika Isai
(Japan, 1821–1880), illustrator
From *Bambutsu zukai* (Isai's drawing method); 1864
woodblock printed illustrated book; ink on paper
9 x 6 1/8 in. (22.8 x 15.6 cm)
Gift of Mrs. Jared K. Morse, 1997
Museum of Fine Arts, Boston
1997.1

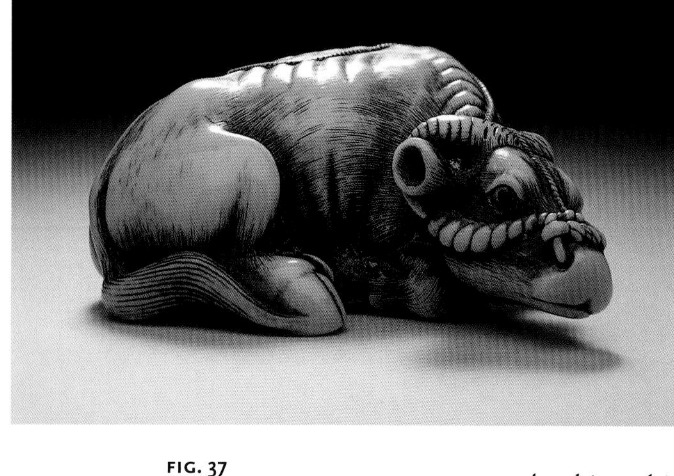

FIG. 37
Tomotada
(Japan, active before 1781)
Resting Ox
ivory with staining, sumi, inlays
AC1998.249.126
CAT. 269

Because netsuke carving is a reductive rather than an additive process—in other words, the carver can only remove material to reveal a form—it would be difficult for carvers to conceive their subjects in the manner suggested by Ōkyo. However, when one compares netsuke made before the naturalism movement and science boom to those made after (around the third quarter of the eighteenth century), it is evident that carvers had developed a new respect for anatomy. Skeletal structure is obvious and clearly creates a framework, along with muscles, on which the skin or hide is draped (FIG. 37). Ōkyo said in his instructions that if one were to attempt a mythological or foreign animal subject, such as *kirin* and dragons, or tigers, one could use a common animal, such as a dog, cat, or monkey, to understand the basic anatomy and movement and then invent, in the case of foreign animals, by viewing skins and skulls.[39] The latter would be especially relevant in the treatment of tigers, whose skins were imported bereft of the animal inside (FIG. 38).

FIG. 38
Sekiran
(Japan, circa 1800–circa 1870)
Crouching Tiger
mid- to late 19th century
bamboo with sumi, inlays
AC1998.249.117
CAT. 281

FIG. 39
Attributed to Gechū
(Japan, active 18th century)
Baku: Monster That Eats Nightmares
ivory with staining, sumi, traces of red pigment
AC1998.249.63
CAT. 212

When a few netsuke from earlier in the eighteenth century are compared to those created after the influence of Ōkyo, the differences are striking. This mid-eighteenth-century nightmare-eating *baku* (FIG. 39) is a quintessential product of the Kamigata region. Some of its hide has been left free of carving to allow the quality and patina of the ivory to glow through the design. The animal is posed in profile, making its defining anatomical characteristics and magnificent flowing tail and mane clearly readable from a distance. The manner of carving is such that, through the working of the surface with broad curls and curves, combined with fine sanding that leaves no sharp edges, a sculpture is created that is weighty; warm to the touch, as smooth ivory tends to be; and softly modeled for an extremely pleasing tactile sensation. Carved areas are balanced with those left uncarved to keep the fingers stimulated. This emphasis on tactility was part of the aesthetic of the Chinese toggle, although here it is taken to a new level of perfection.

A Chinese lioness and cub (FIG. 40), signed by the Kyoto artist Tomotada (active before 1781), was made around the third quarter of the eighteenth century. Tomotada's work is still hefty, although slightly less massive than its precursors, and with similarly styled

FIG. 40, FRONT AND BACK
Tomotada
(Japan, active before 1781)
Chinese Lion and Young
ivory with staining, sumi, inlays
M.87.263.140
CAT. 196

fur and curls. Visual stimulus is beginning to override tactile sensation, and Tomotada is no longer trying to balance smooth and textured areas. As with prints from this period (after 1765), the surface is suddenly densely designed and elaborately worked.[40] Much greater prominence is given to skeletal and muscle structures in this post-Ōkyo period; also in the Ōkyo manner, each hair is carefully placed.

FIG. 41
Tametaka
(Japan, active circa 1730–1790)
Kirin
wood
AC1998.249.244
CAT. 193

BEYOND KAMIGATA

The same evolutionary track is seen in netsuke from the Nagoya area, which is located between Kyoto and Edo. Tametaka (active ca. 1730–1790) was an early carver there, but like Yoshimura Shūzan, his exact style was not carried through by later generations of carvers in the area. Tametaka's wood reclining kirin (FIG. 41), shown twisting his head back to howl, is less elongated than early Kamigata work; rather, it is tightly compacted in a manner more pervasive in late-eighteenth- and early-nineteenth-century Nagoya. As seen in the ivory netsuke from Kamigata, the sharp edges have been worn away. These were probably originally sanded, but they also have been smoothed by use. As with earlier Kamigata netsuke, areas of fine hair work and flying spikes of beard are balanced by softly modeled areas on the haunches that invite one's touch. The quality of the wood grain, its whorls and depth, is also visible between carved areas.

A pile of seven rats (FIG. 42) by the later Nagoya-area artist Ittan (ca. 1820–1877) is part of the explosion of zodiac animals seen both in prints, especially *surimono*

FIG. 42
Ittan (Japan, circa 1820–1877)
Seven Rat Group
wood with inlays
M.87.263.117
CAT. 268

FIG. 43
Seiyōdō Tomiharu
(Japan, 1733–1811)
Frog on Taro Leaf
1782
boxwood
M.91.250.13
CAT. 413

(privately published luxury woodblock prints), and in netsuke in the first decades of the nineteenth century. Often, rats, turtles, or other small animals were shown in groups of three, five, or seven, all *yang* numbers considered lucky. When making a piece for a samurai, a carver would need to use five rats, while for a daimyo or someone else of very high stature, seven would be required.[41] Ittan also takes the compacting of overall form several steps further than Tametaka, and fine hair work covers the sculpture from end to end. Created later than the Chinese lions by Tomotada, this netsuke has broken away from the frontal, 45 degree, or profile pose: it is carved to be seen and appreciated from all angles. Again, after the manner of Ōkyo, the rats are carefully observed, from details of skull and claws to particulars of movement and pose.

By this time, all across central and western Japan, several groups of netsuke carvers had set up shop and created diverse styles of carving within the parameters described above for their time period. For example, in far-flung Iwami (part of present-day Shimane prefecture), a province located to the west in Honshū on the Japan Sea, a group of carvers used local materials and subjects in a very original manner. Headed by Seiyōdō Tomiharu (also called Iwao Tomiharu; 1733–1811) and his family, these carvers at the core of the Iwami School lived along the road between Iwami and Nagasaki, an old route that had been used to carry silver from Iwami to the harbors for overseas shipping (FIG. 43). They specialized in boar tusk as a base for their netsuke (FIG. 44), a material plentiful in that area but rarely used by carvers elsewhere. Their carving style was superrealistic, and Tomiharu in particular used a complex surface treatment for wood called *ukibori*[42] to give an intensely naturalistic feel to the "skin" of his reptilian and amphibian subjects. This was another area of specialization in subject for Iwami carvers: the use of small invertebrates (such as insects) and vertebrates (such as frogs and lizards), which could be observed directly. Though they made the occasional dragon (FIG. 45), these carvers seemed to favor dealing with the visible and the humble rather than the imaginary or auspicious.

43

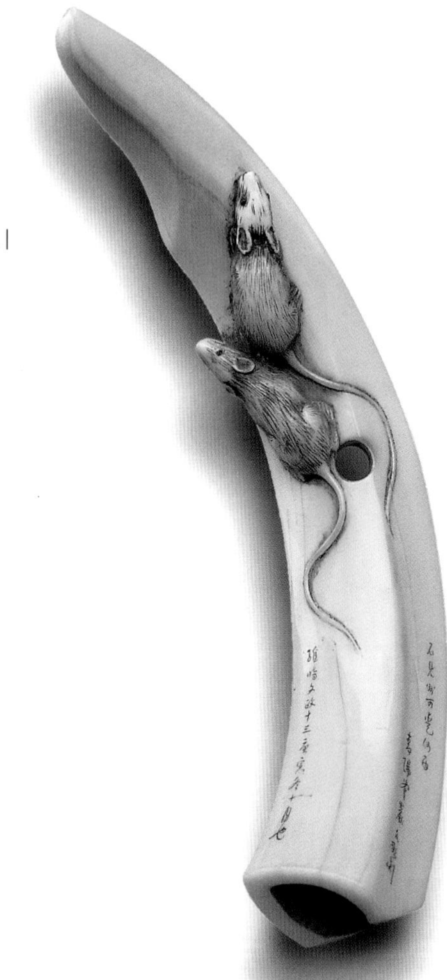

FIG. 44
Seiyōdō Gansui
(Japan, 1809–1848)
Rats on Boar Tusk
1830
boar tusk with inlays
M.91.250.33
CAT. 266

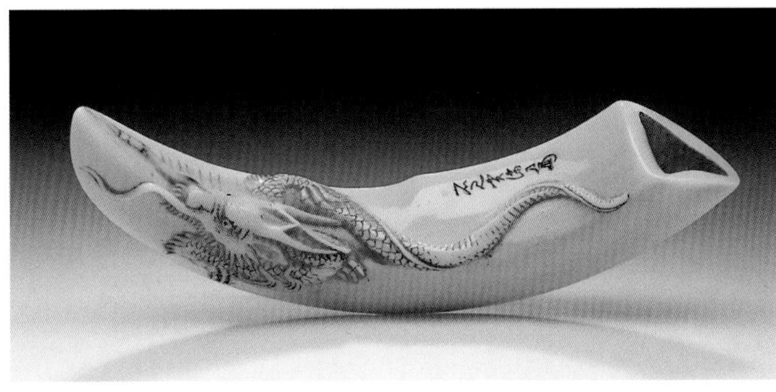

FIG. 45
KANMAN (Japan, 1793–1859)
Dragon on Boar's Tusk
boar tusk
AC1998.249.218
CAT. 302

46

FIG. 46
NAITŌ TOYOMASA
(Japan, 1773–1856)
Rabbit and Monkey
wood with inlays
M.87.263.105
CAT. 287

Development of the five major highways leading to Edo—including the Tōkaidō and Kisokaidō (also called the Nakasendō), which allowed easy travel between Edo and the Kamigata region—meant that provincial carvers could find a steady customer base in the larger cities.[43] Localized groups of carvers were organized throughout Honshū—in addition to the major Kamigata centers and Nagoya—in Ise, Tamba, Hida, and elsewhere, and were centered around talented carvers who created netsuke for local fief daimyo[44] or supplied the enormous demand in Edo. Especially in the first half of the nineteenth century, there was a proliferation of school styles, subject matter, and media in the production of netsuke. In Tamba (north of Kyoto), Naitō Toyomasa (1773–1856) led a school of carvers who adopted his personal style: the figures, frozen in motion, have broad faces, rectangular inlaid eyes, and a naturalistic surface treatment. The strong contrast between sumi-stained areas and wood left its original color gives an illusion of light and shade (FIGS. 46 and 47). The Hida mountains of present-day Gifu prefecture were home to the extraordinary carver of amphibians and reptiles, Matsuda Sukenaga (1800–1871). Sukenaga's work evinces his interest in science, and he created especially perceptive portrayals of toads—how they moved and reacted, the precise texture of their skin—forming these little harbingers of spring into perfect, compact, and tactile netsuke (FIG. 48).

In various kiln sites in Kyoto and Kyūshū, potters also filled the demand for netsuke, creating manjū and katabori in overglazed stoneware (FIGS. 49 and 50), in

47

FIG. 47
NAITŌ TOYOMASA
(Japan, 1773–1856)
Immortal with Toad: Gama Sennin
wood with inlays
M.87.263.97
CAT. 52

48

FIG. 48
MATSUDA SUKENAGA
(Japan, 1800–1871)
Toad on Roof Tile
wood with inlays
M.91.250.142
CAT. 419

49

50

FIG. 49
KENYA (Japan, active 1825–1889)
Okame
glazed pottery; manjū type
M.87.263.62
CAT. 181

FIG. 50
KENYA (Japan, active 1825–1889)
Dog-Shaped Box
pottery with glazes and overglaze enamels
M.87.263.63
CAT. 730

celadon-glazed and blue-glazed porcelain (FIGS. 51 and 52), and even in Raku ware, a low-fired ware produced by the Raku family in Kyoto (FIG. 53). In the larger netsuke-carving communities of Kyoto, Osaka, and Edo, carvers began to experiment with lacquers (FIG. 54) and various inlays, a trend that would peak toward the end of the nineteenth century.

FIG. 51
Chinese Lion
Japan, 19th century
porcelain with celadon glaze
M.87.263.56
CAT. 206

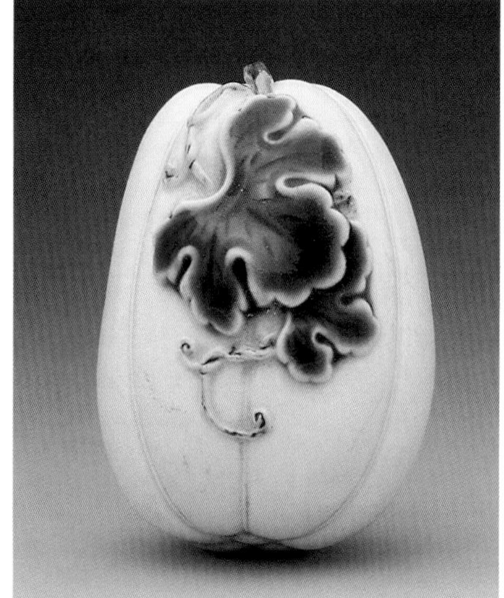

52

FIG. 52
Pumpkin
Japan, 19th century
Hirado ware; porcelain with blue glaze
M.87.263.59
CAT. 486

EDO CARVERS

Edo was, and Tokyo still is, unlike any other place in Japan in terms of demographics and patterns of behavior. By the 1720s, Edo was already the world's most populated city, with more than one million inhabitants. The demographics of the city were artificial, based on the structure of government politics. Unlike typical castle towns, where the local daimyo was native to the area and samurai and townspeople shared loyalties and worked in a symbiotic relationship, during the Edo period all of the daimyo in Japan were forced to live in Edo for regulated periods of time during the year. Foes of the Tokugawa shogun were assigned to live next to the shogun's allies, partly so that pro-Tokugawa daimyo could watch those of questionable loyalty. In the seventeenth and early eighteenth centuries, living arrangements in Edo changed constantly based on shifting loyalties and the requirements of shogunal security. This was the basis for a city in which inhabitants and neighbors felt profoundly unsettled, and were frequently mutually distrustful. Around the daimyo and shogunal leaders, retinues of samurai formed a bureaucracy, and artisans throughout Japan moved into Edo to outfit the homes of samurai and daimyo. This process of outfitting and re-outfitting never slowed, because

FIG. 53
Simplified Animal
Japan, 19th century
Raku ware; stoneware
M.87.263.68
CAT. 351

FIG. 54
School of Koma Bunsai
(Japan, 19th century)
Noh Actor in a Shishiguchi Role
gold and colored lacquer
M.87.263.43
CAT. 573

frequent fires in the congested city occasioned rebuilding. In addition, successful businesses from Kyoto and Osaka had offices in Edo, to which they sent staff on a rotating basis.

All of these factors meant that the population was constantly ebbing and flowing, with daimyo returning to their estates periodically, branch company staff returning to their home offices, and rural workers coming to the city to seek their fortune.[45] Several defining features of Edo life arose as a result. Townspeople had no loyalty to samurai and developed an attitude of rebelliousness toward authority that pervaded their arts. Also, the group of townspeople who stayed in Edo and put down roots, becoming known as Edokko, developed an insular language and set of social priorities. This created a definite "in-group" versus "out-group" culture, each of whose mannerisms was described in literature and theater as well as netsuke (FIG. 55).

FIG. 55
Man with Exaggerated Topknot
Japan, early 19th century
wood
M.91.250.163
CAT. 610

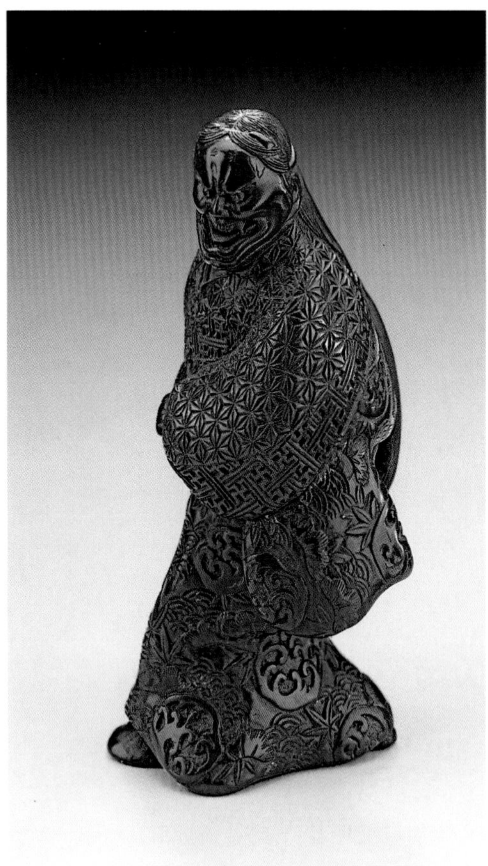

FIG. 56, FRONT AND BACK
MATSUKI HŌKEI (Japan, active Meiji period, 1868–1912)
Noh Actor in the Role of Hannya
carved red lacquer
M.87.263.47
CAT. 577

Edo carvers, more than any other group in Japan, specialized in depicting various characters seen on the street, clearly distinguishing the rude and rustic from the sophisticated. A huge consumer population developed in Edo, centered around merchants who were catering to the samurai class, with artisans filling the demands of both, and Edo was now the major center for entertainment. Staging performances of noh was still the reserved right of the samurai class, though now all classes could perform noh chant, telling the story without the costuming, dance, and music (FIGS. 56 and 57).[46] Kabuki theater, initially for the townspeople and becoming an elite entertainment only in the twentieth century, was hugely popular. In the second quarter of the nineteenth century, government censorship led to the addition of artificial didactic "messages" to kabuki plays, and legendary tales from the *Gikeiki* (Chronicle of Yoshitsune) and other hero tales came into fashion. Multi-figure netsuke depicting tableau of ancient heroes also proliferated. These themes would have always appealed to the samurai customers

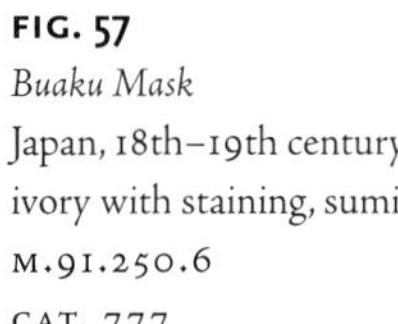

FIG. 57
Buaku Mask
Japan, 18th–19th century
ivory with staining, sumi
M.91.250.6
CAT. 777

FIG. 58
SCHOOL OF NAGAI RANTEI
(Japan, mid- to late 19th century)
Itinerant Entertainers
ivory with staining, sumi
M.87.263.123
CAT. 588

59

FIG. 59
JŪGETSU (Japan, active 19th century)
Daikoku As a Raconteur
ivory with staining, sumi
M.91.250.158
CAT. 165

of netsuke carvers, but theater helped to promote them generally. Pairs of entertainers telling funny tales (FIG. 58) or men reciting stories (FIG. 59) were common sights in small temporary theaters.

More than one hundred types of street performance were practiced in Edo as well.[47] Child acrobats (FIG. 60) were simultaneously admired and pitied for their hard work, and monkey trainers, among others, entertained passersby (FIG. 61). Some artists considered street life itself to be entertainment. It was not politically incorrect at that time to make fun of blind men, whose

FIG. 60
Acrobat
Japan, 18th century
wood with inlays
M.91.250.128
CAT. 578

affliction was considered karmic retribution for errors in a past life; however, they were welcomed into the guild of masseurs, and lifted heavy stones to build up their arm muscles for the job (FIG. 62). This gave carvers an opportunity to document silly and distorted facial expressions, which they emphasized by enlarging the head. The blind were also observed struggling to remove stones from their wooden clogs (*geta*) (FIG. 63). Shouting peddlers, people dressing after a bath, and quarreling couples all became thematic fodder for the carvers' knives, and for their sharp wit. The irreverence of many of these netsuke fed on the undercurrent of rebelliousness mentioned previously. Netsuke in which the villain is shown winning, such as a demon overcoming Shōki (FIG. 64), were probably a covert reference to the decline of the samurai class and the government in the waning years of the shogunate.

Not only did new subjects proliferate in Edo during these years, manners of carving did as well. A lineage of carvers who called themselves "Miwa" shows one form of evolution from an eighteenth- to a nineteenth-century style there. Earlier carvers of the Miwa name fed off the brusque, heavily masculine, competitive atmosphere of Edo when it was dominated by samurai, carving elongated figures that stretch themselves to the point of anguish (FIG. 65). A Miwa School carving of the nineteenth century shows the same tumultuous tone, now between a temple guardian and demon (representing good and evil) locked in the

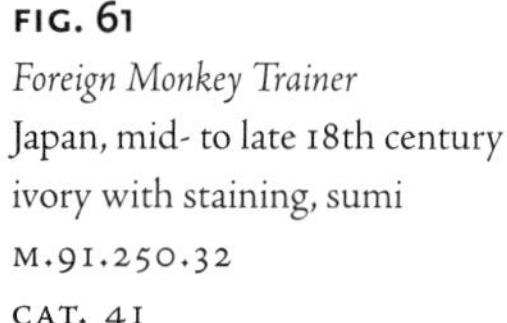

FIG. 61
Foreign Monkey Trainer
Japan, mid- to late 18th century
ivory with staining, sumi
M.91.250.32
CAT. 41

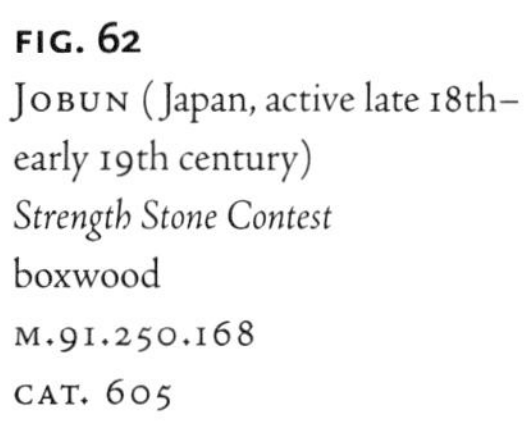

FIG. 62
JOBUN (Japan, active late 18th–early 19th century)
Strength Stone Contest
boxwood
M.91.250.168
CAT. 605

62

FIG. 63
SUGANOYA SHŌKO
(Japan, active circa 1840–1880)
Blind Man with Stone in Clog
wood
M.91.250.160
CAT. 600

63

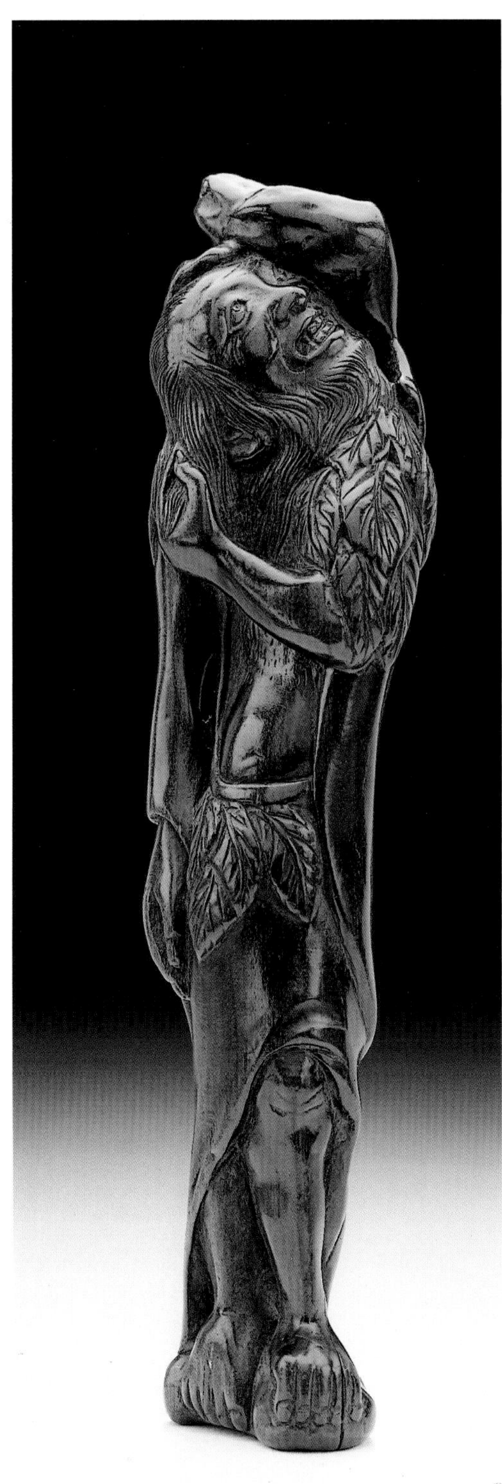

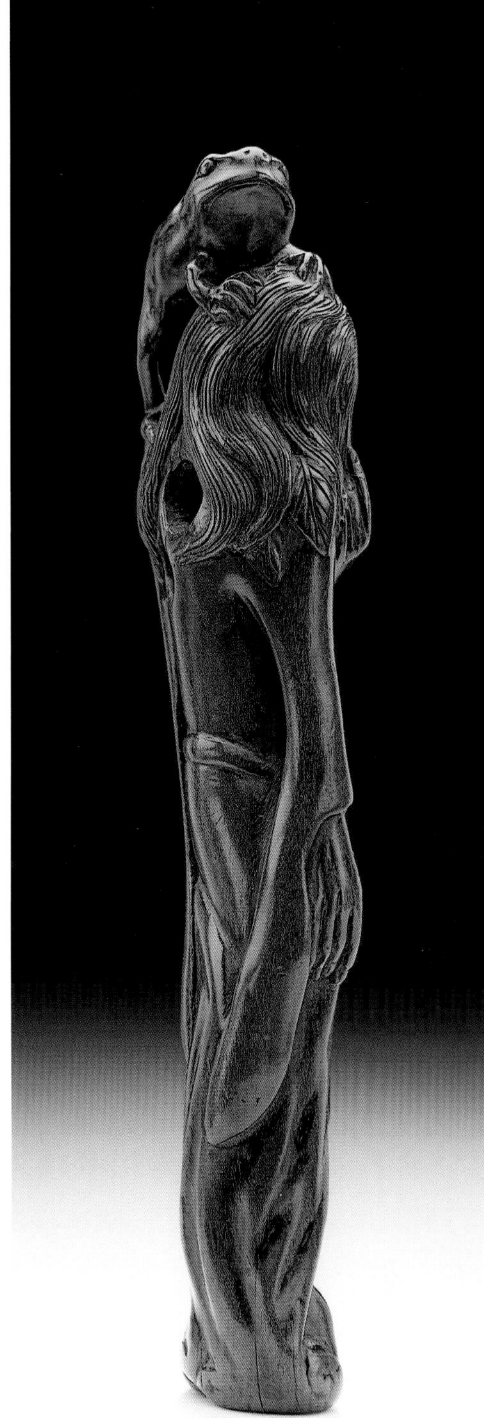

FIG. 64
School of Nagai Rantei
(Japan, mid- to late 19th century)
Shōki and Demon
ivory with staining, sumi, inlays
M.91.250.61
CAT. 507

FIG. 65, FRONT AND BACK
School of Miwa
(Japan, late 18th–19th century)
Immortal with Toad: Gama Sennin
late 18th century
cherry wood
AC1998.249.265
CAT. 51

sumo *kawazugake* throw (FIG. 66). Proportions and anatomy follow the national trend toward naturalism in the later carvings, but the nineteenth-century artist has maintained the quality and patina of sculpted wood, abstaining from overall surface carving that would become pervasive elsewhere.

FIG. 66
School of Miwa
(Japan, late 18th–19th century)
Temple Guardian and Demon Wrestling
mid-19th century
wood
M.87.263.135
CAT. 131

A group of carvers living in the mid-nineteenth century in Shiba and Asakusa, centered around Ozaki Kokusai (FIG. 67) and Ishikawa Rensai (FIG. 68), developed a mannerist style. Many of these carvings were done in stag antler and depended for their flavor in part on the pocked and mottled quality of the material. Kokusai (1835–ca. 1892) was a professional jester as well as a carver,[48] and this humor is revealed in his consciously distorted forms, and sometimes hidden signature (FIG. 69). His associate, Rensai (active mid- to late nineteenth century), worked in a similar manner, stylizing details of his creatures to the point of fascinating abstraction.

Minkoku's elegant netsuke (FIG. 70) brought some of the essence of Kamigata style to Edo. Faces are idealized rather than distorted, and poses generally show more grace than humor.

FIG. 67
Ozaki Kokusai
(Japan, 1835–circa 1892)
Distorted Monkey
stag antler; sashi type
M.87.263.9
CAT. 327

FIG. 68
Ishikawa Rensai (Japan, active mid- to late 19th century)
Chinese Lion Incense Burner
narwhal tusk with inlays
M.91.250.66
CAT. 704

THE NINETEENTH CENTURY: A NATIONAL STYLE

By the second quarter of the nineteenth century, improved logistics for travel and trade encouraged netsuke artists across Japan to work in a more unified manner. Although netsuke began to show similarities of small size, dense and refined surface treatment, naturalism, a new and burgeoning taste for inlay, and greater emphasis on subject matter drawn from daily experience, the underlying philosophical distinctions between Edo and Kamigata artists remained.

The artistic differences among netsuke produced in Edo and those made in Kyoto were based on the divergent aesthetic priorities of their local art patrons. As a comparison, one can look at two contemporary netsuke that are based on the same general subject matter: the first, from Edo (FIG. 71), is of a kite of a *yakko* (footman); the second, from Kyoto (FIG. 72), is of a pair of standing dolls.

The yakko kite, depicting a low-level samurai who has been given policing duties, shows the forceful demeanor and brusque attitude that would have been familiar to Edo clientele. The pair of standing dolls represents a type of doll seen in Kyoto, a city whose central character is defined by the presence of the imperial residence, located in Kyoto for one thousand years. The demeanor of the Kyoto dolls is self-restrained and, in opposition to the blustering features

FIG. 69
Ozaki Kokusai
(Japan, 1835–circa 1892)
Stylized Rakan Mask
stag antler with inlays
AC1998.249.222
CAT. 826

FIG. 70, FRONT AND BACK
Genryōsai Minkoku II (Japan, active early to mid-19th century)
Diving Girl and Octopus
early 19th century
ivory with staining, sumi, lacquer, crystal inlays
M.90.186.13
CAT. 627

FIG. 71
Hōboku (Japan, active 19th century)
Kite in the Form of a Footman: Yakko
gold and colored lacquer
M.87.263.53
CAT. 739

of the yakko kite, almost unexpressive. The stylization of the Edo netsuke—bolder, more graphic, and more playful—is also different from the Kyoto piece. Some of its charm arises from it being a netsuke in the form of a kite which itself is in the form of a yakko. The raison d'être of the doll netsuke is elegance: two highly idealized figures are standing within a cherry blossom, an exquisite flower with historical poetic meaning.

An artist whose work sums up the sophistication and refinement of the mid-nineteenth-century national style is Ōhara Mitsuhiro (1810–1875). Mitsuhiro was born in Onomichi (in present-day Hiroshima prefecture) and spent about thirty years, from age seventeen to forty-eight, in Osaka, training to become and then becoming a master carver. (Later in life, following a bout of ill health, he returned to Onomichi.)[49] Mitsuhiro's work is characterized by mild humor and restrained lyricism of a type engendered in haiku poetry. As in haiku, Mitsuhiro's treatment of his subject indicates a search for its essence—he tended to depict themes in a simple way that revealed larger overtones of meaning. The quintessential example of a netsuke representing this idea is his *Frog-Shaped Seal* (FIG. 73). As a seal, carved to fit easily into the hand, the netsuke has the literary function of authenticating a piece of writing. The frog is simplified to its fundamental form and is precisely sculpted from a high-quality piece of ivory.

The frog itself may have been intended as a reference to Ono no Tōfū (also called Ono Michikaze; 896–966), one of the three great calligraphers of the tenth century. According to legend, Ono was frustrated at having failed the government exams seven times. Walking one day, Ono stopped to watch a frog that was trying to leap into the branches of a willow tree. The frog persevered until he triumphed on his eighth try. This inspired Ono to continue with his efforts and eventually succeed. The intent and rigid little frog of Mitsuhiro's seal is a reminder that one should strive to overcome obstacles.

FIG. 72
Naoaki (Japan, active late 19th–early 20th century)
Standing Dolls
ivory with light staining, sumi; manjū type
M.87.263.32
CAT. 737

One of Mitsuhiro's favored topics, and one often copied by his followers, was that of a tea bowl with a whisk for blending powdered tea (FIG. 74). Using ivory partially treated with lacquer, Mitsuhiro brilliantly juxtaposed the pliant texture of a bamboo whisk and the rustic, tactile form of low-fired tea ware. The aesthetic differences between this object of specialized daily use, with its precisely achieved, naturalistic treatment of surface detail, and the boldly carved eighteenth-century netsuke of mythical immortals and beasts suggest the evolutionary track that netsuke carvers across Japan took as the nineteenth century proceeded. The mid-nineteenth century was a pivotal period for netsuke artists: They sought the beauty in quotidian detail, and the quintessentially ridiculous or sublime within fine gradations of miniaturized expression.

FIG. 74
Ōhara Mitsuhiro
(Japan, 1810–1875)
Tea Bowl and Whisk
wood with lacquer, ivory
M.91.250.323
CAT. 706

FIG. 73, TOP AND BOTTOM
Ōhara Mitsuhiro
(Japan, 1810–1875)
Frog-Shaped Seal
ivory with staining, red seal pigment
M.91.250.44
CAT. 697

1 Arakawa Hirokazu, *The Gō Collection of Netsuke, Tokyo National Museum* (Tokyo and New York: Kodansha International Ltd., 1983), pp. 187–88.

2 Schuyler Van Rensselaer Cammann, *Substance and Symbol in Chinese Toggles: Chinese Belt Toggles from the C. F. Bieber Collection* (Philadelphia: University of Pennsylvania Press, 1962), p. 41.

3 Ibid., pp. 32–37.

4 Karen M. Gerhart, *The Eyes of Power: Art and Early Tokugawa Authority* (Honolulu: University of Hawaii Press, 1999), p. 40.

5 Ibid., p. 26.

6 Cammann, *Substance and Symbol in Chinese Toggles*, p. 42.

7 Ibid., pp. 42–43.

8 Ibid., p. 50.

9 Ibid., p. 51.

10 Gerhart, *The Eyes of Power*, p. 25.

11 Ibid., pp. 27–28.

12 Cammann, *Substance and Symbol in Chinese Toggles*, p. 78.

13 Ibid., p. 52.

14 Ibid., p. 53.

15 Ibid., p. 63.

16 Ibid., pp. 64–65.

17 Ibid., p. 66.

18 Ibid., p. 67.

19 Ibid., p. 68.

20 Contantine N. Vaparis, "Caveat Viator: Advice to Travelers in the Edo Period," *Monumenta Nipponica* 44, no. 4 (winter 1999), p. 480.

21 Joe Earle, *Netsuke: Fantasy and Reality in Japanese Miniature Sculpture* (Boston: Museum of Fine Arts, Boston, 2001), p. 22.

22 William H. Coaldrake, *Architecture and Authority in Japan*, Nissan Institute/Routledge Japanese Studies Series (New York and London: Routledge, 1996), pp. 188–89.

23 Timon Screech, *Sex and the Floating World: Erotic Images in Japan, 1700–1820* (Honolulu: University of Hawaii Press, 1999), p. 116.

24 For an explanation of influence of samurai arts in netsuke, see Matthew Welch and Sharen Thane Chappell, *Netsuke: The Japanese Art of Miniature Carving* (Minneapolis: Minneapolis Institute of Arts; Chicago: Paragon Press, 1999), pp. 22–23.

25 Cammann, *Substance and Symbol in Chinese Toggles*, p. 146.

26 Ibid., p. 147.

27 Stimulated by the presence of Ōbaku-sect Chinese monks who were granted land south of Kyoto for a temple complex, this group of intellectuals endeavored to emulate the activities and style of life of the Chinese *wenren* (literati). The wenren practiced an amateur artist's mindset allowing themselves full freedom of personal expression.

28 Watanabe Masanori, "Thoughts on Early Netsuke in Relation to *Kokon meiga mitate zumo*," *International Netsuke Society Journal* 18, no. 4 (winter 1998), pp. 34–37.

29 Coaldrake, *Architecture and Authority in Japan*, p. 188.

30 For examples of seventeenth-century netsuke of the toggle type, see Welch and Chappell, *Netsuke*, pp. 17–20.

31 Earle, *Netsuke*, pp. 23–25.

32 Traditionally, the Kano surname of the Kano School of painters has been pronounced with a long "o," indicated by a macron (ō) in English transliteration. Recent Japanese scholarship has moved toward pronunciation with a short "o."

33 The seven gods of good fortune were meant to symbolize seven virtues considered essential: longevity, fortune, popularity, candor, amiability, dignity, and magnanimity. Gods were chosen from Daoism, Buddhism, Shinto, and Hinduism to form the group of seven.

34 In 1639, Tokugawa shogun Iemitsu ended all commerce with the outside world, except for regulated trade with the Chinese and Dutch at Nagasaki. In March 1854, Tokugawa shogun Iesada signed a treaty with American naval officer Matthew Perry, granting trading rights to the United States at two ports: Hakodate and Shimoda. Iesada was forced to grant similar concessions to England and Portugal in 1855.

35 Timon Screech, *The Western Scientific Gaze and Popular Imagery in Later Edo Japan: The Lens within the Heart* (Cambridge, England: Cambridge University Press, 1996), pp. 16–18.

36 Various authors have suggested a Chinese source for these patterns. Indeed, Chinese ivories do include portrayals of Dutchmen closely resembling later netsuke, although without patterned clothing.

37 Screech, *The Western Scientific Gaze*, p. 89.

38 Ibid., p. 169.

39 Timon Screech, *The Shogun's Painted Culture: Fear and Creativity in the Japanese States, 1760–1829*, Envisioning Asia (London: Reaktion Books, 2000), pp. 193–94.

40 Nishiyama Matsunosuke, *Edo Culture: Daily Life and Diversions in Urban Japan, 1600–1868* (Honolulu: University of Hawaii Press, 1997), p. 71.

41 In both Chinese and Japanese, the word for the number four (Ch., *si*, J., *shi*) is a homonym for the word meaning "death." Although four thus becomes the least lucky number, the use of other even numbers is avoided by association; odd numbers were considered lucky. Imbued with *yang* (positive male energy), the numbers three, five, and seven were used in Chinese design in a hierarchical manner, especially when they pertained to the dragon as a symbol of power. For example, if a dragon was used to decorate an item of clothing, the number of claws represented the rank of the wearer. A seven-clawed dragon was the most powerful and could only be used to represent the emperor, while five-clawed dragons symbolized esteemed government officials. Only dragons with three claws were acceptable on non-official garments and decorative items.

Similarly, a gift to the emperor or shogun would need to represent seven lucky motifs, such as seven Chinese boys, seven pots, seven coins, etc. A person of substantial rank would receive a gift with five repeated motifs, while those of less exalted status would receive objects that depicted three matched motifs.

The hierarchical position of the number seven is understood by the seven lucky gods (*shichifukujin*) to represent the seven aspects of good character; see Merrily Baird, *Symbols of Japan: Thematic Motifs in Art and Design* (New York: Rizzoli International Publications, Inc., 2001), especially pp. 198–201, 230–31. For an explanation and examples of the centrality of the number five in Chinese symbolism, adopted into Japan, see Baird, *Symbols of Japan*, pp. 28–31. The importance of a combination of three can be gleaned from the selection of three imperial regalia: the Yata mirror, the Kusanagi sword, and the Yasakani curved jewels; see Baird, *Symbols of Japan*, p. 232.

42 Joe Earle, *The Robert S. Huthart Collection of Iwami Netsuke* (Hong Kong, 2000), p. 10. For a description and examples of the *ukibori* technique, see pp. 81–82 of Odile Madden's essay, in this volume.

43 See Nishiyama, "Provincial Culture of the Kasei Period (1804–1830)," chap. 6 in *Edo Culture*.

44 Hata Mitsuru, "Naitō Toyomasa: Han Artist of the Sasayama Domain," in *Netsuke no shizuku* (Tokyo: Nihon Netsuke Kenkyūkai, 2000), pp. 125–28.

45 Nishiyama, *Edo Culture*, p. 41.

46 Ibid., p. 185.

47 Various performance types are explained in "Itinerants, Actors, Pilgrims," chap. 7 of Nishiyama's *Edo Culture*.

48 Shimatani Yoichi, "Red Robe Kokusai," ed. and trans. Nori Watanabe, *International Netsuke Society Journal* 19, no. 2 (summer 1999), p. 29.

49 Katsuhide Akabane, "Mitsuhiro and *Takarabukuro*," in Mitsuhiro, *Takarabukuro: A Netsuke Artist Notebook*, adapted by Charles Temple, trans. Misao Mikoshiba (Chicago: Art Media Resources, Ltd., 2001), pp. 17–18.

Sebastian Izzard

THE RAYMOND AND FRANCES BUSHELL collection of netsuke was made in the grand tradition of the late-nineteenth- and early-twentieth-century collectors. At its height, the collection numbered in the thousands, and every school and tradition was represented within it with superb examples. In important ways, however, Raymond and Frances had their own approach to the subject. Each collector reflects his or her generation in the values, tastes, judgments, and approach brought to bear on the subject. Early netsuke collectors, for example, had a taste for intricate, figurative pieces—which often portrayed the legends and tales of Japan—in part because the themes and elaborate carving appealed to the late-nineteenth-century aesthetic, and in part because the buyers had a Victorian respect for hard work and craftsmanship.

Netsuke of the Meiji, Taishō, and Shōwa Eras (1868–1989)

FIG. 1
KAIGYOKUSAI MASATSUGU
(Japan, 1813–1892)
Buddhist Jewel of Wisdom Carved with Mountain Pavilions
ivory with staining, sumi, inlays
M.91.250.224
CAT. 495

Raymond and Frances's acquisitions evolved out of the circumstances in which they lived. Unlike their netsuke-collecting predecessors, they resided for many years in Japan, and one result is that their collection mirrors the native taste for netsuke. Indeed Raymond, through his books on netsuke and collecting, and his patronage of the great twentieth-century carver Masatoshi (Nakamura Tokisada, 1915–2001), could be said to have moved from merely reflecting a taste to creating one. His concerns with the nature of collecting and its effect on the relationship between collector and artist were deeply felt, as were his ideas about collecting as a discipline, and these he expressed succinctly and with humor in his many books and articles.

The wealth of netsuke by later carvers in the Bushell collection attests to Raymond and Frances's more modern approach. The collection contains a superb selection of the works of Kaigyokusai Masatsugu (1813–1892). Like many master artisans of his generation, Kaigyokusai lived in uncertain times, achieving success in a career that saw famine and social revolution during the late Edo period, and the rapid industrialization of Japan during the following Meiji era (1868–1912). Despite a natural conservatism, his skill was such that he was able to transcend changed circumstances, adapt himself to the times, and yet never lose his artistic integrity. Although he used a wide range of materials, he is most famous for employing *tōkata*, the finest-quality ivory from the tusks of the elephant herds of Southeast Asia. Kaigyokusai had the ability to carve intricate and fully functional netsuke with exquisite detail, and at his best he imbued his work with an almost lifelike quality.

Raymond's feelings regarding Kaigyokusai are best expressed in his own words: "A netsuke by Kaigyokusai at his greatest is no less than sublime, a piece of utter perfection and purity."[1] These were not netsuke made for the European and American globe-trotters who were now visiting Japan and for whom netsuke had become suitable tourist souvenirs. The high quality of Kaigyokusai's netsuke and the materials he used precluded this type of client. He instead marketed his wares to the wealthy merchant community of Osaka and to former samurai who were doing well in the rapidly growing modern Japanese economy. They kept their treasures safely stored, bringing them out on special occasions and in moments of relaxation, when traditional clothing was worn and new purchases could be shown for the admiration of friends and acquaintances.

During his early career, Kaigyokusai is thought to have specialized in making pieces with fine interior carving, such as shells or pine cones that open to reveal an intricate landscape. The netsuke in the shape of a Buddhist "jewel of wisdom" (FIG. 1) is an example. Here the netsuke does not open, but it is carved out with great skill to represent a Chinese-style landscape with scholars' pavilions wrapped in clouds in the mountains. The fine-grained ivory has a moist feeling typical of the tōkata that Kaigyokusai invariably selected. The

FIG. 2
Kaigyokusai Masatsugu
(Japan, 1813–1892)
Fox and Drum
ivory with sumi, inlays
M.91.250.218
CAT. 560

resting fox (FIG. 2), with its paw casually slung through the cord of its hand drum, is an example from Kaigyokusai's middle period. Each detail is carefully and realistically carved, while the playful subject is rendered with charming whimsy. Kaigyokusai's *Floating Crane* (CAT. 370, illustrated on p. 13) is a masterpiece from the early Meiji era. The body is formed in a compact manner perfectly suited to its use, with no protruding features that could easily be broken off or damaged. The eye stares at you with an alertness in direct contrast to the bird's neatly folded body. Each feather appears individually carved.

Despite the social changes brought about by the imperial restoration, Kaigyokusai was able to retain his traditional market. The Edo-period system of long apprenticeship encouraged exemplary attention to detail and technical skill. Other equally talented men, some of whom ran large studios, such as the lacquer artist and painter Shibata Zeshin (1807–1891), were forced to look outward, to Europe and the United States, and marketed their wares on an international level (FIG. 3). Yet others, such as the metalworker Kanō Natsuo (1828–1898), who specialized in sword furniture, essentially lost their livelihood when in 1876 new laws forbade the wearing of swords in public except by military officers. These artists were compelled by circumstance to change their trade.

Suzuki Tōkoku (1846–1913) belongs to the next generation of netsuke artists. Three artists are thought to have used this name, the second two being descendants of the first. The lacquer and wood *manjū* netsuke decorated with an owl (FIG. 4) is thought to date

FIG. 3
Shibata Zeshin
(Japan, 1807–1891)
Box with Teakettle Design
bamboo, lacquer
M.87.263.49
CAT. 710

FIG. 4
Suzuki Tōkoku
(Japan, 1846–1913)
Owl
wood with inlays, lacquer; manjū type
M.91.250.238
CAT. 381

from the late nineteenth to the early twentieth centuries, a time when Tōkoku's signature style had already emerged. Tōkoku was highly skilled in the fine use of inlay, which is rendered with such detail and precision that his netsuke have never been successfully emulated. While *Daruma Yawning* (FIG. 5) is an early example of his work, *Seal Group* (FIG. 6), constructed in a mosaic of different woods and other materials, is typical of this inlay type of netsuke.

The recognition of Buddhist icons as objects of aesthetic appreciation was one of the radical changes brought about by Japan's industrialization. In the early Meiji era, the government felt that it needed a state religion and, because Buddhism and Confucianism had both been imported, Shinto, as the only indigenous religion, was chosen. Some Buddhist temples were demolished and their art discarded. By the 1880s, however, the mood had changed, and Buddhist artworks were being removed from temples and placed in museums or sold to local or foreign collectors. In its humble way, the netsuke of Bukan and a tiger (FIG. 7), a beloved image among Zen Buddhists, reflects this greater reverence.

FIG. 5
SUZUKI TŌKOKU
(Japan, 1846–1913)
Daruma Yawning
wood with inlays
M.91.250.74
CAT. 121

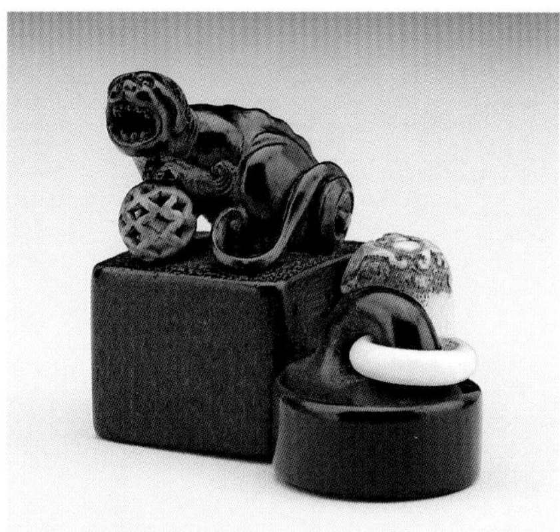

FIG. 6
SUZUKI TŌKOKU
(Japan, 1846–1913)
Seal Group
wood, ivory with staining
M.91.250.240
CAT. 699

FIG. 7
TŌKOKU II or TŌKOKU III
(Japan, late 19th–early 20th century)
The Zen Master Bukan
early 20th century
ivory with staining, sumi, red pigment, inlays
M.91.250.242
CAT. 113

FIG. 8
Ozaki Kokusai
(Japan, 1835–circa 1892)
Elongated Kappa
stag antler; obihasami type
M.91.250.276
CAT. 249

The resurgence of interest in Buddhism can also be seen in the imagery of the so-called Asakusa School of carvers, led by Ozaki Kokusai (1835–ca. 1892), who worked mostly in stag antler. Several carvers of this school lived near the great Kinryūzan Sensōji temple—also known as the Asakusa Kannon Temple—a religious complex in a district of downtown Tokyo. Often their netsuke, pouch clasps, and pipe cases took as a point of reference religious objects such as rosaries, and the begging bowls used by the mendicant monks who wandered the area. Other subject matter included everyday utensils, animals, and blossoming flowers. The *obihasami* netsuke (FIG. 8) is unusual in its secular theme of a *kappa*, a mythical beast that lurked in streams and ponds, waiting to ensnare careless children.

By the 1890s, an industrial policy had been established that encouraged the manufacture of traditional craft goods for export as well as local consumption. Through exhibitions in Europe and the Americas, Japanese art objects became known to a much wider audience. Leading artists such as Shibata Zeshin had become preservationists who strove to maintain traditional skills. Another preservationist was Ishikawa Kōmei (ca. 1848/52–1913), a celebrated ivory carver born to a family of sculptors in Asakusa, Tokyo. In 1891, he became a professor at the Tokyo School of Fine Arts, which had been established in 1887. His ivory netsuke of a monkey (FIG. 9) is an excellent example of his academic style, loosely based on European models.

The Bushell collection is particularly rich in the work of the Sō School. The move to meticulous and realistic carving seen with Kaigyokusai further evolved at the end of the nineteenth and early twentieth centuries with the work of Sōko (Morita Kisaburō, 1879–1943) and Ōuchi Gyokusō (1879–1944), the school's main proponents. The early twentieth century was a prosperous time for Japan. These netsuke were marketed to an affluent class of merchants and industrialists, who could afford such painstakingly carved and finished works. Raymond himself remarked on the many gorgeous smoking sets bearing Sō School netsuke that he had encountered, which belonged to descendants of wealthy late Meiji and Taishō families.[2]

Miniaturization of everyday objects such as crates of oranges, bundles of firewood, bound rocks used as bulwarks for rivers, string-bound sake bottles, and flower blossoms now became fashionable. Carved in incredible detail and rendered as though it had been carelessly

FIG. 9
Ishikawa Kōmei
(Japan, circa 1848/52–1913)
Monkey
ivory
M.91.250.77
CAT. 330

discarded by an errant child, the box of traditional children's toys by Sōko (FIG. 10) is a fine example of the type. The different surfaces of the various toys are carefully polished and finished to bring out the natural luster of the wood. This devotion to finish, with even the most inaccessible areas being polished to the same standard as the rest of the netsuke, is characteristic of Sōko's work. The taste for realism can also be found in his *naruko*, a noisemaker for scaring birds (FIG. 11), and in his almost baroque *Demon Soliciting Alms* (FIG. 12).

Sōko, however, could work in several styles at the same time, and this dexterity is a hallmark of all members of the Sō School. His walking mountain ascetic (*yamabushi*) is a subject typical of netsuke of the late Edo period (FIG. 13), but the carefully carved surfaces, expressive face, and minutely rendered detail make it a fine example of the Sōko manner.

FIG. 10
Sōko (Morita Kisaburō)
(Japan, 1879–1943)
Toy Box
wood
AC1998.249.85
CAT. 748

FIG. 11
Sōko (Morita Kisaburō)
(Japan, 1879–1943)
Bird Scare
wood
AC1998.249.120
CAT. 751

FIG. 12
Sōko (Morita Kisaburō)
(Japan, 1879–1943)
Demon Soliciting Alms
wood
M.91.250.247
CAT. 143

FIG. 13
Sōko (Morita Kisaburō)
(Japan, 1879–1943)
Mountain Ascetic
wood
M.91.250.318
CAT. 149

Gyokusō also made netsuke in a style grounded in the traditions of nineteenth-century netsuke. His wandering *Tanuki* (FIG. 14), with a gourd-shaped sake bottle slung over its shoulder, for example, is reminiscent of Kaigyokusai's *Fox and Drum* (see FIG. 2), whose style Gyokusō attempted to emulate. He captured the same late-Edo-period feeling in his *Courtesan Eguchi no Kimi As Fugen, Bodhisattva of Universal Wisdom* (FIG. 15). Here, the figure, dressed in the robes of a high-ranking courtesan of the late Edo period, reads a love letter. The reference is to Fugen, who is usually shown seated on a recumbent elephant. During the eighteenth and nineteenth centuries, it became common to represent Fugen as Eguchi, a prostitute who famously turned away the poet-priest Saigyō (1118–1190) when he sought shelter for the night. Presenting the bodhisattva in the guise of a prostitute demonstrates the Buddhist concept that appearances are illusory and that there is no fundamental difference between sanctity and impurity. This juxtaposition appealed to wits in the late Edo era, and the theme became popular.

FIG. 14
Ōuchi Gyokusō
(Japan, 1879–1944)
Tanuki
ivory with staining, sumi, red pigment, inlays
M.91.250.122
CAT. 238

FIG. 15
Ōuchi Gyokusō
(Japan, 1879–1944)
The Courtesan Eguchi no Kimi As Fugen, Bodhisattva of Universal Wisdom
ivory with light staining, sumi
M.91.250.80
CAT. 543

FIG. 16
Sōju (Japan, born 1918)
The Demon of Rashōmon
wood
AC1998.249.1
CAT. 226

The Sō School then embarked on trying to create netsuke that were miniature three-dimensional versions of imagery found in prints and paintings. Sōju (b. 1918) for example, rendered in netsuke the image of Ibaraki, the demon of the Rashōmon gate, retrieving her severed arm (FIG. 16). Around 1840, Shibata Zeshin had been commissioned by an association of sugar wholesalers to make a votive tablet, and he chose this portrayal of Ibaraki as his theme. His painting was so popular that Zeshin was catapulted to nationwide fame, and he continued to use the composition on paintings, screens, and lacquer. More than thirty years later, the star kabuki actor Onoe Kikugorō V (1844–1903) commissioned the playwright Kawatake Mokuami (1816–1893) to write a play about Ibaraki, featuring the actor in the main role. Zeshin painted the play's billboard, which was later donated to Sensōji temple, where it can still be found. Sōju's three-dimensional version is obviously based on Zeshin's composition (FIG. 17).

Gyokusō's son Ōuchi Sōsui (1911–1972) pursued a similar path with netsuke based on famous Japanese prints. In the early 1920s, the Parisian jeweler Henri Vever (1854–1943) sold his renowned collection of Japanese woodcut prints to Matsukata Kōjirō, a wealthy Japanese industrialist, who later gave the collection to the Tokyo National Museum. One of the most important works in the collection was an oversize print by Torii Kiyomasu I featuring the actor Ichikawa Danjūrō I (1660–1704) as Soga no Gorō uprooting a bamboo

FIG. 17
Shibata Zeshin
(Japan, 1807–1891)
Ibaraki Retrieving Her Severed Arm
(detail)
1882
pair of two-panel screens; ink, color, and gold on paper
66 3/8 x 65 3/8 in. (168.6 x 166 cm)
signed: Zeshin
sealed: Tairyūkyo
Mary and Jackson Burke Foundation
Photograph by Sheldan Comfert Collins

FIG. 18
Torii Kiyomasu I
Ichikawa Danjūrō I As Soga no Gorō Uprooting a Bamboo
18th century
woodblock print with hand-applied color
Tokyo National Museum, Tokyo

FIG. 19
Ōuchi Sōsui (Japan, 1911–1972)
Soga no Gorō
ivory with staining, sumi
M.91.250.211
CAT. 541

(FIG. 18). This dynamic print has been certified as an Important Cultural Property and has even been featured on a Japanese postage stamp. This latter miniaturization of the image undoubtedly inspired Sōsui to make his ivory three-dimensional version (FIG. 19). Other works in the same genre by Sōsui include a netsuke featuring a double portrait by the great portraitist of actors Tōshūsai Sharaku (active 1794/95).

The period following World War II saw foreign influences affecting netsuke. Obviously the American occupation of Japan—Raymond himself arrived in September 1945—brought netsuke carvers a new clientele and broadened their horizons. Raymond's interest was sincere, and he attempted to advise carvers how to improve their market, not always successfully. He wrote: "For a time, I tried to direct Sōsui's effort towards single figures and simple designs as being much less time-consuming than his usual tours de force. . . . Sōsui attempted this new approach for a couple of years but finally quit in a state of exasperation, directed at me, and reverted to his former style." [3] Although Sōsui's preferred subjects were complex figure carvings—for example, scenes from *Genji monogatari* (The tale of Genji) or passengers on a ferry boat—many of his more interesting netsuke are based on anthropomorphic bronze vessels like those exca-

FIG. 20
Ōuchi Sōsui (Japan, 1911–1972)
Hawk Stylized As Chinese Bronze
ebony with inlays
M.91.250.227
CAT. 705

vated in China (FIG. 20), while his *Mother and Child* seems to refer to a Western sculptural tradition (FIG. 21). It may have been this type of netsuke, with cleanly cut, simple lines, that Raymond tried to steer the artist toward.

The flamboyant boxwood netsuke of Sōsui's contemporary Shōko (Nishino Shōtarō, 1915–1969) are also reworkings of imagery in the Edo tradition. His *Ghosts of Oiwa and Kohei* (FIG. 22), for example, is based on a horrific and highly popular play *Tōkaidō Yotsuya kaidan* (Ghost story of Yotsuya on the Tōkaidō), written and staged by the dramatist Tsuruya Nanboku IV (1755–1829) in 1825. The plot involved a dissolute samurai, Tamiya Iemon, who poisoned his wife, Oiwa, and then killed Kobotoke Kohei, his former servant and the dupe who obtained the poison for him. He tied both their bodies to a door and dumped the door into a river. Needless to say, their angry spirits came back to haunt him. Shōko's seated Inkada Sonja (FIG. 23) is characteristic of his typical work. The religious spirit that infused much of his output ultimately led him to cease making netsuke in the early 1960s to carve Buddhist statuary.

21

22

FIG. 21
Ōuchi Sōsui (Japan, 1911–1972)
Mother and Child
wood
M.91.250.212
CAT. 636

FIG. 22
Shōko (Nishino Shōtarō)
(Japan, 1915–1969)
Ghosts of Oiwa and Kohei
1959
boxwood
M.91.250.84
CAT. 681

23

FIG. 23
Shōko (Nishino Shōtarō)
(Japan, 1915–1969)
Inkada Sonja: Disciple of the Buddha with Long Eyebrows
1955
wood
M.91.250.231
CAT. 93

FIG. 24
Masatoshi (Nakamura Tokisada) (Japan, 1915–2001)
Benten Kozō
July 1957
ivory with staining, sumi, red and gold pigments
M.91.250.98
CAT. 546

FIG. 25
Masatoshi (Nakamura Tokisada) (Japan, 1915–2001)
Kappa with Cucumbers in Head Bowl
December 1978
boxwood with inlays
AC1998.249.141
CAT. 254

It is natural, given Raymond's long and fruitful relationship with Masatoshi, that the Bushell collection contains many superb examples of Masatoshi's work; in 1981, Raymond wrote that for thirty years he and the artist had been bound together in a congenial relationship.[4] Masatoshi's netsuke are firmly rooted in traditional Japanese imagery. His depiction of the heroic villain Benten Kozō, completed in 1957 (FIG. 24), is taken from kabuki theater. The character snarls as he reveals his tattoos to the hapless manager of the Hamamatsuya drapery stores, whom he has tricked, and his disguise—a woman's wig—is now askew. Both the seated kappa feeding himself cucumbers stored in the depression on top of his head (FIG. 25), and the *sashi* netsuke of a cicada made from a hippopotamus tooth (FIG. 26), are representative of Masatoshi's work in the 1970s. As his career progressed, Masatoshi became more eccentric. His *Monster in the Guise of the Goddess of Mercy*, a creature that laughs to himself as he saunters along, disguised as Kannon (FIG. 27), is in a tradition of Japanese monster imagery that goes back to medieval times, yet is strangely modern in

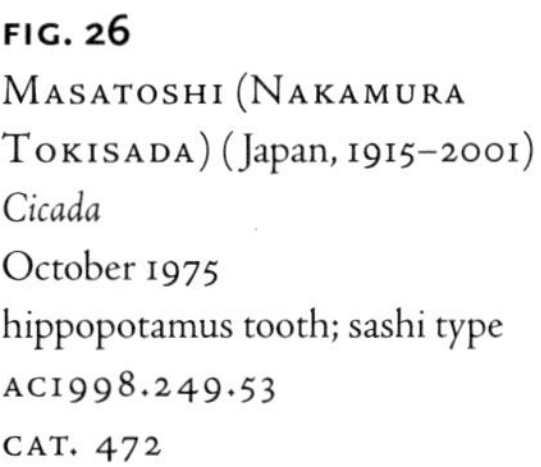

FIG. 26
Masatoshi (Nakamura Tokisada) (Japan, 1915–2001)
Cicada
October 1975
hippopotamus tooth; sashi type
AC1998.249.53
CAT. 472

FIG. 27
Masatoshi (Nakamura Tokisada) (Japan, 1915–2001)
Monster in the Guise of the Goddess of Mercy
July 1976
ivory with staining, sumi
M.91.250.95
CAT. 227

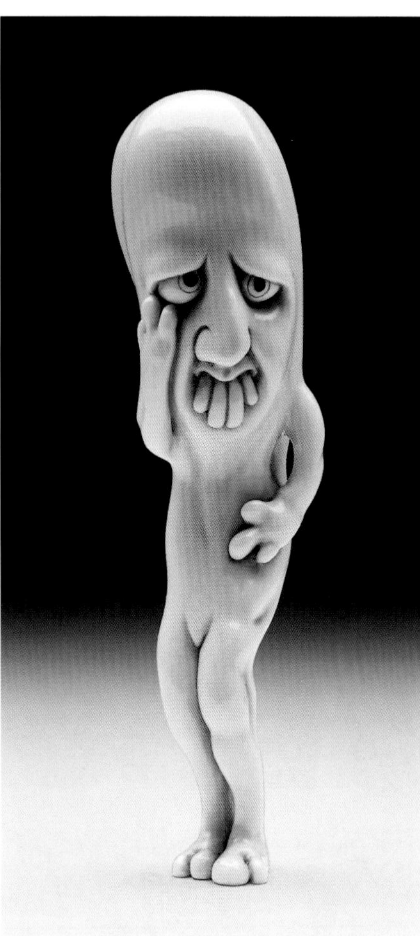

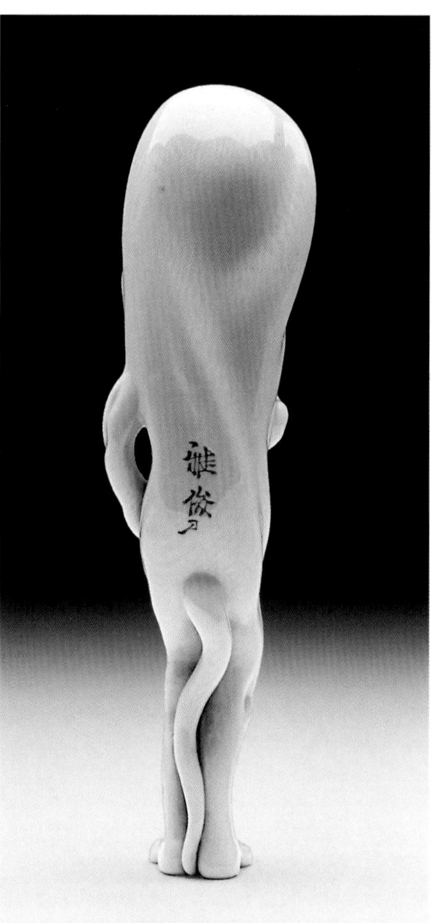

FIG. 28, FRONT AND BACK
MASATOSHI (NAKAMURA TOKISADA) (Japan, 1915–2001)
Biron: Monster Made of Jelly
October 1978
ivory with light staining, black coral inlays
M.91.250.91
CAT. 230

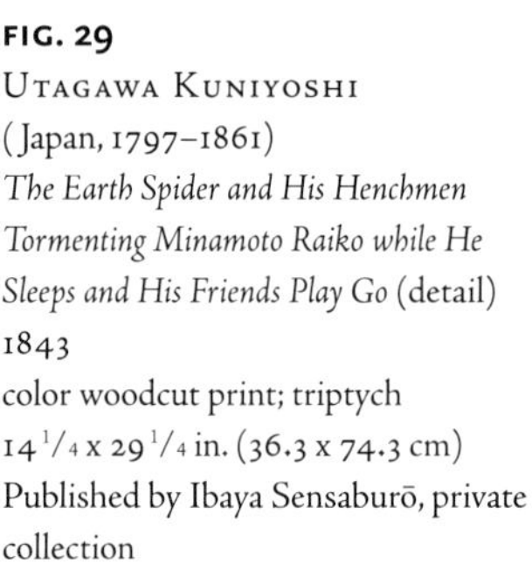

FIG. 29
UTAGAWA KUNIYOSHI (Japan, 1797–1861)
The Earth Spider and His Henchmen Tormenting Minamoto Raiko while He Sleeps and His Friends Play Go (detail)
1843
color woodcut print; triptych
14 1/4 x 29 1/4 in. (36.3 x 74.3 cm)
Published by Ibaya Sensaburō, private collection

feeling. The same is true of his *Biron* (FIG. 28), a jelly-bodied creature, which, while also harking back to earlier monster imagery, especially that found in the works of Utagawa School printmakers of the nineteenth century (FIG. 29), could also have been conjured up by a modern Japanese *manga* artist.

Raymond's interest in supporting contemporary netsuke carvers kept him active as a patron of the most recent generation. The netsuke by Meikei (b. 1932) of Endō Moritō holding the head of Kesa is an example in the collection of a current master's work (FIG. 30).

Raymond Bushell was a dedicated collector deeply committed to his subject. Nor was his interest in the arts of Japan limited to netsuke alone. He possessed small yet choice collections of inrō, sword fittings, prints, and paintings, as well as Chinese jades and snuff bottles. It was with netsuke, however, that his mark was made. Here he showed himself to be exceptional, both for the extraordinary quality and range of his Edo-period pieces and for his interest in modern and contemporary examples. The latter concern shows him to have been a skilled acquirer; his devotion to netsuke led him to help and sustain working artists, and he left his chosen field a better place. Raymond and Frances Bushell's gift of the finest netsuke in their collection to the Los Angeles County Museum of Art, exhibited in its own gallery, seems a fitting conclusion to an exemplary collecting career.

1 Raymond Bushell, *Collectors' Netsuke* (New York: Walker/Weatherhill, 1971), p. 87.
2 Ibid., p. 142.
3 Ibid., p. 185.
4 Masatoshi, *The Art of Netsuke Carving*, as told to Raymond Bushell (Tokyo and New York: Kodansha International Ltd., 1981), p. 8.

FIG. 30, FRONT AND BACK
Meikei (Japan, born 1932)
Moritō and Kesa
wood
AC1998.249.89
CAT. 547

Odile Madden

Whereas significant scholarship has been devoted to the art of netsuke, relatively little attention has been paid to the techniques by which they are fabricated; this study seeks to fill that void, specifically with regard to netsuke carved from ivory. The research took place in 1999, during a technical study and cleaning of approximately one hundred ivory netsuke in the collection of the Los Angeles County Museum of Art (LACMA). This presented a special opportunity to glean information about materials and techniques that was previously available only in anecdotal form from a handful of artists and collectors. In the study, the primary facts come from the netsuke themselves, because each retains evidence of its manufacture that can be witnessed and understood through careful visual examination. By combining these observations with available literary sources, we can draw conclusions about the ways in which ivory netsuke from the seventeenth through the twentieth centuries have been fabricated.

Techniques of netsuke carving have traditionally been held as close trade secrets that are handed down directly from master to apprentice, without the use of formal manuals. Said netsuke carver Masatoshi (1915–2001), "I have never joined organizations or clubs for promotion of ivory carving or for the discussion and study of methods and techniques. . . . Admittedly, the secrecy sometimes resulted in the loss of unique methods."[1]

Ivory Netsuke: Techniques and Materials

Octopus
Japan, mid-19th century
ivory with staining, sumi, double inlays
AC1998.249.92
CAT. 450

Because there are no manuals, it is rare to find first-hand accounts by artists of their materials and techniques. However, with the growing popularity of netsuke among collectors and a concomitant shift in the netsuke carver's role from craftsman to artist, there has been increased impetus for the carvers to share information.[2] Masatoshi gives the most notable example of such accounts in his *Art of Netsuke Carving*: He describes his tools and materials, as well as carving, coloring, and finishing techniques. He was taught these techniques by his father, who in turn was apprenticed at the beginning of the Meiji era (1868–1912) to his uncle, Toshiaki (1854–1896), a carver of *okimono* (small, decorative ornaments). Consequently, Masatoshi's account lends insight into netsuke-carving methods from the mid-nineteenth through the twentieth centuries. Because the book is also a catalogue of his work, the techniques Masatoshi describes are illustrated with specific netsuke he has carved, many of which are now in the Bushell collection at LACMA.

Netsuke carved from ivory first appeared in the seventeenth century as a byproduct of the *shamisen* industry.[3] The strings of the shamisen, a Japanese musical instrument, are plucked with a heavy ivory plectrum. When the plectrum is carved, several pieces of waste ivory are created, namely, the pointed cone at the end of the tusk and others with rounded or slanting sides.[4] It is reported that netsuke made from this waste ivory were of ordinary quality and intended for the general population.[5]

As ivory grew in popularity as a netsuke material, the more skilled carvers of that time, including Kaigyokusai Masatsugu (1813–1892), began to choose *tōkata* (the finest-quality ivory, usually found in Siamese and Annamese tusks) rather than shamisen remnants.[6] Ivory netsuke became extremely popular during the Edo period (1615–1868) and into the Meiji era, when netsuke fell out of fashion in Japanese dress but grew in desirability among collectors and in the export market. This trend continued until World War II, when luxury materials such as ivory became scarce.

Today, ivory is still used as a netsuke medium. Miriam Kinsey reports that the majority of ivory in the 1970s was imported to Japan from Africa. Though harder ivory varieties from India and Thailand were reportedly preferable for netsuke carving, the export of ivory from those countries had by that time been restricted. Subsequent restrictions on the trade of African ivory have made it difficult for the netsuke carver to obtain this material. However, when Kinsey's book was published in 1977, lengths of African elephant tusk could still be purchased from a number of Japanese importers.[7] In recent decades, carvers have begun to experiment with more readily available ivory-like materials, including fossilized mammoth tusk, fossilized walrus tooth, and hippopotamus tooth obtained from zoos.[8]

IVORY STRUCTURE AND COMPOSITION

True ivory is derived from elephant tusks, which are overdeveloped teeth. The upper incisors grow continuously during the elephant's life to a length disproportionate with the other teeth. Though the length and shape of the tusk varies with the species, sex, and age of the elephant, all share a basic structure (FIG. 1).[9] Elephant tusks are solid except for the root, which is embedded in the skull and makes up approximately one-third of the total tusk length. The pulp cavity, a hollow at the center of the root, houses the nerves and blood vessels of the living tusk. This cavity is only present in a fraction of the tusk length, tapering to a narrow nerve channel that runs longitudinally through the center of the rest of the tusk.

The bulk of the tusk is composed of dentin, a dense white material contained within a protective shell. Dentin, the material prized by ivory carvers, is composed of a mineral

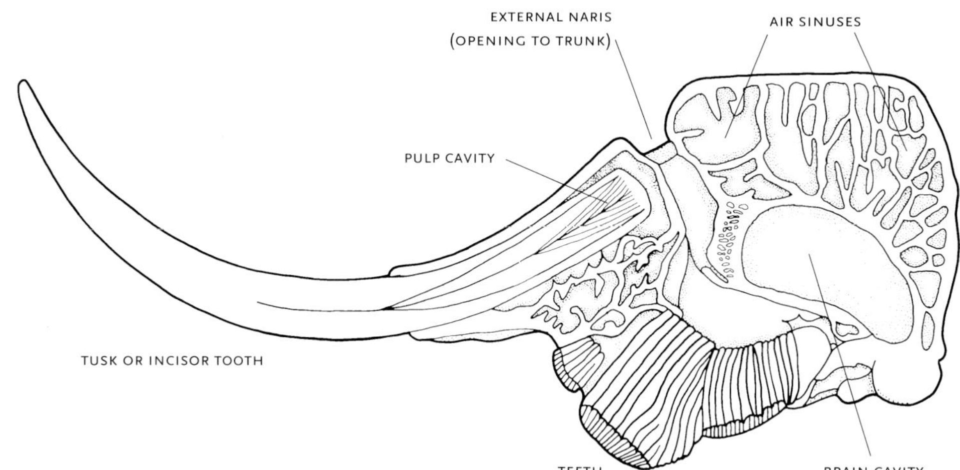

FIG. 1
This cross section shows the physiology of an elephant's cranium and tusk.

phase that is primarily calcium phosphate (64%), an organic phase (24%) that is primarily the protein collagen (18%), and water (11.15%).[10] It is relatively soft (2.5 on the Mohs' scale[11]) and can be worked with tools similar to those used by woodcarvers.[12] The density of the material and the high proportion of collagen allow ivory to be polished to a high gloss and translucent sheen.

During the elephant's life, nutrients and waste are transported between the pulp cavity and the dentin layer through radiating microscopic channels as narrow as 0.0169 millimeter in diameter.[13] Viewed in cross section, these channels form a system of intersecting arches called the Shreger pattern. This structure is unique to elephant ivory and is the basic diagnostic tool for distinguishing it from other ivory-like materials (FIG. 2).

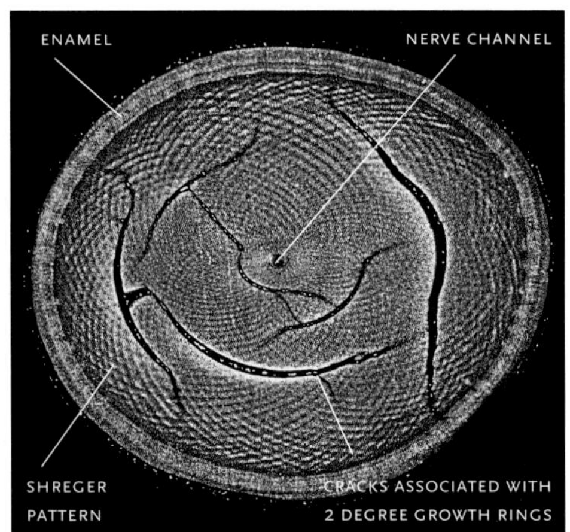

FIG. 2
A polished cross section of elephant ivory, shown actual size, with individual features highlighted.

The outer surfaces of the tusk are covered with a hard cementum layer, also referred to as the rind, that ranges in thickness from approximately 2 to 7 millimeters. Cementum is brittle and generally undesirable for carving.[14] However, some netsuke retain remnants of cementum, visible as lozenge-shaped stacks of alternating dark- and light-colored layers, perhaps because the piece of ivory being carved was small. The cementum layer tends to exhibit different coloration than the adjacent dentin.[15]

The structure and chemical composition described here are general characteristics. The quality of ivory varies greatly among tusks and even within the same tusk, and the species, habitat, and diet of the animal influence tusk size, hardness, texture, and color.[16] Such variations can affect the ease with which a piece of ivory can be carved and polished. Tusks may also have internal irregularities (for example, cracks, and small lumps of ivory resembling peanuts) that form inside the pulp cavity or within the tusk wall as a pathological condition.

The texture and shape of ivory also depend on its position in the tusk. Masatoshi's diagram (FIG. 3) shows his interpretation of the different sections of an elephant tusk.[17] According to him, the tip and second quarter are particularly prized for their fine grain.[18]

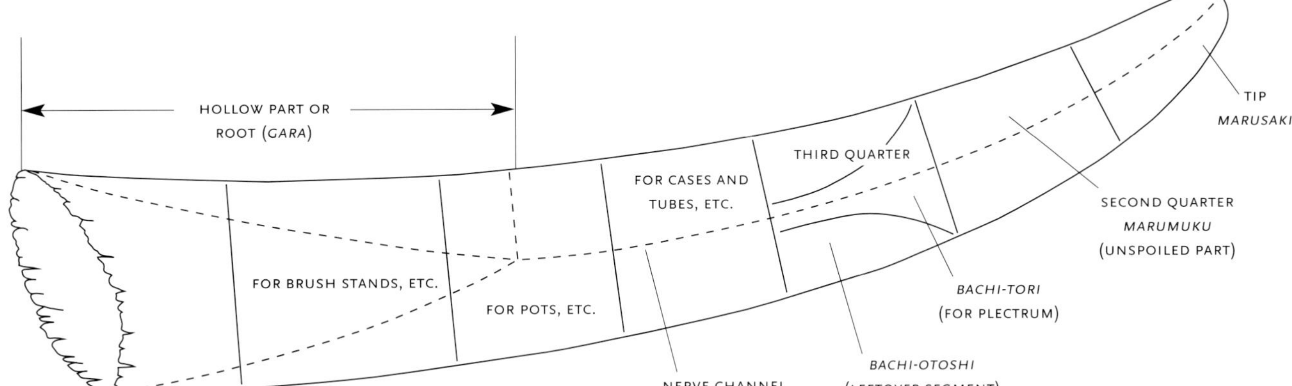

FIG. 3
Masatoshi's diagram from *The Art of Netsuke Carving* illustrates his interpretation of the different sections of an elephant tusk and the products derived from them.

Netsuke made from these sections can sometimes be identified by the presence of the nerve channel, a hole measuring a few millimeters in diameter. In netsuke, this hole may be filled in naturally, with a small ivory pin, or with another material such as ivory dust mixed with fish glue (*nikawa*), or it might be worked into the design (FIGS. 4 and 4a).[19]

Even if there is no nerve channel, the position of a netsuke relative to the tusk from which it was carved can sometimes be deduced from a visual examination. The presence of the Shreger pattern will confirm that the material is elephant ivory and will indicate the orientation of the tusk cross section. Examining the side of the netsuke that corresponds with the tusk cross section may also indicate the direction the netsuke faces within the tusk. In addition to the Shreger pattern, the cross section of an elephant tusk exhibits concentric growth rings. When a portion of a ring is visible on a netsuke, the entire ring can be approximated; the ring's center indicates the location of the nerve channel.

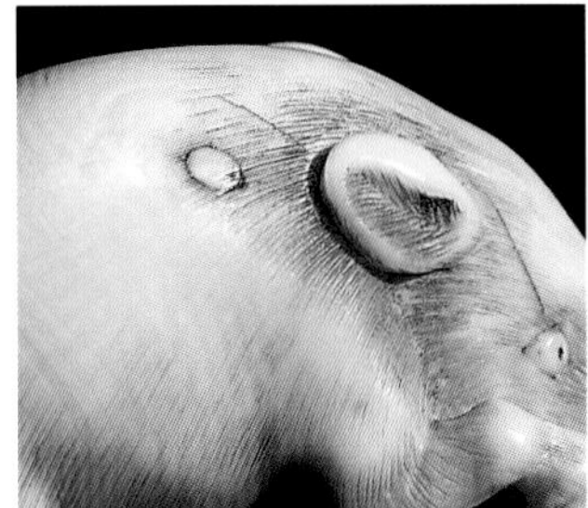

FIG. 4, OVERALL AND DETAIL
Wild Boar Rooting
Japan, 19th century
ivory with staining, sumi
M.91.250.48
CAT. 343

Note the small, round ivory plug (above) that disguises the nerve channel in *Wild Boar Rooting*.

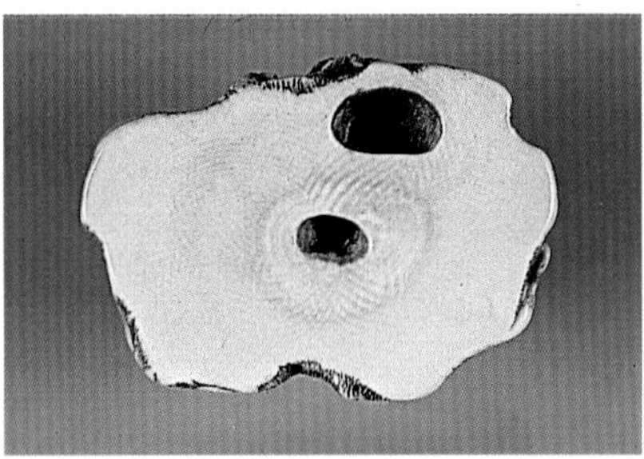

FIG. 4a
This view of the underside of *Wild Boar Rooting* shows the other end of the nerve channel (which has been enlarged to form the smaller hole of the *himotōshi*), Shreger pattern, and secondary growth rings.

The direction the netsuke faces within the tusk can provide useful historical information about carving technique. According to Masatoshi, eighteenth- and nineteenth-century netsuke that depict standing figures tended to be carved from thin longitudinal sections of ivory, with the front of the figure facing the center of the tusk. This is substantiated by LACMA's netsuke.

The quality of ivory also depends upon the quality of the environment in which the material is stored after it is removed from the elephant. Ivory's collagenous component is susceptible to cracking in dry conditions. The cracks in ivory generally form in concentric circles when the tusk is viewed in cross section and run longitudinally along the length of the tusk (see FIG. 2). Other conditions common to ivory that has been poorly stored include mold growth, mold staining, and staining from contact with corroding metals.

It is evident, therefore, that netsuke carvers must choose their material carefully. A carver would rarely purchase an entire tusk; instead, he would find a fine piece of an appropriate size that possessed the desired texture and was free of anomalies.

FIG. 5
Tiger Licking Its Paw
Japan, 18th century
ivory with staining, sumi
AC1998.249.125
CAT. 273

TOOLS

The netsuke carver has traditionally made his own tools, which include a variety of metal saws, files, chisels, drills, and knives.[20] Power tools, such as electric drills, are frowned upon and should be used only sparingly.

The carver works a netsuke against a small, notched slab of wood that is solidly mounted to the workbench. Some carvers may also use a vise. To begin, the carver cuts a piece of ivory from the tusk with a handsaw and draws guidelines for the design onto the ivory block. The carver will then rough out the general shape with flat files, curved "clam" files, and chisels.[21] File marks from this step are rarely found on the finished piece, having most often been removed by polishing.

Once the netsuke's general shape has been achieved, details are rendered with knives and chisels. According to Masatoshi, traditional knives have a solid, triangular, three-dimensional blade with the cutting edge on either the left or the right. A wide range of sizes and shapes are used to achieve a variety of carving depths and surface effects.[22] The most common tool mark encountered on the netsuke examined in this study is the V-shaped line (FIGS. 5a and 5b), which was probably carved with traditional triangular knives.

Chisels may be square or round. The former produce a flat face or edge, while the latter produce "a curved surface, a rounded edge, or a groove."[23] Chisel marks are sometimes accompanied by "chatter," a series of ridges running perpendicular to the carved line that are caused by the vibration of the tool.

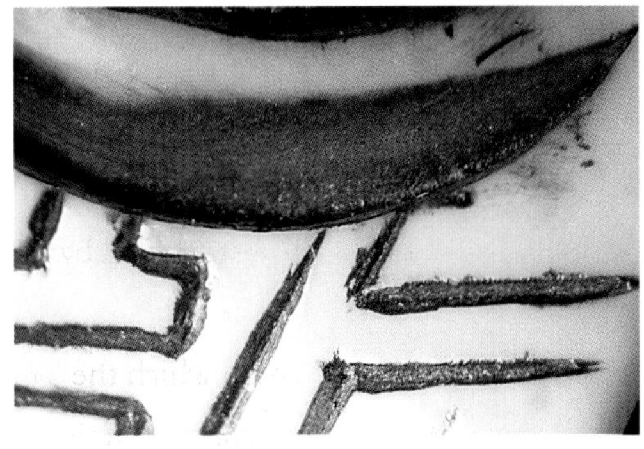

FIGS. 5a and 5b
Examples of V-shaped carved lines can be seen in these details of *Tiger Licking Its Paw*.

Drills are used to form the *himotōshi* (cord hole) and to make deep cuts. Hand drills are traditional, although contemporary carvers may also use electric dental drills.[24] If the surface of the hole has not been smoothly polished, the drill marks may be distinguishable as concentric circles around the walls. The point of the drill tip may also be visible at the bottom of the hole.

CARVING TECHNIQUES

Using the limited number of tools described above, netsuke carvers achieve myriad effects, such as enhancing the illusion of depth or simulating textures such as those of textiles, hair, and skin. One technique is *arashi*, or roughening the surface, which is used for background effects and to simulate textured surfaces, including textiles and rocks. In arashi, delicate round chisels or straight drills are bounced over the ivory to produce an overall surface pattern of small gouges (FIG. 6).[25] The roughened surface is often colored with a material such as black sumi ink to further emphasize the tooled effect (FIG. 6a).

Ukibori is an effect employed by some carvers to raise features such as inscriptions, pimples, warts, and veins on the surfaces of wood and ivory netsuke. A popular means of rendering signatures, ukibori is sometimes called the "relief carving" technique. True ukibori is practiced on wood. Areas that will stand in relief are impressed into the wood surface with a hard tool.[26] The surrounding areas, which will be recessed, are cut down to the level of the

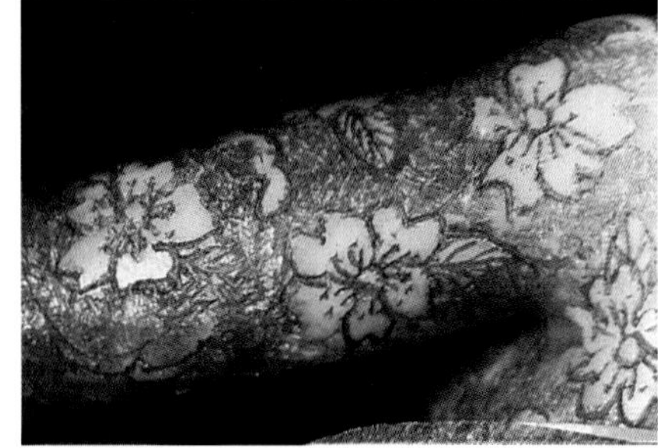

FIG. 6
MASATOSHI (NAKAMURA TOKISADA) (Japan, 1915–2001)
Benten Kozō
July 1957
ivory with staining, sumi, red and gold pigments
M.91.250.98
CAT. 546

FIG. 6a
The detail (above) of the tattoo on Masatoshi's *Benten Kozō* illustrates the technique of *arashi*, or roughening the surface. Often, as seen here, the roughened surface is colored with a material such as black sumi ink for emphasis.

FIG. 7
Octopus
Japan, mid-19th century
ivory with staining, sumi, double inlays
AC1998.249.92
CAT. 450

impressed wood. Finally, the wood of the compacted area is relaxed with moisture, which makes it expand to its full size above the pared background.

It is unclear how ukibori is executed on ivory. Raised details encountered on the ivory netsuke examined in this study, such as the suckers on the underside of *Octopus* (FIG. 7a), tend to have been individually carved in relief.

FIG. 7a
The suckers on the underside of *Octopus* show the faceted irregularities indicative of tool carving.

Carvers of the Iwami School, founded by Seiyōdō Tomiharu (1733–1811), are famous for their skill in ukibori,[27] and the surface of Seiyōdō's *Snail* (FIG. 8) provides a delicate example of the effect. The bumps are round, without the faceted irregularities seen on *Octopus*. Masatoshi suggests that the ridges in the snail's shell may have been achieved with an acid and lacquer resist technique (FIGS. 8a and 8b).[28] He achieved a similar effect using this technique on the surface of his *Peace and Harmony*.[29]

Netsuke are often inlaid with materials such as tortoiseshell, coral, amber, hornbill, shell, metal, or lacquer to emphasize details, such as the eyes, or to embellish a surface. The inlays, typically cylindrical plugs, are inserted into holes that have been drilled in the netsuke and held in place with an adhesive and friction. According to Masatoshi, sealing wax was used in old netsuke to secure inlays in conical holes. He laments that the sealing wax tended to dry out and lose its adhesive properties over time, resulting in loss of the inlays.

FIG. 8
SEIYŌDŌ TOMIHARU
(Japan, 1733–1811)
Snail
ivory with dark staining, sumi
AC1998.249.144
CAT. 454

FIGS. 8a and 8b
As a comparison to figure 7a, the bumps on the skin of *Snail*, and the ridges on its shell, do not show obvious tool marks. In *The Art of Netsuke Carving*, Masatoshi suggests that these details may have been rendered with an acid and lacquer resist technique. He had achieved similar effects experimenting with such a technique on one of his netsuke.

Masatoshi provides a more permanent attachment for his inlays by first carving a perfectly cylindrical hole and then inserting a plug into the hole so that it fits tightly, without any play. Epoxy resin is applied to all contact surfaces to anchor the inlay securely for the life of the netsuke.[30]

As Masatoshi describes, he shapes and polishes the protruding end of an inlay *after* the inlay is fixed in its socket. This tendency is often visible on netsuke with inlays that are flush with the surrounding ivory surface, such as the eyes of *Weird Frog* (see FIG. 25). Abrasion marks cross continuously over both the ivory and the inlay.

More elaborate inlay forms include double inlays, used for the eyes of *Whitebait Group* (FIG. 9a). The white of each eye consists of an inlay of mother-of-pearl shell into which a pupil of a black material, possibly tortoiseshell, is inlaid. Masatoshi also describes a technique called *happōnirami* (literally, "glaring in eight directions") for creating eyes, in which the eye inlay is made from white tortoiseshell, a transparent, light brown material. The bottom (that is, the innermost end) of the plug is hollowed out at the center and filled with lampblack pigment before the inlay is placed in the ivory eye socket. The result, seen in Kaigyokusai's *Floating Crane* (CAT. 370, illustrated on p. 13), is that of a netsuke whose gaze seems to follow the viewer (FIG. 10).[31] Kaigyokusai used a less refined version of this technique in his *Wild Boar* (FIG. 11). Here, the pupil is drilled slightly on the outer surface of the inlay material and filled with black pigment (FIG. 11a).

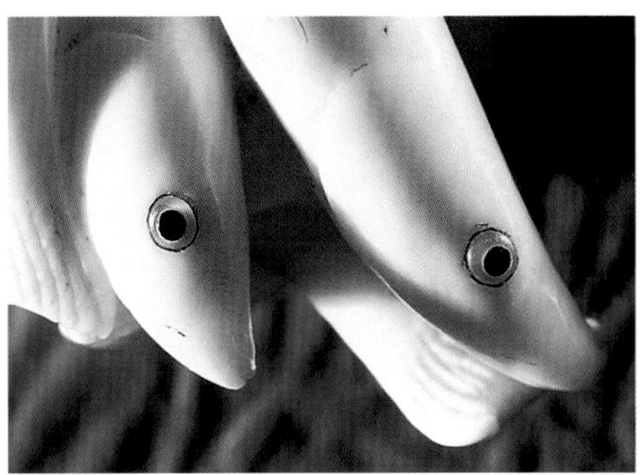

FIG. 9
Ryūkōsai Jugyoku II
(Japan, circa 1815–1877)
Whitebait Group
ivory with sumi, double inlays
AC1998.249.55
CAT. 721

FIG. 9a
The eyes of *Whitebait Group* exemplify the double inlay technique, in which one inlay is used for the white of the eye and another inlay forms the pupil.

FIG. 10
The eyes of Kaigyokusai's *Floating Crane* (CAT. 370; illustrated on page 13) are rendered in the *happōnirami* (literally, "glaring in eight directions") technique, creating an effect in which the crane's gaze seems to follow the viewer.

FIG. 11
Kaigyokusai Masatsugu
(Japan, 1813–1892)
Wild Boar
ivory with sumi, inlays
AC1998.249.172
CAT. 344

FIG. 11a
The recessed pupils of the amber eyes of Kaigyokusai's *Wild Boar*, in which a pupil is drilled slightly on the outer surface of the inlay material and filled with black pigment, are a simplified version of the *happōnirami* technique seen in figure 10.

POLISHING

A netsuke may be polished repeatedly during its production. This process removes tool marks and scratches, as well as oils, resins, and fingerprints, and it creates a smooth surface that emphasizes the lustrous quality of ivory. Polishing may also be alternated with staining, so that the netsuke is stained, some color is removed through polishing, and it is stained again until the desired effect is achieved.

Traditional polishing materials include leaves of the *muku* tree, *gokuzuihi* (a fine-grit powder with an off-white color), *tonoko* (an orange yellow powder), and *tsunoko* (burnt stag antler powder).[32] Though contemporary carvers use a range of these substances, some use new materials derived from modern sources. Even Masatoshi claims to have used sandpaper and emery paper in the early polishing stages.[33]

For some artists, the final step in polishing is to coat the netsuke surfaces with a material such as almond oil or *ibotarō*, a waxy secretion of the male larvae of the insect *Ericerus pela*.[34] Masatoshi reports having rubbed all of his netsuke with ibotarō, which has been melted and impregnated into the weave of a soft cloth. Ibotarō and other coatings can be recognized on the netsuke's surface as small, slightly raised smears or spots, or as a difference in sheen.

COLORATION: STAINS AND PAINTS

Ivory is generally associated with a translucent, creamy white color. However, most ivory netsuke, and many ivory artifacts in general, are colored locally or overall to enliven the carving. Deliberate coloration on netsuke is frequently overlooked or misinterpreted as a natural sign of age. For collectors and art conservators, recognizing and understanding the types of coloration encountered on netsuke is of the utmost importance; routine handling and treatments such as cleaning can easily damage or remove these delicate layers. Also, for those who appreciate the beauty of netsuke, to ignore the coloration is to fail to grasp one of the more finely developed skills of the artist.

Surface coloration on ivory can be very fragile and easily marred by careless cleaning. For this reason, netsuke should never be washed. Water (and saliva) can remove *yasha* dye (described on p. 86), sumi ink, and colored pigments. Solvents and polishes can also disturb surface layers. Gentle cleaning with a small feather duster or soft artist's paintbrush is usually sufficient to remove dust. Any further cleaning should be entrusted to a trained conservator. Due to the size of netsuke, even small losses of color are significant.

Because netsuke are so small, color can be especially important. Details tend to be carved in millimeter-scale depth, and ivory's light color does not produce strong shadows.

12

13

The subtleties of a delicately carved face can be emphasized by placing a darker color in the contours, and adding a dark color to shallowly incised lines draws attention to surface detailing that would otherwise go unnoticed. Two netsuke by the celebrated carver Kaigyokusai illustrate this concept. Both depict zodiac animals and are nearly identical in terms of carving; however, one is uncolored (FIG. 12), while the other has been stained light brown overall and detailed locally with black sumi ink (FIG. 13). The uncolored version appears static despite the dynamic entwining of the animals, while the addition of stain and painted color brings the tumultuous tangle to life.

Color can heighten the sense of realism or simulate an antique appearance. Human figures are often elaborately decorated, with dark, glossy hair, and colorful hair ornaments (FIG. 14); and stains of a soft brown tone give a semblance of age (FIGS. 15 and 16).

FIG. 12
Kaigyokusai Masatsugu
(Japan, 1813–1892)
Zodiac Animals
ivory with sumi, inlays; ryūsa type
AC1998.249.57
CAT. 346

FIG. 13
Kaigyokusai Masatsugu
(Japan, 1813–1892)
Zodiac Animals
ivory with staining, sumi, inlays; ryūsa type
M.87.263.41
CAT. 345

Two versions of the zodiac by Kaigyokusai illustrate how color can enliven an ivory netsuke.

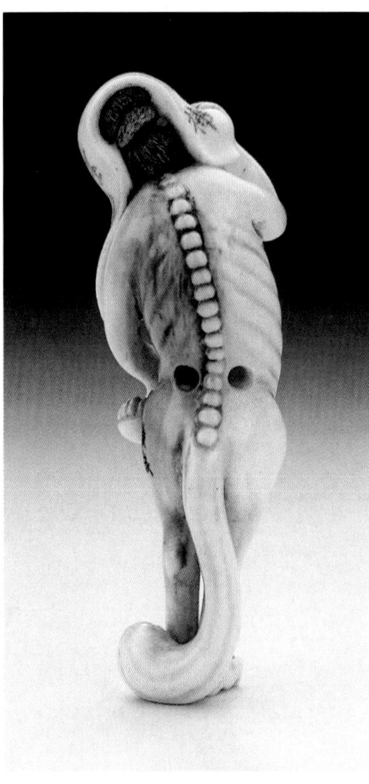

FIG. 14, FRONT AND BACK
Masatoshi (Nakamura Tokisada) (Japan, 1915–2001)
Fox Wife
ivory with staining, sumi, red and gold pigments
AC1998.249.195
CAT. 246

Front and back views of *Fox Wife* show how Masatoshi has decorated the netsuke with black hair, colored hair ornaments, and green staining.

FIG. 15
Ōhara Mitsuhiro
(Japan, 1810–1875)
Gooseneck Gourd
ivory with light staining, sumi
AC1998.249.191
CAT. 488

FIG. 16
Masanobu (Adachi Tomoshichi) (Japan, born 1838)
Stylized Swimming Duck
ivory with staining, sumi
M.91.250.262
CAT. 374

Mitsuhiro's *Gooseneck Gourd* and Masanobu's *Stylized Swimming Duck* have been stained with soft brown tones to give a semblance of age.

The two methods used to color ivory—staining and painting—differ in materials, in bonding properties, and in visual effect. In staining, a dissolved colorant, or dye, penetrates the superficial layers of the ivory. Cleaning or wiping the surface will not remove the stain, although polishing away the surface layers where the dye is most concentrated may lighten the tone. Conversely, paint sits *on* and does not penetrate the ivory surface.

Most ivory netsuke are stained, typically overall and with colors ranging from light to dark brown. Numerous materials can be used to stain ivory, including natural and synthetic dyes and household items such as tea or coffee. Accounts provided by netsuke carvers tell us that particular dyes have traditionally been used, and that they continue to be employed by contemporary carvers.

Perhaps the most commonly used stain for ivory netsuke is *yashabushi* (also called *yashadama* or *yasha*), a dye extracted from the cones of a species of alder tree. As Masatoshi writes:

> I make the dye by infusing a few cones in boiling water in an earthenware pot; I pour off the liquid and set it aside, add fresh water to the cones, and boil them a second time; again, I pour off the liquid; lastly, I mix the two infusions together and give them a long final boil. By the time half the liquid has evaporated, the dye is ready for use.[35]

The dye improves with age, and artists may maintain a batch for a number of years by replenishing the original supply with new infusions.

Netsuke artists have individual methods of applying the dye, and the length of time in the dye bath and rinsing processes also vary. Before dyeing, the netsuke surface must be free of oils or waxes; otherwise, these substances (such as oily fingerprints) can act as a dye resist and will be recorded permanently upon the surface as a lighter color. Surface cleaning is accomplished by polishing with a variety of powders that abrade and absorb substances that may impede staining. Some artists, including Masatoshi, treat the surface with acetic acid, which reportedly acts as a fixative, before dipping the netsuke into the yasha bath.[36] Once the surface is prepared, the netsuke is typically dipped into a warm or hot bath of the yasha infusion.

Experiments staining yasha on ivory piano keys show that residues ranging from a fine, matte grit to a shinier resinous accretion are deposited on the ivory surface in the course of dyeing (FIG. 17). Like the stain, these residues are soluble in water and saliva and can be removed by polishing. In general, these residues will have been polished or washed away from the netsuke surface, but they may remain in small amounts in recessed and protected areas. An example of the typical color attained by yasha can be seen in *Family Crests* (FIG. 18).

Yasha staining is often used in conjunction with sumi ink, and this combination can result in shades of brown, purplish brown, and gray-black, as well as the silvery green tinge of bamboo leaves in Masatoshi's *Ming Bowl with Fish* (FIG. 19).

The dye *kuchinashi* (also known as gamboge) is made from the berries of the gardenia plant. Kuchinashi imparts a yellow color to ivory and is applied in the same way as yasha. Masatoshi describes having maintained a ten-year-old solution of kuchinashi during his life.[37] As demonstrated by the uneven colors on this piano key, staining with gamboge can be difficult (FIG. 20); certain varieties of the pigment can be sticky and difficult to dissolve in water. This is particularly true of varieties sold in lump form rather than powder form. The carver Hideyuki described very long dyeing times to achieve the desired tint. For a deep stain, he placed the netsuke in a strong solution of kuchinashi for two to three hours. For a more subtle tone that enhanced the natural color of ivory, he placed the ivory in a weaker dye solution for up to forty-eight hours.[38] A long

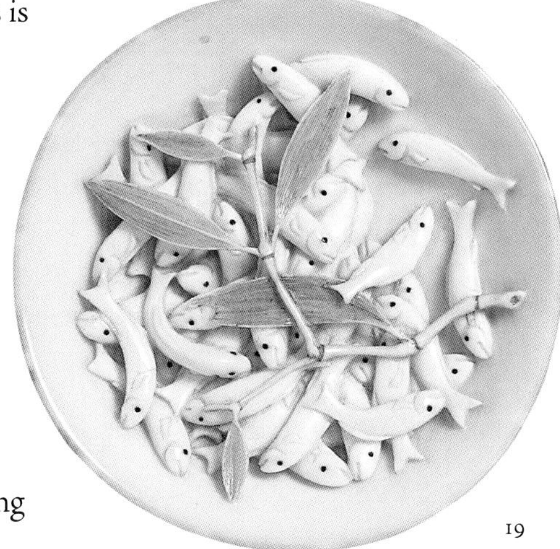

19

19 DETAIL

FIG. 19, OVERALL AND DETAIL
MASATOSHI (NAKAMURA TOKISADA) (Japan, 1915–2001)
Ming Bowl with Fish
January 1957
ivory with staining, sumi, inlays, red lacquer
AC1998.249.56
CAT. 725

The silvery green tinge of the bamboo leaves in Masatoshi's *Ming Bowl with Fish* was created by first staining with *yashabushi* and then applying black sumi ink.

FIG. 17
This ivory piano key shows the brown tone that can be obtained by staining with *yashabushi*. Residues deposited on the ivory surface during the dyeing process are visible on the upper portion of the key. The bottom of the key, also stained with yashabushi, has had the residues removed.

18

FIG. 18
Family Crests
Japan, late 19th century
ivory with staining, sumi; ryūsa type
M.87.263.40
CAT. 673

The brown tone of *Family Crests* resembles that achieved in experiments with *yashabushi*. Dark, powdery residues, visible in the recessed areas, are also similar.

FIG. 20
An ivory piano key stained with *kuchinashi* (also known as gamboge), a dye derived from the berries of the gardenia plant, exhibits colors ranging from bright yellow to a subtle heightening of the ivory's natural white tone.

dyeing time may be how Masatoshi achieved with kuchinashi the gentle golden tone of his *Heron* (FIG. 21).

In *ibushi*, the netsuke is fumigated with incense. The hot smoke penetrates the ivory and imparts an uneven stain. The result is a color simulating natural aging and resembling "that of Buddhist images that have stood for centuries with incense slowly burning at their feet."[39] During fumigation, resins and residues from the smoke accumulate on the ivory surface and can accentuate surface flaws. Masatoshi claims to mitigate this problem by wiping the netsuke surface with ethanol, which dissolves the residues. The solubility of ibushi in ethanol can aid in its identification. Masatoshi used this technique on his *Biron* (CAT. 230, illustrated on p. 74).

FIG. 21
Masatoshi (Nakamura Tokisada) (Japan, 1915–2001)
Heron
June 1974
ivory with light staining, sumi, black coral inlays
M.91.250.89
CAT. 404

A long dyeing time in a weak solution of *kuchinashi* may be how Masatoshi achieved the gentle golden tone of his *Heron*.

Silver nitrate ($AgNO_3$), or *shōsangin*, is a chemical that imparts a stain ranging in color from brown to purple to black. A solution of silver nitrate in water is initially colorless but turns dark when exposed to light. It also penetrates deeply and, because you cannot see it, it is difficult to apply in a controlled manner (FIG. 22). Masatoshi said that he applied silver nitrate to specific areas of the netsuke with a thin stick of willow wood.[40]

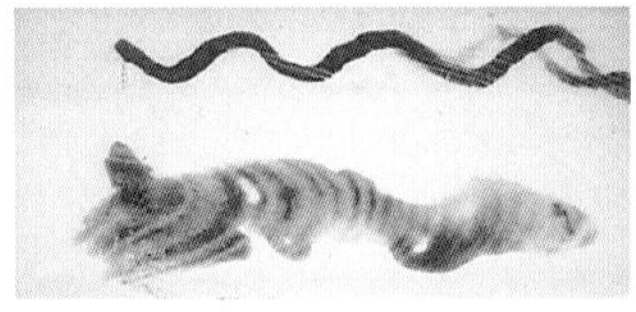

FIG. 22
This ivory piano key was stained with silver nitrate. Silver nitrate in water is colorless when first mixed with water and impossible to see during application; the characteristic purple-black color only appears after the solution is exposed to light for several hours. The solution was applied with a wooden skewer, and the wavering edges of the lines and smears illustrate the impreciseness of the application of this invisible dye.

The spotted skin of Masatoshi's *Salamander* (FIG. 23) was first executed with silver nitrate and then colored by ibushi to mellow "the metallic quality of the silver."[41] To simu-

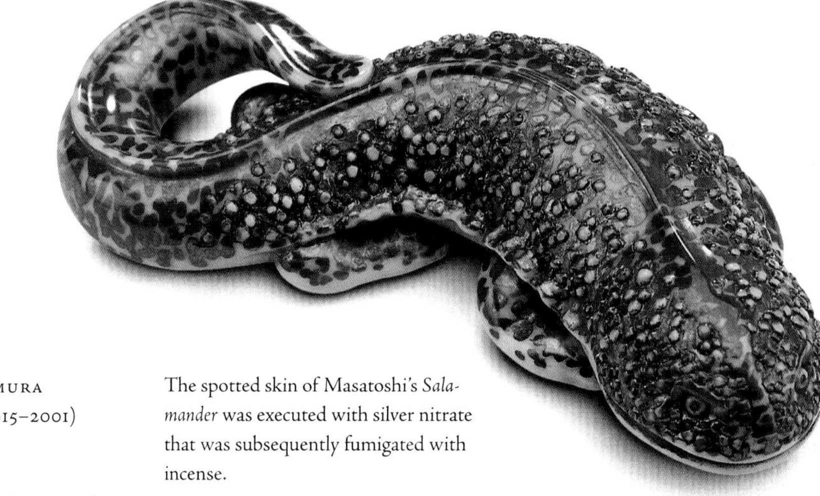

FIG. 23
Masatoshi (Nakamura Tokisada) (Japan, 1915–2001)
Salamander
January 1970
whale tooth with silver nitrate, sumi, black tortoiseshell inlays
AC1998.249.189
CAT. 430

The spotted skin of Masatoshi's *Salamander* was executed with silver nitrate that was subsequently fumigated with incense.

late the appearance of reptilian skin, the back has been textured with carved bumps and spots of silver nitrate. The irregular shape of the colored spots and lines, and the uneven edges of the spots, intimates the more freestyle approach with which this dye must be applied. The different shades of color are due to varying concentrations of the dye.[42]

Though artist accounts as well as the examination of LACMA's netsuke suggest that a core of traditional dyes continues to be used today by carvers, synthetic dyes may also be encountered on contemporary netsuke. The carver Michael Webb describes using a mixture of "commonly available cloth dyes" to color some netsuke.[43] Yasuaki's *Okame As a Demure Beauty* (FIG. 24) wears a vivid green undergarment that may have been stained with a synthetic dye (FIG. 24a).

Potassium permanganate, a chemical dye, is commonly found on contemporary African tourist art. Masatoshi describes using potassium permanganate to color boxwood, though he does not use it on ivory. However, it is mentioned here because it might be encountered on ivory netsuke of low quality, or on fakes. Potassium permanganate ($KMnO_4$) forms a bright fuchsia-colored solution when mixed with water, and the ivory is dipped into this solution. The resultant stain is dark brown and tends to be superficial.[44] Fuchsia-colored residues may also be visible on the surface of the object.

Paints consist of pigment particles and binder (the glue that holds the pigment particles to the object's surface and to each other). Pigments that do not dissolve in the binder or the solvent in which it is applied will not penetrate ivory. Literary sources suggest that the most common binders are water-soluble materials that may be protein (*nikawa*), starch, or lacquer (*urushi*). These binder materials differ in composition, durability, and visual effect. A variety of pigments can be mixed with nikawa or urushi and used to paint netsuke. The ground black carbon or charcoal found in sumi ink, as well as shell gold and red pigments, are common.

Nikawa, a protein glue that may be derived from fish, is quite soft and easily abraded. Pigments bound with nikawa can have a satin, sometimes grainy sheen. In some instances, where the pigment-to-binder ratio is high, the paint has a powdery texture, as can be seen in *Shōjō the Sea Sprite in Sake Bowl* (see CAT. 260).

Sumi is a calligraphy ink composed of ground black carbon pigment bound in nikawa. Sumi coloration goes hand-in-hand

FIG. 24
YASUAKI (Japan, active late 19th–early 20th century)
Okame As a Demure Beauty
early 20th century
ivory with staining, sumi, inlays, red pigment
AC1998.249.106
CAT. 186

FIG. 24a
Okame's vivid green undergarment may have been stained with a synthetic dye.

FIG. 25
MASATOSHI (NAKAMURA TOKISADA) (Japan, 1915–2001)
Weird Frog
January 1976
ivory with light staining, sumi, black coral inlays
M.91.250.90
CAT. 428

FIG. 25a
The use of sumi can be recognized by the presence of a fine layer of evenly dispersed, slightly splintery black pigment, evident in this signature detail of Masatoshi's *Weird Frog*.

with ivory netsuke: black residue resembling sumi was observed on seventy-nine of the approximately one hundred netsuke examined in this study. Hair, pupils, and incised lines are colored with densely pigmented sumi, and it is easily recognizable (for an example, see the detail of *Benten Kozō* in FIG. 6a). However, very fine washes of sumi are often used to emphasize contours of the body and face, or to provide depth to a background scene. In these cases, such as with Masatoshi's *Weird Frog* (FIG. 25), sumi can be recognized by the presence of a fine layer of evenly dispersed, slightly splintery black pigment (FIG. 25a). The satin sheen of the binding medium, which differs subtly in appearance from highly polished ivory surfaces, is also characteristic. Sumi ink is soft, easily abraded, and soluble in water and saliva. Recognizing this omnipresent but fragile colorant is integral to its preservation when handling and cleaning netsuke.

The combination of pigments with lacquer, or urushi, produces a durable surface that is not easily abraded and is invulnerable to many common solvents including water and saliva.[45] Unlike nikawa, which has a matte and often grainy texture, urushi has a glossy appearance that is heightened by polishing. The underside of Masatoshi's *Ming Bowl with Fish* is an example of urushi (FIG. 26). Masatoshi first coated the outside of the bowl with red-tinted lacquer. Once the lacquer cured, he scratched it away to reveal the natural color of the ivory beneath.

Lacquer can be difficult to apply: urushi polymerizes with atmospheric moisture, without which it will not cure properly. According to Masatoshi, he made two versions of *Ming Bowl with Fish*.[46] On the first, the red lacquer on the bowl's exterior curled because it did not dry properly. His second attempt, shown here, has an even, well-adhered red lacquer finish. Lacquer can also flake due to poor adhesion to the ivory substrate.

FIG. 26
The underside of *Ming Bowl with Fish* (CAT. 725) provides an example of painting with tinted *urushi*. Masatoshi first coated the exterior with red lacquer. Once the lacquer cured, he selectively scratched it away to reveal the natural color of the ivory beneath.

1 Masatoshi, *The Art of Netsuke Carving*, as told to Raymond Bushell (Tokyo and New York: Kodansha International Ltd., 1992), p. 24.

2 Miriam Kinsey, *Contemporary Netsuke* (Rutland, Vt.: Charles E. Tuttle Co., 1977), p. 38.

3 Mary Louise O'Brien, *Netsuke: A Guide for Collectors* (Rutland, Vt.: Charles E. Tuttle Co., 1981), p. 19.

4 Ibid.

5 Ueda Reikichi, *The Netsuke Handbook of Ueda Reikichi*, adapted from the Japanese by Raymond Bushell (Rutland, Vt.: Charles E. Tuttle Co., 1961), pp. 74–75.

6 Kinsey, *Contemporary Netsuke*, p. 39; Ueda Reikichi, *Netsuke Handbook*, pp. 74–75.

7 Kinsey, *Contemporary Netsuke*, pp. 40–41.

8 British Museum, *Treasured Miniatures: Contemporary Netsuke*, exh. cat. (London: British Museum, 1994); Kinsey, *Contemporary Netsuke*, p. 66.

9 An African savanna bull (*Loxodonta africana africana*) has long, curved tusks that average 2 meters (approximately 6.5 feet) in length and weigh about 23 kilograms (approximately 51 pounds). An African forest elephant (*Loxodonta africana cyclotis*) has straighter, thinner tusks that are better suited to thrashing about in a habitat of dense foliage. The females of both African species tend to produce smaller tusks. Male Asian elephants (*Elephas maximus*) are smaller than their African counterparts and grow tusks that average 1.5 meters (approximately 5 feet) in length and weigh around 16 kilograms (approximately 35 pounds). Female Asian elephants often do not produce any tusks. From *Grolier Multimedia Encyclopedia*, s.v. "ivory and ivory carving"; Doran H. Ross, ed., *Elephant: The Animal and Its Ivory in African Culture* (Los Angeles: Fowler Museum of Cultural History, University of California, Los Angeles, 1992), p. 44.

10 The values presented here describe an average chemical composition of ivory as cited in *Chinese Ivories from the Shang to the Qing*, exh. cat. (London: Sotheby Publications, 1984), p. 11. The residual < 1% is made up of calcium carbonate and other trace elements. This is only one interpretation of ivory composition, however, and the source of the results is not cited. Therefore, the exact percentages should be interpreted loosely. Further analyses of a variety of samples are needed to gain a more precise understanding of ivory composition.

11 *Chinese Ivories from the Shang to the Qing*, p. 11. The Mohs' scale is used to rate the hardness of a mineral numerically. On this 1 to 10 scale, 1 is the softest (talc) and 10 is the hardest (diamond).

12 Masatoshi, *Art of Netsuke Carving*, pp. 25–32.

13 *Chinese Ivories from the Shang to the Qing*, p. 11.

14 Peter Barnet, "Gothic Sculpture in Ivory: An Introduction," in *Images in Ivory: Precious Objects of the Gothic Age*, ed. Peter Barnet (Detroit, Mich.: Detroit Institute of Arts, 1997), p. 5.

15 It is reported that the rind is also more porous than dentin and therefore absorbs dyes more readily. See Masatoshi, *Art of Netsuke Carving*, pp. 35, 52.

16 Ibid., p. 13.

17 Ibid., p. 34.

18 Ibid.

19 Masatoshi, *Art of Netsuke Carving*, p. 35.

20 Ibid., pp. 30–31.

21 Kinsey, *Contemporary Netsuke*, pp. 67, 130, 135.

22 Masatoshi, *Art of Netsuke Carving*, p. 24.

23 Ibid.

24 Kinsey, *Contemporary Netsuke*, pp. 135–37.

25 Masatoshi, *Art of Netsuke Carving*, p. 30.

26 Ibid., p. 24.

27 Ibid., p. 228.

28 Ibid., p. 24.

29 Ibid., p. 48.

30 Ibid., p. 43.

31 Ibid., p. 46.

32 Ibid., p. 50.

33 Ibid.

34 Miriam Kinsey, *Living Masters of Netsuke* (Tokyo and New York: Kodansha International Ltd., 1985), p. 43; Masatoshi, *Art of Netsuke Carving*, p. 50.

35 Masatoshi, *Art of Netsuke Carving*, p. 53.

36 Ibid., p. 54.

37 Ibid., pp. 55–56.

38 Kinsey, *Living Masters of Netsuke*, p. 48.

39 Masatoshi, *Art of Netsuke Carving*, p. 52.

40 Ibid., p. 56.

41 Ibid.

42 Experiments show that a 10% weight/volume solution of silver nitrate in water will produce dark purple-black shades, while a 1% weight/volume solution gives a barely perceptible tone.

43 Kinsey, *Living Masters of Netsuke*.

44 The superficial nature of potassium permanganate stain may be more related to the low quality of the material and dyeing technique rather than an inherent trait of the colorant.

45 Freshly cured *urushi* is impermeable to most common solvents. However, urushi is vulnerable to ultraviolet radiation and, once degraded, can be drastically affected by solvents.

46 The first version can be found in Masatoshi, *Art of Netsuke Carving*, p. 186.

Foreigners and Outsiders

In 1587, when Toyotomi Hideyoshi, then leader of the central military government, launched a campaign in Kyūshū to defeat its ruling family, he had been shocked by the expansion and influence there of the Portuguese Jesuit missionaries. Fearing that Japan would go the way of the Philippines, which had converted to Catholicism and then been colonized by the Spaniards in 1565, Hideyoshi began to close access to Japan by missionaries from abroad. In 1639, under the Tokugawa shogunate, Japan entered a long period of self-imposed isolation. Almost all foreigners were banned, and trade became extremely limited, with foreign ships allowed to dock only in Nagasaki.

Japan nonetheless required some contact with foreign countries as well as information about the world beyond its borders. Dutch and Chinese traders had no evident motives beyond those of commerce, and their emissaries, isolated in Nagasaki and on the tiny constructed island of Dejima off its coast, were allowed to remain. The Dutch were confined to Dejima, although each year representatives traveled to Edo to pay tribute to the shogun.

This isolation caused the Japanese to look at European foreigners with both curiosity and fear during the Edo period (1615–1868). The relatively simplistic image of foreigners engendered by such limited contact manifested itself in the netsuke produced during the 1700s and 1800s. Those Japanese who were not specifically interested in Dutch interpretations of the sciences, arts, or military strategy tended to view these people as objects of fascination, outside the set social pattern and therefore unpredictable and rather dangerous. In netsuke, Dutchmen were made approachable by being depicted rather derisively (CAT. 5). Their strange clothing, features, hairstyles, behavior, and habits made them exotic, and netsuke carvers brought these curious figures to life while keeping them at a safe distance (CAT. 8).

LEFT: *Dutchman* (CAT. 8); RIGHT: *Chinese Woman and Dog* (CAT. 11)

China, however, was venerated as a rich source of philosophy, laws, and the arts. The Chinese people in netsuke, though exotically clothed, were typically given "noble" features. Physiognomic studies, which began in China and spread from there to Japan in the 1750s, maintained that people who were noble, intelligent, and sophisticated tended to have long, oval-shaped heads, aquiline noses, and relatively high foreheads, a type seen in several Bushell netsuke of Chinese (CATS. 9, 11).

Fantastic stories of weird peoples (Mongolians, Polynesians, Southeast Asians, or fantastic tribes) were spread by imported Chinese books, and they were identified by their exotic dress and features. In netsuke, north Asians were frequently shown as warlike, perhaps a lingering memory of Mongol-led attempted invasions of Japan in 1274 and 1281, while island peoples were portrayed as more passive. Chinese books also provided pictorial sources for the legendary symbiotic tribes of long-armed and long-legged people (Tenaga and Ashinaga) and other outlandish creatures. Members of the symbiotic tribes seemed to be most popular in netsuke, perhaps because they were emblems of the virtue of fulfilling one's appointed role in society.

In 1720, Tokugawa Tsunayoshi, fearing that Japan would be left hopelessly behind in the development of technology and thus open itself to invasion, issued an edict lifting the ban on the import of most Western literature, and these books increased people's curiosity about the outside world. Because the Japanese were still restricted from leaving the country, and threatened with execution upon return, imported literature and arts in the form of illustrated books, portable carved ivory or stone figures, painting, lacquer, and ceramics formed the basis for iconographic characteristics. These sources became the models for early netsuke, many of which, like their Chinese toggle or carved ivory counterparts, dealt with the world beyond the boundaries of common daily experience.

I BACK

1 | **Dutchman with Child**

Japan, 18th century
ivory with staining, sumi, inlays
4 1/16 x 1 7/16 x 1 1/8 in. (10.3 x 3.6 x 2.8 cm)
M.91.250.70

LITERATURE: AMICO, 2001–present; Bushell, *An Introduction to Netsuke*, fig. 1, p. 29

PROVENANCE: Sammy Yukuan Lee

A Dutchman glares down in alarm as the exquisitely dressed Chinese boy he is holding yanks on his beard. The Dutchman's rigid stance is countered by subtle movement in the fringe of his knee-length coat, and by the heavy contrast between the sumi-stained and the lightly colored ivory. It is unlikely that the horn stuffed into the back of the Dutchman's belt was an item carried by Dutch seafaring merchants, but it may have been a motif seen in Western paintings and adopted in netsuke. HG

2 | **Dutchman with Deer Carcass**

Illustrated on page 42
Japan, 18th century
ivory with staining, sumi
4 3/4 x 1 1/4 x 1 3/8 in. (12.1 x 3.2 x 3.5 cm)
AC1998.249.61

LITERATURE: AMICO, 2001–present; Bushell, *An Exhibition of Netsuke*, fig. 301, p. 61; Bushell, *The Wonderful World of Netsuke*, fig. 5, p. 17; Hill and Johnson, "The Raymond Bushell Netsuke Exhibition," fig. 301, p. 35

PROVENANCE: Morita Masao

With a fawn slung over his shoulder, this elongated Dutchman assumes a natural stance, right foot slightly forward, head turned to the right. Sumi-stained patterning is reserved for the perimeter of the design, legs, garment edge, hair, and hide. Areas with no incision and staining show softer textures: modeled drapery, soft-brimmed hat, and pudgy, glowering face. Carved from a triangular piece of ivory, this sculpture is fully realized in the round. HG

3 | Dutchman Holding Dog

Front illustrated on page 43
Japan, 18th century
ivory with staining, sumi, inlays
$3^{15}/_{16}$ x 1 x $^{7}/_{8}$ in. (10 x 2.6 x 2.3 cm)
M.87.263.1

LITERATURE: AMICO, 1999–present; Bushell, *The Wonderful World of Netsuke*, fig. 4, p. 16

PROVENANCE: Frances Numano

The static stance of this broad-nosed, staring Dutchman is relieved by the varied positioning of his arms, which bend to hold a longhaired Pekinese. Except for the broad-brimmed hat, fully modeled face, and shoes, the figure is incised, stippled, inlaid, and stained with sumi for a rich textural effect. Circles on his stockings and inlaid bosses on his coat have the appearance of bubbles that have been sprayed from the sea-foam design on the coat's bottom. HG

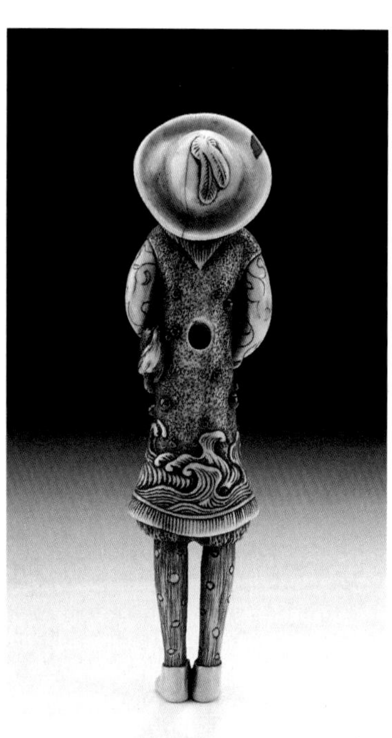

3 BACK

4 | Dutchman Holding Dog

Illustrated on page 42
Japan, 18th century
ivory with staining, sumi
$4^{1}/_{4}$ x $1^{1}/_{2}$ x $1^{1}/_{4}$ in. (10.8 x 3.8 x 3.1 cm)
AC1998.249.66

LITERATURE: AMICO, 2001–present; Atchley, "The Pavilion for Japanese Art in Los Angeles," p. 20; Bushell, *An Exhibition of Netsuke*, fig. 300, p. 61; Bushell, *The Wonderful World of Netsuke*, fig. 4, p. 16

PROVENANCE: Jeffrey Moy; Asian Art Museum of San Francisco; Avery Brundage; Elizabeth Humphreys-Owen

Differing markedly from the surface graphic treatment of the previous Dutch figure (CAT. 3), this attenuated man holding a puppy is enlivened with patterns of low-relief carving. Scarves twist across his legs, and his curling beard is deeply drilled. As he turns to speak to someone, his eyebrows are raised and his mouth is open with happy chatter. Perfunctory treatment of some details is balanced here by an overall sense of animation. HG

5 | Dutchman Holding Puppy

JOBUN, Japan, active late 18th–early 19th century
boxwood with inlays
$3^{3}/_{4}$ x $^{15}/_{16}$ x $^{11}/_{16}$ in. (9.5 x 2.3 x 1.7 cm)
M.90.186.20
incised: *Jobun*

LITERATURE: AMICO, 2001–present; Bushell, *Collectors' Netsuke*, fig. 72, p. 64; Hurtig, *Masterpieces of Netsuke Art*, fig. 231, p. 73; Okada and Neill, *Real and Imaginary Beings*, fig. 31, pp. 51–52; Stratos, "The Netsuke Carvings of Jobun," fig. 25, p. 20

PROVENANCE: William G. Bosshard; Dr. Joseph Kurstin; Charles A. Greenfield; Richards collection

5

This figure clasps his head in astonishment after being soiled by the puppy in his arms (as evidenced by the spot on the left side of his jacket). The costume of this Dutchman is more realistic than the sea-foam-decorated, ruffled-collar versions seen earlier (CATS. 2–3). Jobun probably had access to *Nagasaki-e* (printed pictures documenting the life of foreigners in Dejima and Nagasaki), which were sold as souvenirs throughout Japan. HG

6 | **Dutchman Holding Rooster**

Japan, 18th century
boxwood
$4\frac{1}{8}$ x $1\frac{1}{4}$ x $\frac{3}{4}$ in. (10.4 x 3.2 x 1.8 cm)
M.87.263.2

LITERATURE: AMICO, 1999–present; Bushell, *An Exhibition of Netsuke*, fig. 302, p. 24; Hurtig, *Masterpieces of Netsuke Art*, fig. 124, p. 48

Although, with its straightforward stance and rudimentary detail, this appears to be a folk carving, it is nonetheless filled with energy. Dutchmen were often portrayed holding roosters, and various connoisseurs have theorized that cockfights were held in the Dutch quarters on Dejima, or that the red comb of the rooster was reminiscent of the so-called red-haired (*kōmō*) northern Europeans. The rooster is a symbol of male good looks and virility, but, considering the appearance of the figure that holds him, it is doubtful that that association is intended here. HG

6

7 | **Dutchman**

Illustrated on page 43
Japan, 18th century
wood
$3\frac{5}{8}$ x $1\frac{7}{16}$ x $\frac{13}{16}$ in. (9.2 x 3.6 x 2.1 cm)
M.87.263.115
incised: *Dōraku* [added later]

LITERATURE: AMICO, 2001–present; Lazarnick, *Netsuke and Inro Artists*, vol. 1, p. 357

Holding a long pipe in his knobby fingers, this Dutchman juts his head forward to the left, resting his right hand on his hip. The netsuke's shallow but skillful carving, restraint of design, and size and heft indicate that it is an eighteenth-century work, which was inscribed later with the name of a nineteenth-century carver, Dōraku. HG

8 | **Dutchman**

Illustrated on page 92
Japan, late 18th–early 19th century
mother-of-pearl with sumi
$2\frac{11}{16}$ x $\frac{7}{8}$ x $\frac{7}{16}$ in. (6.8 x 2.2 x 1.1 cm)
M.91.250.336

LITERATURE: AMICO, 2001–present; Bushell, *The Wonderful World of Netsuke*, fig. 3, p. 15

PROVENANCE: B. K. Denton; Baron Masuda

Delicate and jewel-like in appearance, this magnificent piece of mother-of-pearl was carved as a three-dimensional bas-relief. Even though the material, formed from thin layers of nacre, is intractable and temperamental, this anonymous carver was able to create an exquisite and energetic composition. HG

9 | **Chinese Mandarin**

Japan, 18th century
wood
$4\,^{7}/_{8}$ x $1\,^{3}/_{8}$ x $^{15}/_{16}$ in. (12.5 x 3.5 x 2.3 cm)
M.87.263.3

LITERATURE: AMICO, 1999–present; Bushell, *An Exhibition of Netsuke*, fig. 305, p. 24; Bushell, *The Wonderful World of Netsuke*, fig. 88, p. 65

PROVENANCE: William Wilberforce Winkworth

Identified by his stiff, upright collar and button-topped hat as a Chinese court official, or Mandarin, this figure exudes dignity and solidity. Carved with exceptionally simple features that define the costume, much of this netsuke's warmth comes from the wood grain, which is plain and highly polished. HG

10

10 | **Chinese Pilgrim**

Japan, 18th century
bronze
$2\,^{7}/_{16}$ x $1\,^{1}/_{8}$ x 1 in. (6.3 x 2.8 x 2.5 cm)
M.87.263.86

LITERATURE: AMICO, 2000–present; Bushell, *Netsuke Familiar and Unfamiliar*, fig. 363, p. 154

PROVENANCE: Harry Pincus

An unusual netsuke, this relatively heavy figure is thought to represent a Chinese pilgrim because he carries a large gourd on his back, which probably would have contained liquid. His heavy, tripartite beard and mustache, narrow and extended eyes, and strange whorls in his hair define him as both eccentric and foreign. The space between the neck of the gourd and his body could serve as a *himotōshi*. HG

11 | Chinese Woman and Dog

Illustrated on pages 39 and 93
Japan, early 18th century
ivory with staining, sumi, metal fitting
6 1/4 x 1 5/8 x 1 5/16 in. (15.8 x 4.1 x 3.4 cm)
AC1998.249.60

LITERATURE: AMICO, 2001–present; Behrens, *Netsuke*, fig. 815, pl. 17; Bushell, *Collectors' Netsuke*, back of slipcase; Bushell, *An Exhibition of Netsuke*, fig. 304, p. 24; Davey, *Netsuke*, fig. 1037, p. 342; Hill and Johnson, "The Raymond Bushell Netsuke Exhibition," fig. 304, p. 28; Joly and Kumasaku, *Japanese Art and Handicraft*, fig. 74, pl. 53

PROVENANCE: Mark T. Hindson; Sir Frank Brangwyn; S. D. Bles; Walter Lionel Behrens

This is not a typical depiction of a Chinese woman with a dog, because the so-called dog she clasps by the neck appears in fact to be a Chinese lion (see CATS. 195–211), sometimes called a "lion dog." She might be a denizen of an exotic utopia: Her figured cloth bloomers, shaped, scrolling shoes, tunic with ruffled edges and arabesque pattern, layered collar, and elaborate hairstyle all hint at pure fantasy. Her elongated oval face reflects the contemporary physiognomists' view of nobility. This figure is fitted with a metal loop and, because of its substantial weight, probably counterbalanced a hefty tobacco case. This is an exceptional netsuke both for its fluid sculpting and its fine, variegated line work. HG

12

12 | Chinese Guardian

TAMETAKA, Japan, active circa 1730–1790
wood with sumi
3 1/8 x 1 1/16 x 7/8 in. (7.9 x 2.7 x 2.2 cm)
M.91.250.273
incised: *Tametaka*; kakihan

LITERATURE: AMICO, 2001–present; Bushell, *Collectors' Netsuke*, fig. 28, p. 34; Bushell, *An Exhibition of Netsuke*, fig. 18, p. 32; Mikoshiba and Bushell, "Netsuke and the *Sōken kishō*," p. 112

Tametaka has conceived this Chinese guardian simply, but there is a clear anatomy and weight beneath his draperies. The overall gouged texture makes the clothing appear rough, but it also enhances draping patterns over the body. The wild, crooked, and oversize face on this figure brings to mind the words "foreign devil"; whatever the netsuke's intended meaning, it shows extreme intensity. Tametaka added unusual rectangular *himotōshi* to the back of the figure. HG

13 BACK

13 | **Chinese Man**

Chingendō Hidemasa, Japan, active early 19th century
ivory with staining, sumi
$2\,^1/_2$ x $1\,^1/_8$ x $^3/_4$ in. (6.4 x 2.8 x 1.8 cm)
M.87.263.137
incised and stained: *Masanao* [added later]

LITERATURE: AMICO, 1999–present; Bushell, *Collectors' Netsuke*, fig. 19, p. 30; Hurtig, "Masanao," fig. 28, p. 37

PROVENANCE: William Wilberforce Winkworth

In *Collectors' Netsuke* (p. 115), Raymond Bushell pointed out that Hidemasa sometimes signed his work with the name of Masanao, and this netsuke is such a case. It is typical of Hidemasa's work, however, for the face's degree of personality, and for its broad-nosed, wizen-eyed features. Hidemasa's technique is also evinced by the deeply carved drapery folds, the carefully considered anatomy and stance, and the sumi-stained embellishments on the sleeves, stomach guard, and shoulder scarf. HG

14 | **Chinese Scholar with Fly Whisk**

Kimura Ryūmin, Japan, active mid- to late 19th century
ivory with staining, various inlays including malachite, metal, coral, mother-of-pearl; manjū type
$1\,^9/_{16}$ x $^{11}/_{16}$ in. (3.9 x 1.7 cm)
AC1998.249.200
incised on inlaid metal plaque: *Ryūmin*; kakihan

LITERATURE: Bushell, *Netsuke Familiar and Unfamiliar*, fig. 281, p. 141

This heavily encrusted *manjū* shows a Chinese scholar seated on a mat and holding a fly whisk while he contemplates the view. To his left is a teakettle for *sencha*, a type of leaf tea made popular in eighteenth-century Japan with the spread of the literati movement. Japanese intellectuals emulated Chinese amateur scholar-artists, adopting their tea-drinking habits along with other facets of their lifestyle. The large green rock against the fence has chrysanthemums growing before it, indicating that this figure may be Tao Yuanming (365–427), a Chinese poetic genius known for his love of the flower. HG

16

15 | **Mongolian Archer**

Illustrated on page 38
Japan, 18th century
wood
$3^{13}/_{16}$ x $1^{1}/_{8}$ x $^{13}/_{16}$ in. (9.8 x 2.8 x 2.1 cm)
M.91.250.107

LITERATURE: AMICO, 2001–present; Bushell, *Netsuke Familiar and Unfamiliar*, fig. 37, p. 95

This north Asian bowman shrieks with rage as he draws his double-barbed arrow into his bow. His narrow body is as rigid as his arrow, his deeply carved mouth is agape with anger, and his eyes are like slits beneath his furrowed brow. The figure's elaborate costume is so sharply carved that its edges have suffered considerable wear through the centuries. HG

16 | **Mongolian Archer**

Japan, 18th century
ivory with staining, sumi
$3^{7}/_{16}$ x $1^{5}/_{16}$ x $^{13}/_{16}$ in. (8.7 x 3.4 x 2 cm)
M.91.250.108

LITERATURE: AMICO, 2001–present; Bushell, *An Exhibition of Netsuke*, fig. 307, p. 24; Bushell, *Netsuke Familiar and Unfamiliar*, fig. 36, p. 95

This archer is dressed in garb that seems more Chinese than Mongolian. He wears a wide hip guard, and flowing drapery is tied under his substantial belly. In contrast to the previous piece (CAT. 15), this figure is stockier and filled with motion: He turns his face in profile and reaches for his quiver while his draping skirts move with him. The sculpture, fully realized in the round, is stained in incised areas with sumi for a rhythmic effect. HG

17 | **Mongolian Archer**

Follower of Yoshimura Shūzan, Japan, late 18th century
soft wood with pigments
3 5/8 x 1 3/16 x 1 in. (9.3 x 3 x 2.6 cm)
M.87.263.91

LITERATURE: AMICO, 1999–present; Bushell, *Collectors' Netsuke*, fig. 3, p. 25

PROVENANCE: Hans Conried

This alert soldier is carved of soft wood and painted in the manner of Yoshimura Shūzan, who was listed in Inaba Tsūryū's *Sōken kishō* as being the finest in the field of netsuke carving. Although this netsuke is less animated than some created in Shūzan's style, its artist has captured the soldier's droll expression, solid stance, and elaborate costuming, adding multiple colors. Pictures of exotic foreigners were available to eighteenth-century artists through encyclopedias, which were proliferating in Japan at that time. HG

17 BACK

18 | **Pacific Islander Holding Lobster**

Garaku, Japan, active before 1781
narwhal tusk with sumi, red pigment, inlays
2 7/8 x 1 1/16 x 9/16 in. (7.3 x 2.7 x 1.5 cm)
M.91.250.304
incised on raised oval: *Garaku*

LITERATURE: AMICO, 2001–present; Bushell, *Collectors' Netsuke*, fig. 49, p. 40; Bushell, *An Exhibition of Netsuke*, fig. 28, p. 32; Bushell, *An Introduction to Netsuke*, fig. 14, p. 50; Mikoshiba and Bushell, "Netsuke and the *Sōken kishō*," p. 112

PROVENANCE: Peter Shimojo; Itō Kazuo

Grasping a lobster, this islander emerges from the sea, water still streaming down his legs. The figure is dressed in the same garb as a Japanese fisherman, but his wide, round eyes declare his foreign extraction. Garaku, in the late-eighteenth-century manner, paid attention to anatomical detail and finely differentiated texture. He was also noted for using expensive pieces of narwhal tusk, with its variegated coloration and spiraling patterns, which he emphasized on the raised cartouche where he incised his name. HG

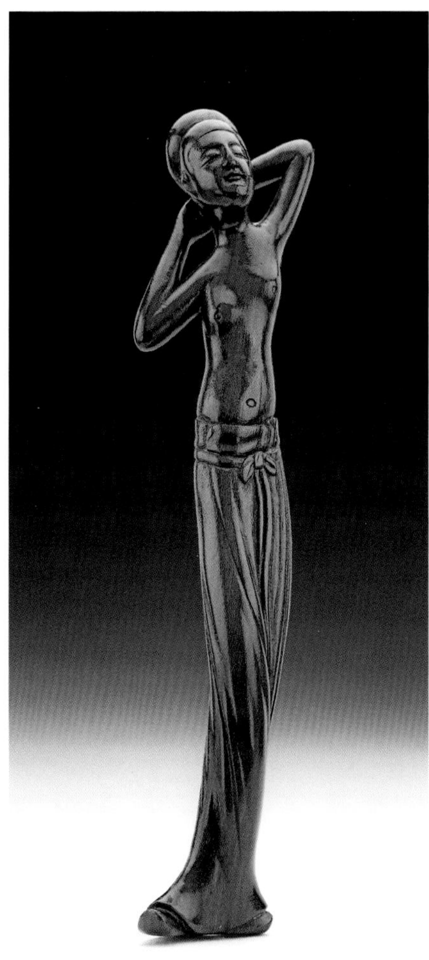

19

19 | Oceanian Woman Wearing Sarong

Hisatoshi, Japan, active 18th century
wood
$4^{13}/_{16}$ x $1^{1}/_{8}$ x $1^{1}/_{8}$ in. (12.3 x 2.8 x 2.8 cm)
AC1998.249.130
incised: *Hisatoshi*

LITERATURE: Bushell, *An Exhibition of Netsuke*, fig. 308, p. 24; Hurtig, *Masterpieces of Netsuke Art*, fig. 111, p. 45

Closing her eyes and soaking in the sunshine, this extraordinarily attenuated figure exudes ease and relaxation. The artist has created a very fluid and expressive figure within the narrow confines of his wood medium, which has miraculously survived more than two centuries. This may have been utilized as a *sashi* netsuke and inserted into the obi. HG

20 | Melanesian with Drum

Attributed to Miwa, Japan, active 18th century
red sandalwood with inlays
$4^{15}/_{16}$ x $1^{9}/_{16}$ x $^{15}/_{16}$ in.
(12.6 x 3.9 x 2.4 cm)
M.91.250.99
incised: [undecipherable]

LITERATURE: Bushell, *An Exhibition of Netsuke*, fig. 12, p. 31; Bushell, *Netsuke Familiar and Unfamiliar*, fig. 733, p. 223; Mikoshiba and Bushell, "Netsuke and the *Sōken kishō*," p. 109

This figure and the drummer in a following piece (CAT. 23) are closely related works in the manner of the early generation Edo carver called Miwa. Both netsuke emphasize solid substance and a fluid, polished surface rather than accurately proportioned anatomy. Dark coloration is countered by light-toned eyes, here inlaid with horn, and painted with *gofun* (shell-white gesso) in *Melanesian Drummer* (CAT. 23). The lighter eyes bring focus and immediacy to the expressions on their elongated and hollow-cheeked faces. One notable peculiarity of Miwa's carving style is the use of highly arched and sometimes overlapping feet. HG

20

20 BACK

This tall figure's dignified stance and the graceful details of drum embellishment, carrying cord, and drapes imbue her with elegance. The base is carved as a seal and, having few projections, the figure would be easily grasped for this use. Impressive for its dual functionality, the netsuke well represents interests in both exoticism and literacy. HG

22 | **Oceanian Drummer**

Japan, 18th century
wood
4 3/4 x 1 5/16 x 1 1/8 in. (12 x 3.3 x 2.8 cm)
M.90.186.1

LITERATURE: Trower, *Catalogue of the H. Seymour Trower Collection of Japanese Art*, fig. 30, pl. 1

PROVENANCE: Harry Seymour Trower; Marcus B. Huish

Titled *Oceanian Drummer*, this long-legged figure sports an offbeat mélange of clothing styles: He wears a grass fishing skirt, an elaborately figured shirt and collar, and a button-topped hat. The look of wild glee on his face could be a reaction to his elaborate game of dress-up. The artist probably combined elements he saw in illustrated encyclopedias, but he added a dash of anatomical realism to the sinewy legs and feet. HG

22

21 | **Oceanian Woman with Drum**

SHŪSHI, Japan, active 18th century
boxwood
4 1/16 x 7/8 x 7/8 in. (10.3 x 2.2 x 2.2 cm)
M.90.186.2
incised: *Shūshi*; kakihan
seal, carved on base: *Shizan*

LITERATURE: Bushell, *An Exhibition of Netsuke*, fig. 314, p. 24; Lazarnick, *Netsuke and Inro Artists*, vol. 1, p. 369

PROVENANCE: Charles A. Greenfield

21 SEAL

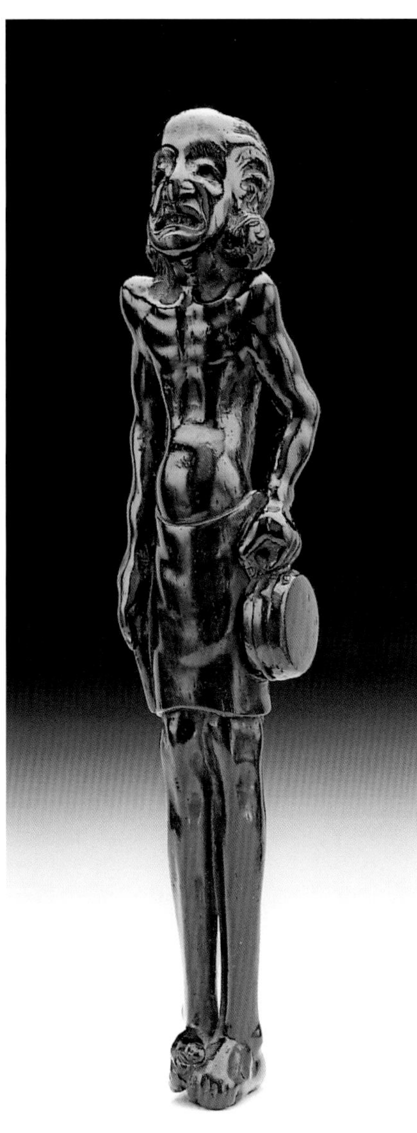

25 | **Malay Looking toward Heaven**

Japan, 18th century
wood
$4\,^1/_4 \times 1\,^1/_4 \times 1$ in. (10.7 x 3.2 x 2.6 cm)
M.91.250.103

LITERATURE: Bushell, *An Exhibition of Netsuke*, fig. 309, p. 62; Bushell, *Netsuke Familiar and Unfamiliar*, fig. 29, p. 94; Davey, *Netsuke*, fig. 1188, p. 400

PROVENANCE: Mark T. Hindson; M. Isobel Sharpe

This figure's curling beard and sarong indicate his South Seas origin. The carving is extremely simple, with some emphasis given to tendons in the neck, and to the shoulder blades. The pacific calm of his expression epitomizes the Japanese view of the Malay people. A cord would have run through the arms, as no *himotōshi* was drilled. HG

24 | **Melanesian Drummer**

RYŪKEI I, Japan, active late 18th–early 19th century
wood with inlays
$3\,^3/_4 \times 1\,^1/_4 \times 1\,^3/_8$ in. (9.5 x 3.2 x 3.5 cm)
AC1998.249.142
incised: *Ryūkei saku* / "made by Ryūkei"

LITERATURE: AMICO, 2001–present; Behrens, *Netsuke*, fig. 4586, pl. 62; Davey, *Netsuke*, fig. 331, p. 115; Lazarnick, *Netsuke and Inro Artists*, vol. 2, p. 892; Meinertzhagen, *The Meinertzhagen Card Index*, pt. B, p. 671

PROVENANCE: Carlo Monzino; Mark T. Hindson; William Wilberforce Winkworth; Frederick M. Meinertzhagen; Walter Lionel Behrens

More than any other in this group, Ryūkei's drummer convincingly participates in a ritual chant and dance with drum accompaniment. The varied positioning of his legs and arms both balance and animate the figure. The artist has given greatest emphasis, however, to the large head and face, with its contrasting inlaid eyes, and to the drummer's sunken, wind-beaten skin and curling hair. HG

23 | **Melanesian Drummer**

ATTRIBUTED TO MIWA, Japan, active 18th century
late 18th century
red sandalwood with pigment, inlays
$5\,^1/_4 \times 1\,^1/_{16} \times {}^3/_4$ in. (13.3 x 2.7 x 1.9 cm)
AC1998.249.271
effaced signature

LITERATURE: AMICO, 2001–present; Bushell, *Collectors' Netsuke*, fig. 43, p. 38

See catalogue 20.

26 | **South Seas Islander**

Illustrated on page 43
Japan, 18th century
wood
5 1/2 x 1 3/16 x 13/16 in. (13.9 x 3 x 2 cm)
AC1998.249.291

LITERATURE: AMICO, 2001–present

The extreme eccentricity of this figure relates him to the fashion for individualism that took hold in Japan around the end of the eighteenth century. This netsuke could represent one of the servants, typically dark-skinned Southeast Asians, who accompanied the Dutch. HG

27 | **Island Primitive**

GESSHŌ (or GESSEI), Japan, active late 18th–early 19th century
late 18th century
wood
2 7/8 x 13/16 x 7/8 in. (7.3 x 2.3 x 2.2 cm)
AC1998.249.25
incised: *Gesshō*

This drummer is roughly carved, in keeping with the primitive subject matter; however, the instrument he beats resembles a *tsuzumi*, a double-ended drum normally used in noh drama, rather than the round drum usually associated with this subject. The artist probably chose this type of drum for its potential for deep carving and interesting texture, which balances the figure's hollowed-out mouth, bold and grotesque facial features, and protruding Adam's apple and ribs. Though Gesshō's netsuke tended toward the inelegant, they were powerful and filled with rhythmic movement. HG

28 | **Pacific Islander Using Spyglass**

RYŪKEI I, Japan, active late 18th–early 19th century
wood
2 15/16 x 1 1/16 x 13/16 in. (7.5 x 2.7 x 2 cm)
M.91.250.306
incised: *Ryūkei*; kakihan

LITERATURE: Bushell, *An Exhibition of Netsuke*, fig. 315, p. 62; Chappell, "Stylistic Developments in the Tokyo (Edo) School," fig. 6, p. 24

Like *Oceanian Drummer* (CAT. 22), this islander wears fanciful dress, here consisting of a combination of fur boots and sarong, with his torso left bare. Anatomy is somewhat generally carved. Focus moves to his facial features, which are oddly pinched by his efforts to see through his spyglass. Prints of seafaring Dutchmen accompanied by Southeast Asian shipmates often show these figures peering through spyglasses, which were becoming a popular import to Japan in the 1750s. HG

29 | Melanesian Coral Diver

Japan, 19th century
ivory with staining, sumi, coral, red pigment
$1\frac{5}{8} \times 1\frac{5}{16} \times 1\frac{1}{2}$ in. (4.2 x 3.3 x 3.8 cm)
M.91.250.189

LITERATURE: AMICO, 2001–present

Both this netsuke and the next (CAT. 30) depict a theme popular in nineteenth-century carving—switching size relationships between two objects for comic effect. Combining disparate materials such as ivory or *umimatsu* (black coral or sea pine) with coral and metal also grew more fashionable as the nineteenth century progressed. Large pieces of coral are seen as "found-object" netsuke in eighteenth- and nineteenth-century literature and painting. These two works go further by combining a strengthened interest in genre detail with this luxury material. HG

29

30

30 | Coral Diver

TOSHINAGA, Japan, active mid- to late 19th century
umimatsu (black coral or sea pine), coral, woven metal cord, inlays
$1\frac{3}{4} \times 1\frac{1}{8} \times \frac{7}{8}$ in. (4.4 x 2.8 x 2.2 cm)
AC1998.249.14
incised: *Toshinaga*

See catalogue 29.

31 | Ashinaga and Tenaga

Illustrated on page 40
Japan, 18th century
stag antler with inlays
$6\frac{7}{16} \times 1\frac{3}{4} \times \frac{15}{16}$ in. (16.3 x 4.5 x 2.3 cm)
M.91.250.111

LITERATURE: AMICO, 2001–present; Bushell, *Netsuke Familiar and Unfamiliar*, fig. 417, p. 166

This and the next four netsuke depict members of two neighboring tribes who, according to legend, lived by the coast in eastern China. One tribe had unnaturally long legs (Ashinaga) and the other, long arms (Tenaga), so they developed a cooperative relationship: Ashinaga would wade into deep water with Tenaga on his back, who could then reach down into the water and pluck out fish. Some netsuke (CATS. 31, 33) show the figures fishing; others (CATS. 32, 35) play with the idea of Ashinaga being set upon by an octopus, which Tenaga madly tries to pluck off. Formulas for these figures came from Chinese pictorial encyclopedias, among the most popular of which was translated into Japanese as *Wakan sansai zue* in 1716. Later, Hokusai (1760–1849) included Ashinaga and Tenaga in his manga painting manuals. HG

32 | Ashinaga and Tenaga

Illustrated on page 40
Japan, 18th century
ivory with staining, sumi
$3\frac{3}{16} \times 1\frac{3}{8} \times 1\frac{1}{16}$ in. (8.2 x 3.5 x 2.7 cm)
M.91.250.113

LITERATURE: AMICO, 2001–present; Bushell, *An Exhibition of Netsuke*, fig. 259, p. 56

See catalogue 31.

33 | **Ashinaga and Tenaga**

Japan, late 18th–early 19th century
wood with metal
4 7/16 x 1 5/16 x 1 1/4 in. (11.2 x 3.3 x 3.2 cm)
M.91.250.112

LITERATURE: Bushell, *An Exhibition of Netsuke*, fig. 258, p. 56

This depiction of Ashinaga and Tenaga is unusual for its use of an inlaid copper alloy fish, placed in the delighted Tenaga's left hand. HG

34 | **Ashinaga Applying Moxa Treatment**

HOKKYŌ SESSAI, Japan, 1820–1879
wood with inlays
1 15/16 x 5/8 x 3/4 in. (5 x 1.5 x 1.9 cm)
AC1998.249.145
incised: *Sessai*

LITERATURE: Hurtig, *Masterpieces of Netsuke Art*, fig. 94, p. 42

Later artists explored other content about these tribes (see CAT. 31), such as how Ashinaga dealt with his ungainly legs on a day-to-day basis. Here, Ashinaga engages in a Chinese medicinal technique called moxibustion, in which a burning pellet of moxa is applied to an acupuncture point. The treatment is thought to stimulate and strengthen the blood and the life energy. HG

34 BACK

33

35 BACK

35 | Ashinaga and Tenaga

HIDEAKI (or SHŪMEI), Japan, active mid- to late 19th century
ivory with staining, sumi
$2\,^1/_4$ x $1\,^1/_{16}$ x $^{13}/_{16}$ in. (5.7 x 2.7 x 2 cm)
AC1998.249.194
incised and stained: *Hideaki* (or *Shūmei*)

LITERATURE: AMICO, 2001–present

In addition to content (see CAT. 34), artists explored new forms for Ashinaga and Tenaga. Here, Hideaki (or Shūmei) has created a more open composition than was seen earlier. HG

36 | Senkyō

Front illustrated on page 41
RYŌSAI, Japan, active 19th century
wood
$1\,^7/_8$ x $1\,^7/_8$ x $^{13}/_{16}$ in. (4.7 x 4.7 x 2.1 cm)
M.91.250.64
incised and stained with sumi: *Ryōsai*

LITERATURE: AMICO, 2001–present; Bushell, *An Exhibition of Netsuke*, fig. 113, p. 41; Bushell, *Netsuke Familiar and Unfamiliar*, fig. 532, p. 188; Bushell, "Netsuke: Miniature Sculptures," p. 36; Bushell, "Travels by Netsuke," fig. 30, p. 109; Lazarnick, *Netsuke and Inro Artists*, vol. 2, p. 886; Phillips, ed., *The Collectors' Encyclopedia of Antiques*, p. 569

Senkyō, another legendary tribe, had a convenient hole running through their chests. When one was tired, his companions could insert a pole into this hole to carry him. This netsuke is typical of work from the 1800s for its small size, lightweight, open carving, and inclusion of multiple figures. HG

36 BACK

37 | **Foreign Archer**

Japan, 18th century
ivory with staining, sumi, inlays
$4\,^{5}/_{16}$ x $1\,^{7}/_{16}$ x $1\,^{1}/_{8}$ in.
(10.9 x 3.7 x 2.9 cm)
M.91.250.297

LITERATURE: AMICO, 2001–present; Bushell, *An Exhibition of Netsuke*, fig. 306, p. 62

This figure's broad-brimmed hat, curling hair and beard, and protruding eyes give him a European appearance; however, his other clothing and his quiver seem to resemble those from north Asia. Even though the figure's costume evinces mixed sources, the carver paid close attention to details of clothing and its movement on the body. This netsuke type, with the foreign archer of unknown origin reacting happily to hitting his mark, appears repeatedly in the mid- to late eighteenth century. HG

38 | **Long-Haired Foreigner**

Japan, 18th century
tooth with staining, sumi
$2\,^{1}/_{2}$ x $^{15}/_{16}$ x $^{15}/_{16}$ in. (6.4 x 2.3 x 2.4 cm)
M.91.250.329

LITERATURE: Bushell, *Netsuke Familiar and Unfamiliar*, fig. 667, p. 212; Mikoshiba and Bushell, "Netsuke and the *Sōken kishō*," p. 105

This netsuke may date to the seventeenth century, although we have given it a more conservative eighteenth-century date. The subject, recorded but not titled in Inaba Tsūryū's *Sōken kishō*, is here executed very primitively. Objects are reduced to their simplest forms: cross-hatching represents ground and a simple fleur-de-lis shape indicates plant life. The figure is itself abbreviated, except for the dramatic expression and glaring eyes; this type of intensity was sometimes associated with practitioners of wizardry, such as Daoist hermits. The netsuke was carved from a tooth, possibly that of a whale. HG

38 BACK

39 | Barbarian Warrior

AFTER YOSHIMURA SHŪZAN, Japan, late 18th–19th century
19th century
wood with pigments
$3^{5}/_{8}$ x $1^{1}/_{8}$ x $1^{1}/_{8}$ in. (9.3 x 2.8 x 2.9 cm)
AC1998.249.263

LITERATURE: AMICO, 2001–present

Judging from illustrations in the *Sōken kishō*, this figure captures some of the concentration and movement of Yoshimura Shūzan's style, but it is too realistic and carefully proportioned to have been done in his time. Evidently an homage work, it has a singular personality that bristles with potential energy. HG

40 | Foreigner in Fanciful Dress

Japan, 18th century
boxwood with inlays
$3^{5}/_{16}$ x $1^{1}/_{16}$ x $^{7}/_{8}$ in. (8.5 x 2.7 x 2.2 cm)
AC1998.249.267

LITERATURE: AMICO, 2001–present

This is the same model as that used for *Mongolian Archer* (CAT. 17), probably carved somewhat later and kept in plain wood rather than polychromed. The beard has been simplified and the lion's face on the stomach protector is more readable, being carved instead of painted. This artist and that of *Mongolian Archer* may have seen the same book illustration or early netsuke for their subject. HG

41 | Foreign Monkey Trainer

Illustrated on page 54
Japan, mid- to late 18th century
ivory with staining, sumi
$3^{9}/_{16}$ x $1^{1}/_{4}$ x $^{13}/_{16}$ in. (9.1 x 3.1 x 2 cm)
M.91.250.32

LITERATURE: AMICO, 2001–present; Bushell, "Travels by Netsuke," fig. 14, p. 107

The monkey trainer with his improbably tall hat may be a foreigner—the goatee and the shape of the eyes represent a European—or a Japanese dressed in exaggerated Dutch-style clothes, popular with eighteenth-century performers. As the trainer grapples with his monkey, which is stained with sumi, his long draperies swirl in reaction to his movement. The figure's contrapposto stance helps this netsuke work as a composition from all angles. HG

42 | **Foreign Drum Master**

Illustrated on page 18
TANAKA MINKŌ, Japan, 1735–1816
wood with inlays
4 1/2 x 1 1/2 x 1 1/4 in. (11.4 x 3.8 x 3.1 cm)
AC1998.249.65
incised: *Minkō*; kakihan

LITERATURE: AMICO, 2001–present; Bushell, *An Exhibition of Netsuke*, fig. 25, p. 17, and front cover; Bushell, *Netsuke Familiar and Unfamiliar*, fig. 145, p. 116; Hill and Johnson, "The Raymond Bushell Netsuke Exhibition," fig. 25, p. 29; Lazarnick, *Netsuke and Inro Artists*, vol. 1, p. 762; Mikoshiba and Bushell, "Netsuke and the *Sōken kishō*," p. 111

PROVENANCE: Jeffrey Moy; Asian Art Museum of San Francisco; Avery Brundage

Tanaka Minkō, the head of a carving studio in Ise, devised a bold, broadly conceived style filled with energy and movement. Here, his foreigner wears late-eighteenth- to early-nineteenth-century Dutch dress; he has broad eyes inset under heavy brows and an ample mouth and ears. He holds a drum more often associated with Chinese or Polynesian tribes, decorated on its skin with a rain dragon. Drums such as this might have been used in rain-supplication ceremonies. The figure's lithe body sways in its snugly fitting clothes, while exaggerated facial features add both intensity and personality. HG

43 | **Foreign Archer with Monkey**

Illustrated on page 19
RYŪSAI, Japan, active late 18th century
wood with inlays
4 5/8 x 1 9/16 x 1 1/4 in. (11.6 x 4 x 3.2 cm)
M.91.250.30
incised: *Ryūsai*

LITERATURE: Bushell, *An Exhibition of Netsuke*, fig. 303, p. 61; Ueda, *The Netsuke Handbook of Ueda Reikichi*, fig. 193, p. 186

Like Minkō's figure (CAT. 42), this archer appears to be of mixed ancestry. His tall stature, curling hair, and eyes that have been inlaid to emphasize their wide stare suggest that he may be European. His long, draping coat with wave motifs and inlaid buttons is fanciful. The disparate combination of a pet monkey and archery equipment seems to create a mélange of all things exotic. This netsuke is very similar to one recently displayed in Minneapolis (see Welch and Chappell, *Netsuke*, p. 36). HG

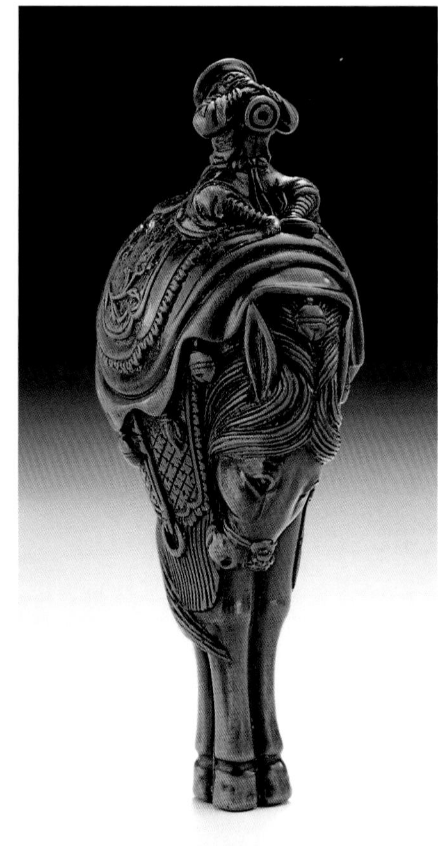

44 | **Foreigner on Horse**

ATTRIBUTED TO TSUJI, Japan, active late 18th century
wood
3 1/16 x 1 5/16 x 1 in. (7.7 x 3.4 x 2.5 cm)
AC1998.249.97
incised: kakihan

LITERATURE: AMICO, 2001–present; Bushell, *An Exhibition of Netsuke*, fig. 312, p. 62; Bushell, *Netsuke Familiar and Unfamiliar*, fig. 742, p. 224

PROVENANCE: Mark T. Hindson

This tiny figure in Dutch clothing is dwarfed by the elaborately caparisoned horse on which he perches. Dressed in softly flowing drapery, the person sits forward of the center of the horse's back, energizing an otherwise symmetrically arranged composition. For its enormous size, the horse appears sweet and gentle; its heavy-lidded eyes peer upward, and its head, legs, and tail are tucked into a compact pose. HG

45 | **Giraffe and Foreigners**

Kazuyoshi, Japan, active 19th century
ivory with staining, sumi
$1\,^{3}/_{16}$ x $1\,^{15}/_{16}$ x $^{7}/_{8}$ in. (3 x 5 x 2.2 cm)
M.87.263.119
incised and stained: *Kazuyoshi*

LITERATURE: AMICO, 2000–present; Hurtig, *Masterpieces of Netsuke Art*, fig. 95, p. 42

Similar to *Foreign Monkey Trainer* (CAT. 41), the figures here are in pseudo-European dress and have foreign features, but they might also represent Japanese men in costume. The artist has somewhat successfully captured the characteristics of a giraffe, although its proportions are fanciful. The use of multiple figures arranged on a base became more common in nineteenth-century netsuke. HG

46 | **"Hairy" Ainu**

Japan, 19th century
wood
$3\,^{1}/_{8}$ x $1\,^{1}/_{2}$ x $1\,^{1}/_{2}$ in. (7.9 x 3.8 x 3.8 cm)
M.90.186.17

LITERATURE: Bushell, *The Wonderful World of Netsuke*, fig. 2, p. 2

PROVENANCE: Cornelius Van Schaak Roosevelt

Though simple in technique, this netsuke is most interesting for its unusual subject matter. The aboriginal tribe called Ainu or Ezo, or by the epithets "hairy Ainu" or "shaggy people" for their hirsute features, made its home in Hokkaidō, which came entirely under Japanese governmental rule only in 1869. A stocky and heavy-set people, the Ainu had a traditional style of clothing, represented here, with bold, appliquéd border designs on plain-weave jackets. This figure is shown returning from a seal hunt. HG

47 | **European Lady**

Japan, late 19th–early 20th century
ivory with colored lacquer; manjū type
$1\,^{5}/_{8}$ x $^{3}/_{4}$ in. (4.2 x 1.8 cm)
M.87.263.33

LITERATURE: AMICO, 2000–present; Bushell, *Netsuke Familiar and Unfamiliar*, fig. 151, p. 117

Throughout the eighteenth and nineteenth centuries, Europeans had been traveling to Japan, bringing pictures of their loved ones—either to be worn or displayed—in the form of medals or miniature reverse paintings on glass. This *manjū* of a woman dressed in the Victorian manner represents such a medallion portrait. Enhancing the exotic feel of the subject, the artist has worked in colored lacquers to show his model's light-colored hair and brown eyes. HG

Religious Figures

Broadening the theme of life beyond daily experience in early netsuke, carvers often portrayed figures of those who led a religious life and were free from rigid social structures. Carvers seldom chose objects of serious worship, such as the Buddha or bodhisattva: The tendency at the time was to make netsuke that evoked the human end of the religious spectrum. There was also a strongly held belief that Daoist immortals, *rakan* (the most worthy direct disciples of the historical Buddha), gods of good fortune, and Buddhist guardians could help a person through trials of daily life. Among eighteenth-century netsuke, one sees a plethora of exotic, perfected humans, especially Daoists and Daoist immortals such as Seiōbo (cat. 58), Buddhist rakan (cats. 83–110), Zen Buddhist patriarchs such as Daruma (cat. 119), and the Seven Gods of Good Fortune (cats. 162–70).

Religious figures were admired for their discipline, their piety, and for living a solitary life of meditation outside the social order. They were notable for their extraordinary appearance, and for their enhanced psychic power and longevity. In netsuke, images of Daoist immortals and Buddhist rakan, for example, have distorted features that indicate advanced age and supernatural powers. Daoists were shown wearing mugwort leaves and mendicant Buddhists wore patched clothing, both of which told of a life beyond societal restrictions and niceties. Extreme expressions such as hilarity or deep concentration were the result of an existence unfettered by mundane thought and common human intercourse. Wearing the image of a religious figure as a netsuke could signal a desire to escape society's norms.

left: *Windblown Daruma* (cat. 119); right: *Seiōbo: Queen Mother of the West* (cat. 58)

Among the most popular of early netsuke subjects, Daoist immortals may have made their appearance after a boom in Daoist studies in Ming dynasty (1368–1644) China, which preceded the export of auspicious literary, medicinal, and decorative items to Japan. Japan's interest in China, its advanced philosophies, and the lives of its literati was also stimulated by the emigration to Japan in 1654 of an important group of Chinese monks representing the Ōbaku sect of Zen (Ch., Ch'an) Buddhism. Eventually the monks were granted land near Uji, south of Kyoto, which enabled the Japanese literati to gain greater access to them and their libraries and art collections. Study of China was enhanced considerably after 1720, when restrictions on book imports into Japan were relaxed.

Shinto, Japan's indigenous religion, was based on the worship of natural spirits (*kami*) that were said to be present in all things. Its disparate local beliefs, objects and figures of worship, and mythologies were organized into a coherent religious system after the introduction of Buddhism, but there continued to be much interaction between the two religions, and they coexist peacefully to this day. In this catalogue, netsuke based on Shintoism have been grouped with figures from folk religions.

Daoist Subjects

Daoism, an ancient and complex religion, involves geomancy, the reading of trigrams, and the worship of a pantheon of deities. These deities represented various constellations, leaders of multiple heavens, and their associated officials and guardians. Fortunetellers and geomancers employed the principles of Daoism, but there was no widespread worship of the Daoist pantheon among the masses in Japan.

Daoist immortals were characterized in East Asian art by their eccentric features and appearance; they were often shown wearing medicinal mugwort leaves, carrying an elixir of longevity in a gourd, or accompanied by a magical beast (CAT. 48). The extraordinary exotic dress seen in netsuke by Yoshimura Shūzan and followers of his style is immediately traceable to prints and paintings of Daoist guardian figures, which are among the most elaborately garbed of those depicted in orthodox Daoist painting.

The immortals most frequently seen in netsuke were Gama Sennin (Ch., Liuhai Xianren, Hou Xiansheng), Tekkai (Ch., Li Tieguai), and Kinkō (Ch., Qingao), and they remained popular from the eighteenth through the twentieth century. Seiōbo (Ch., Xiwangmu) was favored primarily in the eighteenth century. Exaggerated, elongated, or twisted figures of immortals were especially prized in the eighteenth century, reflecting a contemporary Japanese fascination with eccentricity that extended to artists and writers prized for both their genius and their bizarre tendencies.

Daoist immortals were identified by their dress and attributes, but they were also characterized by an intensity of expression, much of which was concentrated around the eyes (CAT. 71). According to Tao Hongjing (456–536), the "ears and eyes are the ladder in the search for the True, the door to gathering up the Divine" (Clunas, *Pictures and Visuality in Early Modern China*, pp. 116–20). Netsuke carvers perhaps understood the fundamental quality of the immortal's gaze and emphasized it.

ABOVE: *Daoist Immortal Riding Hat on Waves* (CAT. 71)

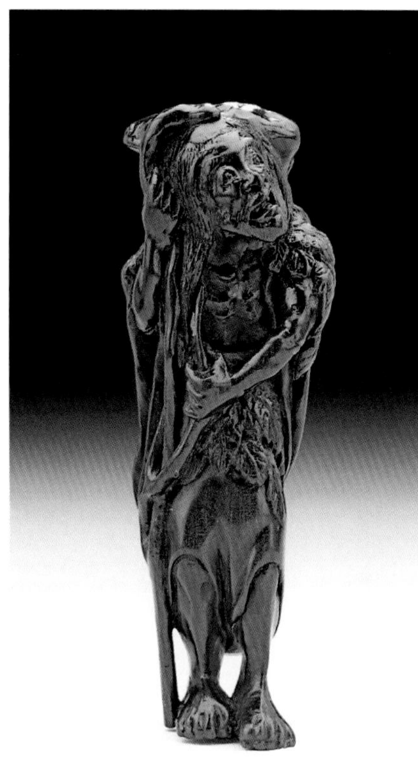

48

48 | Immortal with Toad: Gama Sennin

MIWA, Japan, active 18th century
wood
3 3/16 x 1 1/8 x 15/16 in. (8.2 x 2.9 x 2.3 cm)
AC1998.249.46
incised: *Miwa saku [?]* / "made by Miwa [?]"

LITERATURE: AMICO, 2001–present; Bushell, *An Exhibition of Netsuke*, fig. 11, p. 31; Mikoshiba and Bushell, "Netsuke and the *Sōken kishō*," p. 109

The immortal with a toad, most often called Gama Sennin (Ch., Liuhai Xianren, Hou Xiansheng) in Western sources, was a government official in tenth-century China who was well versed in Daoist practice. One day, he fished out of a well a white toad, which took him on magical journeys. Gama Sennin was a favored motif for early carvers of the late-eighteenth- and nineteenth-century Miwa School in Edo. Edo had a predominantly male population at that time, and Miwa School carvers devised a style that appealed to men: it conveyed qualities of asceticism and struggle. Miwa figures seem to spring from the wood, which retains its knobby texture and grain. Netsuke of this style most closely associated with the Miwa family achieve design cohesion through complete, soft finishing and surface sculpting. HG

49 | Immortal with Toad: Gama Sennin

Japan, 18th century
wood
3 3/16 x 1 1/4 x 1 1/8 in. (8.2 x 3.1 x 2.8 cm)
AC1998.249.137

LITERATURE: Bushell, *An Exhibition of Netsuke*, fig. 173, p. 47

See catalogue 48.

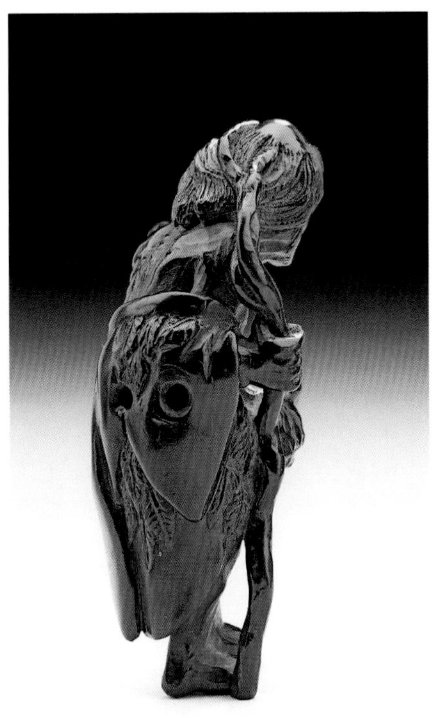

50 BACK

50 | **Immortal with Toad: Gama Sennin**

School of Miwa, Japan, late 18th–19th century
late 18th century
wood
2 9/16 x 1 1/4 x 1 1/8 in. (6.6 x 3.1 x 2.8 cm)
AC1998.249.250
incised: *Miwa*

LITERATURE: AMICO, 2001–present; Lazarnick, *Netsuke and Inro Artists*, vol. 1, p. 793

PROVENANCE: Daniel Rouviere

See catalogue 48.

51 | **Immortal with Toad: Gama Sennin**

Illustrated on page 55
School of Miwa, Japan, late 18th–19th century
late 18th century
cherry wood
5 7/8 x 1 1/4 x 1 7/8 in. (14.9 x 3.2 x 4.8 cm)
AC1998.249.265
incised: *Miwa*; kakihan

LITERATURE: AMICO, 2001–present; Bushell, *Collectors' Netsuke*, fig. 42, p. 38

See catalogue 48.

52 | Immortal with Toad: Gama Sennin

Front illustrated on page 49
Naitō Toyomasa, Japan, 1773–1856
wood with inlays
$2^{13}/_{16}$ x $1^{1}/_{4}$ x $1^{1}/_{4}$ in. (7.1 x 3.1 x 3.1 cm)
M.87.263.97
incised: *Toyomasa*

LITERATURE: AMICO, 2001–present; Bushell, *Collectors' Netsuke*, fig. 90, p. 69; Bushell, *An Exhibition of Netsuke*, fig. 65, p. 36

Naitō Toyomasa and his follower Toyokazu worked for the Aoyama daimyo and lived in Sasayama, Tamba province. Toyomasa's distance from major cities, and therefore other carvers, enabled him to devise his own style. He preferred to enlarge the faces of his figures for readability, adding exaggerated features that he enhanced by inlaying rectangular horn eyes. Gama Sennin was one of his favorite subjects, and he increased the size of the toad to give it nearly equal weight, sometimes making it the dominant figure. Toyomasa shows painstaking attention to naturalistic detail, alternating stained and unstained wood to enhance rhythm and depth. Capturing his figures in a dynamic pose, he excels at freezing a moment of action. HG

52 BACK

53 | Immortal with Toad: Gama Sennin

Toyokazu (Shūgasai), Japan, active early to mid-19th century
wood with inlays
$2^{3}/_{16}$ x $1^{9}/_{16}$ x 1 in. (5.6 x 3.9 x 2.6 cm)
M.91.250.266
incised: *Toyokazu*

LITERATURE: AMICO, 2001–present; Bushell, *An Exhibition of Netsuke*, fig. 172, p. 47

See catalogue 52.

54 | Immortal with Toad: Gama Sennin

Japan, mid-19th century
Hirado ware; porcelain with blue and brown glazes
$2^{3}/_{16}$ x $1^{1}/_{8}$ x 1 in. (5.6 x 2.8 x 2.6 cm)
M.87.263.57

LITERATURE: Ueda, *The Netsuke Handbook of Ueda Reikichi*, fig. 89, p. 89

Showing the "unfettered character" of the Daoist who is one with nature, this Gama giggles hysterically, throwing himself off his feet. Hirado ware was a fief porcelain made for the Hirado daimyo from the late 1600s to the early 1800s, later becoming a commercial product. The astounding quality of some Hirado ware, with its highly refined clay and perfect glazes, reflects this fief heritage. HG

55 | **Immortal with Toad: Gama Sennin**

Kaigyokusai Masatsugu, Japan, 1813–1892
ivory with sumi, inlays
1 5/16 x 1 5/16 x 1 in. (3.3 x 3.3 x 2.5 cm)
M.91.250.222
incised and stained: *Kaigyoku Masatsugu*

LITERATURE: Atchley, "Kaigyokusai," fig. 20, p. 18; Bushell, *Collectors' Netsuke*, fig. 149, p. 105; Hurtig, "Kaigyokusai Masatsugu," fig. 52, p. 21

There was a fashion for naturalistic carving in nineteenth-century Kyoto and Osaka, which Kaigyokusai, who worked in Osaka, embraced. Unlike the style of Miwa (CATS. 48, 50–51), Kaigyokusai's work shows a perfectionist's obsession with surface details and realistic poses. Kaigyokusai used the highest quality ivory, and he gave his full attention to taming his material and finding its ultimate potential. HG

56 | **Seiōbo: Queen Mother of the West**

Illustrated on page 20
Japan, 18th century
ivory with staining, sumi, inlays
3 3/16 x 1 1/16 x 13/16 in. (8.1 x 2.7 x 2.1 cm)
M.91.250.11

LITERATURE: Bushell, *Collectors' Netsuke*, front of slipcase; Bushell, *An Exhibition of Netsuke*, fig. 50, p. 35

Seiōbo (Ch., Xiwangmu), Queen Mother of the West, was a central figure in the Daoist pantheon and the best-known female immortal. She lived with her five "jewel maiden" attendants in the Kunlun Mountains of western China. In her garden were peach trees, which fruited once every three thousand years. Peaches from these trees conferred immortality on those who consumed them and, when the peaches were ripe, Seiōbo held banquets for the immortals and served them the fruit. In paintings, Seiōbo is shown riding a phoenix or crane, her attendants carrying peaches and a fan to cool her. It has been generally assumed that any peach-carrying female immortal in netsuke is Seiōbo, but it is possible that these figures could represent attendants. The four examples in the Bushell collection were all carved in the eighteenth century, though the later artist Hōjitsu (CAT. 59) retro-fitted one figure with ivory inlays. Two netsuke (CATS. 56, 59) are close in manner—the figures shown with complex piled and twisted coiffures, a rounded face of the type considered beautiful in the Chinese T'ang dynasty, and flowing, floor-length dresses. Both are relatively monochromatic (leaving aside Hōjitsu's additions) and accentuate the graceful curves of the figure.

Two examples (CATS. 57, 58), heavily stained with sumi, show a closer relationship to Chinese ivory carvings. In both, the complex surface ornamentation emphasizes the peaches, left in reserve ivory. Both are also triangular in form, although one (CAT. 57) has sculpting to the edge of the material. The very rare work by Sanko (CAT. 58) has more refined finishing, but the sculptor effectively breaks the figure out of the original shape for a dynamic impression. HG

57 BACK

57 | **Seiōbo: Queen Mother of the West**

Japan, 18th century
ivory with staining, sumi
4 3/16 x 1 5/8 x 1 1/16 in.
(10.6 x 4.2 x 2.7 cm)
M.91.250.116

LITERATURE: AMICO, 2001–present; Bushell, *The Wonderful World of Netsuke*, fig. 75, p. 59

PROVENANCE: Yamanaka

See catalogue 56.

58 | **Seiōbo: Queen Mother of the West**

Sanko, Japan, active 18th century
mid-18th century
ivory with staining, sumi
3 x 1 7/16 x 15/16 in. (7.6 x 3.6 x 2.3 cm)
M.91.250.117
incised: *Sanko*

LITERATURE: AMICO, 2001–present; Bushell, *An Exhibition of Netsuke*, fig. 167, p. 46; Mikoshiba and Bushell, "Netsuke and the *Sōken kishō*," p. 114

See catalogue 56.

59 | **Seiōbo: Queen Mother of the West**

Meikeisai Hōjitsu, Japan, died 1872
wood with inlays [inlays applied by Hōjitsu to earlier netsuke]
3 1/16 x 1 1/16 x 13/16 in. (7.8 x 2.7 x 2.1 cm)
M.91.250.118
incised: *Hōjitsu*

LITERATURE: AMICO, 2001–present; Bushell, *An Exhibition of Netsuke*, fig. 168, p. 47

See catalogue 56.

60

60 | Ikkaku: The One-Horned Immortal

Japan, late 18th century
wood with sumi
$3^{1}/_{8}$ x $1^{1}/_{4}$ x $1^{1}/_{4}$ in. (7.9 x 3.1 x 3.1 cm)
AC1998.249.71

LITERATURE: AMICO, 2001–present; Bushell, *An Exhibition of Netsuke*, fig. 182, p. 48

The legend of Ikkaku, the one-horned immortal, began in India in the kingdom of Benares. Born of an immortal and a deer, Ikkaku studied Daoism with his father and became a powerful magician. One day, angry after falling on a rain-slicked rock, he trapped the rain dragon in a cave, causing a drought that could have led to famine. Benares's king sent the most beautiful woman of the court, Lady Shanta, to seduce Ikkaku into releasing the dragon. She succeeded, but Ikkaku fell under the spell of worldly passion and lost his power. In netsuke, Ikkaku is shown carrying Lady Shanta back to the capital, where he would meet his doom. He is usually depicted gazing at her with either adoration or shock.

Netsuke of Ikkaku and Lady Shanta suggest a "beauty and the beast" theme, like the later pairing of a courtesan with Daruma (CAT. 122, illustrated on p. 26). In contrast with Lady Shanta's benign expression, delicate features, elaborate coif, and court garments, Ikkaku is often shown mouth agape, with sunken cheeks, bulging eyes, and trailing hair, and wearing a mugwort skirt and cape over rags. In three examples (CATS. 60, 61, 63), the use of staining has enhanced a sense of movement. HG

61

61 | Ikkaku: The One-Horned Immortal

Japan, late 18th century
ivory with staining, sumi
$2^{5}/_{16}$ x $1^{1}/_{16}$ x 1 in. (5.9 x 2.7 x 2.5 cm)
M.91.250.115

LITERATURE: Bushell, *An Exhibition of Netsuke*, fig. 179, p. 48; Bushell, "Travels by Netsuke," fig. 26, p. 109

See catalogue 60.

62 | Ikkaku: The One-Horned Immortal

Chingendō Hidemasa, Japan, active early 19th century
ivory with staining, sumi
3 1/8 x 7/8 x 15/16 in. (8 x 2.2 x 2.4 cm)
M.91.250.114
incised and stained in irregular cartouche: *Hidemasa*

LITERATURE: AMICO, 2001–present; Bushell, *An Exhibition of Netsuke*, fig. 180, p. 48; Bushell, *The Wonderful World of Netsuke*, fig. 78, p. 60

PROVENANCE: Kimura Waju

See catalogue 60.

63 SIDE

63 | Ikkaku: The One-Horned Immortal

School of Nagai Rantei, Japan, mid- to late 19th century
mid-19th century
ivory with staining, sumi, red pigment, inlays
3 5/8 x 1 3/4 x 1 5/16 in. (9.2 x 4.4 x 3.3 cm)
M.91.250.49
incised in irregular cartouche: *Rantei*

LITERATURE: AMICO, 2001–present; Atchley, "The Pavilion for Japanese Art in Los Angeles," p. 24; Bushell, *Collectors' Netsuke*, fig. 181, p. 122; Bushell, *An Exhibition of Netsuke*, fig. 181, p. 48; Ueda, *The Netsuke Handbook of Ueda Reikichi*, fig. 104, p. 99

See catalogue 60.

63 BACK

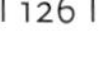

64 BACK

64 | **Daoist Immortal Koreijin and Tiger**

TOMOTADA, Japan, active before 1781
ivory with staining, sumi
1 7/8 x 1 5/8 x 1 1/8 in. (4.7 x 4.2 x 2.8 cm)
AC1998.249.192
incised and stained: *Tomotada*

LITERATURE: Bushell, *Collectors' Netsuke*, fig. 13, p. 28

PROVENANCE: Ouchi Yasushi

Tomotada, one of the three greatest Kyoto carvers, is justifiably famous for the almost palpable interaction between subjects in his multi-figure netsuke. Here, the tiger rubs against the immortal like a gigantic house cat, his right forepaw raised so he can lean into his human companion. The immortal, identified by his animal familiar as Koreijin, looks as if he were comfortably resting against a piece of furniture. HG

65 | **Daoist with Gourd**

Illustrated on page 27
Japan, 18th century
ivory with staining, sumi
4 1/4 x 1 7/16 x 3/4 in. (10.8 x 3.6 x 1.8 cm)
M.91.250.298

LITERATURE: Bushell, *An Exhibition of Netsuke*, fig. 176, p. 47

This could be the immortal Chōkarō (Ch., Zhang Guolao), in which case the large gourd that he clutches would hold his magical horse. It could also be the immortal Kokō, and the gourd would then be the private world into which he retires at night. The figure was carved from the triangular tip of an elephant's tusk, and it closely maintains that shape, with tiny, splayed feet at the pointed end. HG

66 BACK

67 | Daoist Immortal

Illustrated on page 39
Japan, 18th century
boxwood
4 9/16 x 13/16 x 13/16 in. (11.5 x 2 x 2 cm)
M.91.250.100

LITERATURE: AMICO, 2001–present; Bushell, *An Exhibition of Netsuke*, fig. 169, p. 47; Bushell, *Netsuke Familiar and Unfamiliar*, fig. 425, p. 167

This expressive netsuke of an attenuated figure with flowing scarves captures the style of the eighteenth century. The plant the Daoist holds, although not immediately identifiable, is probably intended for an immortality elixir. Details of this netsuke, such as the teeth and backbone, show extremely fine carving. Its length and delicacy suggest that it may have been used as a *sashi*. HG

66 | Daoist Immortal with Sacred Jewel

Japan, 18th century
wood with lacquer, inlays [added later]
4 3/8 x 1 5/8 x 1 3/16 in. (11.2 x 4.2 x 3 cm)
M.91.250.10

LITERATURE: Bushell, *An Exhibition of Netsuke*, fig. 170, p. 47; Ueda, *The Netsuke Handbook of Ueda Reikichi*, fig. 90, p. 92

Overall carving and large size hint that this netsuke was originally sculpted in the eighteenth century; the lacquering and inlays were probably nineteenth-century additions. The jewel he holds is a symbol of purity or Wish-granting Jewel, most often identified with Buddhist figures or with Ryūjin (see CATS. 515–20). It is less common to see it in the hand of a Daoist. HG

68 | **Kirin and Immortal**

Japan, 18th century
ivory with staining, sumi, red pigment
2 13/16 x 1 9/16 x 1 1/4 in. (7.2 x 4 x 3.2 cm)
M.91.250.102

LITERATURE: AMICO, 2001–present; Bushell, *Netsuke Familiar and Unfamiliar*, fig. 768, p. 228; Hill and Johnson, "The Raymond Bushell Netsuke Exhibition," fig. 102, pp. 32, 34

The figures in this netsuke cannot be associated with any known stories. The closest match is Rinreiso (Ch., Lin Lingsu), who is usually depicted seated sideways on a recumbent *kirin* (see CATS. 191–94). This netsuke is of typical eighteenth-century style: it was clearly made from the tip of the elephant's tusk, and the kirin is in a writhing, animated pose, with cross-hatching representing the scales on his back. His unfurling tail intertwines with the flames that rise from below. The hair whorls on his haunches have been worn down with use. HG

69 | **Daoist Immortal with Porcupine**

Japan, 18th century
ivory with staining, sumi, inlays
3 1/2 x 1 1/8 x 13/16 in. (8.9 x 2.9 x 2 cm)
M.91.250.310

LITERATURE: Bushell, *An Exhibition of Netsuke*, fig. 185, p. 48; Bushell, *An Introduction to Netsuke*, fig. 24, p. 67; Bushell, *Netsuke Familiar and Unfamiliar*, fig. 497, p. 179

PROVENANCE: Imai Kenzō

Raymond Bushell initially identified this as a foreigner with a porcupine, although he later decided it was an immortal because the figure holds a magical peach. No stories have been found in which an immortal has a porcupine familiar. HG

70 | **Figure on Baku**

Illustrated on page 39
Japan, 18th century
wood
4 x 1 15/16 x 1 5/16 in. (10.1 x 4.9 x 3.4 cm)
AC1998.249.113
seal, carved on base: *Daimin?* ["great Ming period, 1368–1661"] or *Fukumei?* or *Tenmei?*

LITERATURE: AMICO, 2001–present; Bushell, *An Exhibition of Netsuke*, fig. 38, p. 34, and back cover; Bushell, *Netsuke Familiar and Unfamiliar*, fig. 670, p. 213; Phillips, ed., *The Collectors' Encyclopedia of Antiques*, p. 566

PROVENANCE: Taniguchi Hideo

This magnificent sculpture has been variously identified as a Daoist immortal and as a demon on a *baku* (see CATS. 212–17), although no Daoists are noted as having baku companions. The seated figure has no horns, but it does possess three-clawed hands and feet. It also holds a magical jewel, which suggests a connection with the dragon-king Ryūjin. The roiling and agitated surface of this substantial work imbues the subject with a dreamlike, mystical quality found preponderantly in netsuke of the eighteenth century. HG

70 SEAL

71 | **Daoist Immortal Riding Hat on Waves**

Japan, late 18th–early 19th century
ivory with staining, sumi, inlays
$1^{9}/_{16}$ x $1^{1}/_{4}$ x $1^{1}/_{8}$ in. (3.9 x 3.1 x 2.8 cm)
AC1998.249.166

LITERATURE: AMICO, 2001–present

One day, the immortal Chinnan (also called Nanboku; Ch., Chen Nan) missed a ferry and rode his hat over the waves to meet it. This compact figure fixes the distant ferry in his intense gaze. Chinnan is also known for his ability to call forth a dragon when rain is needed. HG

72 | **Daoist Immortal**

Japan, late 18th–early 19th century
stag antler
$4^{1}/_{2}$ x $2^{1}/_{4}$ x $^{15}/_{16}$ in. (11.4 x 5.8 x 2.4 cm)
M.87.263.12

LITERATURE: AMICO, 1999–present; Ueda, *The Netsuke Handbook of Ueda Reikichi*, fig. 30, p. 39

This hoary figure emerges from the crook of a piece of stag antler, which is hollowed where the marrow crumbled away. The deer was thought to be the only animal capable of rooting out the fungus of immortality, *reishi* (Ch., *lingzhi*), and its life-extending properties were believed to remain in its antlers. Stag antler is an especially appropriate medium for a netsuke of an immortal. HG

73 | **Daoist Immortal, after Yoshimura Shūzan**

RYŌMIN, Japan, active early to mid-19th century
wood
$2^{9}/_{16}$ x $1^{1}/_{8}$ x $^{11}/_{16}$ in. (6.5 x 2.8 x 1.7 cm)
M.87.263.94
incised: *Shūzan kokui Ryōmin utsusu* / "copied by Ryōmin, inspired by Shūzan"

LITERATURE: AMICO, 1999–present; Bushell, *The Wonderful World of Netsuke*, fig. 70, p. 56

PROVENANCE: Mayuyama

The subject, pose, and exaggerated proportions of this netsuke recall the work of Yoshimura Shūzan (d. 1776). Ryōmin, however, working in a nineteenth-century style and with different tools, has shown more realism in the figure's facial features and bare flesh, and in the placement of limbs, fingers, and toes. The surface is polished, as would be expected in a work from this time period. HG

74 | **Daoist Immortal with Crane**

Japan, 19th century
wood with staining, inlays
$1^{11}/_{16}$ x $1^{3}/_{16}$ x $1^{1}/_{8}$ in. (4.3 x 3 x 2.9 cm)
M.91.250.301

LITERATURE: Bushell, *An Exhibition of Netsuke*, fig. 178, p. 48; Bushell, *Netsuke Familiar and Unfamiliar*, fig. 535, p. 188; Bushell, "Travels by Netsuke," fig. 24, p. 108

The delicate carving of this netsuke is a clear sign of its nineteenth-century origins. Several Daoist immortals are associated with the crane, a symbol of longevity, and this is probably Kōhaku. Henri Joly mentions that this immortal traveled to a mountain with a yellow crane and read Daoist texts. HG

75 | **The Daoist Immortal Ryūan**

KAIGYOKUSAI MASATSUGU, Japan, 1813–1892
ivory; manjū type
$2^{5}/_{16}$ x 1 x $^{5}/_{8}$ in. (5.9 x 2.6 x 1.6 cm)
M.87.263.35
incised: *Kaigyokusai Masatsugu*
seal form, incised: [undecipherable]

LITERATURE: AMICO, 2001–present; Atchley, "Kaigyokusai," fig. 29, p. 19; Bushell, *An Exhibition of Netsuke*, fig. 83, p. 19; Lazarnick, *Netsuke and Inro Artists*, vol. 1, p. 564; Ueda, *The Netsuke Handbook of Ueda Reikichi*, fig. 70, p. 83

Kaigyokusai carved tiny figures in bas-relief on this piece of ivory, which is further embellished with billowing clouds and drapery. The subject is Ryūan (Ch., Liu An), who ascended to heaven after drinking an elixir of quicksilver. His rooster and dog imbibed the dregs and accompanied him. HG

76

76 | **Elongated Daoist Immortal**

Japan, mid-19th century
boxwood with inlays
6 x 1 x 13/16 in. (15.4 x 2.5 x 2 cm)
M.91.250.101
incised and stained: *Omitsu [?]*
[undecipherable]

LITERATURE: AMICO, 2001–present; Bushell, *Netsuke Familiar and Unfamiliar*, fig. 774, p. 229

This extremely tall figure either has an odd anatomical structure or has yawned and stretched so much that he has dislocated his rib cage. He appears malnourished, and it is likely that he has been on an ascetic meditation retreat in the woods. Although not the most respectful treatment of a Daoist, the figure has great tensile strength. HG

77 | **The Immortal Roko**

Japan, mid- to late 19th century
wood
2 9/16 x 1 5/8 x 5/8 in. (6.6 x 4.2 x 1.5 cm)
AC1998.249.238
incised: *ittōbori hōzō* / "carved using *ittōbori* [single-knife] technique"

LITERATURE: AMICO, 2001–present

The immortal Roko (Ch., Luao) led a simple existence, riding a long-tailed turtle over the ocean for three thousand years and reading books. Here, he strokes his beard and appears to contemplate a joke as he rides his familiar. Ocean breezes swirl his scant draperies, and aging bones protrude through his sagging skin. HG

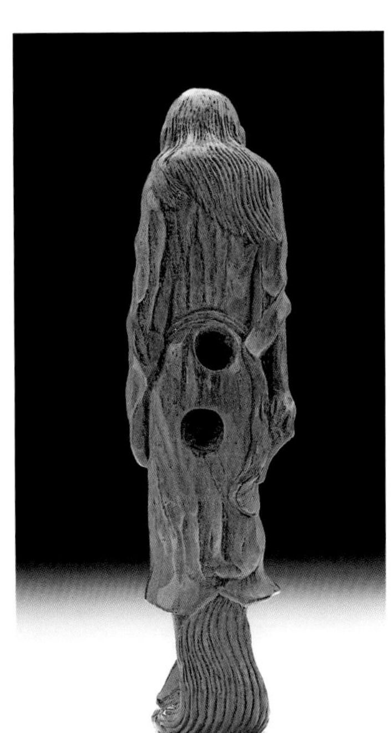

77 BACK

79 | **Daoist Immortal**

Tetsugen (Kyūsai), Japan, 1879–1938
wood with pigments
1 3/8 x 1/2 x 1/2 in. (3.5 x 1.3 x 1.3 cm)
M.87.263.95
incised: *Tetsugen*
seal: [illegible]
ink on box lid: *Kikoku sennin netsuke* / "wood netsuke of an immortal"

LITERATURE: AMICO, 1999–present; Bushell, *Collectors' Netsuke*, fig. 255, p. 154; Bushell, *An Exhibition of Netsuke*, fig. 8, p. 31; Bushell, *An Introduction to Netsuke*, fig. 2, p. 30

PROVENANCE: Matsubara Eizaburo

Intended to be a virtuoso work in miniature, Tetsugen's netsuke has the immortal emerging from a small chip of rough-grained wood. HG

78 BACK

78 | **Immortal with Gourd**

Sekkō (or Yukimitsu), Japan, active late 19th century
wood with inlays
2 13/16 x 1 5/16 x 1 5/16 in. (7.1 x 3.4 x 3.3 cm)
AC1998.249.252
incised: *Sekkō* (or *Yukimitsu*)

LITERATURE: Bushell, *Netsuke Familiar and Unfamiliar*, fig. 761, p. 227

PROVENANCE: Ruth Schneidman

Like *Daoist with Gourd* (CAT. 65, illustrated on p. 27), this immortal could represent either Chōkarō, who kept his horse in the gourd, or Kokō, who slept in his miniature gourd-world each night. Made in the late 1800s, this figure is animated and naturally proportioned. Although smaller than *Daoist with Gourd*, it nonetheless gives an impression of density and weight. HG

79

80 | Daoist Immortal with Dragon

Shōko (Nishino Shōtarō), Japan, 1915–1969
1958
wood
$2^{5}/_{8}$ x $1^{5}/_{16}$ x $1^{3}/_{16}$ in. (6.7 x 3.4 x 3 cm)
M.91.250.86
incised: *Shōko*
ink on box lid: *Toyomasa shiki Hokusōjin Shōko koku* / "carved by Hokusōjin Shōko in the manner of Toyomasa"; kakihan seals on box lid: *Nishino*; *Shōko*

LITERATURE: Bushell, *Collectors' Netsuke*, fig. 335, p. 180; Bushell, *An Exhibition of Netsuke*, fig. 464, p. 78, and front cover; Bushell, "Shōko," p. 59; Hill and Johnson, "The Raymond Bushell Netsuke Exhibition," fig. 464, p. 36

Shōko made this netsuke as an homage to the early-nineteenth-century carver Naitō Toyomasa of Sasayama. It was commissioned by Raymond Bushell, and Shōko was so excited by the concept that he wanted five or six years to complete the netsuke. Bushell convinced him to finish it more quickly. Like the Toyomasa precursor, the immortal seems to be playing a game of "keep away" with a boisterous dragon. In contrast to Toyomasa, Shōko kept the overall tone very even and chose not to use generous inlay. (The Toyomasa netsuke is in the collection of the Metropolitan Museum of Art; see Okada, *Netsuke*, pp. 84–85.) HG

81 | Daoist Monk

Japan, 18th century
wood
$4^{7}/_{16}$ x $1^{1}/_{8}$ x $^{15}/_{16}$ in. (11.3 x 2.8 x 2.3 cm)
M.87.263.118

LITERATURE: AMICO, 1999–present; Bushell, *Netsuke Familiar and Unfamiliar*, fig. 734, p. 223

PROVENANCE: Matsui Yonekichi

The pose of this writhing Daoist suggests that he has either been overcome by something deeply amusing or he has been poisoned. His open mouth is a deeply carved aperture, and his teeth and tongue are carefully detailed. The garments are not typical for an immortal, but his unrestrained behavior is indicative of someone who has removed himself from society. HG

82 | Sage

Japan, early 19th century
stag antler
$2^{7}/_{16}$ x $1^{7}/_{16}$ x $1^{3}/_{16}$ in. (6.2 x 3.7 x 3 cm)
AC1998.221.4
seal, carved on base: [floral design]

LITERATURE: Bushell, *Netsuke Familiar and Unfamiliar*, fig. 682, p. 215

The simple form of this sage was carved from the outer part of an antler with the marrow removed. The netsuke is also a seal, its base an abstract flower. The hollow shape makes the piece easy to hold, and significant surface wear indicates that it was used often. HG

82 SEAL

Buddhist Subjects

Buddhism, unlike Daoism, was a religion of central importance in Japan, and worship of the sixteen most holy *rakan* (Skt., *arhat*, Ch., *lohan*) can be traced back to the eighth century. Rakan, those who had followed the Buddha's Eightfold Path to perfection and achieved enlightenment, were believed to be a bridge between this world and the world of the gods; that is, they could act as a conduit between supplicants on earth and the cosmic Buddha or bodhisattva. Although their bizarre appearance and solitary lifestyle made them similar to Daoist immortals, rakan served a different function as netsuke. Memorial days to rakan were important for the fulfillment of prayers for good luck. After the arrival of the Ōbaku sect of Zen (Ch., Ch'an) Buddhist monks from China in 1654, there was a renewed interest in rakan and they became an essential subject for Zen teaching and painting in the eighteenth and nineteenth centuries. Clearly distinguishing them from Daoist immortals, rakan are shown with shaved heads, elongated ears, and heavy earrings.

Daruma (Skt., Bodhidharma), said to have lived in the sixth century, came from India to China and is considered to be the first patriarch of Zen Buddhism. Stories of Daruma—his strange behavior and extraordinary self-discipline—accrued numerous layers of fantasy with the passage of time. The more popular tales affected image-making of Daruma, evident especially in netsuke and in paintings for townsmen (CAT. 115).

In Buddhism, guardians represent the protectors of the faith, and netsuke often treat guardians and demons (J., *niō* and *oni*) as a metaphor for the fight between good and evil within the human spirit. In eighteenth-century netsuke, guardian figures (CAT. 129) probably were worn to protect the wearer from demons. Later carvers were less reverent, mixing the actions of guardians and demons with those of humans, and this attitude is revealed in *Temple Guardian Weaving Straw Sandal* (CAT. 133). A menacing demon can be seen in *Demon with Spiked Club* (CAT. 135), whose red skin suggests the heat of hell and whose club is ready to inflict pain.

ABOVE: *Daruma, First Patriarch of Zen* (CAT. 115)

83

83 | **Rakan: Buddhist Disciple of Exceptional Merit**

Aoki Mokubei, Japan, 1767–1833
black pottery, rosary glazed gold
2 x 1 x 1 1/8 in. (5.1 x 2.6 x 2.8 cm)
M.87.263.141
impressed: *Mokubei saku* / "made by Mokubei"

LITERATURE: AMICO, 1999–present; Bushell, "Ceramic Netsuke," fig. 2, p. 31; Bushell, *An Exhibition of Netsuke*, fig. 410, p. 73; Bushell, *The Wonderful World of Netsuke*, fig. 19, p. 26

PROVENANCE: Jack Tropp

Images of *rakan* (those who had followed the Buddha's Eightfold Path to perfection and achieved enlightenment), considered to be luck-bringing gifts, were sent as tribute between emperors. Through this tradition, the "grotesque" manner of depicting rakan—that is, as ancient, deformed, hirsute, and wild-looking beings—transferred from China to Japan around the tenth century. Later, the realism of Song dynasty (998–1280) style permeated rakan painting, and the imagery became less iconic and more narrative. The bizarre images that one sees in rakan netsuke were taken directly from the earlier "grotesque" painted portraits. Aoki Mokubei was a literati painter, a designer of Chinese-style leaf-tea (*sencha*) utensils, and a connoisseur of antique ceramics. His pottery studio was most famous for its tea ware, for both sencha and powdered tea (*chanoyū*) gatherings. He also designed other functional ware, including netsuke and incense boxes. The expressive, rough sculpting of this rakan follows the literati aesthetic. HG

84 | **Rakan: Buddhist Disciple of Exceptional Merit**

Illustrated on page 36
After Yoshimura Shūzan, Japan, late 18th–19th century
late 18th century
cypress wood with pigments
3 3/4 x 1 1/8 x 1 in. (9.5 x 2.8 x 2.5 cm)
M.90.186.11

LITERATURE: AMICO, 2000–present; Bushell, *Collectors' Netsuke*, fig. 1, p. 25

PROVENANCE: Cornelius Van Schaak Roosevelt

Richly polychromed and fancifully rendered with a large nose and gaping teeth, this figure is identified as a *rakan* by his dhoti and Wish-granting Jewel; the significance of the ruffled collar and fish-shaped scabbard, however, is unclear. The fish reference might suggest that this represents Ryūjin (CATS. 515–20) with a Tide-ruling Jewel, or it could indicate a wild foreigner. HG

85 | **Handaka Sonja: Disciple of the Buddha with Dragon**

Illustrated on page 41
Follower of Yoshimura Shūzan, Japan, late 18th century
soft wood with pigments
3 3/4 x 1 7/16 x 1 7/16 in. (9.5 x 3.7 x 3.7 cm)
M.87.263.90

LITERATURE: AMICO, 1999–present; Bushell, *An Exhibition of Netsuke*, fig. 4, p. 17; Bushell, *The Wonderful World of Netsuke*, fig. 20, p. 27

PROVENANCE: Honma Kyushiro

The *rakan* Handaka Sonja (Skt., Panthaka) is identified by his dragon companion and often shown with a Wish-granting Jewel. There is great intensity in the glare exchanged by Handaka Sonja and the dragon. Traces of polychrome remain on this worn figure. HG

86 | Handaka Sonja: Disciple of the Buddha with Dragon

Ryūminsai Teikei, Japan, active early 19th century
wood with inlays
$3^{3}/_{8}$ x $1^{1}/_{2}$ x $^{15}/_{16}$ in. (8.6 x 3.8 x 2.3 cm)
M.91.250.40
incised: *Ryūminsai Teikei*; kakihan

LITERATURE: Bushell, *An Exhibition of Netsuke*, fig. 159, p. 46, and back cover; Bushell, *Netsuke Familiar and Unfamiliar*, fig. 735, p. 223; Hill and Johnson, "The Raymond Bushell Netsuke Exhibition," fig. 159, p. 33; Lazarnick, *Netsuke and Inro Artists*, vol. 2, p. 1084

Compared to the previous piece, which was based on the same subject but carved more than fifty years earlier, this netsuke breaks out of the enclosed silhouette. It is dynamically composed, with multiple diagonal elements, and the surface is less pictorial and linear, more fully sculpted. The subject is lighthearted, suggesting a diluted spirituality. HG

87 | Rakan: Buddhist Disciple of Exceptional Merit

Style of Hōshunsai Masayuki, Japan, mid- to late 19th century
wood
$1^{1}/_{2}$ x $1^{9}/_{16}$ x 1 in. (3.8 x 4 x 2.5 cm)
M.91.250.169

LITERATURE: Bushell, *An Exhibition of Netsuke*, fig. 164, p. 46; Bushell, *Netsuke Familiar and Unfamiliar*, fig. 765, p. 228

The *rakan* wears a dhoti and a surplice (*kesa*) over his shoulder. Bald, he has the elongated earlobes and exaggerated Western features typical of nineteenth- and twentieth-century rakan netsuke (compare CATS. 84–85). Masayuki practiced two distinct methods of carving: one, based on the Edo Asakusa type, was mainly reserved for works in stag antler; the other more closely approximated the style of Hara Shūgetsu of Edo and his followers and was used later in his career for works in wood. This netsuke, apparently by Masayuki, typifies the latter style. Masayuki favored Buddhist subjects, and this figure may represent Inkada Sonja, who is often shown holding a Buddhist scepter (*nyoi*). HG

88 | Head of Disciple of the Buddha

Ozawa Shūraku, Japan, 1830–after 1878
silver, mixed-metal disk with inlays, ivory bowl; kagamibuta type
1 15/16 x 3/4 in. (4.9 x 1.8 cm)
M.87.263.81
incised: *Shūraku*; kakihan

LITERATURE: AMICO, 1999–present; Bushell, *Netsuke Familiar and Unfamiliar*, fig. 239, p. 134

Kagamibuta (literally, "mirror lid") netsuke such as this were especially suited for use with tobacco pouches because of their weight. (Heavy netsuke could damage a lacquer inrō.) With the decline in tobacco prices in the 1800s, kagamibuta production increased. Elaborate tobacco utensils became status symbols for townsmen, who, unlike samurai, were not allowed to carry stylishly outfitted swords. Metalsmiths (*kanamonoshi*) created the disks, and *netsukeshi* lathed the ivory or wood holders. Shūraku was among the best known kanamonoshi, although examples in relief by him are rare. The gold eyes, earring, and collar embellishment are inlaid. HG

89 | Disciple of the Buddha in Begging Bowl

Katsuzan or Kuzuyama, Japan, active 19th century
glazed pottery
1 7/16 x 5/8 in. (3.6 x 1.5 cm)
M.87.263.72
incised: *Katsuzan* or *Kuzuyama*

LITERATURE: AMICO, 2001–present

PROVENANCE: Ann Meselson

Ceramic inlay *manjū* netsuke, made famous by Suzuki Tōkoku and his followers, were especially fashionable in the late 1800s. The feather fan may identify this *rakan* as Binzuru Sonja (Skt., Pindola), who was credited with healing powers. The rough surface of the bowl is reminiscent of metal, and the overall texture would have suited the more ascetic taste of a literatus. HG

90 | Disciple of the Buddha in Begging Bowl

Yūkōsai, Japan, active late 19th century
wood with gold leaf
1 3/8 x 3/4 in. (3.5 x 1.8 cm)
M.87.263.37
incised: *Yūkōsai*

LITERATURE: AMICO, 2000–present; Bushell, *An Exhibition of Netsuke*, fig. 177, p. 48; Hurtig, *Masterpieces of Netsuke Art*, fig. 122, p. 48

This image of a *rakan* lacks any identifying features. He sits in a rocky cave, possibly on Mt. Sumeru, and holds a fly whisk (*hossu*) to drive away insects without hurting them. Rough carving reflects the rakan's harsh surroundings. HG

91 | **Disciples of the Buddha Studying Scripture**

Kūya (Nakamura Shinzō), Japan, 1881–1961
ivory with staining, sumi, gold pigment
$1^{7}/_{16}$ x $1^{1}/_{16}$ x 1 in. (3.7 x 2.7 x 2.6 cm)
M.91.250.267
incised and stained with sumi in oval cartouche: *Kūya* [reads left to right]

LITERATURE: Bushell, *Collectors' Netsuke*, fig. 298, p. 162

Rakan are sometimes depicted wearing a dhoti or a surplice (*kesa*). The kesa consists of squares of fabric sewn together into a long panel, which is then draped around the body and over a shoulder, as seen here. Kūya, father of the famous modern carver Masatoshi, created an *okimono* type of netsuke with this pair of rakan. Depicted reciting a sutra, the two have oversize heads with broad features, although other aspects of the netsuke are anatomically accurate and realistically detailed. Kūya has shown his virtuoso talents in surface design in the patterning of the dhoti, kesa, and scroll backings. HG

92 | **Rakan**

Yoshihide, Japan, active early 20th century
wood with inlays
$1^{15}/_{16}$ x $^{13}/_{16}$ x $^{3}/_{4}$ in. (5 x 2.1 x 1.9 cm)
M.91.250.175
incised on inlaid red-lacquer plaque: *Yoshihide*

LITERATURE: Bushell, *Netsuke Familiar and Unfamiliar*, fig. 94, p. 106

The *rakan* Rakora Sonja (Skt., Rahula) is often depicted with a beard and curling hair. Yoshihide is known for his international style, and the fully dimensional layered draperies and piled hair recall images from Indian paintings. This piece is reminiscent of Gandharan portraits of the Buddha. HG

93 | Inkada Sonja: Disciple of the Buddha with Long Eyebrows

Illustrated on page 71
SHŌKO (NISHINO SHŌTARŌ),
Japan, 1915–1969
1955
wood
$1^{7}/_{8} \times 1^{1}/_{2} \times 1^{1}/_{8}$ in. (4.8 x 3.8 x 2.9 cm)
M.91.250.231
incised: *Shōko*
ink on box lid: *Hokusōjin Shōko saku* /
"made by Hokusōjin Shōko"
seals on box lid: *Nishino*; *Shōko*; [abstracted seal script]

LITERATURE: Bushell, *Collectors' Netsuke*, fig. 334, p. 179; Bushell, *An Exhibition of Netsuke*, fig. 463, p. 28; Bushell, "Shōko," p. 60

Inkada Sonja (Skt., Angaja), most often depicted with long eyebrows, is usually shown seated and holding a scepter (*nyoi*). Typical of twentieth-century artists, Shōko has enlarged the figure's head while otherwise maintaining anatomical verisimilitude. Shōko has handled the figure's pose, features, expression, and body with extraordinary care. HG

94 BACK

94 | Hattara Sonja: Disciple of the Buddha with White Tiger

SHŌKO (NISHINO SHŌTARŌ), Japan, 1915–1969
1959
wood
$2^{1}/_{16} \times 1^{3}/_{4} \times 1^{7}/_{16}$ in. (5.3 x 4.5 x 3.6 cm)
M.91.250.176
incised: *Shōko*
ink on box lid: *Hokusōjin Shōko saku* /
"made by Hokusōjin Shōko"; kakihan
seals on box lid: *Nishino*; *Shōko*; [undecipherable]

LITERATURE: Bushell, *An Exhibition of Netsuke*, fig. 465, p. 78; Bushell, "Shōko," p. 61

Hattara or Batora Sonja (Skt., Bhadra) was a magician with a tiger familiar. The shapes around the netsuke base could be interpreted as cloudlike or wavelike, although traditionally the *rakan* and tiger were shown on a rocky mountain amid clouds. Shōko has exaggerated the figure's features and given him an agitated pose. HG

95 | **Hatsura Tasha Sonja**

Masatoshi (Nakamura Tokisada), Japan, 1915–2001
ivory with staining, sumi
2 3/16 x 7/8 x 13/16 in. (5.5 x 2.2 x 2 cm)
m.91.250.381
incised and lightly stained: *Masatoshi tō* / "carved by Masatoshi"

literature: Bushell, *Masatoshi*, front cover; Masatoshi, *The Art of Netsuke Carving*, front of slipcase

Masatoshi carved this set of sixteen *rakan* (cats. 95–110) as his magnum opus. The sixteen rakan were the original disciples to whom the Buddha entrusted the dissemination of his teachings. Raymond Bushell suggested that one could understand the artist's sources by referring to William H. Edmunds's book *Pointers and Clues to the Subjects of Chinese and Japanese Art*. Masatoshi, however, used artistic license in these portraits, simplifying his sculptures so that many are portraits of advanced age and deep thought; it is quite difficult to identify positively individual rakan. Throughout the set, Masatoshi made the bodies smaller and emphasized the head, hands, and feet. Light staining with sumi highlights specific details. hg

96 | **Kiyataka Hasha Sonja**

Masatoshi (Nakamura Tokisada), Japan, 1915–2001
ivory with staining, sumi
2 3/16 x 1 x 13/16 in. (5.6 x 2.5 x 2 cm)
m.91.250.382
incised and lightly stained: *Masatoshi*

literature: Bushell, *Masatoshi*, back cover; Masatoshi, *The Art of Netsuke Carving*, back of slipcase

See catalogue 95.

97 | **Dakaharita Sonja**

Masatoshi (Nakamura Tokisada), Japan, 1915–2001
ivory with staining, sumi
1 15/16 x 15/16 x 7/8 in. (5 x 2.3 x 2.2 cm)
m.91.250.383
incised and lightly stained: *Masatoshi tō* / "carved by Masatoshi"

literature: Bushell, *Masatoshi*, back cover; Masatoshi, *The Art of Netsuke Carving*, back of slipcase

See catalogue 95.

98 | **Sohinda Sonja**

MASATOSHI (NAKAMURA TOKISADA), Japan, 1915–2001
ivory with staining, sumi
2 1/8 x 7/8 x 7/8 in. (5.4 x 2.2 x 2.2 cm)
M.91.250.384
incised and lightly stained: *Masatoshi tō* / "carved by Masatoshi"

LITERATURE: Bushell, *Masatoshi*, front cover

See catalogue 95.

99 | **Dakora Sonja**

MASATOSHI (NAKAMURA TOKISADA), Japan, 1915–2001
ivory with staining, sumi
2 1/4 x 1 x 1 1/8 in. (5.7 x 2.6 x 2.9 cm)
M.91.250.385
incised and lightly stained: *Masatoshi tō* / "carved by Masatoshi"

LITERATURE: Bushell, *Masatoshi*, front cover; Masatoshi, *The Art of Netsuke Carving*, back of slipcase

See catalogue 95.

100 | **Hattara Sonja**

MASATOSHI (NAKAMURA TOKISADA), Japan, 1915–2001
ivory with staining, sumi
2 1/16 x 15/16 x 15/16 in. (5.2 x 2.4 x 2.4 cm)
M.91.250.386
incised and lightly stained in oval reserve cartouche: *Masatoshi*

LITERATURE: Bushell, *Masatoshi*, front cover; Masatoshi, *The Art of Netsuke Carving*, back of slipcase

See catalogue 95.

101 | **Kari Sonja**

MASATOSHI (NAKAMURA TOKISADA), Japan, 1915–2001
ivory with staining, sumi
2 1/8 x 1 x 15/16 in. (5.4 x 2.5 x 2.4 cm)
M.91.250.387
incised and lightly stained: *Masatoshi tō* / "carved by Masatoshi"

LITERATURE: Bushell, *Masatoshi*, back cover

See catalogue 95.

102 | **Hattora Sonja**

MASATOSHI (NAKAMURA TOKISADA), Japan, 1915–2001
ivory with staining, sumi
2 1/4 x 13/16 x 15/16 in. (5.8 x 2.1 x 2.4 cm)
M.91.250.388
incised and lightly stained: *Masatoshi tō* / "carved by Masatoshi"

LITERATURE: Bushell, *Masatoshi*, front cover; Masatoshi, *The Art of Netsuke Carving*, back of slipcase

See catalogue 95.

103 | **Shūbaka Sonja**

MASATOSHI (NAKAMURA TOKISADA), Japan, 1915–2001
ivory with staining, sumi
2 1/4 x 15/16 x 13/16 in. (5.8 x 2.4 x 2 cm)
M.91.250.389
incised and lightly stained: *Masatoshi tō* / "carved by Masatoshi"

LITERATURE: Bushell, *Masatoshi*, back cover; Masatoshi, *The Art of Netsuke Carving*, front of slipcase

See catalogue 95.

104 | **Handaka Sonja**

Masatoshi (Nakamura Tokisada), Japan, 1915–2001
ivory with staining, sumi
2 3/8 x 1 x 13/16 in. (6 x 2.5 x 2.1 cm)
M.91.250.390
incised and lightly stained: *Masatoshi tō* / "carved by Masatoshi"

LITERATURE: Bushell, *Masatoshi*, back cover

See catalogue 95.

105 | **Rakora Sonja**

Masatoshi (Nakamura Tokisada), Japan, 1915–2001
ivory with staining, sumi
2 3/16 x 15/16 x 13/16 in. (5.5 x 2.4 x 2.1 cm)
M.91.250.391
incised and lightly stained: *Masatoshi*

LITERATURE: Bushell, *Masatoshi*, back cover; Masatoshi, *The Art of Netsuke Carving*, back of slipcase

See catalogue 95.

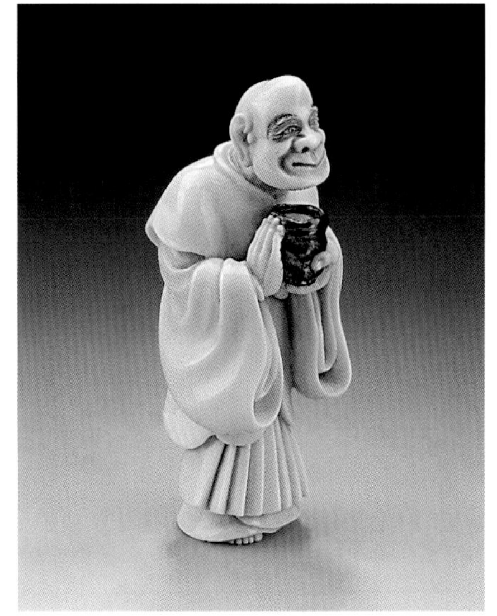

106 | **Nakasaina Sonja**

Masatoshi (Nakamura Tokisada), Japan, 1915–2001
ivory with staining (silver nitrate?), sumi
2 3/16 x 15/16 x 15/16 in. (5.5 x 2.4 x 2.3 cm)
M.91.250.392
incised and lightly stained: *Masatoshi tō* / "carved by Masatoshi"

LITERATURE: Bushell, *Masatoshi*, back cover; Masatoshi, *The Art of Netsuke Carving*, front of slipcase

See catalogue 95.

107 | **Inkada Sonja**

MASATOSHI (NAKAMURA TOKISADA), Japan, 1915–2001
ivory with staining, sumi
2 1/16 x 7/8 x 15/16 in. (5.2 x 2.2 x 2.4 cm)
M.91.250.393
incised and lightly stained: *Masatoshi tō* / "carved by Masatoshi"

LITERATURE: Bushell, *Masatoshi*, back cover; Masatoshi, *The Art of Netsuke Carving*, back of slipcase

See catalogue 95.

108 | **Hatsunabashi Sonja**

MASATOSHI (NAKAMURA TOKISADA), Japan, 1915–2001
ivory with staining, sumi
2 3/16 x 15/16 x 13/16 in. (5.6 x 2.3 x 2.1 cm)
M.91.250.394
incised and lightly stained: *Masatoshi tō* / "carved by Masatoshi"

LITERATURE: Bushell, *Masatoshi*, front cover; Masatoshi, *The Art of Netsuke Carving*, front of slipcase

See catalogue 95.

109 | **Ashita Sonja**

MASATOSHI (NAKAMURA TOKISADA), Japan, 1915–2001
ivory with staining, sumi
2 1/4 x 1 1/8 x 1 in. (5.8 x 2.8 x 2.5 cm)
M.91.250.395
incised and lightly stained: *Masatoshi tō* / "carved by Masatoshi"

LITERATURE: Bushell, *Masatoshi*, back cover; Masatoshi, *The Art of Netsuke Carving*, back of slipcase

See catalogue 95.

110 | **Chuda Handaka Sonja**

Masatoshi (Nakamura Tokisada), Japan, 1915–2001
ivory with staining, sumi
2 3/8 x 1 x 15/16 in. (6 x 2.6 x 2.3 cm)
M.91.250.396
incised and lightly stained: *Masatoshi tō* / "carved by Masatoshi"

Literature: Bushell, *Masatoshi*, back cover

See catalogue 95.

111 | **The Zen Master Bukan**

Attributed to Unjudō Shumemaru, Japan, active before 1782
boxwood
2 3/8 x 1 x 7/8 in. (6 x 2.5 x 2.2 cm)
AC1998.249.76

Literature: AMICO, 2001–present; Bushell, *An Exhibition of Netsuke*, fig. 27, p. 32; Bushell, *Netsuke Familiar and Unfamiliar*, back cover; Bushell, "Questions & Answers" (1976b), figs. 8d, e, and f, pp. 50–51; Lazarnick, *Netsuke and Inro Artists*, vol. 2, p. 994; Mikoshiba and Bushell, "Netsuke and the *Sōken kishō*," p. 107; Ueda, *The Netsuke Handbook of Ueda Reikichi*, fig. 59, p. 54

This tiny, light figure came in an original box signed "Unjudō Shumemaru," and Ueda Reikichi believed this netsuke was a rare work from the hand of that carver. Bukan (Ch., Fenggan) was a seventh-century Chinese monk from Mt. Tiantai. Although Bukan and his tiger are schematically rendered, there is much character and energy in this small piece. The figures are posed to be viewed from all angles. HG

111 side

112 BACK

112 | **The Four Sleepers: Bukan, Kanzan, Jittoku, and the Tiger**

Japan, 18th century
wood
$2^{9}/_{16} \times 1^{15}/_{16} \times 1^{3}/_{16}$ in. (6.6 x 5 x 3 cm)
M.91.250.170

LITERATURE: Atchley, "The Tiger in Netsuke," fig. 15, p. 7; Bushell, *An Exhibition of Netsuke*, fig. 53, p. 35; Bushell, *Netsuke Familiar and Unfamiliar*, fig. 767, p. 228; Phillips, ed., *The Collectors' Encyclopedia of Antiques*, p. 563

Shown in this unsigned netsuke are Kanzan and Jittoku (Ch., Hanshan and Shide), both depicted as innocent boys, the older Bukan (Ch., Fenggan), who was their teacher, and Bukan's animal familiar, a tiger. They are unselfconscious and fearless, keeping with the idea that all four are part of a continuum within the Buddha nature. It has been suggested that the four sleepers represent the calm of enlightenment. This sizable netsuke is broadly and simply carved, and Bukan is depicted in Chinese clothing (compare CATS. 111, 113). HG

113 | The Zen Master Bukan

Illustrated on page 65
Tōkoku II or Tōkoku III, Japan, late 19th–early 20th century
early 20th century
ivory with staining, sumi, red pigment, inlays
1 7/16 x 1 1/4 x 1 1/4 in. (3.7 x 3.1 x 3.2 cm)
M.91.250.242
seal form in carved red lacquer: *Bairyū*

LITERATURE: AMICO, 2001–present; Bushell, *Collectors' Netsuke*, fig. 224, p. 147; Bushell, *An Exhibition of Netsuke*, fig. 377, p. 70

This and similar netsuke have traditionally been identified as the Zen master Bukan, but his dhoti, arm circlet, gold earrings, and scepter (*nyoi*) suggest Hattora Sonja. The figure's anatomy is carefully rendered, suggesting that the artist may have taken a life-drawing class or worked from photographs. Classes with live models became available to Japanese art students in the late 1800s, when Western artists were invited to demonstrate their manner of instruction. The tiger, however, is more fancifully and less carefully carved. Tōkoku's use of multiple colors and inlays was carried on by his descendants. HG

114 | Kanzan and Jittoku: Two Zen Worthies

Japan, late 18th century
wood
1 3/4 x 1 1/4 x 3/4 in. (4.4 x 3.1 x 1.9 cm)
M.91.250.171

LITERATURE: Bushell, *An Exhibition of Netsuke*, fig. 162, p. 46; Bushell, *The Wonderful World of Netsuke*, front cover; Dillon, "Philadelphians Display Netsuke," p. 16; Hill and Johnson, "The Raymond Bushell Netsuke Exhibition," fig. 162, p. 33

These two characters are identified by their youthful appearance and humorous expressions, as well as by the poetry scroll that Kanzan clasps in his left hand. Although minimally carved, this netsuke conveys a sense of charm and camaraderie. HG

115 | Daruma, First Patriarch of Zen

Tanaka Minkō, Japan, 1735–1816
wood
1 9/16 x 1 5/16 x 15/16 in. (3.9 x 3.3 x 2.4 cm)
M.90.186.8
incised: *Minkō*; kakihan

LITERATURE: AMICO, 2000–present

PROVENANCE: Robert Fleischel

The story of Daruma (Skt., Bodhidharma) was embellished over time. One such tale, depicted here, involves the atrophy of Daruma's legs during his nine years of meditation. He is commonly depicted seated, or unable to use his legs, and this inspired the creation of a good-luck wishing doll in the form of Daruma, bereft of arms and legs but weighted to right itself after being toppled (see CAT. 732). It was also said that Daruma, angered by falling asleep during meditation, ripped off his eyelids. The first tea plants sprang from the spot where the lids fell, and monks since then have drunk tea to remain awake during meditation. Attention to details of Daruma's face, drapery, limbs, hands, and feet suggest that this netsuke may have been done late in the career of Minkō, who was by trade a carver and painter of household Buddhist altars (*butsudan*). HG

116 | Daruma on Reed

HIDETSUNE, Japan, active 19th century
ivory with staining, sumi, red pigment
1 7/8 x 15/16 x 13/16 in. (4.8 x 2.4 x 2 cm)
M.91.250.177
incised and stained with sumi in soft rectangular cartouche: *Hidetsune*

LITERATURE: AMICO, 2001–present; Bushell, *The Wonderful World of Netsuke*, fig. 9, p. 20

PROVENANCE: Ugo Alphonse Casal

According to legend, after his interview with Emperor Wu, Daruma crossed the Yangtze River on a reed and went to the Shaolin temple to meditate. The ancient Chinese words for "reed" and "reed boat" were similar, however, and later artists may have misinterpreted this piece of iconography. Hidetsune's work is deeply carved to accentuate Daruma's stance, balancing on the reed as it pulls him across the river. HG

117 | Daruma Emerging from Scroll

ISSHINSAI MASANAO, Japan, active late 18th–early 19th century
early 19th century
wood with inlays
1 13/16 x 1 5/16 x 7/8 in. (4.6 x 3.3 x 2.2 cm)
AC1998.249.270
incised: *Isshinsai*

LITERATURE: AMICO, 2001–present

In the late 1700s, *ukiyo-e* (pictures of the floating world) printmakers and illustrators began to play with the idea of figures in scrolls "coming to life" and leaving their paintings. In this netsuke, Daruma's scroll has not yet fully unrolled as he attempts to climb out. He holds a fly whisk (*hossu*) and wears a robe with a cowl, both iconographic elements of his period of meditation at Shaolin. His eyes, glaring beneath heavy brows, convey his philosophy of looking into one's own heart to find the Buddha. HG

118 | Daruma, First Patriarch of Zen

Japan, 19th century
red coral
1 9/16 x 1 5/16 x 5/8 in. (3.9 x 3.4 x 1.6 cm)
M.91.250.257

LITERATURE: AMICO, 2001–present; Bushell, *An Exhibition of Netsuke*, fig. 360, p. 68; Bushell, *Netsuke Familiar and Unfamiliar*, fig. 345, p. 151

PROVENANCE: Murray Sprung

Coral was a highly coveted luxury material, and lower-class citizens could be arrested if seen wearing it in public. To capture the intensity of Daruma's gaze, this artist has bored holes for his pupils. HG

119 | **Windblown Daruma**

Front illustrated on page 114
Shūkōsai Anraku, Japan, active early to mid-19th century
mid-19th century
wood with various inlays including gold, silver, lacquer
$2^{7}/_{16}$ x $1^{5}/_{16}$ x $^{7}/_{8}$ in. (6.3 x 3.4 x 2.2 cm)
AC1998.249.148
incised: *Anraku*

LITERATURE: AMICO, 2001–present

PROVENANCE: Douglas collection

Anraku helped stimulate the fashion for using inlay and multiple materials in netsuke. His stout figure stands against the wind in the pose Daruma took when crossing the Yangtze River on a reed (see CAT. 116). His large whisk is tucked into his belt, ready to repel insects or other distractions in his quest for enlightenment. HG

119 SIDE

120 | **Daruma, First Patriarch of Zen**

Morikawa Toen, Japan, 1820–1894
wood
$2^{9}/_{16}$ x 1 x $^{3}/_{4}$ in. (6.6 x 2.5 x 1.9 cm)
AC1998.249.251
incised: kakihan

LITERATURE: AMICO, 2001–present; Ueda, *The Netsuke Handbook of Ueda Reikichi*, fig. 40, p. 45

Toen worked in the *ittōbori* (single-knife carving) technique that distinguished the doll-making style of Nara. The cowled figure of Daruma was an excellent subject for his simplified and abstract manner of carving. HG

121 | **Daruma Yawning**

Illustrated on page 65
Suzuki Tōkoku, Japan, 1846–1913
wood with inlays
$1^{9}/_{16}$ x $1^{1}/_{16}$ x $^{13}/_{16}$ in. (3.9 x 2.7 x 2.1 cm)
M.91.250.74
incised: *Tōkoku*
seal form, incised: *Bairyū*
ink on box lid: *Suzuki Tōkoku*
seal on box lid: *Bairyū*

LITERATURE: Bushell, *An Exhibition of Netsuke*, fig. 379, p. 26; Ueda, *The Netsuke Handbook of Ueda Reikichi*, fig. 76, p. 87

Suzuki Tōkoku popularized this compact, inlaid, half-toothless model of Daruma yawning. Few can look dignified while yawning, and netsuke artists loved to play with this unguarded moment, combining it for comic effect with Daruma's distended stomach, atrophied legs, and lidless, staring eyes. HG

122 | **Cleaning Daruma's Ears**

Front illustrated on page 26
Suzuki Tōkoku, Japan, 1846–1913
wood with inlays
$1^{9}/_{16} \times 1^{1}/_{4} \times 1^{1}/_{16}$ in. (3.9 x 3.2 x 2.7 cm)
M.91.250.241
incised: *Tōkoku*
seal form, incised: *Bairyū*

LITERATURE: AMICO, 2001–present; Bushell, *An Exhibition of Netsuke*, fig. 383, p. 70; Hurtig, *Masterpieces of Netsuke Art*, fig. 992, p. 228

PROVENANCE: Adolph Kroch

Tōkoku's exquisite carving lends a note of realism to this netsuke, which suggests a "beauty and the beast" theme. In Japan, as in other cultures, it was considered humorous to combine extremely disparate people or elements. HG

122 BACK

123 | **Daruma with Fly Whisk and Begging Bowl**

Tōkoku I or Tōkoku II, Japan, late 19th–early 20th century
wood with inlays
$1^{5}/_{16} \times {}^{15}/_{16} \times {}^{15}/_{16}$ in. (3.3 x 2.4 x 2.4 cm)
AC1998.249.297
incised: *Tōkoku*
seal form, carved and inlaid in blue lacquer: *Bairyū*
ink on box lid: *Tōkoku Fūzui*
seal on box lid: *Bairyū*

LITERATURE: AMICO, 2001–present; Bushell, *An Exhibition of Netsuke*, fig. 384, p. 70

See catalogue 121.

124 | **Daruma with Fly Whisk and Begging Bowl**

Tōkoku II or Tōkoku III, Japan, late 19th–early 20th century
wood with inlays
$1^{9}/_{16} \times 1^{7}/_{16} \times 1^{1}/_{4}$ in. (3.9 x 3.6 x 3.1 cm)
AC1998.249.259
incised: *Tōkoku*
seal form, inlaid in carved red lacquer: *Bairyū*

LITERATURE: AMICO, 2001–present

See catalogue 121.

125 | **Daruma, First Patriarch of Zen**

NISAI, Japan, late 19th–early 20th century
wood with lacquer, inlays
$3\,^{3}/_{16}$ x $^{7}/_{8}$ x $^{3}/_{4}$ in. (8.2 x 2.2 x 1.9 cm)
AC1998.249.242
incised: *Nisai tō* / "carved by Nisai"

LITERATURE: AMICO, 2001–present; Bushell, *Collectors' Netsuke*, fig. 295, p. 162

Nisai's work leaned toward simplification and caricature. Here the carver emphasizes Daruma's deep disappointment at failing to communicate his message to Emperor Wu by giving the Zen patriarch the expression of a sad dog. HG

126 | **Daruma Reading a Salacious Romance**

SŌKO (MORITA KISABURŌ), Japan, 1879–1943
ivory with light staining, sumi, red pigment
$^{7}/_{8}$ x $1\,^{1}/_{2}$ x $^{15}/_{16}$ in. (2.2 x 3.8 x 2.4 cm)
M.91.250.250
incised and stained with sumi: *Sōko tō* / "carved by Sōko"
incised and stained with vermilion: kakihan

LITERATURE: Bushell, *Collectors' Netsuke*, fig. 268, p. 156

At the center of Japanese humor is play on the unexpected, and netsuke artists often used this device in their carvings of Daruma, exemplified here in Sōko's netsuke of the Zen patriarch reading a risqué novel. The humor is found in the master of austere Zen practice succumbing to the quick thrill of a lurid romantic tale. While this is entirely out of character for Daruma, it also reveals the relationship between Daruma and the courtesan: he is engaging in one of her typical habits, as both are manifestations of the dharma. The details of the drapery, fingers and toes, and carefully written text exemplify the meticulous realism that permeates Sōko's work. HG

127 | **Bishamonten in Scroll**

Juhōsai Tsunemasa, Japan, active 18th century
ivory with staining, sumi, inlays
2 3/8 x 1 3/16 x 3/4 in. (6.1 x 3 x 1.9 cm)
AC1998.249.173
incised and stained: *Juhōsai Tsunemasa*; kakihan

Like Isshinsai's *Daruma Emerging from Scroll* (CAT. 117), Juhōsai explores the concept of a character in a work of art "coming to life." This is a guardian figure in warrior's garb, whose image likely would be displayed on Boys' Day (fifth day of the fifth month). It represents one of the great protectors of Buddhist law, Bishamonten (Skt., Vaishravana). As head of the Four Heavenly Kings (Shitennō) who guarded the cardinal directions, Bishamonten was protector of the north, the most dangerous quadrant. He traditionally carries a *stupa* or pagoda in his raised hand and a staff in the other. Here, the stupa is indicated by the position of his hand; the stupa has been stolen by the demon on the back of the netsuke. HG

127 BACK

128 | **Temple Guardian**

School of Miwa, Japan, 18th–19th century
wood with inlays
2 1/4 x 1 1/8 x 15/16 in. (5.8 x 2.8 x 2.3 cm)
M.87.263.134
incised: *[?] Aoyama ni Miwa haka* / "[?] the Miwa tomb in Aoyama"

LITERATURE: AMICO, 1999–present; Bushell, *Collectors' Netsuke*, fig. 41, p. 38; Bushell, *An Exhibition of Netsuke*, fig. 13, p. 31; Mikoshiba and Bushell, "Netsuke and the *Sōken kishō*," p. 109; Ueda, *The Netsuke Handbook of Ueda Reikichi*, fig. 3, p. 28

PROVENANCE: Henry T. Reiss

Miwa has miniaturized one of the grand gate Guardian Kings (*niō*) whose images stand at the entrance to Buddhist temple compounds. Considering the wrathful visage of this figure, his image was probably thought to have a protective, talismanic effect. He stands on a rock, a symbol for Mt. Sumeru, showing his unwavering determination and strength. With mouth closed and arms lowered, the figure protects the esoteric aspects of Buddhism, although he should hold a thunderbolt (*vajra*) in his left hand according to literary iconography. HG

129 | **Temple Guardian**

Japan, 18th–19th century
ivory with sumi
2 5/16 x 1 5/16 x 7/8 in. (5.9 x 3.3 x 2.2 cm)
M.91.250.12

LITERATURE: Atchley, "The Pavilion for Japanese Art in Los Angeles," p. 23; Bushell, *An Exhibition of Netsuke*, fig. 157, p. 21; Bushell, *Netsuke Familiar and Unfamiliar*, fig. 85, p. 104

This carver of this temple guardian goes beyond Miwa in surface detail and exaggeration of musculature, reflecting the style of full-size sculptures. This guardian also diverges from standard iconography for hand placement and attributes, but his stance captures the ferocious protector's power and rage. HG

129 BACK

130 | **Demon with Temple Guardian in Bath**

SCHOOL OF MIWA, Japan, late 18th–19th century
mid-19th century
wood
1 7/16 x 1 3/16 x 1 1/8 in. (3.6 x 3 x 2.9 cm)
M.91.250.320
incised: *Miwa*; kakihan

LITERATURE: AMICO, 2001–present; Bushell, *An Exhibition of Netsuke*, fig. 15, p. 31; Bushell, *Netsuke Familiar and Unfamiliar*, fig. 747, p. 225

Here, the demon is probably either enslaved by or currying favor with the guardian protector he bathes. This Miwa School carver eloquently captures the movement of figures and water, distorting musculature and facial expression for comic effect. HG

131 | **Temple Guardian and Demon Wrestling**

Also illustrated on page 56
SCHOOL OF MIWA, Japan, late 18th–19th century
mid-19th century
wood
2 7/8 x 1 7/16 x 1 7/16 in. (7.3 x 3.6 x 3.7 cm)
M.87.263.135
incised in oval cartouche: *Miwa*

LITERATURE: AMICO, 1999–present; Bushell, *An Exhibition of Netsuke*, fig. 14, p. 31; Ueda, *The Netsuke Handbook of Ueda Reikichi*, fig. 71, p. 84

A number of Edo carvers explored the struggle of good and evil through the sumo technique *kawazugake*. Good will win, because the guardian (who is being lifted) has hooked his left leg and arm around the demon and will soon overthrow him. The carvers who depicted this theme emphasized or exaggerated its different aspects. Here the carver focused on the musculature around the knees and lower legs; in the next piece (CAT. 132), the carver concentrated on the rib cage. These are *okimono*-type netsuke, better suited for display than for use. The Miwa School carver has given the surface a particularly fine polish. HG

131

132 SIDE

132 | **Temple Guardian and Demon Wrestling**

Hōzan, Japan, active late 19th century
wood with inlays
$2^1/_4$ x $1^1/_8$ x 1 in. (5.7 x 2.8 x 2.5 cm)
AC1998.249.258
incised: *Hōzan*; kakihan

LITERATURE: AMICO, 2001–present

See catalogue 131.

133 | **Temple Guardian Weaving Straw Sandal**

Sōko (Morita Kisaburō), Japan, 1879–1943
wood
$1^7/_8$ x $1^5/_{16}$ x $1^1/_8$ in. (4.7 x 3.4 x 2.8 cm)
AC1998.249.84
incised in inlaid gold plaque with green-stained horn or antler surround: *Sōko*

LITERATURE: AMICO, 2001–present; Bushell, *An Exhibition of Netsuke*, fig. 433, p. 75

PROVENANCE: Nakajima Meiken

Sōko's extremely refined carving reveals the importance he placed on distinguishing textures and mass. The laboring guardian sits on the Buddha's enormous sandal, which curves up at the edges. Intricately carved details such as the raised scarf suggest that this netsuke would be displayed rather than worn. HG

133

134 | Temple Guardian and Demon

Sōko (Morita Kisaburō), Japan, 1879–1943
1940
boxwood
$1^{15}/_{16}$ x $1^{1}/_{2}$ x 1 in. (5 x 3.8 x 2.5 cm)
AC1998.249.121
incised: *Sōko tō* / "carved by Sōko"
seal form, inlaid in gold and lacquer: *Morita*
ink on interior box lid: *Shōwa ka no e tatsu toshi aki* / "autumn 1940"; *Sōko koku* / "carved by Sōko"; *Nihon bijutsu Kyōkai hyaku jushichi kai tenrankai mukansa shuppinsu* / "submitted to the unjuried Japan Art Association 117th exhibition"
seal on box lid: *Sōko*

LITERATURE: AMICO, 2001–present; Bushell, *An Exhibition of Netsuke*, fig. 434, p. 27; Bushell, "Questions & Answers" (1977), fig. 19b, p. 47; Hill and Johnson, "The Raymond Bushell Netsuke Exhibition," fig. 434, p. 29; Ueda, *The Netsuke Handbook of Ueda Reikichi*, fig. 198, p. 189

A guardian and demon enjoy a temporary truce during the Obon festival (held in midsummer), when ancestors return from their various spirit worlds to the family village. The demon carries water and the guardian carries flowers to wash and decorate the graves of their ancestors in a ritual welcoming them home. The textures and details here give the piece an overall uniformity of effect. HG

134

135 | Demon with Spiked Club

Japan, 18th century
red and black Negoro lacquer with inlays
$3^{3}/_{16}$ x $1^{9}/_{16}$ x $1^{1}/_{2}$ in. (8.1 x 4 x 3.8 cm)
M.91.250.133

LITERATURE: AMICO, 2001–present; Bushell, *An Exhibition of Netsuke*, fig. 400, p. 72; Ueda, *The Netsuke Handbook of Ueda Reikichi*, fig. 172, p. 175, and front cover

PROVENANCE: Meidbrodt collection

Demons come in a variety of forms, from disease carriers to poltergeists that run wild at night to minions of the King of Hell, Enma, and this demon appears to be one such minion. His solid stance, enormous club, and focused, straightforward gaze imply the presence of one who is guarding territory rather than sneaking about to wreak havoc. The Negoro style of lacquer, layered with red thinly applied over black (here artificially aged), emphasizes the demon's musculature. HG

136 BACK

136 | **Thunder Demon on Drum**

TANAKA MINKŌ, Japan, 1735–1816
wood with inlays
4 x 1 x $^{3}/_{4}$ in. (10.1 x 2.5 x 1.9 cm)
AC1998.249.176
incised: *Minkō*; kakihan

LITERATURE: Bushell, *Collectors' Netsuke*, fig. 34, p. 36

This thunder demon is poised to pound his drum and strike terror into the hearts of mortals. His broad, rough features are typical of Minkō's style, as is the generalized carving. The artist inlaid the demon's horns and the tacks on the drum skin. This netsuke appears to have been carved in two parts, with the drum and feet attaching to the legs at the ankles. HG

137 | **Demon**

Illustrated on page 18
AFTER YOSHIMURA SHŪZAN, Japan, late 18th–19th century
soft wood with pigments
3 $^{1}/_{8}$ x 1 $^{7}/_{16}$ x $^{15}/_{16}$ in. (8 x 3.7 x 2.4 cm)
M.87.263.89

LITERATURE: AMICO, 1999–present; Bushell, *Collectors' Netsuke*, fig. 4, p. 26; Bushell, *An Exhibition of Netsuke*, fig. 7, p. 31; Bushell, *Netsuke Familiar and Unfamiliar*, back cover; Falkove, "The Unique, the Extraordinary, and the Unusual," fig. 6, p. 27; Mikoshiba and Bushell, "Netsuke and the *Sōken kishō*," p. 106

PROVENANCE: Cornelius Van Schaak Roosevelt

Because this figure has been variously identified as a *kirin*, the god of Mt. Shitsugozan, and a *shokuin* (a composite creature), it seems more practical to refer to it with the term *demon* until further evidence is found. This particular demon, with its aggressive stance, is recorded in the *Sōken kishō* as a type carved by Yoshimura Shūzan (d. 1776), and the delicate surface painting suggests his style as well. HG

138 | Demons Carrying Rich Man to Hell

Ikkōsai Tōun, Japan, active 1830–1843
ivory with staining, sumi
1 3/8 x 1 5/8 x 7/8 in. (3.5 x 4.2 x 2.2 cm)
M.91.250.134
incised and stained with sumi in oval reserve: *Tōun*

LITERATURE: Ueda, *The Netsuke Handbook of Ueda Reikichi*, fig. 129, p. 136

This arrogant, wealthy man has hired a palanquin, carried by the servants of hell, to bring him to his final destination. Calmly sucking on his pipe while seven demons hoist him across Sanzu no Kawa, the Buddhist equivalent of the river Styx, he seems oblivious to the horrors that await him. Bushell interpreted this scene as depicting the proverb "Even the judgments of hell are influenced by money." HG

139 | Raijin: God of Thunder

Front illustrated on page 24
Kaigyokusai Masatsugu, Japan, 1813–1892
ivory with staining; manjū type
2 x 1/2 in. (5.1 x 1.2 cm)
M.87.263.34
incised and lightly stained: *Kaigyokudō Masatsugu*

LITERATURE: AMICO, 1999–present; Atchley, "Kaigyokusai," fig. 10, p. 11; Bushell, *Collectors' Netsuke*, fig. 152, p. 106; Bushell, *An Exhibition of Netsuke*, fig. 98, p. 39, and front cover

Unlike the later realist carver Sōko (see CAT. 134), whose even, overall treatment of detail sometimes makes his work hard to read, Kaigyokusai, famous for his naturalistic style, was a master of rhythms of light and dark. Here he distinguishes the thunder god and his drums from the roiling clouds by altering the density of staining. Kaigyokusai's mastery of the levels of depth in a shallow carving field is evident in the interweaving of drums and drapery with the clouds. HG

139 BACK

140 | Shōzuka no Baba

Soshin, Japan, active late 19th–early 20th century
wood with inlays
4 1/8 x 1 7/16 x 1 1/8 in. (10.4 x 3.6 x 2.8 cm)
AC1998.249.133
incised: *Soshin tō* / "carved by Soshin"

LITERATURE: AMICO, 2001–present; Bushell, *An Exhibition of Netsuke*, fig. 130, p. 42; Bushell, *Netsuke Familiar and Unfamiliar*, fig. 749, p. 225; Lazarnick, *Netsuke and Inro Artists*, vol. 2, p. 1307; Phillips, ed., *The Collectors' Encyclopedia of Antiques*, p. 570

Shōzuka no Baba is a terrifying minion of hell who takes people's clothing as they cross over the Sanzu no Kawa (see CAT. 138). The weight of the clothes helps determine the heft of a person's sins. Soshin has carved her with sharp strokes in a grotesque and repellent manner, suggesting the horror she would provoke. HG

141 | Demon Pelted with Beans at New Year

Ueda Kōhōsai, Japan, died circa 1907
late 19th–early 20th century
ivory with staining, sumi
1 3/4 x 1 5/16 x 1 1/4 in. (4.4 x 3.4 x 3.1 cm)
AC1998.249.21
incised and stained: *Kōhōsai*

LITERATURE: Ueda, *The Netsuke Handbook of Ueda Reikichi*, fig. 163, p. 154

The deep trepidation felt about demons in earlier times had declined by the Meiji period (1868–1912), when these (CATS. 141–43) were sculpted. Demons from this period became, in effect, cute: they appeared harassed or tried to win a reprieve by pretending to do good works. Ueda Reikichi describes Kōhōsai as a resident of Osaka; however, by the late 1800s, a general acceptance of realism and the popularity of Edo-type humor had diluted regional styles in favor of a national style. HG

142 | Demon Soliciting Alms

Eisai, Japan, 19th century
late 19th century
mixed-metal disk, ivory bowl; kagamibuta type
1 15/16 x 11/16 in. (4.9 x 1.7 cm)
M.87.263.75
incised: *Eisai*; kakihan

LITERATURE: AMICO, 1999–present; Lazarnick, *Netsuke and Inro Artists*, vol. 1, p. 361; Ueda, *The Netsuke Handbook of Ueda Reikichi*, fig. 13, p. 32

See catalogue 141.

143 | Demon Soliciting Alms

Illustrated on page 67
Sōko (Morita Kisaburō), Japan, 1879–1943
wood
2 1/16 x 1 3/16 x 1 in. (5.2 x 3 x 2.6 cm)
M.91.250.247
incised: *Sōko tō* / "carved by Sōko"

LITERATURE: Bushell, *Collectors' Netsuke*, fig. 267, p. 156

See catalogue 141.

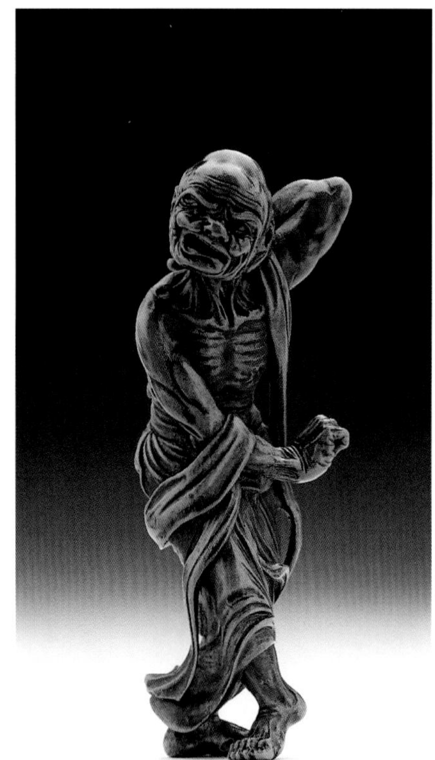

144 | **Struggle against Temptation**

Japan, 18th century
wood with sumi
3 3/8 x 1 3/4 x 1 in. (8.6 x 4.5 x 2.5 cm)
AC1998.249.115

LITERATURE: Behrens, *Netsuke*, fig. 414, pl. 9; Bushell, *An Exhibition of Netsuke*, fig. 166, p. 46; Bushell, *Netsuke Familiar and Unfamiliar*, fig. 84, p. 104

PROVENANCE: Mark T. Hindson

The monk is completely entangled in a rope, here symbolizing the soul's connection to the world of desires, and strikes a pose recalling a dance of Hindu gods. His right arm is elongated for effect and the rest of his anatomy is rendered simplistically, suggesting a date around 1750. The artist used sumi to create a harsh surface contrast that complements the theme. HG

145 | **Ancient Worthy with Buddhist Scepter**

Japan, late 18th–early 19th century
wood
2 7/8 x 1 1/8 x 1 in. (7.3 x 2.8 x 2.5 cm)
AC1998.249.114

LITERATURE: Bushell, *An Exhibition of Netsuke*, figs. 165a and b, p. 46; Bushell, *The Wonderful World of Netsuke*, fig. 45, p. 42; Hill and Johnson, "The Raymond Bushell Netsuke Exhibition," figs. 165a and b, p. 33

PROVENANCE: Matsui Yonekichi

This figure may represent the *rakan* Inkada Sonja, usually identifiable by long eyebrows and a scepter (*nyoi*). Here the figure strains to scratch an itch with the scepter, his twisting stance enabling the carver to study anatomy and drapery flow. Sumi emphasizes the sharp bones, tendons, and wrinkles of this ancient worthy. HG

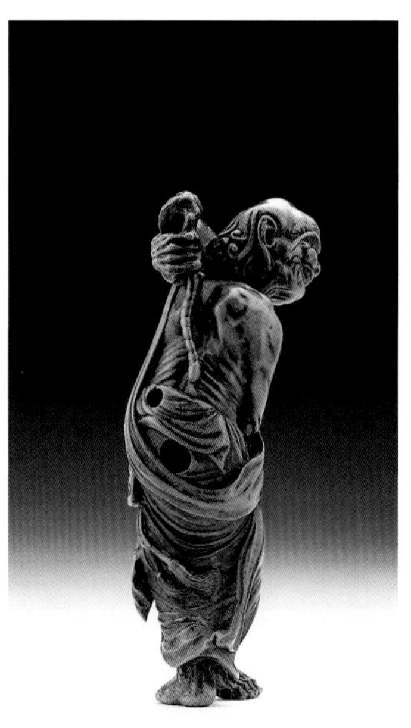

145 BACK

146

146 | **Basū Sennin**

Japan, 19th century
wood with green and brown lacquer
$3^{1}/_{16}$ x $^{15}/_{16}$ x $^{7}/_{8}$ in. (7.8 x 2.4 x 2.3 cm)
M.91.250.172

LITERATURE: Bushell, *An Exhibition of Netsuke*, fig. 158, p. 46; Bushell, *Netsuke Familiar and Unfamiliar*, fig. 77, p. 103

Basū Sennin is recognized by the sutra scroll in his left hand and the staff in his right, and by being clothed only from the waist down. He is a messenger of the Thousand-armed Kannon, and his best-known image, of which this is a close reproduction, is a sculpture at the Sanjūsangendō temple in Kyoto. HG

147 | **Itinerant Monk**

Japan, 19th century
wood
$3^{1}/_{16}$ x $1^{1}/_{4}$ x $1^{3}/_{16}$ in. (7.8 x 3.2 x 3 cm)
M.91.250.293

LITERATURE: Bushell, *Netsuke Familiar and Unfamiliar*, fig. 76, p. 103; Bushell, "Travels by Netsuke," fig. 7, p. 106

The monk with shaved pate wears tall clogs (*geta*) to stay above the mud. In his right hand he holds a string of prayer beads, and over his back he has slung a fish-shaped wooden gong (*mokugyo*), which he steadies with his left hand. For a fee, this type of monk would recite sutras to dispel demons. HG

147

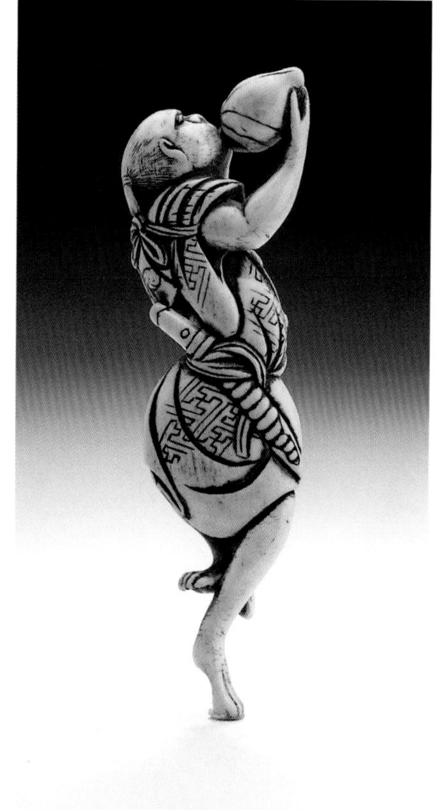

148 BACK

148 | **Mountain Ascetic Sounding Signal**

Japan, early 19th century
ivory with staining, sumi, red pigment
$3^{7}/_{16}$ x $1^{1}/_{8}$ x $^{5}/_{8}$ in. (8.8 x 2.8 x 1.5 cm)
AC1998.249.132

LITERATURE: Bushell, *An Exhibition of Netsuke*, fig. 293, p. 60

Mountain ascetics (*yamabushi*) in Japan, seen here and in the following netsuke, were practitioners of a discipline called Shugendō. It originated in the ancient Japanese veneration of mountains and their attendant gods (*kami*), but was eventually organized around esoteric Buddhist practice. By making a circuit up a mountain and performing ascetic rituals and meditation, a yamabushi traveled metaphorically through the ten stages of existence, beginning in hell and progressing to Buddhist perfection (Addiss, *Ghosts*, p. 107). Yamabushi tended to be tough and intense individuals, hardened by such practices as confessing their sins while hanging from a cliff. This netsuke is carved from a thin sliver of ivory and cannot stand on its own. HG

149 | **Mountain Ascetic**

Illustrated on page 68
Sōko (Morita Kisaburō), Japan, 1879–1943
wood
$2^{3}/_{16}$ x $1^{3}/_{16}$ x $1^{1}/_{8}$ in. (5.5 x 3 x 2.9 cm)
M.91.250.318
incised: *Sōko saku* / "made by Sōko"
ink on box lid: *Shōwa tsuchi no to mi shōka* / "Shōwa, Younger Brother of Earth, Year of the Serpent [1929] early summer"; *Sōko saku* / "made by Sōko"
seal on box lid: *Sōko*

LITERATURE: Bushell, *An Exhibition of Netsuke*, fig. 428, p. 75, and front cover; Bushell, "Travels by Netsuke," fig. 10, p. 106; Hill and Johnson, "The Raymond Bushell Netsuke Exhibition," fig. 428, p. 36; Hurtig, "Collecting Legends," p. 18

This netsuke, sculpted more than one hundred years later than the anonymously carved *Mountain Ascetic Sounding Signal*, functions better as a small *okimono*. Sōko's netsuke are so detailed that one could use them for sociological study, although obviously the carver's desire was less reportage than to capture the spirit of the dancing figure. (On *yamabushi*, see CAT. 148.) HG

150

151 | **Chinese Gong**

Japan, late 18th–early 19th century
wood
3 x 1$^{5}/_{16}$ x $^{13}/_{16}$ in. (7.6 x 3.4 x 2 cm)
AC1998.249.24

LITERATURE: AMICO, 2001–present; Ueda, *The Netsuke Handbook of Ueda Reikichi*, fig. 48, p. 48

The animal supports on this gong, carved in the symmetrical Chinese style, seem to have come to life. Two dragons and a Chinese lion join to keep demons away and protect the Buddhist law. In China, the gong served to dispel demons and, in temple rituals, to attract the attention of the spirits. HG

151

150 | **Gong with Elephant Handle**

Japan, 18th century
ivory with staining, sumi
4$^{5}/_{16}$ x 2$^{1}/_{16}$ x 1$^{3}/_{8}$ in. (10.9 x 5.3 x 3.5 cm)
M.87.263.138

LITERATURE: AMICO, 2000–present; Bushell, *Netsuke Familiar and Unfamiliar*, fig. 666, p. 212

The elephant is one of the Seven Jewels that aid the Universal King in understanding Buddhist law. Here the elephant stands on a gong used to punctuate the reading of sutras, the animal and gong tied with the rope by which souls are brought to Buddhist law. HG

152 | **Dragons on Gong**

Asakusa School, Japan, mid- to late 19th century
mid-19th century
stag antler
1 1/2 x 1 1/4 x 1 in. (3.8 x 3.1 x 2.5 cm)
AC1998.249.165

LITERATURE: Bushell, *Netsuke Familiar and Unfamiliar*, fig. 390, p. 161

PROVENANCE: Yamada collection

The type of gong most commonly used in Japan, called a *mokugyo*, was made of wood and carved to resemble fish. The shape was derived from a pair of fish facing head-to-head and tail-to-tail, representing two goldfish, one of the Eight Treasures of Buddhism. On this mokugyo, dragon heads form handles and a juvenile dragon crawls over the surface. HG

153 | **Buddhist Monk Sleeping on Gong**

Tetsugen (Kyūsai), Japan, 1879–1938
wood with lacquer, pigments
1 5/8 x 1 3/16 x 13/16 in. (4.1 x 3 x 2.1 cm)
AC1998.249.302
incised: *Ikkyū tō* / "carved by Ikkyū" [Tetsugen's art name]

LITERATURE: Bushell, *Collectors' Netsuke*, fig. 247, p. 153; Bushell, *Netsuke Familiar and Unfamiliar*, fig. 101, p. 108

Though this appears to be a charming image, the monk sleeping on a wooden gong (*mokugyo*) was a metaphor for one who failed to reach enlightenment. He is using the gong as a headrest rather than seeking and understanding the profound power of its message. HG

154 | **Buddhist Bell**

Japan, 19th century
bamboo root
2 1/4 x 2 1/4 x 1 1/2 in. (5.8 x 5.7 x 3.8 cm)
AC1998.249.161

LITERATURE: Bushell, *Netsuke Familiar and Unfamiliar*, fig. 387, p. 160

In this netsuke, a found object—a bamboo root—has been carved slightly to make it resemble more closely a recognizable object. Though not often published, found-object netsuke were fairly common. HG

155 | **Confucian Devotee**

Japan, 18th century
wood
$2\frac{5}{8}$ x $1\frac{7}{16}$ x $\frac{13}{16}$ in. (6.7 x 3.6 x 2 cm)
M.91.250.292

LITERATURE: Bushell, *An Exhibition of Netsuke*, fig. 280, p. 58; Bushell, *Netsuke Familiar and Unfamiliar*, fig. 367, p. 155

This is a simply carved folk netsuke of a very rare subject. The devotee's peach offering indicates that he is taking part in a Confucian ritual. HG

156 | **A Confucian Paragon: Dutiful Son with Blind Father**

DŌRAKU (SAI), Japan, active early 19th century
ivory with staining, sumi
$1\frac{7}{8}$ x $1\frac{1}{4}$ x $\frac{13}{16}$ in. (4.8 x 3.1 x 2.1 cm)
M.91.250.197
incised and stained: *Dōraku*

LITERATURE: AMICO, 2001–present; Ueda, *The Netsuke Handbook of Ueda Reikichi*, fig. 53, p. 51

One of the virtues espoused in Confucianism was to love and care for one's parents, and Confucian theorists in China selected twenty-four models, or "paragons of filial piety." The story of the young man assisting his blind father is not told in the paragons, but in the first story, Emperor Shun's father is called Gushou, or "Blind Old Man." In the tale, Emperor Shun had an unappealing family, but his love for his parents was so great that the beasts were moved to help him plow and weed their land. In this netsuke, the sighted young man's pupils have been filled in while those of the blind old man have not. HG

157 | A Confucian Paragon: Saishi Feeding Her Toothless Great-Grandmother-in-Law

MIURA YOSHINAGA, Japan, active late 19th century
ivory with sumi
$3\,^{3}/_{16}$ x $2\,^{1}/_{4}$ x $1\,^{5}/_{16}$ in. (8.2 x 5.8 x 3.4 cm)
AC1998.249.90
incised and lightly stained: *Miura shi Yoshinaga*

LITERATURE: AMICO, 2001–present; Bushell, *An Exhibition of Netsuke*, fig. 267, p. 23; Bushell, *Netsuke Familiar and Unfamiliar*, fig. 517, p. 184; Davey, *Netsuke*, fig. 933, p. 307; Hill and Johnson, "The Raymond Bushell Netsuke Exhibition," fig. 267, p. 34; Lazarnick, *Netsuke and Inro Artists*, vol. 2, p. 1239; Phillips, ed., *The Collectors' Encyclopedia of Antiques*, p. 567

PROVENANCE: Mark T. Hindson; Guest collection

Saishi (Ch., Cui Nanshan) had an aging relative by marriage, Madame Zhangsun. Each day, Saishi would wash her face, comb her hair, and feed her with her own milk, for Madame Zhangsun was toothless. By these means, Saishi kept Madame Zhangsun healthy for several years. HG

157 BACK

158 | Angel Finial

Japan, 17th century
wood (cypress?) with pigments, lacquer, gilt
$2\,^{9}/_{16}$ x $^{11}/_{16}$ x $^{7}/_{16}$ in. (6.5 x 1.7 x 1.1 cm)
AC1998.249.303

LITERATURE: Bushell, *Netsuke Familiar and Unfamiliar*, fig. 78, p. 103

Heavenly spirits, called Tennin or Hiten, or the half-bird called Karyōbinga, were servants and attendants to the Buddhist gods and demigods. They were not themselves objects of worship. In painting or sculpture, these spirits were found in the celestial zone, either playing instruments, praying, or carrying or riding lotuses whose petals they scatter. The Karyōbinga was the Kalavinka of Indian mythology, a Himalayan half-bird, half-person with a beautiful singing voice. This has been called an angel finial because it appears to be a tiny ornament that was retrofitted as a netsuke. Sculpted of very light wood, it is lacquered and gilded. HG

159

161

159 | **Heavenly Spirit: Karyōbinga**

Japan, 18th century
ivory with staining, sumi
2 5/8 x 1 1/4 x 1 1/16 in. (6.7 x 3.2 x 2.7 cm)
M.91.250.294

LITERATURE: Behrens, *Netsuke*, fig. 273, pl. 5; Bushell, *An Exhibition of Netsuke*, fig. 161, p. 46; Bushell, "Travels by Netsuke," fig. 27, p. 109

This Karyōbinga with a lotus is made from a small, triangular section of ivory that has been heavily carved over the entire surface. When worn, it would appear to fly along the upper edge of the obi. (On Karyōbinga, see CAT. 158.) HG

160 | **Heavenly Spirit: Karyōbinga**

Illustrated on page 19
Japan, 18th century
ivory with dark staining, sumi
2 3/8 x 1 1/2 x 1 in. (6 x 3.8 x 2.5 cm)
AC1998.249.110

LITERATURE: Bushell, *An Exhibition of Netsuke*, fig. 49, p. 18; Bushell, *Netsuke Familiar and Unfamiliar*, fig. 539, p. 189; Hill and Johnson, "The Raymond Bushell Netsuke Exhibition," fig. 49, pp. 32, 40; Phillips, ed., *The Collectors' Encyclopedia of Antiques*, p. 566

The Southeast Asian flavor of this netsuke, and cord holes which appear retrofitted, might indicate a foreign source, or at least foreign inspiration. HG

161 | **Heavenly Spirit: Karyōbinga**

KYOKUSEN, Japan, active early 19th century
wood with inlays
1 x 2 7/16 x 1 1/2 in. (2.5 x 6.3 x 3.8 cm)
AC1998.249.15
incised: *Kyokusen*

Kyokusen carved his Karyōbinga in a nearly solid agglomeration of gauzy scarves and feathers, using a Toyomasa-like rubbing style to highlight exposed edges after deep staining. HG

Folk Religion and Shinto Subjects

The Seven Gods of Good Fortune (J., Shichifukujin)—Jurōjin, Fukurokuju, Hotei, Daikoku, Ebisu, Bishamonten, and Benzaiten—were originally individual deities from India and China as well as Japan, and they were believed to bring wealth and long life. The first four gods in particular were highly popular with netsuke carvers. Both Jurōjin and Fukurokuju are venerated as deities of longevity. They were initially associated with Daoism, and their netsuke images tend to reflect Chinese carved figures that were used for good luck. Hotei (Ch., Budai), a wandering Zen monk, was believed to be the incarnation of the bodhisattva Maitreya. He begged for food and alms, which he placed in a large sack for safekeeping until he could redistribute them to children. Daikoku (Skt., Mahakala), deity of the field, was originally an Indian god who fought the forces of evil. Ebisu, usually shown with a *tai* (red sea bream), was the god of fishing. Daikoku and Ebisu together were worshiped as gods of the kitchen. Bishamonten had an equally important role in Buddhist cosmology, and he is shown in that section (see CAT. 127).

Auspicious figures in this catalogue consist of Chinese boys and images of Okame. Chinese boys are usually dressed in belted silk robes and silk shoes, and wear their hair in two tufts or buns on the sides of their head. As auspicious symbols of fertility, they were often depicted in groups of three, five (CAT. 172), or seven, which were all propitious numbers.

Okame, of purely Japanese origin, is based on the mythological character Ame no Uzume, a fat, jolly goddess whose bawdy dance lured Amaterasu no Ōmikami from her cave. In kyōgen drama, Uzume appeared in caricature form as a character later known as Okame (or Otafuku), who represented a woman who reveled in her sensuality. In netsuke, Okame is depicted in all of these guises.

ABOVE: *Group of Five Chinese Boys* (CAT. 172)

162 BACK

162 | **Hotei and Chinese Boys**

KAGETOSHI, Japan, active early to mid-19th century
ivory with staining, sumi
$1^{5}/_{16} \times 1^{1}/_{2} \times 1$ in. (3.4 x 3.8 x 2.5 cm)
AC1998.249.235
incised on raised rectangular reserve:
Kagetoshi

LITERATURE: AMICO, 2001–present

Hotei (Ch., Budai), one of the Seven Gods of Good Fortune, was adopted as a god of contentment and magnanimity although originally he was a wandering Zen monk. As a monk, he preferred the company of children to that of adults, and his bag contained the alms he received from begging. The Chinese boys that surrounded Hotei became an emblem of multiple heirs, and the bag was thought to be full of treasures.

Here and in the next piece, the carvers show two fashions in later Edo-period netsuke. Kagetoshi, known for minute and intricate carvings, groups child musicians with Hotei, dispersing the activity around a relatively empty center. The netsuke's miniaturized complexity embodies a trend in the 1800s. HG

163 | **Hotei Dreaming on His Bag of Treasures**

ATTRIBUTED TO TOYOSUKE, Japan, circa 1788–1858
stoneware with gold and brown lacquer
$1^{1}/_{2} \times 1^{1}/_{8} \times 1^{1}/_{8}$ in. (3.8 x 2.8 x 2.8 cm)
M.87.263.70

LITERATURE: AMICO, 2000–present; Bushell, "Ceramic Netsuke," fig. 39, p. 30; Bushell, *Netsuke Familiar and Unfamiliar*, fig. 452, p. 171

PROVENANCE: Ikeda Shun'ichirō

Toyosuke mixes disparate materials, including lacquer with suspended metal flecks and ceramic. He then adds intentional ambiguity, as Hotei's stomach flows over his bag, with no clear demarcation between stomach and bag, making the fused mass a joint metaphor for plenty. HG

164 | Daikoku and Ebisu: Gods of Wealth and Commerce

Japan, 18th century
ivory with staining, sumi
$2\,^{1}/_{4}$ x $1\,^{9}/_{16}$ x $^{15}/_{16}$ in. (5.7 x 4 x 2.3 cm)
M.91.250.173

LITERATURE: Bushell, *The Wonderful World of Netsuke*, fig. 31, p. 34

PROVENANCE: Sakai Shoji

In netsuke, Daikoku and Ebisu, two of the Seven Gods of Good Fortune, are sometimes depicted as sumo wrestlers. Sumo has been associated with Shinto since the eighth century, and its rituals still influence the sport. Here the figures are arranged in a stack that makes superb wearable art: the netsuke is balanced around a central axis and has completely rounded contours, yet encapsulates dramatic tension and energy. Earle has suggested that the lower figure could be Hotei rather than Ebisu (Earle, *Netsuke*, p. 157). HG

165 | Daikoku As a Raconteur

Illustrated on page 53
JŪGETSU, Japan, active 19th century
ivory with staining, sumi
$2\,^{7}/_{16}$ x $^{7}/_{8}$ x $1\,^{1}/_{16}$ in. (6.2 x 2.2 x 2.7 cm)
M.91.250.158
incised and stained: *Jūgetsu*

LITERATURE: Bushell, *Netsuke Familiar and Unfamiliar*, fig. 179, p. 122; Lazarnick, *Netsuke and Inro Artists*, vol. 2, p. 998

Daikoku, recognizable by his hat and extended earlobes, is clothed here in townsman's garb and beats his left hand with a fan, giving emphasis to points in his comic tale. His expression suggests that he is humorously exaggerating his story, and his drooping eyes add a note of realism. HG

166 | Fukurokuju: God of Wisdom

Illustrated on page 39
Japan, 18th century
ivory with staining, sumi
$2\,^{7}/_{16}$ x 2 x $1\,^{3}/_{16}$ in. (6.2 x 5.1 x 3 cm)
M.91.250.174

LITERATURE: Dillon, "Philadelphians Display Netsuke," p. 16

Fukurokuju, whose name means "luck, official status, longevity," is known for his distended cranium, which holds the wisdom gained during his long life. He is also one of the Seven Gods of Good Fortune. Fukurokuju netsuke of the 1700s (CATS. 166–67) tend to show him in a forward-facing pose often seen in Ming dynasty Chinese ivories, with everything except his macrocephalic head truncated severely. In nineteenth-century versions, seen in work by Ōhara Mitsuhiro (CAT. 168), Fukurokuju is more naturally proportioned. HG

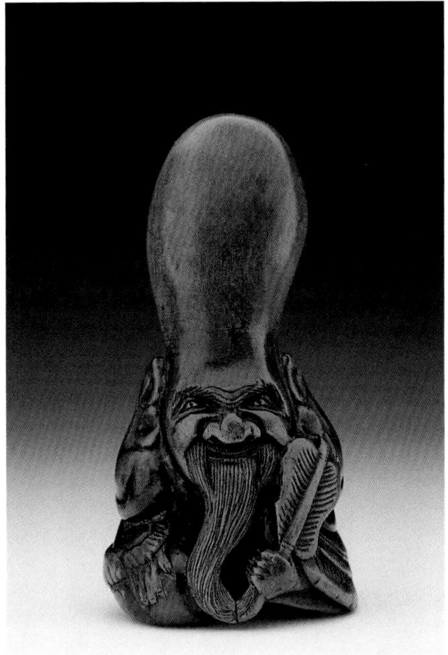

167 | Fukurokuju: God of Wisdom

Sueyoshi Sekishū, Japan, active late 18th–early 19th century
wood
$2^{1}/_{4}$ x $1^{5}/_{8}$ x $^{7}/_{8}$ in. (5.7 x 4.1 x 2.2 cm)
AC1998.249.18
incised: *Sekishū*

LITERATURE: AMICO, 2001–present; Bushell, *An Exhibition of Netsuke*, fig. 184, p. 48

See catalogue 166.

168 | Fukurokuju on Clouds

Ōhara Mitsuhiro, Japan, 1810–1875
ivory with staining, sumi
$1^{9}/_{16}$ x $1^{1}/_{16}$ x $1^{3}/_{16}$ in. (3.9 x 2.7 x 3 cm)
AC1998.249.174
incised and stained: *Mitsuhiro*

PROVENANCE: Takama collection

Mitsuhiro seems to have been looking at Daoist or Chinese-style literati paintings when he designed his Fukurokuju. The figure, hands hidden in sleeves, holds up his arms before his face in a Chinese gesture of honor and obeisance. HG

169 | **Jurōjin, God of Longevity, As Turtle**

JUICHI (or TOSHIKAZU), Japan, active late 19th century
ivory with staining, sumi
2 1/16 x 1 9/16 x 3/8 in. (5.2 x 4 x 1 cm)
M.91.250.300
incised and stained with sumi: *Ju*; kakihan

LITERATURE: Bushell, *An Exhibition of Netsuke*, fig. 154, p. 45

Like Fukurokuju, Jurōjin (Ch., Shoulao) had a large head to hold the accumulated wisdom of his advanced age. Jurōjin's name includes the Chinese character meaning "longevity," and he is sometimes accompanied by a stag, the only animal believed capable of rooting out and ingesting the fungus of immortality. Jurōjin is also associated with the turtle, which is known for its long life. This artist has doubled his wish for longevity by creating a figure that reads as a turtle on one side and as Jurōjin on the other. HG

170 | **Jurōjin Mounted on His Stag**

KEISUKE, Japan, active late 19th–early 20th century
late 19th century
painted wood
1 15/16 x 1 5/8 x 1 1/4 in. (5 x 4.1 x 3.1 cm)
AC1998.249.77
incised: *Gofuku tenrai zu baku Chokunyū ō Keisuke tō* / "design of five treasures gifted by heaven, copied from old man Chokunyū [Tanomura Chokunyū, 1814–1907], carved by Keisuke"

LITERATURE: AMICO, 2001–present; Bushell, *An Exhibition of Netsuke*, fig. 373, p. 69; Bushell, *Netsuke Familiar and Unfamiliar*, fig. 415, p. 164; Lazarnick, *Netsuke and Inro Artists*, vol. 1, p. 608

According to the inscription, Keisuke modeled his netsuke on a painting by Tanomura Chokunyū, a *nihonga* artist working in a traditional Japanese style during the Meiji period (1868–1912), when many artists turned to Western styles and techniques. Chokunyū was from an eminent lineage of artists who followed the Nanga style, based on interpretations of Chinese literati painting. Both the structure and the surface of this netsuke are extremely delicate and, though tiny, it was probably best used as an *okimono*. HG

171 | **Chinese Boy with Cat**

Japan, 18th century
ivory with staining, sumi
2 3/16 x 13/16 x 13/16 in. (5.6 x 2.1 x 2.1 cm)
M.91.250.278

LITERATURE: AMICO, 2001–present; Bushell, *The Wonderful World of Netsuke*, fig. 33, p. 35

PROVENANCE: Horie Zenshiro

Images of Chinese boys, typified by their costume and distinctive coif, were emblems of good fortune carried by those who hoped to produce heirs. Except for softness of contour, figures of boys carved in the eighteenth century tended to resemble shrunken adults. The size of the cat indicates how small the boy is, who appears iconic and doll-like when compared to the animal. HG

172 | **Group of Five Chinese Boys**

KAGETOSHI, Japan, active early to mid-19th century
ivory with sumi
1 9/16 x 1 1/16 x 1 1/16 in. (4 x 2.7 x 2.7 cm)
M.91.250.132
incised in rectangular reserve cartouche: *Kagetoshi*

LITERATURE: AMICO, 2001–present; Bushell, *Collectors' Netsuke*, fig. 198, p. 125; Bushell, *An Exhibition of Netsuke*, fig. 281, p. 58

Kagetoshi's boys, like those surrounding Hotei (CAT. 162), are arranged around a hollow center so that each figure can be seen individually. The proportions and avid expressions show the greater realism of nineteenth-century netsuke. HG

172 BACK

173 | **Chinese Boy**

Japan, 19th century
porcelain with red overglaze and gold enamels
$1\frac{3}{4} \times 1\frac{9}{16} \times 1\frac{9}{16}$ in. (4.5 x 4 x 3.9 cm)
M.91.250.317

Composed in a simple, triangular form, this elaborately dressed boy could easily have been produced from a mold. Ceramics workshops throughout Japan, but especially in Kyūshū, increased their netsuke production in the nineteenth century. HG

174 | **Chinese Boy and Water Buffalo**

Shūkōsai Anraku, Japan, active early to mid-19th century
mid-19th century
ivory with staining, sumi
$1\frac{3}{4} \times 1\frac{1}{2} \times \frac{15}{16}$ in. (4.5 x 3.8 x 2.4 cm)
M.87.263.122
incised and stained: *Shūkōsai Anraku*

LITERATURE: AMICO, 1999–present; Ueda, *The Netsuke Handbook of Ueda Reikichi*, fig. 55, p. 52

Anraku's netsuke on a plinth is carefully elaborated, with varied surface textures and multiple layers of staining and sumi. The theme of the Chinese ox-herding boy comes from a series of Zen paintings that use the pair to illustrate a Zen acolyte's progress toward enlightenment. This work could represent either the beginning, where the boy thinks he knows the ox, or the final stage, where he knows the true nature of the ox. HG

174 BACK

175 | **Chinese Boys**

Japan, mid-19th century
Hirado ware; porcelain with purple, green, brown, and black glazes
1 15/16 x 1 1/8 x 7/8 in. (5 x 2.9 x 2.2 cm)
M.87.263.58

LITERATURE: Bushell, "Ceramic Netsuke," fig. 43, p. 30; Bushell, *An Exhibition of Netsuke*, fig. 413, p. 73; Bushell, *Netsuke Familiar and Unfamiliar*, fig. 444, p. 170

Chinese boys were a popular motif in Hirado porcelain. This charming netsuke—showing a boy and his baby brother, who affectionately mimics his attitude—has multiple colored glazes, and details painted with black glaze. The effect is highly ornamental, typifying later Hirado ware. HG

176 | **Chinese Boy with Puppy**

Illustrated on page 28
Japan, mid-19th century
wood
1 5/8 x 1 3/16 x 1 9/16 in. (4.2 x 3 x 3.9 cm)
M.91.250.131

LITERATURE: AMICO, 2001–present; Bushell, *An Exhibition of Netsuke*, fig. 284, p. 59

Comparing this mid-nineteenth-century carving of a boy with the next, dated around 1900, reveals some aspects of early-twentieth-century carving. The netsuke are relatively similar except for the miniaturized and closely spaced features on Sōsai's *Chinese Boy Playing Drum*. The same tendency toward delicate facial features with a hint of Western realism can be seen in prints from that period. The Sōsai netsuke is smaller than the boy with puppy by one-eighth to three-eighths of an inch, showing a move away from functionality, and the hair is less stylized and more realistic. HG

177 | **Chinese Boy Playing Drum**

SŌSAI, Japan, active late 19th–early 20th century
boxwood with inlays
1 1/8 x 1 1/8 x 1 1/8 in. (2.8 x 2.8 x 2.9 cm)
AC1998.249.285
incised: *Sōsai*; kakihan

See catalogue 176.

177 BACK

178 | **Uzume**

Chingendō Hidemasa, Japan, active early 19th century
wood
3 1/4 x 1 3/4 x 1 9/16 in. (8.3 x 4.5 x 4 cm)
M.91.250.37
incised: *Hidemasa*

LITERATURE: Bushell, *An Exhibition of Netsuke*, fig. 273, p. 57; Hurtig, *Masterpieces of Netsuke Art*, fig. 920, p. 218

PROVENANCE: Avery Brundage

A rare wood netsuke by Hidemasa, this Uzume (whose full name was Ame no Uzume no Mikoto) with a movable tongue, posed during her performance for Amaterasu no Ōmikami, has the broad face, wide, triangular nose, and large mouth seen in so many works by this master. Hidemasa excels at showing the mass and sagging weight of the figure, sculpting and polishing the wood to bring out the best in the material. HG

178 BACK

179 | **Uzume**

Miyagi Chokusai (Masanosuke), Japan, born 1877
ivory with staining, sumi
2 1/4 x 1 x 3/4 in. (5.7 x 2.5 x 1.9 cm)
AC1998.249.155
incised and lightly stained: *Chokusai*

Chokusai's Uzume appears to be yawning rather than singing, with her eyes nearly shut and her arms stretched above her. This figure has lost some of the expressiveness of exaggeration seen in the previous netsuke, while gaining realism in anatomy and surface detail. HG

180 | **Okame**

Japan, 19th century
Banko ware; ceramic with overglaze enamel and colored glaze
1 15/16 x 1 3/16 x 1 1/16 in. (5 x 3 x 2.7 cm)
M.87.263.65

LITERATURE: AMICO, 2001–present; Bushell, "Ceramic Netsuke," front cover

Overglazed enamel portraits of Okame tend to reflect formulas from noh theater or festival masks and costumes, here seen in the ornate dress, placid expression, and loosened tresses near her forehead. Okame is usually shown covering her smile with her left hand. Kenya's Okame *manjū* (CAT. 181) is related to a painting theme of the Rimpa School. Kenya belonged to an offshoot group of Rimpa, a community of artists who worked in a stylized decorative manner and catered to nobility. One of the oft-repeated designs that passed through generations of Rimpa painters placed Okame's visage at the right edge of a fan or roundel that was then mounted on a silk background of a different color. The flowers at the left of Kenya's manjū do not follow that model; they are close to motifs created by Ogata Kenzan (1663–1743), the first Rimpa artist to make ceramics into a format for painted compositions. HG

180

181 | **Okame**

Illustrated on page 50
KENYA, Japan, active 1825–1889
glazed pottery; manjū type
1 9/16 x 1 9/16 x 5/8 in. (4 x 4 x 1.6 cm)
M.87.263.62
black on white glaze in rectangular reserve: *Kenya*

LITERATURE: AMICO, 2001–present; Atchley, "The Pavilion for Japanese Art in Los Angeles," p. 25; Bushell, "Ceramic Netsuke," fig. 29, p. 29; Bushell, *The Inrō Handbook*, fig. 47, p. 72; Bushell, *The Wonderful World of Netsuke*, fig. 74, p. 58

PROVENANCE: Imai Kenzō

See catalogue 180.

182 | **Okame**

KENYA, Japan, active 1825–1889
stoneware with colored glazes and overglaze enamels
1 11/16 x 7/8 x 13/16 in. (4.3 x 2.2 x 2 cm)
M.91.250.73
black on white glaze in oval cartouche: *Kenya*
ink on box lid: *Tōbu domin Kenya tsukuru* / "made by Kenya, a native of Edo"; *Otogoze* / "mask of Oto [Okame]"

LITERATURE: Bushell, "Ceramic Netsuke," p. 29; Bushell, *An Exhibition of Netsuke*, fig. 418, p. 73; Lazarnick, *Netsuke and Inro Artists*, vol. 1, p. 611; Ueda, *The Netsuke Handbook of Ueda Reikichi*, fig. 91, p. 93

See catalogue 180.

183 | **Okame**

ATTRIBUTED TO KENYA, Japan, active 1825–1889
glazed pottery
1 3/8 x 1 1/8 x 1 1/8 in. (3.5 x 2.9 x 2.9 cm)
AC1998.249.111

LITERATURE: Bushell, "Ceramic Netsuke," fig. 26, p. 28; Bushell, *An Exhibition of Netsuke*, fig. 411, p. 26; Bushell, *Netsuke Familiar and Unfamiliar*, fig. 462, p. 173

This group of four netsuke illustrates the divergent approaches in the late 1800s and early 1900s. Like the previous overglazed enamel Okame group, all but the example by Shō (CAT. 185) show the character fully dressed and with one hand inside a sleeve that delicately covers her smile. The Raku-type Okame here is roughly modeled and painted in restrained tones, making it appropriate for wear to a casual poetry or literati gathering. The Koma School *makie* lacquer version would more likely be worn with elaborate clothing and inrō on a formal occasion. Shō's reclining woman is the ultimate in relaxed inelegance, and this netsuke could have been worn while one visited close friends. Yasuaki's elaborate ivory Okame is a magnet for close inspection, finely carved and colored on all sides and carried to be enjoyed by like-minded collectors. Yasuaki's netsuke could have been displayed as an *okimono*. HG

184 | **Okame**

KOMA KANSAI SCHOOL, Japan, late 19th–early 20th century
gold and colored lacquer
1 7/8 x 1 9/16 x 1 1/4 in. (4.7 x 4 x 3.2 cm)
M.91.250.71
makie inscription: *Kansai saku* / "made by Kansai"

LITERATURE: Bushell, *An Exhibition of Netsuke*, fig. 403, p. 72; Ueda, *The Netsuke Handbook of Ueda Reikichi*, fig. 196, p. 188

See catalogue 183.

184

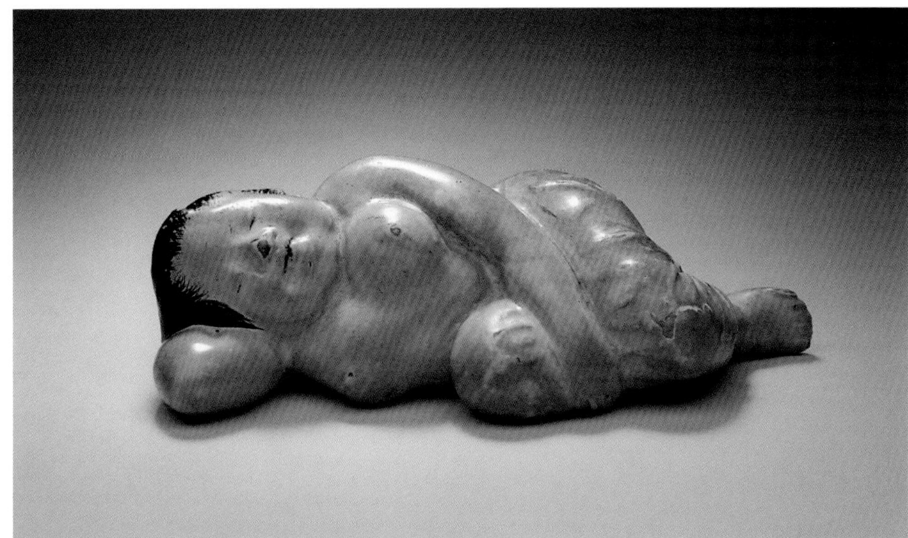
185

185 | **Okame, the Homely Daughter**

SHŌ, Japan, active early 20th century
wood with pigments
2 7/8 x 1 1/4 x 1 1/16 in. (7.4 x 3.2 x 2.7 cm)
M.91.250.202

LITERATURE: Bushell, *The Wonderful World of Netsuke*, fig. 73, p. 58

PROVENANCE: Cherry Ishihara

See catalogue 183.

186 | **Okame As a Demure Beauty**

Illustrated on page 89
YASUAKI, Japan, active late 19th–early 20th century
early 20th century
ivory with staining, sumi, inlays, red pigment
1 7/8 x 7/8 x 3/4 in. (4.8 x 2.2 x 1.9 cm)
AC1998.249.106
incised and stained: *Yasuaki*
seal form, incised on inlaid metal: *Kōdama*

PROVENANCE: Hauptner collection

See catalogue 183.

187 | **Bugaku Bird Headdress**

Japan, early 19th century
ivory with staining, sumi
$2^{1}/_{4}$ x $1^{7}/_{8}$ x $1^{1}/_{8}$ in. (5.7 x 4.7 x 2.8 cm)
M.91.250.198

LITERATURE: Bushell, *An Exhibition of Netsuke*, fig. 321, p. 25; Bushell, *Netsuke Familiar and Unfamiliar*, fig. 531, p. 188

This headdress is called a layered bird helmet (*kasane-torikabuto*). It was used in bugaku, a form of Shinto ritual dance used in the imperial court that was most popular during the Heian (794–1185) and Kamakura (1185–1333) periods. Performances, initially held at court but later at shrine festivals, featured a combination of two dances: one with music from China ("dances of the left") and one with music from Korea ("dances of the right"). This helmet would be used for dances of the right. HG

188 | **Musical Instruments for Kagura Ceremony**

Sō, Japan, active second half of the 19th century
walrus tusk; manjū type
$1^{5}/_{8}$ x $1^{5}/_{16}$ x $^{3}/_{4}$ in. (4.1 x 3.4 x 1.9 cm)
AC1998.249.153
seal form, carved: *Sō*

Sō's elaborate *manjū* takes its theme from shrine festivals where bugaku and native-style kagura ritual dances were performed. It depicts helmets that were used in various bugaku performances. The mouth organ (*shō*), panpipes, small drum, and *gohei* paper streamers could be used either in gagaku music (the traditional Japanese court music that accompanies bugaku) or in kagura performances, created to propitiate the Shinto gods. HG

189 | **Cluster of Felicitous Symbols**

GYOKUZAN, Japan, active late 19th century
ivory with staining, sumi, and metal and other inlays; ryūsa type
2 x 7/8 in. (5.1 x 2.2 cm)
M.91.250.283
incised and stained with sumi: *Ōju Gyokuzan saku* / "made by request, by Gyokuzan"

LITERATURE: Bushell, *An Exhibition of Netsuke*, fig. 100, p. 39; Ueda, *The Netsuke Handbook of Ueda Reikichi*, fig. 19, p. 35

This two-part *ryūsa* netsuke is hollowed out and carved on multiple levels with an agglomeration of "things to be grateful for." Clustered on the verso side are symbols of the Seven Gods of Good Fortune: Ebisu's fan, Daikoku's drum, and Hotei's sack. Dragons, cranes, and *minogame* (raincape turtles) rim the *manjū*, along with other animals including Ebisu's *tai* (red sea bream) fish and Daikoku's rat. Scattered on the netsuke's face are all types of treasures: foods from sea and land, a stick horse for festival-dance use, gold coins, magic jewels (*tomoe*), and a cat (probably a friend of the carver). This type of virtuoso carving was practiced in a spirit of competition—with the material and with each other—by late-nineteenth-century *netsukeshi*. HG

189

190 | **Inari Fox**

MASATOSHI (NAKAMURA TOKISADA), Japan, 1915–2001
boxwood with sumi
2 1/4 x 1 9/16 x 1 1/16 in. (5.8 x 3.9 x 2.7 cm)
AC1998.249.198
incised: *Masatoshi*

To identify itself as a messenger of the god of rice, Masatoshi's fox holds a banner reading "great god Inari." The Shinto deity Inari was especially important to farmers, rice merchants, and sake brewers, but he was also widely popular for his ability to feed the entire populace. In addition, he was the protector of homes. In the ancient transcription of his name, Uka no Mitama, one character could also mean "fox," and some speculate that this was how the fox came to be considered Inari's messenger. Masatoshi's netsuke is unstained and has fine overall hair work. HG

Mythical Creatures and Supernatural Animals

THE *KIRIN*, CHINESE LION, AND *BAKU*—all creatures from myth—were popular netsuke subjects in the seventeenth and eighteenth centuries. In his book *Netsuke: Fantasy and Reality in Japanese Miniature Sculpture*, Joe Earle pointed out that these subjects predominated in the Kamigata area, and that models came from illustrated books.

The kirin's extraordinary speed enabled it to elude capture, and its antler, believed to have properties similar to those of rhinoceros horn, could alleviate the effects of poison. Because the kirin's size was not recorded, it could be portrayed in netsuke as enormous in relation to humans, or left indeterminate.

The Chinese lion, also called a Korean dog, is a long-held symbol in Buddhism that originated in India. The lion embodies the existence of the Buddha nature, which is present equally in each hair on the beast as in its entire being, just as it is distributed through all phenomena in the universe. The lion's image served as a guardian figure, fiercely defending a sacred space against both evil and ignorance. In the home, images of Chinese lions deflect evil; as netsuke, they may have been used to repel personal demons.

The *baku*, possibly originating from the Chinese tapir, has a head like an elephant's, a trunklike nose, small, floppy ears, and a body like that of a Chinese lion, with a mane, curling tail, and spotted hide. Its main talent was its ability to eat anything, including nightmares. Its image was used to fend off dreams that might adversely affect one's future.

LEFT: *Baku: Monster That Eats Nightmares* (CAT. 217); ABOVE: *Tanuki Covered with Lotus Leaves* (CAT. 235)

All three creatures possessed virtues and protective capacities and were worn as talismans. Reduction and refinement to essentials, an idea central to Japanese aesthetics, is clearly expressed in these magnificent animals captured as miniature sculpture. Especially during the eighteenth century, carvers invoked the energy and power of supernatural creatures, and the heft of these netsuke reminds us of their strong and muscular presence.

While beneficent animals were popular with artists of Kyoto and Osaka, carvers in Edo (now Tokyo) tended to depict beasts of a malevolent nature. Using the "hair of the dog" theory of protecting oneself from evil by wearing its image, customers throughout Japan wore netsuke of *tengu* (mountain goblins, often a beaked and winged man-shaped beast), monsters, shape-shifters such as foxes and *tanuki* (raccoon-dogs), *kappa* (water spirits), and earthquake fish.

Supernatural ghouls abound in Japanese lore and art of the eighteenth and nineteenth centuries. Among the types of monsters noted by Nikolas Kiej'e in *Japanese Grotesqueries* are animals or objects possessed by nature spirits; utilitarian objects and architectural forms animated by disembodied souls; freaks of nature born of a human and a god, demon, animal or other creature; and shape-shifting animals. Examples of all of these types are found in netsuke.

Netsuke of monsters in the Bushell collection were primarily made by twentieth-century carvers such as Shōko (1915–1969) and Masatoshi (1915–2001). For subjects, carvers drew on ancient legends, paintings, and their own imaginations.

Trickster animals such as the kappa, fox, and tanuki were of Japanese origin, although some fox stories also came from China. The kappa and the fox were messengers of Shinto gods—the kappa representing the river god, and the fox the god of rice and agriculture, Inari. Although they were affiliated with the gods, their behavior was often destructive. The fox was the primary trickster, and it was feared the most because its spirit could possess a person and assume his or her form. According to lore, the fox usually chose to possess a woman and, once bewitched, this woman might then seduce and defraud a male victim. Among trickster animals, the most lecherous were kappa and tanuki. Both were shape-shifters, but they differed in other respects: The kappa devoured their human prey, while tanuki played malicious although sometimes deadly jokes. The lasciviousness of both kappa and tanuki separated them from other monsters.

191 | **Kirin**

Illustrated on page 38
Attributed to Tomotada, Japan, active before 1781
ivory with staining, sumi
$4\,^{1}/_{2} \times 1\,^{7}/_{8} \times 1\,^{5}/_{16}$ in. (11.4 x 4.7 x 3.4 cm)
AC1998.249.64

LITERATURE: AMICO, 2001–present

Tomotada's *kirin* sits primly with feet together while extending its neck and raising its head to bay. It has a narrow and graceful silhouette. Signed and unsigned versions exist; several are similar in composition and sensibility, suggesting that Tomotada, and perhaps his studio, created numerous examples of this popular design. The Tomotada style—elegant, elongated, and large—is typical of the fashion in Kyoto at the time. HG

192 | **Kirin**

径Tametaka, Japan, active circa 1730–1790
wood with inlays
$1\,^{7}/_{8} \times 1\,^{3}/_{4} \times 1\,^{1}/_{8}$ in. (4.7 x 4.4 x 2.8 cm)
AC1998.249.30
incised on raised oval reserve: *Tametaka*

LITERATURE: Bushell, *An Exhibition of Netsuke*, fig. 17, p. 17; Mikoshiba and Bushell, "Netsuke and the *Sōken kishō*," p. 112

In contrast to Tomotada's netsuke (CAT. 191), Tametaka's twisting *kirin* (also CAT. 193) illustrate the aesthetic of the Nagoya carvers. The compactness of Tametaka's compositions, and his preference for wood, prefigured the Nagoya style. The relative roughness and expressiveness of these kirin, however, reflect Tametaka's personal style and would not be carried into later generations. HG

192 BACK

193 | **Kirin**

Also illustrated on page 47
TAMETAKA, Japan, active circa 1730–1790
wood
1 15/16 x 1 3/4 x 13/16 in. (5 x 4.4 x 2 cm)
AC1998.249.244
incised in partial rectangular cartouche: *Tametaka*

LITERATURE: AMICO, 2001–present; Bushell, *Collectors' Netsuke*, fig. 29, p. 34

See catalogue 192.

193

194 | **Kirin**

Japan, date unknown, 18th-century style
ivory with staining, sumi
4 1/4 x 1 1/2 x 1 in. (10.8 x 3.8 x 2.5 cm)
AC1998.249.62

LITERATURE: AMICO, 2001–present; Bushell, *An Exhibition of Netsuke*, fig. 51, p. 18; Hill and Johnson, "The Raymond Bushell Netsuke Exhibition," fig. 51, p. 28

Of uncertain origin, this unsigned, twisting *kirin* has an exquisite, dynamic form that represents a style fashionable in Kyoto in the eighteenth century. HG

195 BACK

195 | **Chinese Lion**

GECHŪ, Japan, active 18th century
ivory with staining, sumi, inlays
$2^{1}/_{4}$ x $2^{1}/_{4}$ x $1^{7}/_{8}$ in. (5.7 x 5.7 x 4.7 cm)
AC1998.249.136
incised and stained with sumi in rectangular reserve: *Gechū*

LITERATURE: Atchley, "The Pavilion for Japanese Art in Los Angeles," p. 22; Bushell, *An Exhibition of Netsuke*, fig. 22, p. 17; Mikoshiba and Bushell, "Netsuke and the *Sōken kishō*," p. 115; Phillips, ed., *The Collectors' Encyclopedia of Antiques*, p. 566

Chinese lion netsuke were most popular from the mid- to late 1700s. The five lions in this group (CATS. 195–99) share stylistic consistencies that suggest similar source material, although there are individual variations based on the carver. Except for *Chinese Lion* (CAT. 197), the lions are from the vicinity of Kamigata and were probably made between the 1750s and 1770s. Here, Gechū has delineated his lion's hair and stained the hide overall; however, unlike the other carvers in this group, he exaggerated the long, looping curls of the lion's beard, mane, and tail. HG

196 | **Chinese Lion and Young**

Illustrated on page 47
TOMOTADA, Japan, active before 1781
ivory with staining, sumi, inlays
$1^{7}/_{16}$ x $2^{3}/_{16}$ x $1^{1}/_{16}$ in. (3.7 x 5.5 x 2.7 cm)
M.87.263.140
incised and stained in rectangular cartouche: *Tomotada*

LITERATURE: AMICO, 1999–present; Bushell, *An Exhibition of Netsuke*, fig. 9, p. 31; Hurtig, "The Tomotada Story," fig. 18, p. 25; Mikoshiba and Bushell, "Netsuke and the *Sōken kishō*," p. 111

All five lions in this group (CATS. 195–99) are heavy and massive, with large skulls, broadly outlined mouths, wide, triangular noses, and relatively short snouts. Each has carefully outlined claw sheathes on large strong paws; a prescribed number of tail, mane, beard, and brow curls; and suggestions of hair whorls on the hide. In this netsuke, Tomotada's lion leans forward to shelter her cub. HG

197 | **Chinese Lion**

Japan, 18th century
ivory with staining, sumi
$2\,^{3}/_{16} \times 1\,^{5}/_{16} \times 1\,^{5}/_{16}$ in. (5.6 x 3.3 x 3.3 cm)
M.87.263.139

LITERATURE: AMICO, 1999–present

The hide of this ivory lion is smooth, unlike the other four in the group (CATS. 195–96, 198–99). This netsuke was either carved earlier than the others (before 1750) or was perhaps made in Edo. The incised circles with radiating lines schematically indicate hair whorls. HG

198 | **Chinese Lion**

Japan, 18th century
wood
$2\,^{1}/_{4} \times 1\,^{5}/_{16} \times 1\,^{3}/_{16}$ in. (5.8 x 3.3 x 3 cm)
M.91.250.200

LITERATURE: AMICO, 2001–present; Bushell, *An Exhibition of Netsuke*, fig. 317, p. 25

PROVENANCE: Burnie M. Craig

This wooden lion dandles its coiling tresses with its hind paw. HG

199 | **Chinese Lion Guarding the Jewel of the Buddha**

Front illustrated on page 25
Japan, 18th century
ivory with staining, sumi, inlays
$2\,^{1}/_{8} \times 1\,^{3}/_{4} \times 1\,^{7}/_{16}$ in. (5.4 x 4.4 x 3.6 cm)
AC1998.249.224

LITERATURE: AMICO, 2001–present; Bushell, *Netsuke Familiar and Unfamiliar*, fig. 603, p. 201

PROVENANCE: Imai Kenzō

This lion, clasping the jewel of the Buddha, has an intense glare that expresses his possessive distrust. HG

199 BACK

200 | **Chinese Lion on Tile**

Tanaka Minkō, Japan, 1735–1816
wood with inlays
1 7/8 x 1 5/16 x 13/16 in. (4.8 x 3.3 x 2 cm)
M.91.250.321
incised: *Tontoku Minkō* [Tanaka Minkō's art name]
seal form, pot-shaped, incised; kakihan

LITERATURE: Bushell, *Collectors' Netsuke*, fig. 39, p. 37; Bushell, *An Exhibition of Netsuke*, fig. 24, p. 32; Mikoshiba and Bushell, "Netsuke and the *Sōken kishō*," p. 111

Carvers of Chinese lion netsuke from the end of the 1700s and into the 1800s broke with earlier formulas. Here, Minkō, an influential carver, places his lion on a roof-tile end. The lion's focused stare and teasing stance give it the appearance of a watchdog. The tile's spiraling three-comma-shaped "magic jewel" design (*mitsu-tomoe*) might indicate an association with a sacred Buddhist structure. HG

201 | **Chinese Lion**

Illustrated on page 33
Japan, late 18th–early 19th century
rhinoceros horn
1 3/4 x 1 5/16 x 1 1/4 in. (4.4 x 3.4 x 3.1 cm)
AC1998.249.124

LITERATURE: Bushell, "Questions & Answers" (1978b), fig. 2, p. 42

PROVENANCE: Lawrence "Johnny" Johnstone

The carvers of these two netsuke (CATS. 201–2) have radically simplified the surface textures of their lions, giving full concentration to facial expression and pose. HG

202 | **Chinese Lion**

Japan, late 18th–early 19th century
bone
$1\frac{5}{8}$ x $1\frac{5}{8}$ x $1\frac{3}{16}$ in. (4.1 x 4.1 x 3 cm)
AC1998.249.273

See catalogue 201.

204

203

203 | **Pair of Chinese Lions**

Kano Tomokazu, Japan, circa 1764/71–circa 1830/43
early 19th century
wood
$1\frac{1}{4}$ x $1\frac{5}{16}$ x $1\frac{1}{8}$ in. (3.1 x 3.3 x 2.8 cm)
AC1998.249.6
incised in oval cartouche: *Tomokazu*

LITERATURE: AMICO, 2001–present; Bushell, *Collectors' Netsuke*, fig. 98, p. 71

Wood netsuke of Chinese lions from the early 1800s (CATS. 203–4) retain the compactness and introversion of earlier examples in other mediums. However, some of the old formulas (see CATS. 195–99) are no longer evident: noses and lip outlines are softened into the surrounding fur, the number of curls is no longer prescribed, and anatomy is more naturally proportioned. The netsuke are also less hefty and more easily grasped. HG

204 | **Chinese Lion Chewing Its Paw**

Tadatoshi, Japan, circa 1780–1844
wood
$1\frac{5}{8}$ x $1\frac{5}{8}$ x $1\frac{1}{2}$ in. (4.1 x 4.1 x 3.8 cm)
AC1998.249.143
ukibori in rectangular reserve: *Tadatoshi*

LITERATURE: Hurtig, *Masterpieces of Netsuke Art*, fig. 100, p. 44

See catalogue 203.

204 SIDE

205 | **Pair of Chinese Lions**

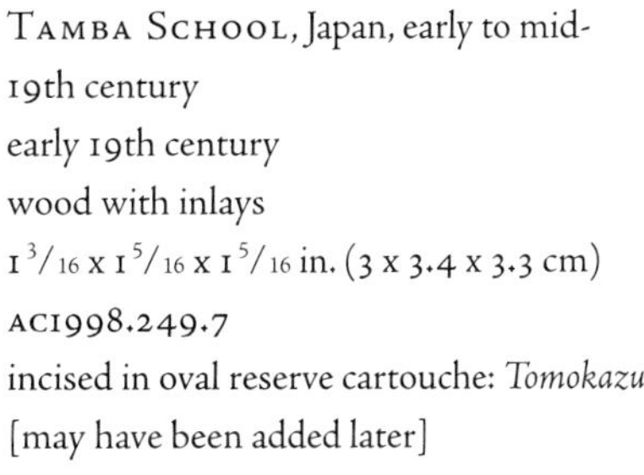

TAMBA SCHOOL, Japan, early to mid-19th century
early 19th century
wood with inlays
$1\,^{3}/_{16} \times 1\,^{5}/_{16} \times 1\,^{5}/_{16}$ in. (3 x 3.4 x 3.3 cm)
AC1998.249.7
incised in oval reserve cartouche: *Tomokazu*
[may have been added later]

LITERATURE: AMICO, 2001–present

205 SIDE

Here, as in Tomokazu's netsuke (CAT. 203), lion cubs wrestle each other instead of fending off evil. HG

206 | **Chinese Lion**

Illustrated on page 50
Japan, 19th century
porcelain with celadon glaze
$2\,^{1}/_{8} \times {}^{15}/_{16} \times 1\,^{1}/_{16}$ in. (5.4 x 2.3 x 2.7 cm)
M.87.263.56

LITERATURE: AMICO, 2001–present; Bushell, "Ceramic Netsuke," fig. 13, p. 26; Bushell, *An Exhibition of Netsuke*, fig. 412, p. 73; Bushell, *Netsuke Familiar and Unfamiliar*, fig. 450, p. 171

PROVENANCE: Frederick M. Jonas

Porcelain netsuke, made from molds, proliferated in the late 1800s with the decline in tobacco prices and the subsequent demand for tobacco pouches; however, few of these fragile netsuke have survived. The pale color and technical perfection of this celadon lion indicate its source: the kilns of the Nabeshima daimyo. HG

207 | **Chinese Lion**

Japan, 19th century
Arita ware; porcelain with red overglaze and gold enamels
$2^{5}/_{16}$ x $1^{9}/_{16}$ x $1^{1}/_{8}$ in. (5.9 x 4 x 2.9 cm)
M.87.263.71

LITERATURE: AMICO, 2001–present; Bushell, "Ceramic Netsuke," fig. 32, p. 29; Bushell, *Netsuke Familiar and Unfamiliar*, fig. 454, p. 172

The Arita kilns were famous for overglaze gold and enamel, seen most often in so-called Imari ware, which was made for export, and Arita potters provided an alternate source of commercial Chinese-style porcelain. This lion is decorated with starburst-type hair whorls that are stylistically more Chinese than Japanese. HG

208 | **Chinese Lion**

KAIGYOKUSAI MASATSUGU, Japan, 1813–1892
ivory
$1^{7}/_{8}$ x $1^{1}/_{8}$ x $^{7}/_{8}$ in. (4.8 x 2.9 x 2.2 cm)
AC1998.249.108
incised in rectangular reserve: *Kaigyokusai*

LITERATURE: Bushell, *Collectors' Netsuke*, fig. 143, p. 104; Bushell, *An Exhibition of Netsuke*, fig. 88, p. 19; Hurtig, "Kaigyokusai Masatsugu," fig. 48, p. 21

Kaigyokusai Masatsugu focused on anatomical realism and fine materials. He has treated the lion's hide in great detail and evoked the presence of the body and musculature beneath. Overwrought muscles similar to those on Buddhist temple guardians (see CATS. 128–29) ripple the surface of the skin. HG

208 BOTTOM

209 | **Chinese Lion Scratching Its Chin**

ATTRIBUTED TO KAIGYOKUSAI MASATSUGU, Japan, 1813–1892
ivory with staining, sumi, inlays
$1^{7}/_{8}$ x $1^{3}/_{16}$ x $1^{1}/_{2}$ in. (4.8 x 3 x 3.8 cm)
AC1998.249.282
incised and stained in oval reserve: *Kaigyokudō Masatsugu*

See catalogue 208.

210 | **Chinese Lion**

ISHIKAWA RENSAI, Japan, active mid- to late 19th century
stag antler with inlays
$^{15}/_{16}$ x $1^{5}/_{8}$ x $1^{5}/_{8}$ in. (2.3 x 4.2 x 4.2 cm)
M.87.263.17
seal form, carved on raised square on base: *Ren*
seal, carved on base: *Nōshinkiin*

LITERATURE: AMICO, 1999–present; Bushell, *Collectors' Netsuke*, fig. 239, p. 151; Bushell, *An Exhibition of Netsuke*, fig. 357, p. 67; Davey, *Netsuke*, fig. 533, p. 180

PROVENANCE: Mark T. Hindson

Unlike Kaigyokusai, Ishikawa Rensai used rough material in a mannered treatment to make his beasts more otherworldly. Rensai focuses almost entirely on facial features and geometric, stylized curls. HG

210 SEAL

211 | **Chinese Lion on Cushion**

ISHIKAWA RENSAI, Japan, active mid- to late 19th century
walrus tusk
$1^{7}/_{16}$ x $1^{3}/_{8}$ x $^{15}/_{16}$ in. (3.7 x 3.5 x 2.3 cm)
M.90.186.5
seal form, carved on raised square: *Ren*

LITERATURE: AMICO, 1999–present

PROVENANCE: Richard Marchant; Terry Wingrove

The inclusion of a fly whisk, a traditional Buddhist accoutrement, makes this one of the few later netsuke to reinforce the Buddhist origin of the Chinese lion. HG

212 | **Baku: Monster That Eats Nightmares**

Illustrated on page 46
ATTRIBUTED TO GECHŪ, Japan, active 18th century
ivory with staining, sumi, traces of red pigment
$3^{3}/_{4}$ x $1^{5}/_{8}$ x $1^{3}/_{16}$ in. (9.5 x 4.1 x 3 cm)
AC1998.249.63
incised and stained in rectangular reserve: *Gechū*

LITERATURE: AMICO, 2001–present; Beckett, *Sister Wendy's American Collection*, p. 253; Bushell, *An Exhibition of Netsuke*, fig. 21, p. 17; Bushell, *Netsuke Familiar and Unfamiliar*, fig. 504, p. 181; Hill and Johnson, "The Raymond Bushell Netsuke Exhibition," fig. 21, p. 29; Lazarnick, *Netsuke and Inro Artists*, vol. 1, p. 399; Mikoshiba and Bushell, "Netsuke and the *Sōken kishō*," p. 115

The *baku*, in the baying pose of a *kirin*, has the flowing mane, tail, and hair whorls of a Chinese lion. Its forepaw rests on a Chinese stool or table, another reference to its origins. This netsuke is attributed to Gechū because of the long, spiraling mane and carefully arranged beard. The alternation of smooth with heavily carved and stained areas also recalls Gechū's style. HG

213 SIDE

213 | Baku: Monster That Eats Nightmares

Front illustrated on page 37
KANKŌ, Japan, active 18th century
ivory with staining, sumi, inlays
1 3/4 x 1 3/8 x 1 1/4 in. (4.4 x 3.5 x 3.2 cm)
AC1998.249.154
incised and stained: *Kankō*

LITERATURE: Hurtig, *Masterpieces of Netsuke Art*, fig. 96, p. 42

This *baku* looks over its shoulder as it clings to a Buddhist Wish-granting Jewel. The baku has no Buddhist connections, and Kankō seems to have borrowed a feature associated with the Chinese lion. This baku has overall hair work and a light sumi stain. While it lacks the textural contrast of the previous piece, the smooth surface of the jewel acts as a foil for the hair work. HG

214 | Baku: Monster That Eats Nightmares

Japan, 18th century
wood
4 3/8 x 1 3/8 x 1 9/16 in. (11.2 x 3.5 x 3.9 cm)
M.91.250.104
seal, carved: *Takara* / "treasure"

LITERATURE: Bushell, *The Wonderful World of Netsuke*, fig. 38, p. 38

PROVENANCE: William Wilberforce Winkworth

The caparisoned creature here, perched on a drum, appears to be a cross between an elephant and a *baku*. Its closed eyes form elongated slits, seen in contemporary elephant netsuke (see CAT. 353), and it has sagging skin on the legs, another elephant trait. The tiny, floppy ears, here tucked into the collar, are more often seen on baku, although it bays like a *kirin*. The tail curls upward in a single thick spiral. The netsuke's shape is appropriate for its dual use as a seal. HG

214 SEAL

215 | **Baku: Monster That Eats Nightmares**

Japan, 18th century
ivory with staining, sumi, inlays
$2\,^{3}/_{8}$ x $1\,^{1}/_{4}$ x 1 in. (6 x 3.2 x 2.6 cm)
M.91.250.105

PROVENANCE: Francis C. Reif

This *baku*, carved from a superior piece of ivory, has very light staining. Although the creature pulls its head upward, it maintains a compact form within an overall triangular shape. HG

216 | **Baku: Monster That Eats Nightmares**

Illustrated on page 27
Japan, 18th century
ivory with staining, sumi
$2\,^{1}/_{8}$ x $1\,^{7}/_{16}$ x 1 in. (5.4 x 3.7 x 2.5 cm)
M.91.250.270

LITERATURE: Bushell, *Collectors' Netsuke*, front of slipcase; Bushell, *An Exhibition of Netsuke*, fig. 55, p. 18

The walking *baku* twists around, as though it has caught the scent of a nightmare or disease demon on which to dine. The concentric curves at the outer edges of his eyes enhance the impression of focused attention. The tail and trunk create a fluid, oval composition and compact form. HG

217 | **Baku: Monster That Eats Nightmares**

Illustrated on page 182
MASATOSHI (NAKAMURA TOKISADA), Japan, 1915–2001
ivory with staining, sumi
$2\,^{11}/_{16}$ x $1\,^{7}/_{8}$ x $1\,^{1}/_{8}$ in. (6.9 x 4.7 x 2.8 cm)
AC1998.249.54
incised and lightly stained: *Masatoshi*

LITERATURE: AMICO, 2001–present

Masatoshi's bumptious *baku* has the appearance of an arrogant, well-fed gentleman after a full-size nightmare dinner. Masatoshi collaborated with Takeda Hideo (b. 1948), a print designer, on a set of four fantastic animals. In addition to the baku, they designed and carved a phoenix, a *kirin*, and a *minogame* (raincape turtle). HG

219 | Mermaid and Child

Kokei, Japan, active circa 1781–1800
wood
$1\,^{3}/_{4}$ x $1\,^{1}/_{4}$ x 1 in. (4.4 x 3.1 x 2.5 cm)
AC1998.249.37
incised on raised oval reserve: *Kokei*

LITERATURE: AMICO, 2001–present; Bushell, *The Wonderful World of Netsuke*, fig. 10, p. 20

PROVENANCE: Matsui Yonekichi

Mermaid and Child is an unusual composition, showing a mermaid merrily suckling her baby. The mother's protective pose gives the netsuke a smooth, curvaceous silhouette, suitable for wear. HG

218 | Mermaid

Japan, 18th century
ebony or black persimmon wood
$3\,^{15}/_{16}$ x $^{7}/_{8}$ x $^{15}/_{16}$ in. (10 x 2.2 x 2.3 cm)
M.91.250.110

LITERATURE: Bushell, *An Exhibition of Netsuke*, fig. 44, p. 35; Bushell, *Netsuke Familiar and Unfamiliar*, fig. 746, p. 225; Davey, *Netsuke*, fig. 1151, p. 383

PROVENANCE: Mark T. Hindson; William Wilberforce Winkworth; Dr. H. A. Gunther

Mermaids and mermen (*ningyo*) were illustrated in imported and locally published encyclopedias distributed in Japan during the 1700s. They fit nicely into the category of anthropomorphic monsters long seen in Japanese art. In the encyclopedias, however, they were classed with mythical peoples such as Ashinaga and Tenaga (see CATS. 31–35). An illustration in Inaba Tsūryū's *Sōken kishō* indicates that ningyo were used as a netsuke subject at least from the late 1700s. Mermaid imagery, considered semi-erotic, reached the height of its popularity in the 1700s and early 1800s, although interest was revived in the late 1800s and early 1900s. During the mid-1800s, female pearl divers fulfilled the demand for semi-erotic netsuke (see CATS. 626–31). Beautiful dark wood distinguishes this mermaid, and netsuke of the same type were published in the recent catalogue from the Museum of Fine Arts, Boston (Earle, *Netsuke*, p. 67). HG

220 | **Mermaid and Monkey**

Also illustrated on page 17
Japan, late 19th–early 20th century
wood with inlays
3 1/8 x 1 1/4 x 1 1/16 in. (7.9 x 3.1 x 2.7 cm)
AC1998.249.73

LITERATURE: AMICO, 2001–present; Bushell, *An Exhibition of Netsuke*, fig. 253, p. 56; Bushell, *Netsuke Familiar and Unfamiliar*, figs. 540a and b, p. 189; Hurtig, *Masterpieces of Netsuke Art*, fig. 97, p. 44

PROVENANCE: Elizabeth Humphreys-Owen

Two creatures are intertwined in a netsuke carved as a perfect, tactile object. The combination of mermaid and monkey might refer to a legend in which the ailing Ryūjin (the ruler of seas and tides) needed the liver of a monkey in order to be healed. In this case, perhaps the mermaid had captured the monkey for Ryūjin's use. HG

220 BACK

221 | **Merman**

FREDERICK M. MEINERTZHAGEN,
England, 1881–1962
mid-20th century
wood
3 x 1 7/8 x 1/2 in. (7.6 x 4.7 x 1.3 cm)
M.91.250.209
incised in rectangular cartouche: *Hagen*

LITERATURE: Bushell, *Netsuke Familiar and Unfamiliar*, fig. 506, p. 181

PROVENANCE: William Wilberforce Winkworth

Frederick Meinertzhagen, known to netsuke collectors as the first Westerner to thoroughly research and classify netsuke, was also occasionally tempted to try his hand at carving. His muscular merman has odd facial features, perhaps playing on the "weird foreigner" aspect of early mermaid illustrations in East Asia. To Western eyes, the face is reminiscent of a gargoyle. HG

222 | **Rain Dragon**

Japan, early 19th century
wood with sumi
3 11/16 x 1 1/8 x 1 3/4 in. (9.4 x 2.9 x 4.5 cm)
M.87.263.96

LITERATURE: Mikoshiba and Bushell, "Netsuke and the *Sōken kishō*," p. 105

Although this subject was classified for years simply as a monster, Joe Earle has recently made a convincing case that it represents a rain dragon (*amaryō*) (Earle, *Netsuke*, pp. 98–99). He notes that the encyclopedia *Kinmō zui* (1666) describes the amaryō as a smooth-skinned, yellow dragon reminiscent of a sea horse. This netsuke is carved from soft, loose-grained wood that lends the dragon an overall rough texture and discourages further ornamental carving. HG

223 | **Long-Necked Goblin**

School of Tomokazu, Japan, early to mid-19th century
early 19th century
wood with inlays
2 7/8 x 1 x 3/4 in. (7.4 x 2.5 x 1.9 cm)
AC1998.249.210
incised: *Tomokazu* [spurious]

LITERATURE: Ueda, *The Netsuke Handbook of Ueda Reikichi*, fig. 136, p. 141

Tales of ghosts and monsters were widely popular in the late 1700s and 1800s, especially those written by Ueda Akinari (1734–1809) in collections such as his *Ugetsu monogatari* (Tales of moonlight and rain, 1776). Ghoulish scenes were also illustrated in print series by Utagawa Kuniyoshi (1797–1861) and Tsukioka Yoshitoshi (1839–1892).

The ghoul in this netsuke has an extendable neck, enabling him to arch over his victim. He is identified as a spiral neck or stretch neck (*rokuro kubi*). The monster holds his hands in the typical "haunting" position and glares with pupil-less eyes. His victim does not react because he is blind. The netsuke evokes the proverb "A blind man does not fear a snake," or "ignorance is bliss." HG

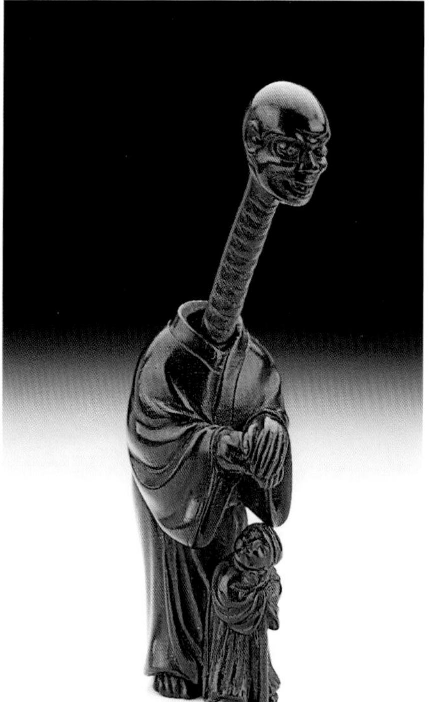

224 | **Weird Demon Tasting His Tail**

Shōko (Nishino Shōtarō), Japan, 1915–1969
wood
1 5/8 x 1 5/16 x 1 5/16 in. (4.1 x 3.4 x 3.3 cm)
M.91.250.230
incised: *Shōko*
ink on box lid: *Hokusōjin Shōko saku* / "made by Hokusōjin Shōko"
seals on box lid: *Nishino*; *Shōko*; [abstracted seal script]

LITERATURE: Bushell, *Collectors' Netsuke*, fig. 333, p. 79; Bushell, *An Exhibition of Netsuke*, fig. 469, p. 79; Bushell, "Shōko," p. 60

In Japan, there is a long tradition of illustrating the "night parade of ghosts and demons" (*hyakki yakō*), featuring ghouls who were thought to roam the streets while people slept. It was considered highly unwise to be caught outside in the midnight hours. Artists exercised their imaginations to create the most beastly monsters, portraying everything from possessed umbrellas to one-eyed, long-necked hags. Shōko in particular dedicated hours to carving these creatures. His *Monster Beating Gong* (CAT. 225) performs the *nembutsu* chant of praise to the Buddha Amida, endeavoring to look up piously beneath his snaking brows. HG

225 | **Monster Beating Gong**

Shōko (Nishino Shōtarō), Japan, 1915–1969
wood
1 11/16 x 1 1/4 x 1 1/8 in. (4.3 x 3.2 x 2.8 cm)
M.91.250.229
incised: *Shōko*

LITERATURE: Bushell, *Collectors' Netsuke*, fig. 337, p. 180; Bushell, "Shōko," p. 60

See catalogue 224.

226 | The Demon of Rashōmon

Front illustrated on page 69
Sōju, Japan, born 1918
wood
2 1/16 x 1 11/16 x 1 1/4 in. (5.2 x 4.3 x 3.2 cm)
AC1998.249.1
incised: *Sōju tō* / "carved by Sōju"

LITERATURE: Bushell, *Collectors' Netsuke*, fig. 283, p. 159

This netsuke, like Keisuke's *Jurōjin Mounted on His Stag* (CAT. 170), illustrates the trend in the late 1800s and 1900s to adapt well-known paintings into netsuke subjects. In this netsuke, Sōju captured the motion and surface elaboration of the character of Ibaraki rendered by artist Shibata Zeshin (1807–1891). HG

227 | Monster in the Guise of the Goddess of Mercy

Illustrated on page 73
Masatoshi (Nakamura Tokisada), Japan, 1915–2001
July 1976
ivory with staining, sumi
2 5/16 x 1 1/8 x 15/16 in. (5.9 x 2.9 x 2.4 cm)
M.91.250.95
incised and lightly stained with sumi: *Masatoshi tō* / "carved by Masatoshi"

LITERATURE: Bushell, *An Exhibition of Netsuke*, fig. 500, p. 81; Bushell, *Masatoshi*, fig. 328, p. 39; Masatoshi, *The Art of Netsuke Carving*, fig. 328, p. 216

In his *Art of Netsuke Carving* (pp. 163, 216, 218), Masatoshi explained each of his monster netsuke, which he carved for personal amusement. From the back, Masatoshi's figure is recognized as the well-known bodhisattva of mercy in feminine form, commonly depicted draped in a white robe that rises high over her elaborate coif. Masatoshi took pleasure in this portrayal because it intensified the shock when the viewer turned the netsuke and saw its horrific face. HG

226 BACK

228 SIDE

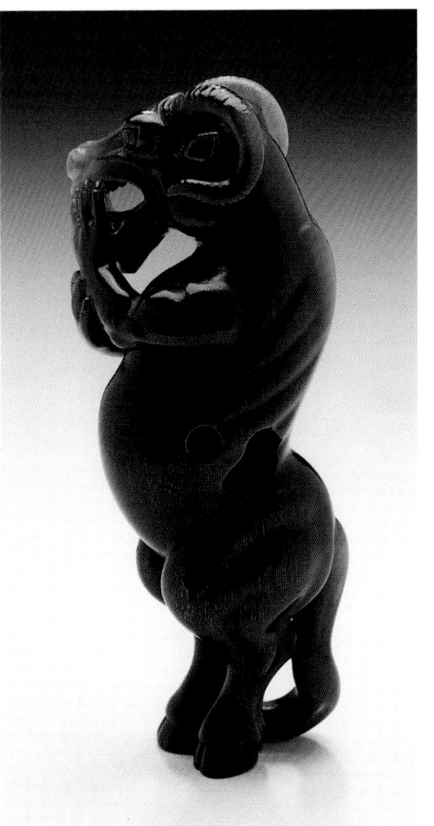

228 BACK

228 | **Goat-Headed Monster**

MASATOSHI (NAKAMURA TOKISADA), Japan, 1915–2001
August 1976
rhinoceros horn
$3^{1}/_{2}$ x $1^{3}/_{8}$ x 1 in. (9 x 3.5 x 2.6 cm)
M.91.250.88
incised: *Saikaku Masatoshi tō* / "carved by Masatoshi from rhinoceros horn"

LITERATURE: Bushell, *An Exhibition of Netsuke*, fig. 496, p. 81; Bushell, *Masatoshi*, fig. 94, p. 10; Hill and Johnson, "The Raymond Bushell Netsuke Exhibition," fig. 496, p. 36; Masatoshi, *The Art of Netsuke Carving*, fig. 94, p. 163

Here, Masatoshi's demonic, fanged goat rises upon its back legs. The artist has chosen an exquisite piece of rhinoceros horn to give this creature a dramatic surface. HG

230 | **Biron: Monster Made of Jelly**

Also illustrated on page 74
MASATOSHI (NAKAMURA TOKISADA), Japan, 1915–2001
October 1978
ivory with light staining, black coral inlays
$3^{3}/_{16}$ x $1^{1}/_{16}$ x $^{7}/_{8}$ in. (8.2 x 2.7 x 2.2 cm)
M.91.250.91
incised: *Masatoshi tō* / "carved by Masatoshi"

LITERATURE: Bushell, *Masatoshi*, fig. 337, p. 16; Masatoshi, *The Art of Netsuke Carving*, fig. 337, p. 218

Masatoshi's jelly monster could be destroyed with salt, like a slug. Here he stands, piteously quaking, ready to flee from his pursuers. HG

229 | **Goat-Headed Monster**

MASATOSHI (NAKAMURA TOKISADA), Japan, 1915–2001
August 1977
ivory with staining, sumi, black coral inlays
$3^{5}/_{16}$ x $1^{1}/_{8}$ x 1 in. (8.5 x 2.8 x 2.5 cm)
AC1998.249.217
incised and stained: *Masatoshi*

LITERATURE: Masatoshi, *The Art of Netsuke Carving*, fig. 327, p. 216

Masatoshi was fascinated by the dog-headed, human-bodied demons in the illustrated encyclopedia *Wakan sansai zue* (1716). He added to the ghoulish array by putting the head of a goat on a masculine human body. With a touch of fierceness in the face, the head is a cross between that of a goat and a dog. HG

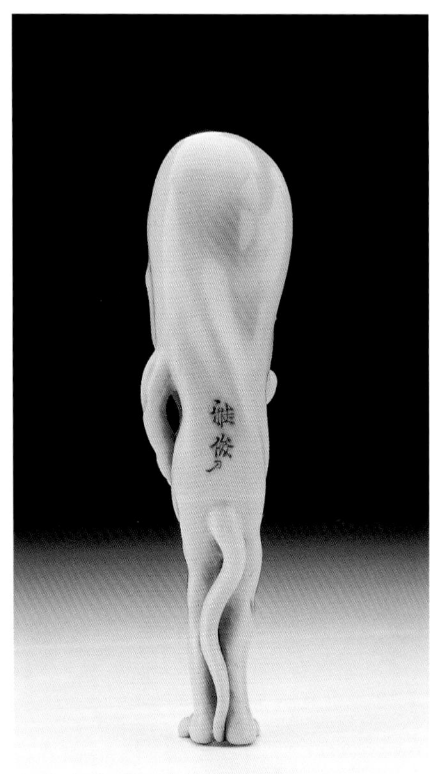

230 BACK

231 | **Tengu**

Japan, early 19th century
wood with inlays
$1^{15}/_{16}$ x $1^{1}/_{16}$ x $^{15}/_{16}$ in. (4.9 x 2.7 x 2.3 cm)
M.91.250.334

LITERATURE: Bushell, *An Exhibition of Netsuke*, fig. 252, p. 56; Hurtig, *Masterpieces of Netsuke Art*, fig. 977, p. 226

The name *tengu* (mountain goblin) may have derived from the mythical Chinese mountain dog (*tiengou*). Its appearance may be based on the Indian Buddhist guardian deity Garuda. A shape-shifter, the tengu would become a warrior-monk or a hawk to find sustenance; his favorite foods were mountain ascetics, especially those who were falsely holy. True holiness and the chanting of protective sutras would repel the tengu (Fister, "Tengu," pp. 103–12). The beaked *karasu tengu* (crow tengu) has eyes that have been inlaid with abalone to emphasize his fearsome, supernatural power. HG

232 | **Tengu King**

OZAWA SHŪRAKU, Japan, 1830–after 1878
iron, mixed-metal disk, wood bowl; kagamibuta type
$1^{3}/_{8}$ x $^{1}/_{2}$ in. (3.5 x 1.3 cm)
M.87.263.82
incised: *Shūraku*; kakihan

LITERATURE: AMICO, 1999–present; Bushell, *Netsuke Familiar and Unfamiliar*, fig. 241, p. 135

Shūraku's *kagamibuta* depicts the long-nosed *tengu*. In this portrait, Sōjōbō, the tengu king, holds a ritual thunderbolt. Shūraku has emphasized Sōjōbō's otherworldly power by inlaying his eyes with gold. Sōjōbō was said to have instructed the great warrior Minamoto Yoshitsune (1159–1189) in the art of war. HG

233 | **Tanuki Disguised As Monk**

MASAKAZU, Japan, late 18th–early 19th century
early 19th century
ivory with staining, sumi, inlays
$2^{1}/_{8}$ x $1^{1}/_{16}$ x $^{5}/_{8}$ in. (5.4 x 2.7 x 1.6 cm)
M.91.250.52
incised in oval reserve cartouche: *Masakazu*

LITERATURE: Bushell, *Collectors' Netsuke*, front of slipcase; Bushell, *An Exhibition of Netsuke*, fig. 218, p. 22

PROVENANCE: David A. Swedlow

The raccoon-dog (*tanuki*), often incorrectly called a badger, was said to disguise itself as a monk so it could trap and eat less-than-holy representatives of the faith. Tanuki in disguise were a favored netsuke theme. In monks' garb, or wrapped in lotus leaves, they allude to sinful monks who wrap themselves in false sanctity. Masakazu depicts his tanuki in midtransformation; the head has already assumed a semihuman appearance. The overall stippling and sumi staining allows the smooth ivory head, teeth, and monks' accoutrements to stand out. HG

235 BACK

234 | **Tanuki Disguised As Monk**

Japan, last half of the 19th century
stag antler
$2^{1}/_{8}$ x $1^{15}/_{16}$ x $1^{5}/_{16}$ in. (5.4 x 5 x 3.4 cm)
AC1998.249.236

This netsuke, made from the corona section of a stag's antler, shows a *tanuki* napping on a Buddhist gong (*mokugyo*), a general metaphor for one who feigns a search for enlightenment. HG

235 | **Tanuki Covered with Lotus Leaves**

TOYOKAZU (SHŪGASAI), Japan, active early to mid-19th century
wood with inlays
$1^{3}/_{4}$ x $1^{1}/_{4}$ x $^{7}/_{8}$ in. (4.4 x 3.1 x 2.2 cm)
AC1998.249.93
incised on raised oval reserve: *Toyokazu*

LITERATURE: AMICO, 2001–present; Bushell, *An Exhibition of Netsuke*, fig. 219, p. 51

Tanuki wrap themselves in the leaves of the lotus (CATS. 235–36), a Buddhist symbol of purity. As conveyed in *Tanuki Disguised As Monk* (CAT. 234), one who is evil at heart can hide his true nature under the guise of holiness. Monks who abused their authority were often the target of such imagery. HG

236 | **Tanuki under Lotus Leaf**

Japan, early to mid-19th century
wood with inlays
1 3/4 x 1 5/16 x 1 in. (4.4 x 3.3 x 2.5 cm)
AC1998.249.193

PROVENANCE: Kaji

See catalogue 235.

237 | **Tanuki**

To (or Tan), Japan, active late 19th–early 20th century
early 20th century
wood with inlays, traces of red and black lacquer
2 x 1 5/8 x 1 3/8 in. (5.1 x 4.2 x 3.5 cm)
M.91.250.121
incised: *To* (or *Tō* or *Tan*) *saku* / "made by To (or Tō or Tan)"

LITERATURE: AMICO, 2001–present; Bushell, *An Exhibition of Netsuke*, fig. 217, p. 51

This *tanuki* is disguised as an entertainer, wearing a red jacket and strumming on a *shamisen* to lull someone into a false sense of relaxation and security. The tanuki works for a meal, which it will pilfer from an unsuspecting guest. Although previously published as a work by To, research suggests the inscription could also be read "Tō" or "Tan." HG

238 | **Tanuki**

Front illustrated on page 68
Ōuchi Gyokusō, Japan, 1879–1944
ivory with staining, sumi, red pigment, inlays
2 3/16 x 13/16 x 1 1/4 in. (5.5 x 2 x 3.1 cm)
M.91.250.122
incised: *Gyokusō tō* / "carved by Gyokusō"

LITERATURE: AMICO, 2001–present; Hurtig, "Collecting Legends," fig. 6, p. 16

Ōuchi Gyokusō, leading realist carver of the Sō School, has outfitted his *tanuki* with a Buddhist fly whisk. The whisk's original function was to chase off insects without harming them, while its metaphorical purpose was to drive away distractions during the single-minded pursuit of enlightenment. The fly whisk, like other Buddhist paraphernalia, is part of the tanuki's disguise, which he occasionally assumes to fool people into giving him food or money. HG

238 BACK

239 | Dancing Fox

Front illustrated on page 25 and front cover
Japan, 18th century
ivory with dark staining, sumi
2 13/16 x 1 1/16 x 15/16 in. (7.1 x 2.7 x 2.3 cm)
AC1998.249.69

LITERATURE: AMICO, 2001–present; Bushell, *An Exhibition of Netsuke*, fig. 212, p. 22; Bushell, *The Inrō Handbook*, fig. 13, p. 26; Bushell, *Netsuke Familiar and Unfamiliar*, fig. 709, p. 219; Hill and Johnson, "The Raymond Bushell Netsuke Exhibition," fig. 212, p. 28

PROVENANCE: Mizutani Yoshijiro

Dancing Fox portrays a fox in midtransformation, probably into a wily woman. The artist's imaginative use of *yashadama* stain to indicate metamorphosis also emphasizes the fox's sensuous curves and coy expression. Her bushy tail arcs up to touch the top of her spine, creating a cord hole. HG

239 BACK

240 BACK

240 | Fox

SHŌMOSAI, Japan, active late 18th–early 19th century
early 19th century
wood with silver lacquer
2 9/16 x 1 1/8 x 11/16 in. (6.6 x 2.9 x 1.8 cm)
M.91.250.39
makie in *makie* cartouche: *Shōmosai*

LITERATURE: AMICO, 2001–present; Bushell, *An Exhibition of Netsuke*, fig. 402, p. 72; Bushell, *Netsuke Familiar and Unfamiliar*, fig. 255, p. 137; Hurtig, *Masterpieces of Netsuke Art*, fig. 90, p. 42; Lazarnick, *Netsuke and Inro Artists*, vol. 2, p. 971

Shōmosai's lacquer fox has a comical, cartoonlike air as he looks slyly behind himself to see if he can spot a potential victim. The rubbery quality of his forelegs enhances his transformative abilities; the leg positions appear anthropomorphic. HG

241 | Fox Disguised As Priest

Illustrated on page 37
Japan, 18th century
ivory with staining, sumi
3 11/16 x 1 3/16 x 9/16 in. (9.4 x 3 x 1.4 cm)
M.87.263.7

LITERATURE: AMICO, 1999–present; Bushell, *Netsuke Familiar and Unfamiliar*, fig. 773, p. 229

The play *Tsurigitsune* (Trapping of the fox) was part of a kyōgen repertoire performed repeatedly from the 1700s through the 1900s. It was about a fox that assumed the guise of the priest Hokuzōsu to escape hunters. In the four netsuke in this group (CATS. 241–44), the fox is on his way home, his power weakening as he resumes his original identity. Emphasis in the netsuke portrayals changed through the generations, first toward surface realism (CAT. 242), then to natural stance and drapery (CAT. 243), and finally to the appearance of old age and decrepitude (CAT. 244). The face of Masatsugu's netsuke (CAT. 244) rotates to reveal that of a fox or a human. HG

242 | **Fox Disguised As Priest**

Kōkoku, Japan, active 1830–1867
wood with lacquer, inlays
$2\,^{1}/_{8}$ x $^{7}/_{8}$ x $^{7}/_{8}$ in. (5.4 x 2.2 x 2.2 cm)
AC1998.249.122
incised: *Kōkoku*
seal form, incised on inlaid silver: *Kōkoku*

LITERATURE: AMICO, 2001–present; Bushell, *An Exhibition of Netsuke*, fig. 399, p. 26; Bushell, *The Wonderful World of Netsuke*, fig. 47, p. 43

PROVENANCE: Marcel Lorber

See catalogue 241.

242

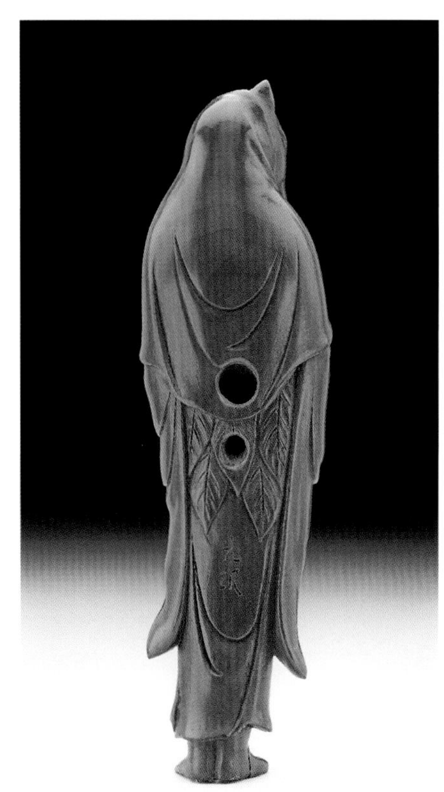

243 BACK

243 | **Fox Disguised As Priest**

Kōmin, Japan, active 19th century
wood
$3\,^{3}/_{4}$ x $1\,^{1}/_{8}$ x $^{15}/_{16}$ in. (9.6 x 2.8 x 2.4 cm)
M.91.250.50
incised: *Kōmin*

LITERATURE: AMICO, 2001–present; Bushell, *An Exhibition of Netsuke*, fig. 214, p. 51; Ueda, *The Netsuke Handbook of Ueda Reikichi*, fig. 131, p. 138

See catalogue 241.

244 | **Fox Disguised As Priest**

MASATSUGU, Japan, active mid-19th century
ebony, movable face in ivory
2 3/8 x 1 1/16 x 1 5/16 in. (6 x 2.7 x 3.3 cm)
AC1998.249.260
incised in mother-of-pearl plaque: *Masatsugu*

See catalogue 241.

244 ALTERNATE FACE

245 | **Fox Fire**

ŌYAMA MOTOZANE IV, Japan, died 1916
silvered bronze, mixed metals; manjū type
1 5/8 x 13/16 in. (4.2 x 2 cm)
M.87.263.83
incised: *Sekijōken* [Ōyama Motozane IV's art name]; kakihan

LITERATURE: AMICO, 2000–present; Bushell, *An Exhibition of Netsuke*, fig. 424, p. 74; Bushell, "Questions & Answers" (1976c), fig. 13, p. 52

Foxes were ascribed a number of magical abilities in addition to their powers of transformation. The phosphorescent "will-o'-the-wisp" emissions often seen in marshy rice fields were attributed to foxes who could set alight their tails or entire bodies to lure nighttime travelers off the road. In this netsuke, a traveler uses the "fox fire" to light his pipe, potentially endangering himself. HG

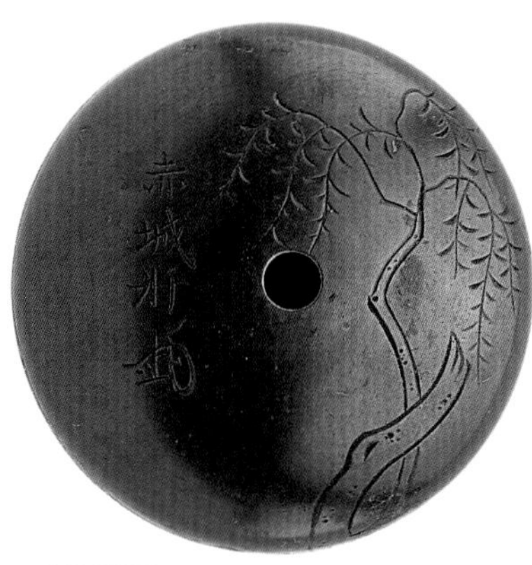

245 BACK

246 | **Fox Wife**

Illustrated on page 85
Masatoshi (Nakamura Tokisada), Japan, 1915–2001
ivory with staining, sumi, red and gold pigments
$3^{1}/_{2} \times 1^{1}/_{4} \times 1^{3}/_{16}$ in. (9 x 3.1 x 3 cm)
AC1998.249.195
incised and stained: *Masatoshi*

literature: AMICO, 2001–present

provenance: Yokomachi[?] Inari Daimyōjin

Masatoshi may be illustrating the story of Kuzunoha, a vixen whose life was saved by a man. In gratitude, she returns in female form, marries the man, and gives birth to a son (said to be Abe no Seimei, the Heian-period court astrologer; see cat. 535). Eventually, she must abandon her human family to return to her lair. She is shown here in partial disguise during a private moment in the bath. The name of the bathhouse is written on her towel. hg

247 back

247 | **Kappa the River Creature on Rock**

Naitō Toyomasa, Japan, 1773–1856
wood with inlays
$1^{5}/_{8} \times 1^{7}/_{16} \times 1^{1}/_{4}$ in. (4.2 x 3.6 x 3.2 cm)
M.91.250.59
incised: *Toyomasa*

literature: AMICO, 2001–present; Dee, "Toyomasa," fig. 4, p. 30

Naitō Toyomasa, resident of Tamba and carver to a daimyo from Mino province, invented a new style for carving wooden netsuke. He was known for his overall working of the surface, use of rectangular horn inlay for eyes, and variegated staining that enhanced light and shadow. However, his most individual aspect was the quality of captured movement. *Kappa the River Creature on Rock* appears ready to jump, while *Kappa Astride Turtle* (cat. 248) is quite relaxed. The surfaces of the two *kappa* (water spirits) are worked for contrast. The kappa on a rock has regular, repetitive stipple marks, and the kappa on the turtle has deeply rumpled skin with a more random pattern. A trickster animal, the kappa was a messenger of the Shinto river god. It had a monkeylike face and a scale-covered body; it inhabited river shallows and would drown passersby to drink their blood or eat their flesh. hg

248 | **Kappa Astride Turtle**

Naitō Toyomasa, Japan, 1773–1856
wood with inlays
1 7/8 x 1 7/16 x 1 1/2 in. (4.7 x 3.6 x 3.8 cm)
M.91.250.60
incised in oval cartouche: *Toyomasa*

LITERATURE: AMICO, 2001–present; Atchley, "The Pavilion for Japanese Art in Los Angeles," p. 23; Bushell, *Collectors' Netsuke*, fig. 93, p. 69

PROVENANCE: Mark T. Hindson

See catalogue 247.

249 | **Elongated Kappa**

Illustrated on page 66
Ozaki Kokusai, Japan, 1835–circa 1892
stag antler; obihasami type
3 13/16 x 13/16 x 11/16 in. (9.7 x 2 x 1.8 cm)
M.91.250.276
seal form, carved: *Koku*

LITERATURE: Bushell, *An Exhibition of Netsuke*, fig. 354, p. 67; Bushell, *The Wonderful World of Netsuke*, fig. 59 (center), p. 49

PROVENANCE: Niwa Curio

This abstract *kappa* is identifiable only by the small indentation in its head. It would have been worn as an *obihasami*, with the head and arms hooked over the top of the obi. The stag antler is thin and delicate; Kokusai has carved away material from the back to make the netsuke less weighty and to form the kappa's legs. HG

250 | **Kappa**

Yoshinobu, Japan, active Meiji period (1868–1912)
silvered bronze, mixed-metal disk, ironwood bowl; kagamibuta type
1 5/8 x 1/2 in. (4.1 x 1.3 cm)
M.87.263.77
incised: *Yoshinobu koku* / "carved by Yoshinobu"

LITERATURE: AMICO, 2001–present; Bushell, *An Exhibition of Netsuke*, fig. 423, p. 74; Bushell, *Netsuke Familiar and Unfamiliar*, fig. 220, p. 131; Lazarnick, *Netsuke and Inro Artists*, vol. 2, p. 1235

The reptilian tongue of this *kappa* tastes the air, and his eyes goggle as he hunts for prey. Yoshinobu has stepped away from the "cute" portrayal of kappa seen in so many netsuke of the 1800s and 1900s. The elongated nose and misshapen ear and jawline give it the appearance of a distorted humanoid. HG

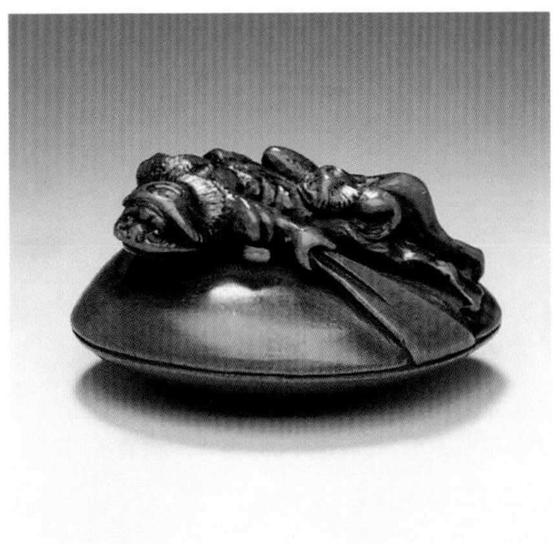

251 | Kappa Caught by Clamshell

Shōtō, Japan, active 1830–1843
wood with inlays
15/16 x 1 13/16 x 1 1/4 in. (2.3 x 4.6 x 3.1 cm)
AC1998.249.4
incised: *Shōtō*; kakihan

LITERATURE: AMICO, 2001–present; Bushell, *An Exhibition of Netsuke*, fig. 114, p. 41

The clamshell (CATS. 251–53) alludes to the *kappa*'s reputation for lasciviousness. Stories abound of kappa transforming themselves or using other methods to seduce females. The clam itself can be a symbol for the female, as the hinge in the back can resemble female genitalia. The kappa caught in a clamshell becomes a metaphor for a man trapped by lust. HG

252 | Kappa and Clam

Rensai, Japan, active late 19th century
stag antler
1 1/8 x 1 7/16 x 1 1/4 in. (2.8 x 3.7 x 3.1 cm)
AC1998.249.49
incised: *Rensai*

LITERATURE: AMICO, 2001–present; Ueda, *The Netsuke Handbook of Ueda Reikichi*, fig. 78, p. 88

See catalogue 251.

253 | Kappa on Clam

Miyagi Chokusai (Masanosuke), Japan, born 1877
early 20th century
ivory with staining, sumi
1 3/4 x 1 5/16 x 1 1/16 in. (4.4 x 3.3 x 2.7 cm)
AC1998.249.184
seal form in inlaid carved red lacquer: *Chokusai*

LITERATURE: AMICO, 2001–present

See catalogue 251.

253 BACK

254 | **Kappa with Cucumbers in Head Bowl**

Illustrated on page 72
MASATOSHI (NAKAMURA TOKISADA), Japan, 1915–2001
December 1978
boxwood with inlays
2 7/16 x 1 3/4 x 1 1/2 in. (6.3 x 4.4 x 3.8 cm)
AC1998.249.141
incised in irregular reserve: *Masatoshi*

LITERATURE: Masatoshi, *The Art of Netsuke Carving*, fig. 83, p. 161

The *kappa* has an indentation on the top of his head that he must keep filled with water to avoid losing power. If the kappa could be tricked into bowing, the water would spill out, he would weaken, and the intended victim could escape. A victim could also distract a kappa by throwing cucumbers, its favorite food. Here the kappa keeps its cucumbers in the head bowl. Masatoshi's kappa is a cartoonlike creature with very simplified anatomy, an oversize head, and enormous eyes. HG

255 | **Dragon-Fish**

Japan, 18th century
wood
3 11/16 x 1 9/16 x 1 1/4 in. (9.4 x 4 x 3.2 cm)
M.91.250.26

LITERATURE: Bushell, *An Exhibition of Netsuke*, fig. 42, p. 34; Bushell, *Netsuke Familiar and Unfamiliar*, fig. 676, p. 213

This subject has been variously interpreted as a flying dragon and as a carp in the midst of transforming into a dragon after climbing the falls at Longmen in China. Details of the composition suggest the latter; its body appears very fishlike and not necessarily aerodynamic. HG

256 | **Pair of Three-Clawed Animals**

Tōmin, Japan, active late 18th–early 19th century
early 19th century
wood with inlays
1 7/16 x 1 5/16 x 1 in. (3.7 x 3.4 x 2.6 cm)
M.91.250.29
incised: *Tōmin*

LITERATURE: Bushell, *Netsuke Familiar and Unfamiliar*, fig. 491, p. 179; Lazarnick, *Netsuke and Inro Artists*, vol. 2, p. 1146; Phillips, ed., *The Collectors' Encyclopedia of Antiques*, p. 566

This pair of unusual animals expresses a yin-yang balance in an arrangement often used in nineteenth-century netsuke. The passive animal sits with its mouth closed; the active one with its mouth open. The origin of these animals is mysterious, although their three-clawed paws, bulging eyes, and oversize mouths give them a demonic quality. HG

256 END

257 | **Unicorn**

Illustrated on page 24
Japan, 19th century
wood; sashi type
6 1/2 x 1 1/4 x 9/16 in. (16.6 x 3.1 x 1.5 cm)
M.91.250.299

LITERATURE: Bushell, *Netsuke Familiar and Unfamiliar*, fig. 578, p. 196

PROVENANCE: Matsubara Eizaburo

This subject has been called a unicorn for lack of any identifiable characteristics aside from the single horn on its head. Its sinuous, elegant form may have been adopted from the simplified juvenile dragon or rain dragon motifs found on Chinese bronzes, porcelain, and ornamental fittings. HG

258 | **Suisai**

Masayoshi, Japan, active early to mid-19th century
mid-19th century
wood with inlays
1 1/4 x 1 1/4 x 1 1/4 in. (3.1 x 3.1 x 3.1 cm)
AC1998.249.182
incised: *Masayoshi*

LITERATURE: Bushell, *An Exhibition of Netsuke*, fig. 257, p. 56; Bushell, *Netsuke Familiar and Unfamiliar*, fig. 500, p. 180; Phillips, ed., *The Collectors' Encyclopedia of Antiques*, p. 568

This mythical creature, habitually mistransliterated as *suisei*, is actually *suisai*, meaning "water rhinoceros." Tachibana Morikuni gives this identification in his illustration in *Ehon shahō bukuro* (An illustrated treasure sack of pictures for copying, 1720). Morikuni describes two types: one is a spotted land animal with three horns, and the other is a water creature with a carapace and one horn on its forehead and a smaller horn on top of its muzzle. Both have three-toed hooves and multiple folds on the neck. Here, Masayoshi's water suisai does not have its smaller horn. HG

259 | **Suisai**

School of Nagai Rantei, Japan, mid- to late 19th century
mid-19th century
ivory with staining, inlays
$1\,{}^{5}/_{16}$ x $1\,{}^{1}/_{8}$ x ${}^{15}/_{16}$ in. (3.4 x 2.8 x 2.4 cm)
M.91.250.58
incised in oval reserve cartouche: *Rantei*

LITERATURE: AMICO, 2001–present; Bushell, "Questions & Answers" (1976b), figs. 4a and b, p. 49

259 BACK

This carver alludes to the *suisai*'s smaller horn by adding bumps along the nose ridge. Both Masayoshi (CAT. 258) and the Rantei School carver have given their suisai two-toed hooves. Morikuni also described a cowlike body, although the bodies seen here are more goatlike. Goats had been imported into Japan by foreigners by at least the late 1700s, if drawings from life by Maruyama Ōkyo (1733–1795) can serve as any indication. HG

259 BOTTOM

260 | **Shōjō the Sea Sprite in Sake Bowl**

Ryūkōsai Jugyoku II, Japan, circa 1815–1877
ivory with staining, sumi, seal paste cinnabar pigment
$1\,{}^{5}/_{16}$ x $1\,{}^{1}/_{4}$ x 1 in. (3.4 x 3.1 x 2.5 cm)
AC1998.249.183
incised: *Jugyoku*

Shōjō, a sea sprite from ancient Chinese legend, was described in the noh play *Shōjō* as having a human or simian face and streaming red hair. The shōjō's weakness was sake, and in various versions of the play he helped a rice seller, Gao Feng, by sharing privileged information after drinking quantities of sake. According to legend, a fisherman who caught a shōjō could sell his hair to make an expensive scarlet dye. The wave motif on the robe indicates the shōjō's sea origins; he shows his devotion to rice wine by crawling on an enormous sake cup. Jugyoku's detailed, anecdotal style is typical of work done in Edo in the mid-1800s. HG

261 | Shōjō: The Drunken Sea Sprite

Dōshōsai, Japan, born 1828
ivory with sumi; manjū type
$1^{5}/_{8}$ x $1^{9}/_{16}$ x $^{1}/_{2}$ in. (4.1 x 4 x 1.2 cm)
M.87.263.27
incised and stained with sumi: *Dōshōsai*

LITERATURE: AMICO, 2001–present; Bushell, *An Exhibition of Netsuke*, fig. 91, p. 39; Bushell, *Netsuke Familiar and Unfamiliar*, fig. 282, p. 142

Dōshōsai's clowning, drunken shōjō sits beside a vat of sake and balances a scoop on his nose. Shōjō are often depicted with chrysanthemums nearby or as part of their costume, as seen here on the sea sprite's Chinese-style clothing. Dew from this flower was considered a potion for long life, perhaps indicating shōjō's longevity. HG

262 | Earthquake Fish: Namazu

Kaigyokusai Masatsugu, Japan, 1813–1892
ebony with inlays; sashi type
$4^{13}/_{16}$ x $1^{1}/_{4}$ x $^{5}/_{8}$ in. (12.3 x 3.1 x 1.6 cm)
M.91.250.219
incised: *Kaigyokusai*

LITERATURE: Atchley, "Kaigyokusai," fig. 28, p. 19; Bushell, *An Exhibition of Netsuke*, fig. 81, p. 37

In 1855, a devastating earthquake destroyed many sections of Edo. Afterward, images of the earthquake fish (*namazu*) proliferated throughout Japan. It was an enormous fish or eel thought to live beneath the islands of Japan and cause earthquakes when it flicked its tail. A namazu netsuke would have been a protective talisman against earthquakes. During the Meiji era (1868–1912), namazu were satirical symbols for government officials. In these sardonic illustrations, namazu-men were often paired with cat-women, who represented the officials' expensive geisha-mistresses. Kaigyokusai's namazu is a model of elegant simplicity. HG

263

263 | Earthquake Fish: Namazu

Masatoshi (Nakamura Tokisada), Japan, 1915–2001
September 1969
black tortoiseshell
$2^{7}/_{16}$ x $^{13}/_{16}$ x $^{1}/_{2}$ in. (6.3 x 2 x 1.3 cm)
AC1998.249.243
incised: *Masatoshi tō* / "carved by Masatoshi"

LITERATURE: Bushell, *Masatoshi*, fig. 181, p. 12; Masatoshi, *The Art of Netsuke Carving*, fig. 181, p. 184

In *The Art of Netsuke Carving*, Masatoshi describes the material he used to create this netsuke (p. 184). He had his tortoiseshell dealer fuse layers of shell together to create a chunk thick enough to carve. The result is a translucent, shiny fish, which glistens as if seen underwater. HG

262

Zodiac Animals

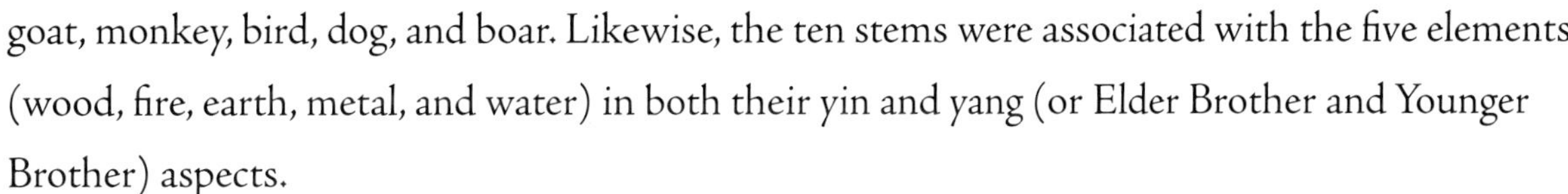

THE CHINESE ZODIACAL CYCLE (J., *jikkan jūnishi*) is an ancient system for counting days, months, and years, as well as for indicating directions and divisions of the day. Two sets of symbols—one called the "twelve branches" and the other the "ten stems"—are combined in two-symbol pairs to create a sixty-year cycle. Around the Later Han (25–220) dynasty, the twelve branches came to be identified with the names of certain animals—rat, bull, tiger, rabbit, dragon, snake, horse, goat, monkey, bird, dog, and boar. Likewise, the ten stems were associated with the five elements (wood, fire, earth, metal, and water) in both their yin and yang (or Elder Brother and Younger Brother) aspects.

It is difficult to pinpoint the exact source for the choice of specific animals, but there are abundant clues: for example, traditional Chinese naturalists include zodiacal animals among the "six domestic animals"—horse, ox, goat, pig, dog, and chicken—all of which were key to survival in an agrarian society and have protective, productive, or fertility associations. Monkeys were believed to have curative powers, especially with horses, and they were commonly kept in stables. In Chinese belief, monkeys also fended off evil spirits. Although Westerners might think of the rat, rabbit, and snake as pests, each had positive attributes that suited their zodiacal roles. When rice was plentiful, rats were too, and they came to be associated with abundance. Rabbits, which reproduce with abandon, were naturally associated with bounty and fertility. The snake, because it shed its skin, symbolized rebirth and regeneration. Farmers also depended on snakes for vermin control, and it was considered bad luck if a snake moved *out* of one's house.

LEFT: *Baby Dragon* (CAT. 295); RIGHT: *Tiger* (CAT. 274)

Together, the dragon and tiger stood for the cycle of life during a year: the dragon (CAT. 295) symbolized birth and efflorescence, while the tiger represented the harvest and death. Expanding on these metaphors, the dragon also represented the east, where the sun rises, and the yang positive principle, while the tiger's direction was west, where the sun sets, and the yin passive principle. Later, these roles shifted. The tiger (CAT. 274), considered a king of fur-bearing animals, took the role of the yang, or male principle, and in art came to signify the warrior's spirit. In later depictions, the tiger also personified wind and the dragon rain.

Four of the twelve animals represent the cardinal directions: the rat is north, the horse south, the rabbit east, and the bird west. The use of animal names for the twelve branches also made the Chinese zodiac more comprehensible as a basis for divination, such as determining auspicious and inauspicious days. Fortunetellers were consulted before major endeavors, and astrologers prepared horoscope almanacs for people born under a specific animal sign and element, guiding them in their conduct during, for example, the dog year, dragon month, first rat day, hour of the rooster, and told them in which directions they should or should not travel at certain times. People born in animal years were ascribed the characteristics of that animal as well: those born in the Year of the Dog are said to be fiercely loyal and humanitarian but often cynical and stubborn, and those born in the Year of the Rat were thought to be industrious but restless.

While ancient beliefs might have contributed to the inclusion of these animals in the zodiacal system, each animal also inspired stories and tales based on its virtues and vices; therefore, wearing netsuke of a zodiacal animal was not only efficacious during the animal's year but might also represent one or more of its ascribed virtues.

264 | **Rat Pair**

Japan, 18th century
ivory with staining, sumi, inlays
1 3/4 x 1 9/16 x 1 1/4 in. (4.5 x 3.9 x 3.1 cm)
M.91.250.280

LITERATURE: AMICO, 2001–present; Bushell, *An Exhibition of Netsuke*, fig. 52, p. 18

The rat, the first zodiac animal, represents the eleventh month, the hours between 11 P.M. and 1 A.M., and the direction north. This netsuke is in Kamigata style: the rats have heavy bodies, thick ears, large, bulging eyes, and long, grasping toes. HG

265 | **Five Rat Group**

IKKAN, Japan, 1817–1893
early 19th century
wood with inlays
1 1/4 x 1 1/8 x 1 1/8 in. (3.1 x 2.8 x 2.8 cm)
AC1998.249.52
incised in oval reserve cartouche: *Ikkan*

LITERATURE: AMICO, 2001–present

This netsuke by Ikkan and another by Ittan (CAT. 268) show approximately contemporaneous approaches to rat groups, in the compact, finely worked style of Nagoya. Ikkan's five rats are individualized, each appearing relatively calm, with the drilled ears placed in a relaxed position. HG

266 | **Rats on Boar Tusk**

Illustrated on page 48
SEIYŌDŌ GANSUI, Japan, 1809–1848
1830
boar tusk with inlays
4 5/16 x 1 9/16 x 11/16 in. (11.3 x 4 x 1.8 cm)
M.91.250.33
incised and stained: *Iwami shū Kawaigawa nishi* / "Iwami, west of Kawai River"; *Seiyōdō Gansui chōkoku* / "sculpted by Seiyōdō Gansui"; *Kore toki Bunsei jūsan ka no e tora fuyu jūgatsu nari* / "Bunsei 13 [1830], Elder Brother of Fire, Year of the Tiger, tenth month"

LITERATURE: AMICO, 2001–present; Bushell, *Collectors' Netsuke*, fig. 61, p. 60; Bushell, *An Exhibition of Netsuke*, fig. 60, p. 36; Hill and Johnson, "The Raymond Bushell Netsuke Exhibition," fig. 60, p. 32; Lazarnick, *Netsuke and Inro Artists*, vol. 1, p. 387

PROVENANCE: Sammy Yukuan Lee

Gansui, from Iwami, studied the rats' movement on the tusk rather than their individual features. HG

267 | **Seven Rat Group**

Chikuyōsai Tomochika, Japan, 1800–1873
ivory with staining, sumi, inlays
1 9/16 x 1 3/16 x 1 1/8 in. (4 x 3 x 2.9 cm)
m.87.263.116
incised and stained with sumi in irregular reserve: *Tomochika*

literature: amico, 1999–present; Bushell, *An Exhibition of Netsuke*, fig. 187, p. 21; Ueda, *The Netsuke Handbook of Ueda Reikichi*, fig. 79, p. 88

Tomochika, who worked in Edo, gives his group of rats the quality of a confused crowd, one rat stepping on the lips of another. Here areas that are incised and sumi-stained contrast with plain ivory. hg

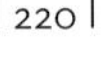

268 | **Seven Rat Group**

Also illustrated on page 48
Ittan, Japan, circa 1820–1877
wood with inlays
1 5/16 x 1 5/16 x 1 9/16 in. (3.3 x 3.4 x 3.9 cm)
m.87.263.117
incised in oval cartouche: *Ittan*; kakihan

literature: Bushell, *Collectors' Netsuke*, fig. 108, p. 90

Ittan concentrates on the pile effect, giving his rats shortened tails and tense, searching expressions. hg

269 | **Resting Ox**

Illustrated on page 46
Tomotada, Japan, active before 1781
ivory with staining, sumi, inlays
2 1/8 x 1 7/8 x 1 1/4 in. (5.4 x 4.7 x 3.1 cm)
ac1998.249.126
incised in rectangular cartouche: *Tomotada*

literature: amico, 2001–present; Bushell, *Collectors' Netsuke*, fig. 15, p. 29; Bushell, *An Exhibition of Netsuke*, fig. 10, p. 31; Mikoshiba and Bushell, "Netsuke and the *Sōken kishō*," fig. 6, p. 111

The ox, the second animal in the zodiac, stands for the twelfth month, the hours from 1 to 3 a.m., and the direction north-northeast. Kyoto artist Tomotada, mentioned in Inaba Tsūryū's *Sōken kishō* as being famous for carvings of oxen, has created one that is softly modeled and burdened by its own weight. It seems to sink into the ground. Tomotada clearly observed from live models. hg

270 | **Resting Ox**

Toyomasa II, Japan, active mid-19th century
boxwood with inlays
$1^{1}/_{16}$ x $2^{1}/_{8}$ x $1^{5}/_{16}$ in. (2.7 x 5.4 x 3.3 cm)
M.87.263.100
incised: *Toyomasa*

LITERATURE: Bushell, *An Exhibition of Netsuke*, fig. 70, p. 36; Tadashi, "Genmatsu Minsho no kometsuke (I)"

Toyomasa II, from Tamba, gives his ox the look of a perky dog, with stylized carving of the ribs and the long fringe on its forehead. Though beautifully sculpted, this ox suggests that the artist did not observe his subject firsthand. HG

271 | **Tiger**

School of Kyoto Masanao, Japan, 18th–early 19th century
18th century
ivory with staining, sumi, inlays
$^{15}/_{16}$ x $1^{9}/_{16}$ x $1^{9}/_{16}$ in. (2.3 x 3.9 x 3.9 cm)
AC1998.249.202

The tiger is the third animal of the zodiac, representing the first month, the hours from 3 to 5 A.M., and the direction east-northeast. The tigers in these three netsuke (CATS. 271–73), with their long snouts, heavily bulging brows, and open circles along the spine, demonstrate the late-eighteenth-century Kyoto carving manner. The surface is incised and sumi-stained overall, except for outlined, curving stripes. These Kyoto tigers are lankier and less like house cats than examples from other regions. HG

271 BACK

272 | **Tiger and Cub**

Illustrated on page 38
TOMOTADA, Japan, active before 1781
ivory with staining, sumi, inlays
1 9/16 x 1 3/8 x 1 1/16 in. (4 x 3.5 x 2.7 cm)
M.90.186.9
incised and stained with sumi in lightly incised rectangle: *Tomotada*

LITERATURE: Bushell, *Collectors' Netsuke*, fig. 8, p. 27; Hurtig, "The Tomotada Story," fig. 20, p. 25

PROVENANCE: E. E. Simmons; George Weil; Major L. A. Luxmore

This grouping by Tomotada is the most impressive of the eighteenth-century tiger netsuke. Tomotada took full advantage of this triangular section of tusk to arch the mother tiger over her cub, which she grooms. The artist seems to have studied the anatomy of the wolf to evoke this animal of prey. HG

273 | **Tiger Licking Its Paw**

Also illustrated on pages 80 and 81
Japan, 18th century
ivory with staining, sumi
1 3/4 x 1 1/2 x 1 1/8 in. (4.4 x 3.8 x 2.8 cm)
AC1998.249.125

LITERATURE: AMICO, 2001–present; Bushell, *Collectors' Netsuke*, front of slipcase; Bushell, *An Exhibition of Netsuke*, fig. 342, p. 25; Bushell, *Netsuke Familiar and Unfamiliar*, fig. 731, p. 222

See catalogue 271.

273 BACK

274 | **Tiger**

TAMETAKA, Japan, active circa 1730–1790
wood
2 3/8 x 2 x 2 in. (6 x 5.1 x 5.1 cm)
AC1998.249.118
incised in oval reserve: *Tametaka*

PROVENANCE: Hans Conried

Tametaka, of Nagoya, and Tanaka Minkō (CAT. 275) moved away from the Kyoto style to create bold, original variations on the tiger theme. Tametaka's tiger, huge for a netsuke, is curled upon itself for ease of wear. The loose-grained wood lends itself to striating and staining, but not to fine detail. HG

275 | **Tiger Pair**

Tanaka Minkō, Japan, 1735–1816
wood with inlays
1 7/16 x 1 1/4 x 1 in. (3.6 x 3.1 x 2.5 cm)
AC1998.249.50
incised: *Minkō*; kakihan

LITERATURE: AMICO, 2001–present; Bushell, *Collectors' Netsuke*, fig. 40, p. 37

This feisty yin-yang pair by Tanaka Minkō, a carver for the Tōdō daimyo of Tsu, seems to be in a face-off. The bodies and legs are shorter than their Kyoto counterparts, and the heads are broader and flatter. Like the Tametaka tiger, the Minkō pair has a roughly carved surface that adds to the sense of wildness. HG

276 | **Lurking Tiger**

Naitō Toyomasa, Japan, 1773–1856
circa 1800
wood with inlays
1 7/8 x 1 5/16 x 7/8 in. (4.8 x 3.4 x 2.2 cm)
M.87.263.98
incised in oval reserve: *Toyomasa*

LITERATURE: Bushell, *Collectors' Netsuke*, fig. 88, p. 68; Bushell, *An Exhibition of Netsuke*, fig. 71, p. 36

Naitō Toyomasa's reclining tiger with inlaid horn eyes has its tail coiled and ready to whip around. The tiger's upturned snout, pointed ears, and elongated fangs lend it a lively and dangerous aspect. Nonetheless, the distorted physiques of Toyomasa's tigers (also CATS. 280, 285) hint that he was looking at paintings and rugs rather than actual animals. HG

277 | **Snarling Tiger**

CHINGENDŌ HIDEMASA, Japan, active early 19th century
ivory with staining, sumi, inlays
1 13/16 x 1 9/16 x 1 in. (4.6 x 4 x 2.5 cm)
M.91.250.36
incised and stained in rectangular reserve: *Hidemasa*; kakihan

LITERATURE: Bushell, *An Exhibition of Netsuke*, fig. 340, p. 66; Bushell, *The Wonderful World of Netsuke*, fig. 41, p. 40

PROVENANCE: Tsuruki Yoshimatsu

Although Hidemasa lived in the early nineteenth century, he preferred working in the eighteenth-century style of Masanao of Kyoto. This tiger is lanky, like the earlier Masanao School example (see CAT. 271), and its hide is decorated in a similar pattern. Both tigers keep their ears tucked flat against their heads. Hidemasa had an excellent sense of proportion and always added character to the face and stance. HG

277 BACK

278 | **Tiger**

MATSUSHITA OTOMAN, Japan, active early to mid-19th century
ivory with staining, sumi, red pigment, double inlays
1 3/4 x 1 11/16 x 1 9/16 in. (4.5 x 4.3 x 4 cm)
M.90.186.19
incised and red-lacquered in rectangular reserve: *Otoman*

LITERATURE: AMICO, 2000–present; Atchley, "The Tiger in Netsuke," fig. 7, p. 6; Hurtig, *The Netsuke Hall of Fame's Record Breakers*, fig. 10, p. 43; Lazarnick, *Netsuke and Inro Artists*, vol. 2, p. 1325

PROVENANCE: William G. Bosshard; Maryott

Otoman, from Kyūshū, created an independent and dynamic style of carving. He sculpted several versions of this standing, snarling tiger with naturalistic stripes of sumi. This one, with its slender legs, open jaws, and retracted lips, is his most successful. Otoman's large, neatly carved signature is on the animal's left flank. HG

281 SIDE

279 | **Tiger and Bamboo Shoot**

MASAHIDE, Japan, active 19th century
early 19th century
wood with inlays
1 5/16 x 1 1/2 x 1 1/4 in. (3.4 x 3.8 x 3.1 cm)
AC1998.249.116
incised in oval reserve cartouche: *Masahide*

LITERATURE: Bushell, *An Exhibition of Netsuke*, fig. 345, p. 25

Followers of Naitō Toyomasa, such as Masahide, used his method for the tiger's hide: incised lines stained with sumi run the length of the animal, crossed by uncarved, outlined bands to represent the tiger's stripes. This cat's stripes are so regularly placed that he appears to be wearing pajamas. HG

280 | **Tiger on Bamboo Shoot**

NAITŌ TOYOMASA, Japan, 1773–1856
wood with inlays
1 7/8 x 1 5/16 x 1 7/16 in. (4.7 x 3.3 x 3.7 cm)
M.87.263.110
incised: *Toyomasa*

LITERATURE: Bushell, *An Exhibition of Netsuke*, fig. 72, p. 19

Toyomasa's pairing of a tiger with bamboo casts the tiger in the symbolic role of the terrestrial realm. The bamboo emphasizes the resiliency of this king of earthly beasts. HG

280 BACK

281 | **Crouching Tiger**

Front illustrated on page 46
SEKIRAN, Japan, circa 1800–circa 1875
mid- to late 19th century
bamboo with sumi, inlays
1 5/8 x 1 5/16 x 1 1/4 in. (4.1 x 3.4 x 3.1 cm)
AC1998.249.117
incised and stained on inlaid ivory plaque: *Nanajūroku Sekiran* / "Sekiran at age seventy-six"

LITERATURE: AMICO, 2001–present; Bushell, *An Exhibition of Netsuke*, fig. 369, p. 26; Bushell, *The Wonderful World of Netsuke*, fig. 42, p. 40; Meinertzhagen, *The Meinertzhagen Card Index*, pt. B, p. 719

PROVENANCE: Frederick M. Meinertzhagen; Harry Seymour Trower

Sekiran is known for his tigers carved from "sesame seed" bamboo, with compelling inlaid ivory eyes. Sumi was used to stain incisions in the hide. The head is large in proportion to the body, emphasizing the personality in the animal's face. HG

282 | **Tiger**

Toyoyasu, Japan, 1810–1883
mid-19th century
wood with inlays
1 1/2 x 1 3/16 x 1 3/8 in. (3.8 x 3 x 3.5 cm)
M.87.263.113
incised in oval reserve: *Toyoyasu*

LITERATURE: Bushell, *Netsuke Familiar and Unfamiliar*, fig. 512, p. 183

Toyoyasu, Toyomasa's son, curled this tiger's tail around its legs rather than placing it in a tense, coiled position on the tiger's back, as his father often did. HG

282 BACK

283 | **Tiger**

Attributed to Unshō Hakuryū, Japan, active 1854–1859
ivory with staining, sumi, inlays
2 x 1 1/4 x 1 3/16 in. (5.1 x 3.1 x 3 cm)
M.91.250.150
incised and stained with sumi: *Hakuryū saku* / "made by Hakuryū" [spurious]

LITERATURE: Bushell, *Collectors' Netsuke*, fig. 187, p. 123; Bushell, *An Exhibition of Netsuke*, fig. 347, p. 66

PROVENANCE: Otsuki Yuzuru

According to Ueda Reikichi, Hakuryū worked in the Gion district of Kyoto. The flattened ears, puffy brows, and texturing of this tiger's hide are all typical of traditional Kyoto style. HG

284 | **Tiger and Monkey**

Japan, 18th century
wood with inlays
2 x 1 7/8 x 1 3/8 in. (5.1 x 4.8 x 3.5 cm)
M.91.250.43

LITERATURE: AMICO, 2001–present; Atchley, "The Tiger in Netsuke," fig. 8, p. 7; Bushell, *An Exhibition of Netsuke*, fig. 201, p. 21; Phillips, ed., *The Collectors' Encyclopedia of Antiques*, p. 563

This piece, created from loose-grained wood, is large and bulky, its surface treated in the manner of Tametaka (see CAT. 274). HG

284 BACK

285 | **Tiger and Monkey**

NAITŌ TOYOMASA, Japan, 1773–1856
wood with inlays
1 5/8 x 1 1/4 x 1 5/16 in. (4.1 x 3.1 x 3.4 cm)
M.87.263.112
incised in oval reserve: *Toyomasa*

LITERATURE: AMICO, 2001–present; Bushell, *Collectors' Netsuke*, fig. 91, p. 69

Toyomasa, using familiar techniques (see CAT. 279), emphasizes the relationship between the tiger and the monkey. HG

285 BACK

286 | **Moon-Shaped Rabbit**

Japan, 18th century
ivory with staining, sumi
1 7/8 x 1 5/8 x 1 in. (4.8 x 4.2 x 2.5 cm)
M.91.250.196

LITERATURE: Bushell, *An Exhibition of Netsuke*, fig. 193, p. 49; Bushell, *Netsuke Familiar and Unfamiliar*, fig. 725, p. 222

PROVENANCE: Frances Numano

The rabbit, the fourth animal in the zodiac, represents the hours from 5 to 7 A.M. and the direction east. The "Rabbit in the Moon" *jataka* (a tale of a prior incarnation of the Buddha) relates a test given to four animals. The god Indra appears in the guise of a beggar to a monkey, a jackal, an otter, and a rabbit and pleads with them to help him find food. The monkey, jackal, and otter in turn bring bananas, an egg, and a fish. The rabbit asks the beggar to build a fire and, when it is ready, leaps into it, sacrificing himself for the beggar's fare. Indra reveals his true identity, pulls the rabbit from the fire, and sets him on the moon, where he serves as a reminder of the rewards of generosity. This netsuke is in the form of a rice sweet bun, also called a *manjū*. HG

287 | **Rabbit and Monkey**

Also illustrated on page 49
NAITŌ TOYOMASA, Japan, 1773–1856
wood with inlays
1 7/16 x 1 5/8 x 1 5/16 in. (3.6 x 4.1 x 3.3 cm)
M.87.263.105
incised in oval reserve: *Toyomasa*

LITERATURE: AMICO, 1999–present; Bushell, *Collectors' Netsuke*, fig. 87, p. 68

Toyomasa's netsuke of a rabbit and monkey in a sumo hold was probably made for a married couple, one born in each of those zodiacal years. The idea of animals engaged in sumo comes from a set of satirical hand scrolls entitled *Chōjū giga* (Frolicking animal scrolls), painted in the early Kamakura period (1185–1249), which cast animals in human roles. HG

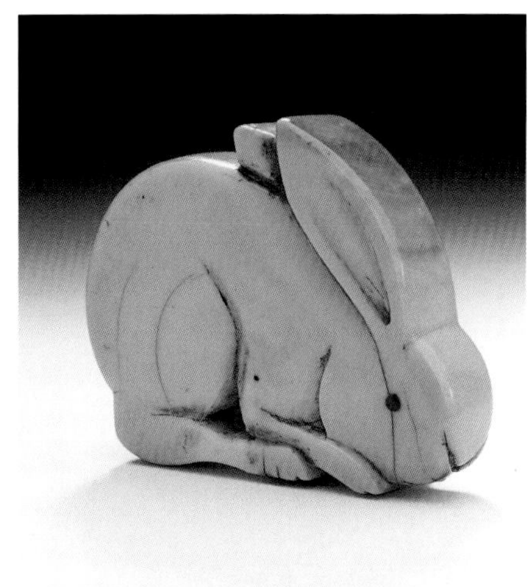

288 | **Rabbit**

School of Tomokazu, Japan, early to mid-19th century
early 19th century
wood with inlays
$1\frac{1}{8}$ x $1\frac{7}{16}$ x 1 in. (2.8 x 3.7 x 2.5 cm)
M.91.250.253
incised in oval reserve: *Tomokazu*

LITERATURE: AMICO, 2001–present; Bushell, *Collectors' Netsuke*, fig. 95, p. 71

This rabbit, shown chewing on vegetation, is carved realistically, apparently observed from life. The even coloration, consistent and fine overall hair work, and compact form reflect the manner of Tomokazu. Tomokazu, a carver from Gifu who worked for a time in Kyoto, was very influential, and it is difficult to authenticate his work. HG

289 | **Rabbit**

Japan, 19th century
Bizen ware; stoneware
$1\frac{3}{16}$ x $1\frac{3}{16}$ x $1\frac{9}{16}$ in. (3 x 3 x 3.9 cm)
M.87.263.66

LITERATURE: AMICO, 2000–present; Bushell, "Ceramic Netsuke," fig. 10, p. 27; Bushell, *An Exhibition of Netsuke*, fig. 409, p. 73; Bushell, *Netsuke Familiar and Unfamiliar*, fig. 448, p. 171

Bizen, a kiln site active since the Kamakura period (1185–1333), produces unglazed, high-fired stoneware. The clay used for Bizen ware is carefully filtered and sifted over a number of years before being used for pottery, resulting in a fine texture. Remarkable color effects are achieved by varying the placement of the pieces within the kiln. The Bizen clay gives this moon-shaped rabbit a strong tactile quality. Apparently mold-made, this type of figure is still produced in Bizen. HG

290 | **Double-Sided Rabbit**

Japan, 19th century
ivory with staining, sumi, inlays
$2\frac{1}{16}$ x $1\frac{5}{8}$ x $\frac{9}{16}$ in. (5.2 x 4.2 x 1.5 cm)
M.91.250.272

LITERATURE: AMICO, 2001–present; Bushell, *An Exhibition of Netsuke*, fig. 192, p. 49; Bushell, *Netsuke Familiar and Unfamiliar*, fig. 776, p. 230

PROVENANCE: Frances Numano

Using half of a slice of elephant tusk, this carver created a simplified and semi-abstract form, emphasizing the silhouette rather than the *manjū*-like qualities of the rabbit. HG

291 | **Rabbit Pair**

Kaigyokusai Masatsugu, Japan, 1813–1892
ivory with inlays
1 9/16 x 1 1/4 x 1 1/16 in. (4 x 3.1 x 2.7 cm)
M.91.250.217
incised in rectangular reserve: *Kaigyokusai*
seal form, incised: *Masa*

LITERATURE: AMICO, 2001–present; Atchley, "Kaigyokusai," fig. 15, p. 15; Bushell, *Collectors' Netsuke*, fig. 151, p. 106; Bushell, *An Exhibition of Netsuke*, fig. 80, p. 19; Hurtig, "Kaigyokusai Masatsugu," fig. 54, p. 21

Kaigyokusai Masatsugu and Ryōkō used a very similar, minutely detailed and naturalistic technique for their albino rabbits. Kaigyokusai, following the standard portrayal of a rabbit pair, shows a rabbit placing his paws on his submissive mate's back. The carver might have observed actual animals, as they appear quite true to nature. HG

292 | **Rabbit**

Ryōkō, Japan, active mid-20th century
ivory with staining, sumi, inlays
1 9/16 x 1 1/4 x 1 1/8 in. (4 x 3.1 x 2.9 cm)
M.91.250.82
incised: *Ryōkō*

LITERATURE: AMICO, 2001–present; Bushell, *An Exhibition of Netsuke*, fig. 190, p. 21; Hurtig, *Masterpieces of Netsuke Art*, fig. 116, p. 47

Ryōkō gives an additional layer of meaning to his rabbit by placing it on cattail reeds, with which the rabbit of legend (see CAT. 286) is said to polish the disk of the moon. HG

292 BOTTOM

293 | **Coiled Dragon**

Attributed to Tomotada, Japan, active before 1781
ivory with staining, sumi, inlays
$2\ ^{3}/_{16}$ x $1\ ^{1}/_{2}$ x $^{13}/_{16}$ in. (5.5 x 3.8 x 2 cm)
M.91.250.27

LITERATURE: Bushell, *The Inrō Handbook*, fig. 107, p. 144

The dragon, the fifth animal in the zodiac, represents the third month, the hours from 7 to 9 A.M., and the direction east-southeast; it was popular as a netsuke subject for its multiple cosmological associations. This carver, possibly Tomotada, carefully differentiated each scale on his coiling subject, rounding off the plates on the chest for greater realism. The dragon's tongue, hanging crookedly out of his mouth, gives him the look of an excited and happy dog. He personifies pure, assertive yang energy. HG

293 BOTTOM

294 | **Dragon**

Japan, 18th century
wood with staining
3 x $1\ ^{5}/_{16}$ x $^{13}/_{16}$ in. (7.6 x 3.3 x 2 cm)
AC1998.249.44

LITERATURE: AMICO, 2001–present; Lazarnick, *Netsuke and Inro Artists*, vol. 2, p. 1311

PROVENANCE: Robert S. Huthart

Shaped like a calligraphy brush rest, this recumbent dragon has an overall stippled surface rather than scales, and subtly modulated staining. The netsuke is both tactile and lightweight. The subject is somewhat abstracted in the style of the 1700s. HG

295 | **Baby Dragon**

Front illustrated on page 216
KANO TOMOKAZU, Japan, circa 1764/71–circa 1830/43
early 19th century
boxwood with inlays
1 5/16 x 1 1/8 x 1 in. (3.4 x 2.8 x 2.5 cm)
AC1998.249.78
incised: *Tomokazu*; kakihan

LITERATURE: AMICO, 2001–present; Bushell, *Collectors' Netsuke*, fig. 97, p. 71, and back cover; Bushell, *An Exhibition of Netsuke*, fig. 62, p. 19; Hill and Johnson, "The Raymond Bushell Netsuke Exhibition," fig. 62, p. 29

Tomokazu has created a very lively figure with softly lumpy skin and sharply focused, darkly inlaid eyes. The tilt of its head and a slight flex in the legs make it appear ready to spring. HG

295 BOTTOM

296 | **Dragon in Clouds**

NAITŌ TOYOMASA, Japan, 1773–1856
wood with inlays
1 3/4 x 1 13/16 x 11/16 in. (4.4 x 4.6 x 1.8 cm)
M.87.263.102
incised: *Toyomasa*

LITERATURE: AMICO, 2000–present; Hata Akira, "Naitō Toyomasa," fig. 18, p. 35

Compared to the two previous dragons, Toyomasa's netsuke (also CAT. 297) are more pictorial than tactile, with many angular elements: hard, overlapping scales, sharply pointed whiskers, and hollowed-out scrolling clouds. Toyomasa most likely planned them from graphic illustrations, as they are carved with linear detail overall and best viewed from the front. HG

297 | **Dragon and Gourd**

NAITŌ TOYOMASA, Japan, 1773–1856
wood with inlays
1 3/4 x 1 15/16 x 13/16 in. (4.4 x 5 x 2 cm)
M.87.263.107
incised: *Toyomasa*

LITERATURE: Bushell, *Collectors' Netsuke*, fig. 92, p. 69; Bushell, *An Exhibition of Netsuke*, fig. 66, p. 19

The theme of the dragon in a gourd could have Daoist overtones—some immortals could produce magical animals from gourds—or it might signify the impossible. HG

298 | **Dragon and Clouds**

OKAKOTO, Japan, active first half of the 19th century
ivory with staining, sumi, inlays; ryūsa type
1 7/16 x 7/8 in. (3.7 x 2.2 cm)
AC1998.249.300
incised and stained in rectangular reserve: *Okakoto*

Okakoto was a pupil of the famous Kyoto carver Yamaguchi Okatomo (see CAT. 332) and maintained the flavor of earlier Kyoto netsuke in his work. His acknowledgment of mid-nineteenth-century changes in netsuke style is seen in the pierced, *ryūsa*-type carving of this *manjū* and the contrast he achieves through sumi staining. HG

299 | **Coiled Dragon**

Japan, first half of the 19th century
wood with inlays
1 9/16 x 1 7/16 x 7/8 in. (3.9 x 3.6 x 2.2 cm)
AC1998.249.253
carved: kakihan of Tomokazu? [undecipherable]

LITERATURE: AMICO, 2001–present

This neatly folded dragon shows distinct similarities to one signed "Ikkan" and published by Paul Moss (Moss, *Zodiac Beasts and Distant Cousins*, pp. 33–34). The pose, the treatment of eyes, brows, and whiskers, and the simply incised scales are similar, suggesting that work was also a product of the Nagoya area. Unlike the Moss example, this netsuke retains details of brow, head, and beard carving that enhance the dramatic intensity of the composition. HG

300 | **Dragon**

Japan, 19th century
bamboo; sashi type
5 x 2 1/4 x 1 in. (12.7 x 5.7 x 2.5 cm)
AC1998.249.68

LITERATURE: AMICO, 2001–present; Bushell, *An Exhibition of Netsuke*, fig. 194, p. 49; Bushell, *Netsuke Familiar and Unfamiliar*, fig. 588, p. 198

PROVENANCE: Mark T. Hindson

Working with bamboo root, the carver of this *sashi* enhanced qualities already present in the material. The found-object roughness of the piece suggests a connection with nature, complementing the cosmic subject matter. HG

301 | **Dragon Standing on Clouds**

After Yoshimura Shūzan, Japan, late 18th–19th century
19th century
wood with pigments
3 9/16 x 1 1/4 x 1 3/16 in. (9.1 x 3.1 x 3 cm)
M.87.263.92

LITERATURE: AMICO, 1999–present; Beckett, *Sister Wendy's American Collection*, p. 253; Bushell, *An Exhibition of Netsuke*, fig. 6, p. 31; Mikoshiba and Bushell, "Netsuke and the *Sōken kishō*," pp. 106, 110; Ueda, *The Netsuke Handbook of Ueda Reikichi*, fig. 144, p. 144

This delicate monster is carved of soft wood and painted in the manner of Yoshimura Shūzan. Only the front half of this animal is dragonlike; its haunches, rear legs, and tail more closely resemble the anonymously carved *Demon* (CAT. 137, illustrated on p. 18) or the monster that Joe Earle calls the God of Shitsugozan (Earle, *Netsuke*, pp. 106–8). The sharpness of the carving makes it unlikely that it was sculpted before 1800. HG

302 | Dragon on Boar's Tusk

Illustrated on page 49
KANMAN, Japan, 1793–1859
boar tusk
$3^{13}/_{16}$ x $^{3}/_{4}$ x $^{7}/_{16}$ in. (9.8 x 1.9 x 1.1 cm)
AC1998.249.218
incised and stained: *Iwami Kanman tō* / "carved by Kanman of Iwami"; kakihan

LITERATURE: AMICO, 2001–present; Bushell, *Collectors' Netsuke*, fig. 62, p. 60; Lazarnick, *Netsuke and Inro Artists*, vol. 1, p. 587

According to Raymond Bushell, Kanman was a student of Seiyōdō Tomiharu, the founder of the Iwami netsuke lineage. Here Kanman has created a bas-relief dragon on a tusk. The use of tusk was typical of the Iwami style, a dragon theme less common; Iwami carvers specialized in small natural subjects. Kanman's dragon has a snakelike body with an oversize rectangular head. HG

303 | Five Dragon Group

IKKŌSAI (SAITŌ ITARŌ), Japan, 1805–1876
ivory with staining, sumi, red pigment, inlays
$1^{7}/_{8}$ x $1^{5}/_{8}$ x $1^{1}/_{16}$ in. (4.7 x 4.2 x 2.7 cm)
M.91.250.57
incised in oval cartouche: *Ikkōsai*

LITERATURE: AMICO, 2001–present; Bushell, *An Exhibition of Netsuke*, fig. 150, p. 45; Bushell, *The Wonderful World of Netsuke*, fig. 94, p. 68; Meinertzhagen, *The Art of the Netsuke Carver*, fig. 98, pl. 11

PROVENANCE: Frederick M. Meinertzhagen

Composed of an intertwined group of two adult and three juvenile dragons, Ikkōsai's netsuke is the polar opposite of heavy, tactile eighteenth-century dragon netsuke. Deeply carved, with each surface crisply textured, this work is coarse to the touch, though the dragons are posed to prevent protruding edges. The size and overlap of each scale is carefully considered, and red staining inside the mouths of the adult dragons heightens the realism. HG

304 | Confronting Dragons

Illustrated on page 24
RYŪKŌ, Japan, active mid-19th century
ivory with staining, sumi; ryūsa type
$1^{5}/_{8}$ x $1^{5}/_{8}$ x $^{9}/_{16}$ in. (4.2 x 4.2 x 1.4 cm)
M.87.263.39
seal form, carved and stained: *Ryūkō*

LITERATURE: Bushell, *Netsuke Familiar and Unfamiliar*, fig. 567, p. 193; Mikoshiba and Bushell, "Netsuke and the *Sōken kishō*," p. 113

Ryūkō has chosen an archaic, symmetrical composition for his *ryūsa manjū*. The dragons' mouths are in "A-Un" positions representing the first and last letters of the Sanskrit alphabet, a Buddhist mantra. The dragons are not arranged end-to-end in the typical yin-yang manner, but rather face each other, like decorative elements in a Middle Eastern or Silk Road design. As in Okakoto's *ryūsa* (CAT. 298), the sumi stain over light ivory creates a strong contrast. HG

305 | Pipe-Smoke Dragon

SHŪZAN, Japan, active mid-19th century
wood with inlays
$2\,^{9}/_{16} \times 1\,^{3}/_{16} \times {}^{11}/_{16}$ in. (6.6 x 3 x 1.7 cm)
AC1998.249.163
incised: *Shūzan*

LITERATURE: AMICO, 2001–present; Bushell, *Netsuke Familiar and Unfamiliar*, fig. 743, p. 224; Lazarnick, *Netsuke and Inro Artists*, vol. 2, p. 1018

Shūzan here playfully brings to life in dragon form the smoke that curls up around a pipe. Shūzan's hard-edged carving and realistic approach are hallmarks of netsuke of the mid-1800s. HG

306 | Dragon Guarding the Jewel of the Buddha

MITSUKIYO, Japan, active 19th century
iron, gilt, diamond
$1 \times 1\,^{1}/_{16} \times {}^{3}/_{8}$ in. (2.6 x 2.7 x 1 cm)
M.87.263.88
incised: *Mitsu*
carved in relief, gilt: *Kiyo*

LITERATURE: AMICO, 2000–present; Bushell, *An Exhibition of Netsuke*, fig. 367, p. 26; Bushell, *Netsuke Familiar and Unfamiliar*, fig. 356, p. 153

Gilded and fitted with a diamond, this *ryūsa*-type ornament was devised by a metalsmith and illustrates the development of nineteenth-century netsuke from sculpture to jewelry. Resembling a fitting on a sword or purse, this netsuke would have been too heavy for an inrō; it was probably used with a tobacco or money pouch. HG

307 | **Snake**

Japan, 18th century
wood
$3\,^1/_4 \times 1\,^{15}/_{16} \times 1\,^1/_2$ in. (8.3 x 5 x 3.8 cm)
M.91.250.146

LITERATURE: AMICO, 2001–present; Bushell, *An Exhibition of Netsuke*, fig. 56, p. 35; Bushell, *Netsuke Familiar and Unfamiliar*, fig. 421, p. 167

The snake is the sixth animal of the zodiac, symbolizing the fourth month, the hours 9 to 11 A.M., and the direction south-southeast. In Buddhism, the snake or *naga* kings had a protective function, sheltering the Buddha during his final meditation. On a practical level, farmers depended on snakes to reduce the vermin population, and it was considered bad luck if a snake moved out of one's house. The snake's ability to shed its skin symbolized rebirth and regeneration. Loosely coiled to add length to its great bulk, this snake shows the wear that has occurred over time to its lightly gouged surface. It would have been a sizable presence on the obi of its wearer. HG

308 | **Snake**

NAGAI RANTEI, Japan, late 18th–early 19th century
ivory with staining, sumi, inlays
2 5/8 x 1 1/2 x 1 5/16 in. (6.7 x 3.8 x 3.3 cm)
AC1998.249.102
incised and stained with sumi: *Rantei*

LITERATURE: AMICO, 2001–present; Bushell, *Collectors' Netsuke*, fig. 177, p. 121; Bushell, *An Exhibition of Netsuke*, fig. 195, p. 49, and back cover; Bushell, *An Introduction to Netsuke*, fig. 5, p. 37; Hill and Johnson, "The Raymond Bushell Netsuke Exhibition," fig. 195, p. 34

PROVENANCE: Spink & Son, Ltd.

The Kyoto carver Rantei enjoyed experimenting with staining, and he gave this snake a golden hue. Darker brown stain has been carefully applied between the scales to enhance the snake's texture. HG

308 BOTTOM

309 | **Snake**

MATSUDA SUKENAGA, Japan, 1800–1871
mid-19th century
wood with inlays
1 3/8 x 1 3/8 x 1 1/16 in. (3.5 x 3.5 x 2.7 cm)
AC1998.249.162
incised: *Sukenaga*

LITERATURE: AMICO, 2001–present; Bushell, *The Wonderful World of Netsuke*, fig. 79, p. 61

PROVENANCE: Shimizu Chōzaburo

These two snakes from the nineteenth century (also CAT. 310) are smaller, lighter, and more compactly arranged than earlier examples. Both are also quite naturalistic in body shape and movement. Sukenaga formed the snake's scales by carving them individually, while Sessai used cross-hatching. Sessai adds tension by posing the snake's head at an angle to stare at the viewer. HG

310 | **Snake**

Illustrated on page 16
HOKKYŌ SESSAI, Japan, 1820–1879
wood with inlays
1 1/2 x 1 1/4 x 3/4 in. (3.8 x 3.2 x 1.9 cm)
AC1998.249.41
incised on raised rectangular reserve: *Sessai*

LITERATURE: AMICO, 2001–present; Bushell, *Collectors' Netsuke*, fig. 157, p. 108; Hillier, "*Sessai Unkin zu fu* (Book of designs) by Sessai Unkin," figs. 12, 13, pp. 257–58

PROVENANCE: Deto Koichi

See catalogue 309.

311 | **Vertical Horse**

Illustrated on page 20
Japan, 18th century
wood with inlays; sashi type
$4^{1}/_{4}$ x $1^{1}/_{2}$ x $1^{1}/_{4}$ in. (10.8 x 3.8 x 3.1 cm)
AC1998.249.67

LITERATURE: AMICO, 2001–present; Bushell, *An Exhibition of Netsuke*, fig. 339, p. 65; Bushell, *Netsuke Familiar and Unfamiliar*, fig. 718, p. 221; Hill and Johnson, "The Raymond Bushell Netsuke Exhibition," fig. 339, p. 35

The seventh animal of the zodiac, the horse represents the fifth month, the hours between 11 A.M. and 1 P.M., and the direction south. To create this knife-shaped horse *sashi*, the carver humorously flattened the beast. The netsuke is quite long but easily grasped for thrusting into the obi. HG

312 BACK

312 | **Grazing Horse**

Japan, 18th century
wood
$3^{5}/_{16}$ x $1^{3}/_{4}$ x $1^{1}/_{8}$ in. (8.4 x 4.4 x 2.8 cm)
M.91.250.282

LITERATURE: Bushell, *Collectors' Netsuke*, back of slipcase; Bushell, *An Exhibition of Netsuke*, fig. 337, p. 65; Bushell, *Netsuke Familiar and Unfamiliar*, fig. 710, p. 220; Hill and Johnson, "The Raymond Bushell Netsuke Exhibition," fig. 337, p. 35

The grazing horse was a common theme in eighteenth-century netsuke. Some have suggested that the shape of the grazing horse in netsuke resembles the head of the immortal Fukurokuju (CATS. 166–68), and therefore may convey a wish for long life. In this netsuke, the anatomy of the horse is treated in an almost rubbery manner. HG

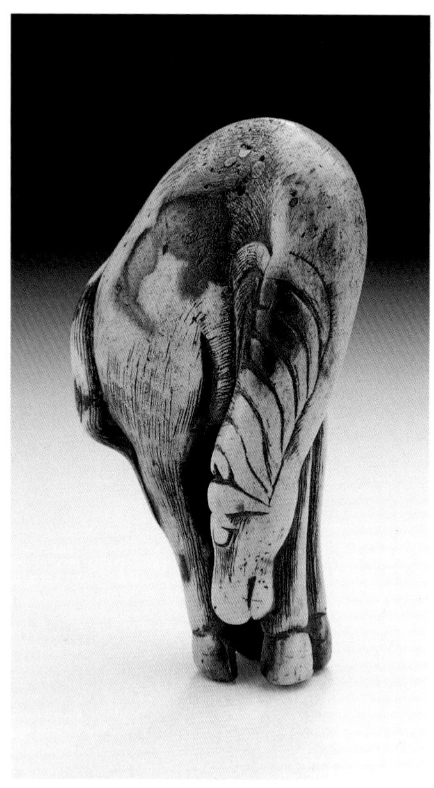

313

314 | **Grazing Horse**

Japan, early 19th century
ivory with staining, sumi
$2^{3}/_{8}$ x $1^{7}/_{16}$ x $^{15}/_{16}$ in. (6.1 x 3.6 x 2.3 cm)
AC1998.249.70

LITERATURE: AMICO, 2001–present; Bushell, *An Exhibition of Netsuke*, fig. 332, p. 25; Hurtig, *Masterpieces of Netsuke Art*, fig. 118, p. 46

The most naturalistic of the three grazing horses emphasizes the bones of the spine and legs. This netsuke, carved from a stunning piece of ivory, gets its tactile qualities from the light hair work on the horse's back. HG

313 | **Grazing Horse**

Japan, late 18th–early 19th century
stag antler with staining, sumi
3 x $1^{5}/_{8}$ x $^{15}/_{16}$ in. (7.7 x 4.2 x 2.3 cm)
M.87.263.14

LITERATURE: AMICO, 2000–present; Bushell, *An Exhibition of Netsuke*, fig. 334, p. 65; Bushell, *Netsuke Familiar and Unfamiliar*, fig. 693, p. 217; Bushell, "Netsuke: Miniature Sculptures," p. 34; Hill and Johnson, "The Raymond Bushell Netsuke Exhibition," fig. 334, p. 35; Phillips, ed., *The Collectors' Encyclopedia of Antiques*, p. 567

The natural color and texture of the stag antler gives this piebald horse its distinctive markings. HG

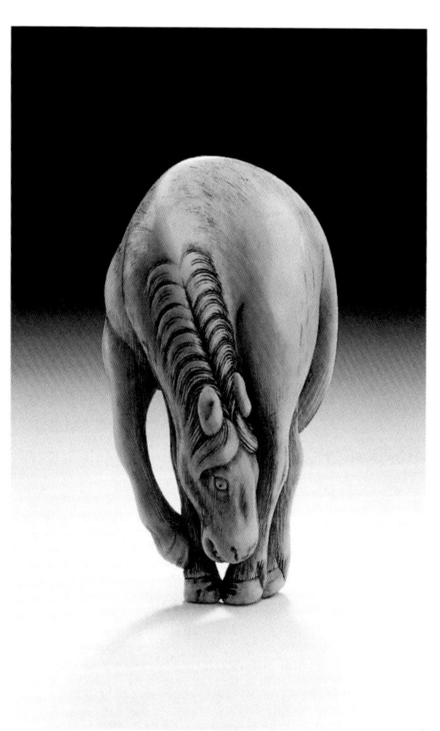

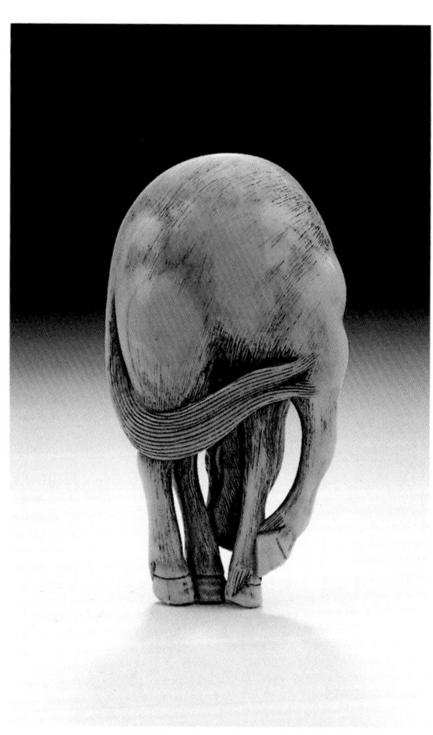

314 BACK

315 | **Shiriya Horse**

Japan, late 18th–early 19th century
wood with sumi
$1^7/_8 \times 1^3/_4 \times 1^3/_{16}$ in. (4.8 x 4.5 x 3 cm)
M.91.250.285

LITERATURE: Bushell, *An Exhibition of Netsuke*, fig. 338, p. 65; Bushell, *Netsuke Familiar and Unfamiliar*, fig. 473, p. 176

PROVENANCE: Akai Shiro

This little horse, standing primly on its four hooves, is a cross between Japanese and Mongolian breeds. These horses, called *kandachime*, run wild in the Shiriya district of Aomori. Once used for food, they are now a tourist attraction. The kandachime's small body and large head make it a suitable netsuke subject. HG

316 | **Horse and Rat**

KANO TOMOKAZU, Japan, circa 1764/71–circa 1830/43
early 19th century
wood with double inlays
$1^7/_8 \times 1^3/_8 \times 1^5/_{16}$ in. (4.8 x 3.5 x 3.3 cm)
AC1998.249.105
incised in oval cartouche: *Tomokazu*

LITERATURE: AMICO, 2001–present; Bushell, *An Exhibition of Netsuke*, fig. 63, p. 36; Bushell, *The Wonderful World of Netsuke*, fig. 17, p. 25

PROVENANCE: Inami Tokuo

Tomokazu's pairing of two zodiac animals is tightly arranged. With its forelegs drawn up, the horse nuzzles itself, ignoring the rat climbing in its tail. The surface is worn and was perhaps waxed, lessening the impact of the fine hair work for which Tomokazu is best known. The reclining horse subject also functioned well as a netsuke. HG

316 SIDE

316 BOTTOM

317 | Resting Horse

Japan, 18th century
ivory with staining, sumi
2 1/16 x 1 1/8 x 15/16 in. (5.3 x 2.9 x 2.3 cm)
M.91.250.144

LITERATURE: Bushell, *An Exhibition of Netsuke*, fig. 330, p. 25; Bushell, *Netsuke Familiar and Unfamiliar*, fig. 727, p. 222

PROVENANCE: Frances Numano

Resting Horse was probably made before the other two reclining horses (CATS. 316, 318). It is smoothly polished, and the carver has paid little attention to anatomy. HG

318 | Resting Horse

SCHOOL OF NAGAI RANTEI, Japan, mid- to late 19th century
mid-19th century
ivory with staining, sumi, inlays
1 1/2 x 1 1/16 x 1 in. (3.8 x 2.7 x 2.5 cm)
M.91.250.28
carved and stained in incised cartouche: *Rantei*

LITERATURE: Bushell, *An Exhibition of Netsuke*, fig. 335, p. 65; Bushell, *Netsuke Familiar and Unfamiliar*, front cover; Ueda, *The Netsuke Handbook of Ueda Reikichi*, fig. 102, p. 98

Rantei's horse is highly animated: its spine slopes sharply down to its tail, its left foreleg is raised, and it whinnies at something behind. The enlarged head is embellished with sumi, as are the mane and tail, enhancing the contrast with the smooth, white body. HG

318 SIDE

319 | **Resting Goat**

MASAYOSHI, Japan, active early to mid-19th century
ivory with sumi
$1^{5}/_{16}$ x $1^{13}/_{16}$ x $^{15}/_{16}$ in. (3.3 x 4.6 x 2.4 cm)
M.91.250.42
incised in inlaid tortoiseshell plaque:
Masayoshi

LITERATURE: AMICO, 2001–present; Bushell, *An Exhibition of Netsuke*, fig. 197, p. 21; Hill and Johnson, "The Raymond Bushell Netsuke Exhibition," fig. 197, p. 34; Phillips, ed., *The Collectors' Encyclopedia of Antiques*, p. 563

The eighth animal of the zodiac, the ram or goat, represents the sixth month of the year, the hours from 1 to 3 P.M., and the direction south-southwest. The carvers of these goat netsuke (CATS. 319–23) probably worked from illustrations; it is doubtful that goats, which were imported, roamed where these artists lived. The wavy hair on Masayoshi's perky goat makes it appear to have ribs running down its haunches. HG

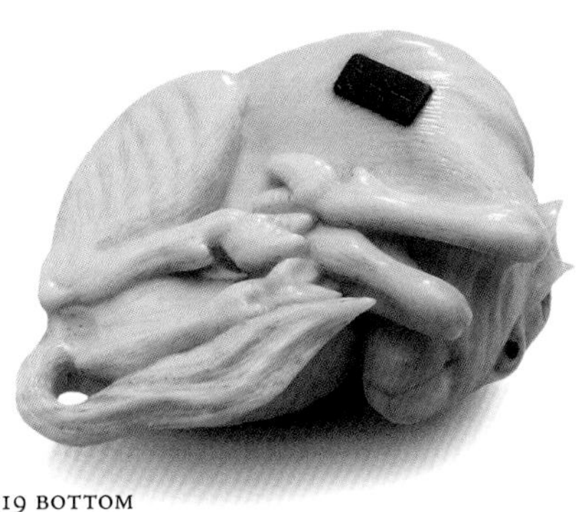

319 BOTTOM

320 | **Goat Pair**

Japan, early 19th century
ivory with staining, sumi, double inlays
$1^{7}/_{8}$ x $1^{1}/_{8}$ x $1^{1}/_{16}$ in. (4.8 x 2.9 x 2.7 cm)
M.91.250.281

LITERATURE: AMICO, 2001–present; Bushell, *An Exhibition of Netsuke*, fig. 198, p. 21; Bushell, *Netsuke Familiar and Unfamiliar*, fig. 729, p. 222

PROVENANCE: Anna L. Wunderlich

The anonymous carver of this longhaired goat pair has covered his beasts with hair arranged in intertwining locks. HG

321 | **Goat Pair**

SUKENAO, Japan, active early to mid-19th century
wood with inlays
1 9/16 x 1 1/4 x 1 3/16 in. (3.9 x 3.1 x 3 cm)
AC1998.249.180
incised in rectangular reserve cartouche: *Sukenao*

LITERATURE: AMICO, 2001–present; Bushell, *An Exhibition of Netsuke*, fig. 200, p. 50; Bushell, *Netsuke Familiar and Unfamiliar*, fig. 714, p. 220

Only Sukenao managed to achieve both movement and some anatomical accuracy in his goats, perhaps by working from animal models of another species. HG

322 | **Goat**

IKKAN, Japan, 1817–1893
wood with double inlays
1 9/16 x 1 1/4 x 1 1/4 in. (4 x 3.2 x 3.1 cm)
AC1998.249.150
incised in oval reserve cartouche: *Ikkan*

LITERATURE: Bushell, *Collectors' Netsuke*, fig. 102, p. 72

It is notable that Ikkan and Tetsugen, two noncontemporaneous artists, looked at the same model for their netsuke. In addition to overall pose, the two share details of leg placement and beard, tail, and haunch shape. The different materials and the divergent approaches of the artists distinguish their work. Although both goats are finely carved with overall hair work, Ikkan's use of pitted wood has added a textural layer, while Tetsugen's high-grade ivory avoids extraneous color and texture. HG

323 | **Goat**

TETSUGEN (KYŪSAI), Japan, 1879–1938
ivory with sumi, inlays
1 1/16 x 1 1/2 x 1 1/8 in. (2.7 x 3.8 x 2.9 cm)
M.91.250.75
incised in oval reserve cartouche: *Tetsugen*
ink on box lid: *Tetsugen*
seal on box lid: *Tetsugen*

LITERATURE: Bushell, *An Exhibition of Netsuke*, fig. 196, p. 49

PROVENANCE: Arthur Jolliffe

See catalogue 322.

324 SIDE

324 | Tiny Monkey on Monkey's Back

ANONYMOUS FOLK ARTIST, Japan, 19th century
wood with lacquer
2 1/4 x 1 1/4 x 1 3/16 in. (5.8 x 3.1 x 3 cm)
M.87.263.133

LITERATURE: AMICO, 2000–present

PROVENANCE: Minagawa Seizan

The monkey, the ninth zodiac animal, symbolizes the seventh month, the hours from 3 to 5 P.M., and the direction west-southwest. This schematically carved monkey with a tiny monkey attached to the top of his spine may be based on a Chinese pun. The phrase "Crazy monkey behind monkey" (*Hou bei feng hou*) is a homonym for "May the later generations [of the family] be ennobled as marquises" (Cammann, *Substance and Symbol in Chinese Toggles*, p. 124). HG

325 | Monkey Pair and Loquat

KANO TOMOKAZU, Japan, circa 1764/71–circa 1830/43
early 19th century
wood with inlays
1 5/16 x 1 3/8 x 1 1/4 in. (3.4 x 3.5 x 3.2 cm)
M.91.250.252
incised in oval reserve: *Tomokazu*

LITERATURE: AMICO, 2001–present

PROVENANCE: David A. Swedlow

Tomokazu portrays a mother and baby macaque grappling over a cluster of loquats. In treatment of surface and anatomy, this monkey pair strongly resembles a single monkey with berries published by Paul Moss (Moss, *Zodiac Beasts and Distant Cousins*, fig. 38). However, the keenly observed carving of the fingers outdoes that published by Moss, perhaps due to greater adaptability of this wood. HG

326 BACK

326 | **Monkey in Chestnut**

NAITŌ TOYOMASA, Japan, 1773–1856
wood with inlays
$1^{11}/_{16}$ x $1^{9}/_{16}$ x $1^{7}/_{16}$ in. (4.3 x 4 x 3.7 cm)
M.87.263.109
incised: *Toyomasa*

LITERATURE: Hata Akira, "Naitō Toyomasa," front cover

Toyomasa's monkey emerges fully formed from a chestnut. The idea of one being revealing itself within another, a common theme in Toyomasa's work, is usually found in netsuke having Daoist overtones. Toyomasa, however, was a devout Buddhist, and this has led to speculation about the meaning of these netsuke. This monkey's anatomy is treated in a manner similar to many other examples of Toyomasa's known work. Here the eyes are double-lidded and inlaid, although not with a rectangular section of horn, as is found elsewhere. HG

327 | **Distorted Monkey**

Illustrated on page 57
OZAKI KOKUSAI, Japan, 1835–circa 1892
stag antler; sashi type
$4^{13}/_{16}$ x $2^{7}/_{8}$ x 1 in. (12.2 x 7.4 x 2.5 cm)
M.87.263.9

LITERATURE: AMICO, 1999–present; Bushell, *An Exhibition of Netsuke*, fig. 356, p. 67; Bushell, *Netsuke Familiar and Unfamiliar*, fig. 691, p. 216

PROVENANCE: Walter Belanger

Kokusai has used pitted stag antler for these comical *obihasami* and *sashi* (CATS. 327–29), adding texture to a schematized and abstract form. Elongated limbs and "orange-slice" mouths are reminiscent of *Toba-e*, a style of satirical drawing. The style is named after the purported artist of the *Chōjū giga* (Frolicking animal scrolls), a work that humorously depicts animals engaged in human activities. For this netsuke, Kokusai has used a branching section of antler. The torso of the monkey would have shown above the obi. One of the netsuke (CAT. 329) also functions as a seal. HG

328 | **Elongated Monkey**

Ozaki Kokusai, Japan, 1835–circa 1892
stag antler; obihasami type
4 3/4 x 11/16 x 13/16 in. (12.1 x 1.8 x 2 cm)
M.87.263.10
seal form, carved: *Koku*

LITERATURE: AMICO, 1999–present; Bushell, *The Wonderful World of Netsuke*, fig. 58 (left), p. 49

PROVENANCE: Nagayama K.

See catalogue 327.

328

329

329 | **Elongated Monkey**

Ozaki Kokusai, Japan, 1835–circa 1892
stag antler; obihasami type
4 1/2 x 1 x 3/4 in. (11.4 x 2.5 x 1.9 cm)
AC1998.249.104
seal form, carved: *Seisai'in* [?] or *Tazai'in* [?]

LITERATURE: Bushell, *An Exhibition of Netsuke*, fig. 355, p. 67; Bushell, *The Wonderful World of Netsuke*, fig. 58 (right), p. 49

PROVENANCE: Itō Kazuo

See catalogue 327.

329 SEAL

330 | **Monkey**

Also illustrated on page 66
Ishikawa Kōmei, Japan, circa 1848/52–1913
ivory
1 5/8 x 1 5/16 x 1 1/4 in. (4.1 x 3.3 x 3.1 cm)
M.91.250.77
incised: *Kōmei*

LITERATURE: AMICO, 2001–present; Bushell, *An Exhibition of Netsuke*, fig. 447, p. 27; Chappell, "Stylistic Developments in the Tokyo (Edo) School," fig. 14, p. 25; Ueda, *The Netsuke Handbook of Ueda Reikichi*, fig. 167, p. 156

Kōmei was part of a new wave of artists working at the beginning of the Meiji era who enthusiastically followed the government's urgings to learn Western artistic techniques. He mastered surface realism, three-dimensional modeling, and exact proportioning so well, he was invited to teach Western-style sculpture at the recently established Tokyo School of Fine Arts. Kōmei may have observed this monkey at the nearby Ueno Zoo in Tokyo and, typical of this artist, carved it from the finest ivory. HG

330 BACK

331 | **Monkeys and Wasp**

Illustrated on page 35
MASANAO II (MIYAKE), Japan, 1848–1922
wood with inlays
$1^{5}/_{16}$ x $1^{5}/_{16}$ x $1^{3}/_{16}$ in. (3.4 x 3.3 x 3 cm)
AC1998.249.27
incised and stained with sumi: *Masanao*

LITERATURE: AMICO, 2001–present; Bushell, *Collectors' Netsuke*, fig. 119, p. 94

This monkey pair with a wasp may be based on Chinese homophonic punning (see also p. 35), in this case expressing a wish for promotion. Masanao II belonged to a clan of carvers that for years had been located in the Ise-Yamada area, and who may originally have been carpenters for Ise Shrine. Monkey netsuke by this group are usually in active poses and uniformly dark in color, with fine hair work over somewhat tubular body parts. The monkey's wincing face, with inlaid ivory teeth, is a compelling focal point. HG

332 | **Chicken Group**

YAMAGUCHI OKATOMO, Japan, active before 1781
ivory with staining, sumi, inlays
$1^{15}/_{16}$ x 1 x 1 in. (5 x 2.5 x 2.5 cm)
AC1998.249.47
incised: *Okatomo*

LITERATURE: AMICO, 2001–present

Okatomo, student of the *Sōken kishō* carver Tomotada, here tackles a Confucian theme as well as a zodiacal one. Chickens were often used to show proper Confucian familial relationships: the male standing guard while the female grooms her chicks. Okatomo used high-quality ivory, which has achieved a soft luster over two centuries. The bird is the tenth animal of the zodiac, representing the eighth month, the hours from 5 to 7 P.M., and the direction west. HG

333 | **Rooster**

Japan, early 19th century
ivory with sumi, red pigment
$1^{7}/_{16}$ x 1 x $1^{3}/_{4}$ in. (3.7 x 2.6 x 4.5 cm)
M.91.250.147

LITERATURE: AMICO, 2001–present; Bushell, *An Exhibition of Netsuke*, fig. 207, p. 50

The peaceful pose of this rooster is well suited to netsuke, having no protrusions on which clothing could snag. Note the complex array of overlapping feathers. This netsuke may have been cleaned by a previous owner who was not aware of the fragility of staining on ivory. HG

335 | **Bitch and Puppies**

Masanao, Japan, active before 1781
wood with inlays
$1^{15}/_{16}$ x $1^{5}/_{8}$ x $1^{1}/_{4}$ in. (5 x 4.2 x 3.1 cm)
M.87.263.136
incised in oval reserve: *Masanao*

LITERATURE: AMICO, 1999–present; Bushell, *Collectors' Netsuke*, fig. 21, p. 31; Mikoshiba and Bushell, "Netsuke and the *Sōken kishō*," p. 114

These Shiba inu (also CAT. 336) are by Masanao, one of the most successful and influential carvers in eighteenth-century Kyoto. Known for his sensitive portrayals of animals, he gave them original poses, expressive features, and naturalistic anatomy. His dogs often have full chests and long snouts. Masanao's skill is evident in the hair work and the treatment of the eyes. HG

335 BACK

334 | **Dog**

Attributed to Gechū, Japan, active 18th century
ivory with staining, sumi, inlays
$2^{1}/_{4}$ x $1^{1}/_{2}$ x $^{7}/_{8}$ in. (5.7 x 3.8 x 2.2 cm)
AC1998.249.94

LITERATURE: AMICO, 2001–present; Bushell, *An Exhibition of Netsuke*, fig. 23, p. 32; Bushell, *The Inrō Handbook*, fig. 92, p. 129; Hill and Johnson, "The Raymond Bushell Netsuke Exhibition," fig. 23, p. 32

The eleventh animal of the zodiac, the dog represents the ninth month, the hours from 7 to 9 P.M., and the direction west-northwest. This lively little animal, proudly displaying its curling locks, is in a style devised by Gechū, who worked in Osaka. This is a fanciful creature, with the face of a Shiba inu and the tail of a Chinese lion. Dog netsuke could function as protective talismans against demons. HG

334 BACK

336 | Household Dog on Embroidered Zabuton

Also illustrated on page 37

MASANAO, Japan, active before 1781
ivory with staining, sumi, inlays
1 3/4 x 1 5/8 x 1 in. (4.4 x 4.1 x 2.6 cm)
AC1998.249.304
incised and stained in oval cartouche: *Masanao*

LITERATURE: AMICO, 2001–present

See catalogue 335.

336 SIDE

337 | Dog Sitting in Padded Basket

ATTRIBUTED TO GARAKU SCHOOL, Japan, late 18th–early 19th century
narwhal tusk with staining, sumi
1 5/16 x 1 5/16 x 7/8 in. (3.4 x 3.4 x 2.2 cm)
AC1998.249.188

LITERATURE: AMICO, 2001–present

Lying comfortably in his padded basket, this Pekinese was probably carved by a member of Garaku's group in Osaka. Garaku, a carver mentioned in Inaba Tsūryū's *Sōken kishō*, liked the unusual texture of narwhal, the distinctive spiral markings of which are evident in the unincised framework of this basket. The netsuke of Osaka carvers are known for their complicated textures and tightly condensed forms. HG

338 | Dog

NAITŌ TOYOMASA, Japan, 1773–1856
wood with inlays
1 13/16 x 1 x 1 5/16 in. (4.6 x 2.6 x 3.4 cm)
M.87.263.99
incised: *Toyomasa*

LITERATURE: AMICO, 2001–present; Hata Akira, "Naitō Toyomasa," fig. 14, p. 34

PROVENANCE: Fred B. Thomas

Toyomasa's spotted Shiba inu puppy resembles a painting subject made popular by Maruyama Ōkyo and his school (see also p. 44). The rounded, compact shape of this roly-poly pup is perfectly suited to netsuke. HG

339 | **Wild Boar**

Japan, 18th century
ivory with staining, sumi, inlays
1 1/16 x 1 1/16 x 1 1/8 in. (2.7 x 2.7 x 2.8 cm)
M.91.250.145

LITERATURE: AMICO, 2001–present; Hurtig, *Masterpieces of Netsuke Art*, fig. 86, p. 41

The boar, the twelfth animal in the zodiac, corresponds to the tenth month, the hours from 9 to 11 P.M., and the direction north-northwest. The boar's pudgy figure made it an emblem for prosperity. This boar, with its oversize head and exaggerated, curving features, shows the stylistic priorities of mid-eighteenth-century carvers. HG

340 | **Resting Boar**

YOSHINAGA, Japan, active before 1781
ivory with staining, sumi, inlays
2 3/8 x 1 3/16 x 7/8 in. (6 x 3 x 2.2 cm)
AC1998.249.103
incised and stained in oval reserve:
Yoshinaga

LITERATURE: AMICO, 2001–present; Bushell, *An Exhibition of Netsuke*, fig. 35, p. 33; Bushell, *The Inrō Handbook*, fig. 51, p. 79; Hill and Johnson, "The Raymond Bushell Netsuke Exhibition," fig. 35, p. 29; Mikoshiba and Bushell, "Netsuke and the *Sōken kishō*," p. 114

Yoshinaga's humorous boar caricature is a model of late-eighteenth-century Kyoto carving. The oddly shaped snout, gaping, toothy grin, beady eyes, and floppy ears typify boar netsuke produced by this school. The body is somewhat naturalistic, although it is overlong and lacks the powerful shoulders of a boar. It has a strong backbone and softly modeled ribs and haunches, on which fine hair work has been incised and stained. HG

340 BOTTOM

341 | **Wild Boar Pair**

Kano Tomokazu, Japan, circa 1764/71–circa 1830/43
early 19th century
wood with inlays
2 x 1 5/16 x 1 1/4 in. (5.1 x 3.3 x 3.1 cm)
M.91.250.335
incised in oval reserve cartouche: *Tomokazu*

LITERATURE: AMICO, 2001–present; Bushell, *The Wonderful World of Netsuke*, fig. 14, p. 22

PROVENANCE: Abram Gercik

Tomokazu's understated naturalistic style here reaches a peak, and this yin-yang pair of boars is a highlight of the Bushell collection. The boars are turned slightly toward each other, the sleeping boar guarded by the alert figure on its back. Subtle changes in hair work and staining give dimension to the sculpture. HG

342 | **Wild Boar**

Naitō Toyomasa, Japan, 1773–1856
wood with inlays
1 7/8 x 1 1/16 x 1 9/16 in. (4.7 x 2.7 x 3.9 cm)
M.87.263.101
incised in oval reserve: *Toyomasa*

LITERATURE: AMICO, 1999–present; Bushell, *Collectors' Netsuke*, fig. 89, p. 68; Bushell, *An Exhibition of Netsuke*, fig. 67, p. 36

The figures in Toyomasa's netsuke often appear frozen in mid-action, as does this boar on the point of standing up. The animal, with its powerful shoulders and sturdy legs, could soon become a threat to any foe. Use of double inlay in the eyes gives them a sharp, wary focus. HG

342 BACK

343 | **Wild Boar Rooting**

Illustrated on page 79
Japan, 19th century
ivory with staining, sumi
1 13/16 x 1 5/16 x 1 3/8 in. (4.6 x 4.1 x 3.4 cm)
M.91.250.48

LITERATURE: Hurtig, *Masterpieces of Netsuke Art*, fig. 113, p. 46

This boar's relatively realistic proportions and his unaffected way of rooting through fallen autumn leaves are evidence of this netsuke's nineteenth-century origins. His wrinkling nose lends a sense of immediacy. HG

344 | **Wild Boar**

Illustrated on page 83
KAIGYOKUSAI MASATSUGU, Japan, 1813–1892
ivory with sumi, inlays
1 5/16 x 1 1/4 x 1 3/16 in. (3.4 x 3.1 x 3 cm)
AC1998.249.172
incised in rectangular reserve: *Kaigyoku*

LITERATURE: AMICO, 2001–present

Kaigyokusai's boar touches its nose delicately to the ground, left fore-hoof *en pointe*, ears tucked modestly back. The change in proportion from head and shoulders to tiny legs suggests that Kaigyokusai has left behind strict realism in favor of a softened, moundlike, wearable netsuke. The exquisite treatment of the surface is a trademark of Kaigyokusai's work. HG

345 | **Zodiac Animals**

Front illustrated on page 85
KAIGYOKUSAI MASATSUGU, Japan, 1813–1892
ivory with staining, sumi, inlays; ryūsa type
1 5/8 x 1 5/8 x 7/8 in. (4.1 x 4.2 x 2.2 cm)
M.87.263.41
incised and lightly stained: *Kaigyokudō Masatsugu*

LITERATURE: AMICO, 2000–present

There are a number of versions of Kaigyokusai's *ryūsa* showing all twelve zodiacal animals (also CAT. 346), and in each the artist continued to challenge himself to make an elegant composition. While other artists piled the animals into a confused mass, or arranged them around a *manjū* or *kagamibuta* form, Kaigyokusai achieved lightness, movement, and flawless finish in these ryūsa. HG

345 BACK

346 | **Zodiac Animals**

Illustrated on page 85
KAIGYOKUSAI MASATSUGU, Japan, 1813–1892
ivory with sumi, inlays; ryūsa type
1 5/8 x 7/8 in. (4.1 x 2.2 cm)
AC1998.249.57
incised on raised rectangular reserve: *Kaigyokusai Masatsugu*

LITERATURE: AMICO, 2001–present

PROVENANCE: Tomita Kumasaku

See catalogue 345.

Living Creatures

NETSUKE OF LIVING CREATURES are superabundant. In this catalogue, for the sake of simplicity, they are loosely organized into mammals, birds, reptiles and amphibians, sea creatures, gastropods (especially snails), insects, and spiders. The Japanese, like the Chinese, ascribed meanings to many native animals, and in art they came to symbolize specific seasons, moods, and other qualities. Large mammals that were not native to Japan, such as the camel, elephant, and giraffe, were imported for display in the nineteenth century; these animals had fewer symbolic associations and were generally considered curiosities.

Numerous birds are represented in netsuke, and many of them also had rich symbolic associations. Preeminent among domestic birds was the crane, which was thought to be long-lived and the bearer of dead souls and immortals into other worlds. Because mandarin ducks were reputed to be true to their mates for life, they were considered felicitous symbols. The sparrow, a harbinger of spring, was also associated with abundant harvest.

Lizards, turtles, and frogs were all popular as netsuke, especially the latter two because their rounded shapes, like the snail, were the perfect forms for netsuke.

Japan, as an island nation, has a wealth of stories and symbols connected with sea creatures and fish. The earliest tribes on the island were ostensibly dependent upon sea creatures for protein; for this reason, sea imagery is used to honor one's ancestors.

LEFT: *Owl and Bat* (CAT. 380); ABOVE: *Snail on Well Bucket* (CAT. 459)

Importing some concepts from China and India, the Japanese expanded upon and enhanced religious, literary, and artistic associations with animals of the sea. Fish, because of the numerous eggs they release when they spawn, became symbols of multiple progeny, and a pair of fish was a reference for a happy marriage. The Bushell collection contains a broad array of sea creatures, including several that are rarely seen in netsuke (CATS. 431–34) and seem never to have accrued symbolic meaning.

Insects in Japan, like insects everywhere, flourish at specific times of year. While they do have seasonal or metaphorical associations, one finds often in netsuke that they are used purely as nature studies.

During the heyday of netsuke, in the eighteenth and nineteenth centuries, there was also a growing passion for categorizing animals and plants. Dozens of encyclopedias were produced in those years, and the painter Maruyama Ōkyo (1733–1795) of Kyoto popularized a style of empirical drawing. Netsuke artists were inspired by these developments to carve animal netsuke more naturalistically. The best netsuke showed not only effective composition and use of material but also keenly perceptive empirical observation of animals and their habits.

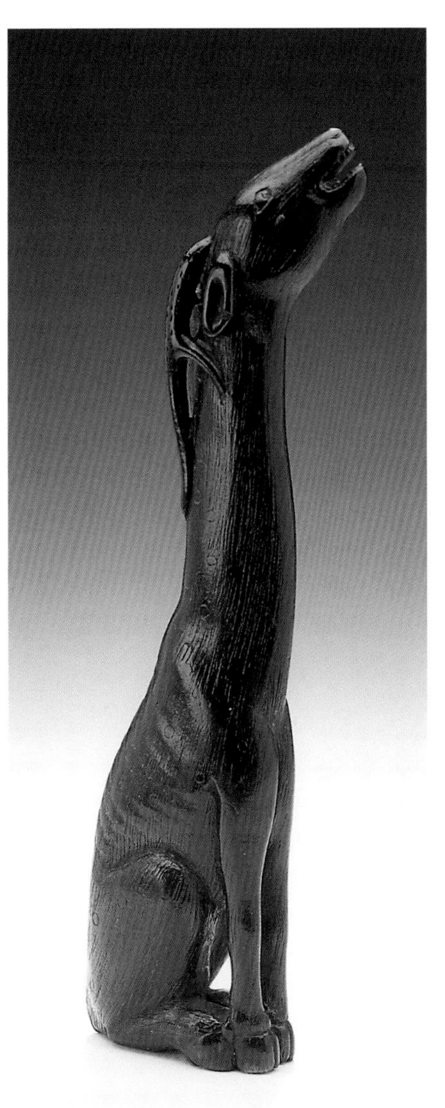

347 | **Stag**

Japan, 18th century
wood
5 x 3/4 x 1 5/16 in. (12.7 x 1.9 x 3.3 cm)
M.91.250.17

LITERATURE: AMICO, 2001–present; Bushell, *An Exhibition of Netsuke*, fig. 46, p. 35; Bushell, *Netsuke Familiar and Unfamiliar*, fig. 703, p. 219; Hill and Johnson, "The Raymond Bushell Netsuke Exhibition," fig. 46, p. 32

Deer had many felicitous associations. Daoists considered deer the only animal capable of rooting out the fungus of immortality, and their antlers were believed to contain traces of this magical substance. Deer were also messengers and bearers of the gods, and they still roam the park around the Kasuga Shrine in Nara. This seated deer with upraised head and open mouth is typical of the popular Kyoto School in the late 1700s, which included artists such as Tomotada and Yamaguchi Okatomo. VA

348 | **Stag**

Japan, 18th century
wood; sashi type
4 7/8 x 1 5/8 x 1 1/16 in. (12.5 x 4.1 x 2.7 cm)
AC1998.249.264

In his book *Takarabukuro* (Treasure bag), Mitsuhiro interpreted humorously conceived stags such as this as representing the animal familiar of the god of longevity, Jurōjin. The hump of the deer's bent back recalls Jurōjin's enlarged cranium. HG

349 | **Stag in Maple Leaves**

KAGETOSHI, Japan, active early to mid-19th century
ivory with sumi
$1\frac{11}{16} \times 1\frac{1}{8} \times 1$ in. (4.3 x 3 x 2.5 cm)
AC1998.249.186
incised in reserve cartouche: *Kagetoshi*

LITERATURE: Bushell, *Collectors' Netsuke*, fig. 195, p. 125

The autumn cry of the deer in rut, which sounds like a wailing child, signals the approaching death of the year. This cry is often used in poetry to evoke the season's melancholy. When shown with maple leaves, a full moon, or chestnuts, deer symbolized fall. Kagetoshi is best known for his skill in deep, minute ivory carving (see CAT. 369). VA/HG

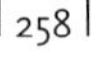

350 | **Stag in Chestnut**

NAITŌ TOYOMASA, Japan, 1773–1856
wood with inlays
$1\frac{9}{16} \times 1\frac{5}{16} \times 1$ in. (3.9 x 3.4 x 2.6 cm)
M.87.263.104
incised in oval reserve: *Toyomasa*

LITERATURE: Hata Akira, "Naitō Toyomasa," fig. 25, p. 35

A deer in a chestnut is a symbol of fall. Because Naitō Toyomasa lived far from major cities, and thus from other carvers, he was able to devise his own style. His treatment of surfaces shows painstaking observation of natural textures. HG

351 | **Simplified Animal**

Illustrated on page 50
Japan, 19th century
Raku ware; stoneware
$\frac{7}{8} \times 1\frac{3}{4} \times \frac{3}{4}$ in. (2.2 x 4.5 x 1.9 cm)
M.87.263.68

LITERATURE: Bushell, "Ceramic Netsuke," fig. 25, p. 28; Bushell, *Netsuke Familiar and Unfamiliar*, fig. 449, p. 171

This netsuke probably depicts a bear. It is modeled on a type of clay toy from Fushimi, south of Kyoto, sold at the Fushimi Inari Shrine and distinguished by the circle on its back. It was produced by the Raku family, which has been creating ceramics since the sixteenth century and is best known for rustic tea ceremony objects. HG

352 | **Camel Pair**

Japan, second quarter of the 19th century
wood with inlays
1 3/4 x 1 5/16 x 15/16 in. (4.4 x 3.3 x 2.3 cm)
AC1998.249.2

LITERATURE: AMICO, 2001–present; Bushell, *An Exhibition of Netsuke*, fig. 222, p. 51; Bushell, *An Introduction to Netsuke*, fig. 25, p. 69; Hill and Johnson, "The Raymond Bushell Netsuke Exhibition," fig. 222, p. 34

PROVENANCE: Frederick M. Meinertzhagen; Uchino Shoei

The Japanese word for "camel" (*rakuda*) is a homophone for the word meaning "comfortable," and the camel could be used as a rebus to wish someone a comfortable life. Also, a pair of camels was exhibited throughout Japan in 1824, and the two animals clearly had great affection for one another. Several artists painted them, and these images came to signify a contented marriage. HG

353 | **Indian Elephant**

Style of Tsuji, Japan, 18th century
boxwood
$2^{7}/_{16} \times 1^{7}/_{8} \times 1^{1}/_{8}$ in. (6.3 x 4.8 x 2.8 cm)
M.91.250.187

LITERATURE: AMICO, 2001–present

This is an exceptionally finely sculpted piece that takes full advantage of the wood. Exaggerated wrinkling on the elephant closely resembles the manner of Tsuji. This carver, unlike Sōichi (CAT. 355), probably relied on his memory of elephants illustrated in books imported from China. HG

353 BACK

354 BOTTOM

354 | **Smiling Elephant**

OZAKI KOKUSAI, Japan, 1835–circa 1892
stag antler
$^{7}/_{8}$ x 1 $^{9}/_{16}$ x 1 $^{1}/_{4}$ in. (2.2 x 3.9 x 3.2 cm)
M.91.250.46

LITERATURE: Bushell, *Collectors' Netsuke*, back of slipcase; Bushell, *An Exhibition of Netsuke*, fig. 352, p. 67; Bushell, *Netsuke Familiar and Unfamiliar*, figs. 692a and b, p. 217

This novel elephant is typical of Kokusai's oeuvre. The compact form, extreme caricature, inventiveness, and geometric abstraction of features are characteristics of this eccentric carver. VA/HG

355 | **Caparisoned Elephant**

SŌICHI, Japan, active late 19th–early 20th century
ivory with light staining, sumi, and inlays including mother-of-pearl
1 $^{5}/_{8}$ x 1 $^{9}/_{16}$ x $^{13}/_{16}$ in. (4.2 x 3.9 x 2 cm)
M.91.250.268
incised on inlaid oval mother-of-pearl plaque: *Sōichi tō* / "carved by Sōichi"

Like camels, elephants were exhibited in Japan in the nineteenth century. In contrast to the carver of *Indian Elephant* (CAT. 353), Sōichi clearly had access either to live models or to drawings made from direct observation. Ornamental inlay was especially popular during the Meiji period. HG

357 | **Distorted Cat**

Japan, 18th century
wood
$1^{7}/_{8}$ x $1^{11}/_{16}$ x $1^{1}/_{8}$ in. (4.7 x 4.3 x 2.9 cm)
M.91.250.140

LITERATURE: AMICO, 2001–present; Bushell, *An Exhibition of Netsuke*, fig. 221, p. 22; Bushell, *Netsuke Familiar and Unfamiliar*, fig. 707, p. 219

This amusing and appealing netsuke of a cat of indeterminate breed capably conveys the spirit of the animal through the tense positions of its legs and ears, although overall the work is schematic. VA/HG

356 | **Giraffe Pair**

SHŌKO (NISHINO SHŌTARŌ), Japan, 1915–1969
1960
boxwood
$1^{3}/_{4}$ x $1^{5}/_{8}$ x $1^{5}/_{16}$ in. (4.4 x 4.1 x 3.4 cm)
AC1998.249.74
incised: *Shōko*
ink on box: *Hokusōjin Shōko saku* / "made by Hokusōjin Shōko"; *Shōko*
seal on box lid: *Shōko*

LITERATURE: Bushell, *An Exhibition of Netsuke*, fig. 471, p. 28; Bushell, "Shōko," p. 57; Bushell, *The Wonderful World of Netsuke*, fig. 35, p. 37

PROVENANCE: Asahi Art

Shōko, a pupil of Sōko (1879–1943), was famous for his caricatured animals and people. Here, however, Shōko has worked in a naturalistic manner, emphasizing the fluid grace of the giraffes' necks. VA/HG

358 | **Sleeping Cat**

KAIGYOKUSAI MASATSUGU, Japan, 1813–1892
ivory with sumi, red pigment
$1^{5}/_{8} \times 1^{1}/_{8} \times 1$ in. (4.1 x 2.8 x 2.5 cm)
AC1998.249.80
incised: *Kaigyoku*

LITERATURE: AMICO, 2001–present; Atchley, "Kaigyokusai," fig. 12, p. 15; Atchley, "The Pavilion for Japanese Art in Los Angeles," p. 23; Bushell, *Collectors' Netsuke*, fig. 148, p. 105; Bushell, *An Exhibition of Netsuke*, fig. 85, p. 38; Hurtig, "Kaigyokusai Masatsugu," fig. 51, p. 21

PROVENANCE: Frances Numano; Tomita Kumasaku

Although the cat initially had negative associations, in later centuries stories of loyal cats proliferated, as did their image in netsuke. This *Sleeping Cat* by Kaigyokusai is especially attractive for its authenticity and sweetness. HG

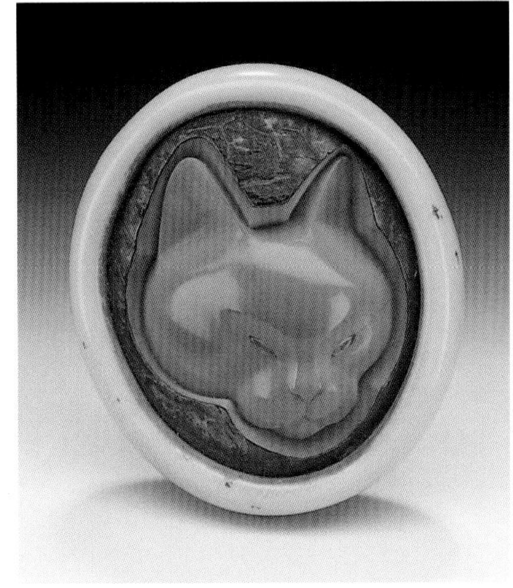

359 | **Cat**

Japan, 20th century
corozo nut and ivory with inlays; manjū type
$2^{1}/_{16} \times 1^{7}/_{8} \times {}^{13}/_{16}$ in. (5.2 x 4.7 x 2 cm)
AC1998.249.221

LITERATURE: Bushell, *Netsuke Familiar and Unfamiliar*, fig. 274, p. 140; Bushell, *Netsuke Masks*, fig. 292

PROVENANCE: Frances Numano

Here, the face of a sleeping cat decorates an ivory bowl. The corozo nut, sometimes called vegetable ivory or tagua nut, is the seed of the ivory palm. These pure cellulose nuts have been used for carving for more than two centuries. VA/HG

360 | **Cat and Lizard**

MASATOSHI (NAKAMURA TOKISADA), Japan, 1915–2001
February 1980
boxwood
$1^{9}/_{16} \times 1^{5}/_{16} \times 1^{5}/_{16}$ in. (3.9 x 3.4 x 3.3 cm)
AC1998.249.216
incised: *Masatoshi tō* / "carved by Masatoshi"

LITERATURE: Bushell, *Masatoshi*, fig. 278, p. 35; Masatoshi, *The Art of Netsuke Carving*, fig. 278, p. 205

In his *Art of Netsuke Carving*, Masatoshi says this cat is bewildered: it thought it had captured the trespassing lizard by biting its tail, but the lizard goes nonchalantly on its way, knowing it can grow another. VA

361 | **Wolf and Whelp**

Japan, 18th century
ivory with staining, sumi, inlays
$1^{7}/_{8}$ x $1^{13}/_{16}$ x 1 in. (4.7 x 4.6 x 2.6 cm)
M.87.263.121

LITERATURE: AMICO, 2001–present; Phillips, ed., *The Collectors' Encyclopedia of Antiques*, p. 567

The wolf was indigenous to Japan, although it is now extinct there. Like the dog, it was believed to deter demons, but it was also known to haunt graveyards and kill travelers. In Chinese legend, it appears as a rapacious creature, willing to eat even one who saves it. The wolf here is fiercely protective of its young. HG

361 BACK

362 | **Wolf Eating Its Own Paw**

Kano Tomokazu, Japan, circa 1764/71–circa 1830/43
early 19th century
wood with inlays
1 7/16 x 1 5/16 x 1 in. (3.7 x 3.4 x 2.6 cm)
M.91.250.256
incised in oval reserve cartouche: *Tomokazu*

LITERATURE: Bushell, *An Exhibition of Netsuke*, fig. 61, p. 36; Bushell, *Netsuke Familiar and Unfamiliar*, fig. 704, p. 219

PROVENANCE: David A. Swedlow

Tomokazu, who carved almost entirely in wood, became famous for his authentic animal netsuke, especially monkeys and turtles. He liked to go into the woods and sketch living creatures, perhaps observing a starving wolf in this posture. VA

363 | **Wolf and Skull**

Japan, 19th century
wood with inlays
3 1/8 x 1 3/4 x 1 5/16 in. (7.9 x 4.4 x 3.4 cm)
AC1998.249.134

PROVENANCE: Betty Jahss

This heavily stylized netsuke of a wolf and skull would have been favored by samurai, who cultivated a stoic attitude about death. HG

364 | **Bear Licking Honey**

Kaigyokusai Masatsugu, Japan, 1813–1892
ebony with inlays
1 3/4 x 1 1/4 x 1 1/8 in. (4.4 x 3.1 x 2.8 cm)
AC1998.249.99
incised: *Kaigyokusai*

LITERATURE: AMICO, 2001–present; Atchley, "Kaigyokusai," fig. 26, p. 19; Bushell, *Collectors' Netsuke*, fig. 144, p. 104; Bushell, *An Exhibition of Netsuke*, fig. 86, p. 38; Hill and Johnson, "The Raymond Bushell Netsuke Exhibition," fig. 86, p. 32; Hurtig, "Kaigyokusai Masatsugu," fig. 49, p. 21

PROVENANCE: Imai Kenzō

This bear is an excellent example of the finely detailed and carefully controlled carving of Kaigyokusai's best work. Note the inlaid horn eyes and the whiskers in relief. The faint crescent moon carved on the bear's chest represents the markings of the Asian black bear. VA/HG

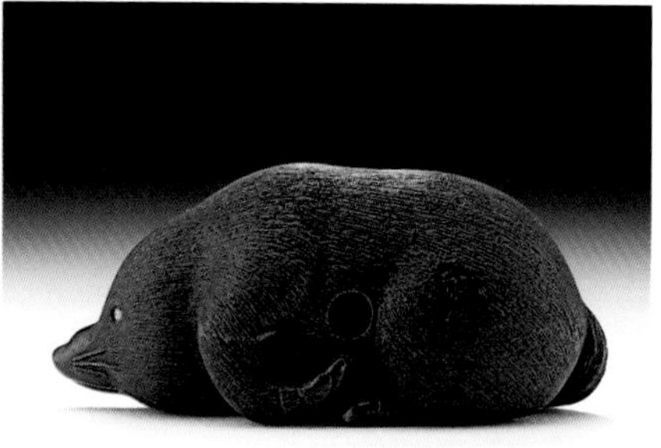

365 BACK

365 | **Mole**

MASATOSHI (NAKAMURA TOKISADA), Japan, 1915–2001
December 1960
ebony with inlays
2 5/16 x 1 x 1 in. (5.9 x 2.6 x 2.5 cm)
AC1998.249.269
incised in irregular reserve: *Masatoshi*

LITERATURE: Masatoshi, *The Art of Netsuke Carving*, fig. 282, p. 206

Like Kaigyokusai's bear, Masatoshi's mole employs hairline engraving, with whiskers in relief. Masatoshi has used ebony to suggest the mole's nocturnal habits. The mole has no symbolic associations and is an unusual subject in Japanese art. VA/HG

366 | **Bat on Roof Tile**

HŌRAKU, Japan, active early to mid-19th century
early 19th century
wood with inlays
1 5/16 x 1 5/16 x 1 3/16 in. (3.4 x 3.4 x 3 cm)
AC1998.249.3
incised in oval cartouche: *Hōraku*

LITERATURE: AMICO, 2001–present; Bushell, *Collectors' Netsuke*, fig. 193, p. 124; Bushell, *An Exhibition of Netsuke*, fig. 233, p. 53

The bat (*fu*) was a favored motif in Chinese art because its homophone means "happiness." In local proverbs, a bat on a roof tile meant that a learned person was in residence. The bat was Hōraku's favorite subject for netsuke, and his portrayals are unusually naturalistic for a subject imported from China. HG

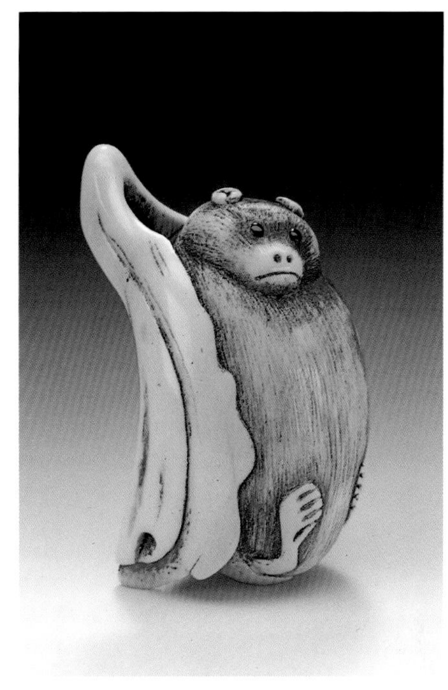

367 | **Stylized Bat**

Japan, mid- to late 19th century
rhinoceros horn or *umimatsu* (black coral)
2 x 1 3/4 x 1 in. (5.1 x 4.5 x 2.5 cm)
M.90.186.16

LITERATURE: AMICO, 2000–present; Hurtig, *Masterpieces of Netsuke Art*, fig. 925, p. 220; Lazarnick, *Netsuke and Inro Artists*, vol. 1, pp. 10, 73

PROVENANCE: George Lazarnick

This is a dramatic rendering of the creature so admired by the Japanese. The material's translucency and polished sheen add lightness to this stylized, elegant treatment. VA/HG

368 | **Bat**

MITSUTOSHI, Japan, active late 19th century
ivory with staining, sumi, inlays
1 7/8 x 1 1/4 x 7/8 in. (4.7 x 3.1 x 2.2 cm)
AC1998.249.286
incised: *Kyō no junin Mitsutoshi koku* / "carved by Mitsutoshi living in Kyoto"

LITERATURE: Hurtig, *Masterpieces of Netsuke Art*, fig. 114, p. 46

Carved from a triangular section of tusk, this bat shows a mixture of styles, with the body rendered naturalistically and the appendages carved in a schematized manner. The abbreviated treatment of appendages indicates the limited size of the artist's raw material. HG

370 | **Floating Crane**

Illustrated on page 13

KAIGYOKUSAI MASATSUGU, Japan, 1813–1892
ivory with staining, sumi, inlays
$1^{13}/_{16}$ x $^{15}/_{16}$ x $^{7}/_{8}$ in. (4.6 x 2.4 x 2.2 cm)
M.91.250.339
incised: *Kaigyokusai*

LITERATURE: AMICO, 1998–present; Atchley, "Kaigyokusai," fig. 1, p. 10; Bushell, *Collectors' Netsuke*, fig. 147, p. 105; Hurtig, "Kaigyokusai Masatsugu," fig. 27, p. 18; Hurtig, *Masterpieces of Netsuke Art*, fig. 437, pp. 114–15

PROVENANCE: Imai Kenzō

This is a famous carving by Kaigyokusai, and it has appeared in many books about netsuke. It is a fine example of his legendary carving skills (also CAT. 358), conveying a full array of textures. The crane's feet show the natural position of a bird at rest. VA/HG

369 | **Crane Group**

KAGETOSHI, Japan, active early to mid-19th century
ivory with sumi
$1^{3}/_{16}$ x $1^{5}/_{8}$ x $1^{1}/_{4}$ in. (3 x 4.1 x 3.1 cm)
AC1998.249.205
incised in rectangular reserve: *Kagetoshi*

LITERATURE: Bushell, *Collectors' Netsuke*, fig. 197, p. 125; Bushell, *An Exhibition of Netsuke*, fig. 146, p. 20

A single crane represented a desire for longevity, and a group of cranes multiplied this desire. Like *Stag in Maple Leaves* (CAT. 349), this piece attests to Kagetoshi's attention to minute detail. VA/HG

371 | **Mandarin Duck**

Japan, late 18th–early 19th century
bronze with gilding
1 15/16 x 1 1/2 x 13/16 in. (5 x 3.8 x 2 cm)
M.87.263.85

LITERATURE: AMICO, 2000–present; Bushell, *An Exhibition of Netsuke*, fig. 358, p. 68; Hurtig, *Masterpieces of Netsuke Art*, fig. 81, p. 41

Ducks were felicitous symbols, especially mandarin ducks. These crested and elegantly colored birds were prized both for their beauty and for their symbolic value. They were reputed to remain true to their mates for life, which made them a perfect motif for wedding gifts. This metal netsuke would have been too heavy for an inrō; it was likely attached to a tobacco pouch. VA/HG

372 | **Simplified Mandarin Duck**

Japan, 19th century
ivory with staining, sumi, inlays, red pigment
1 9/16 x 1 5/16 x 13/16 in. (3.9 x 3.3 x 2 cm)
M.87.263.126

LITERATURE: AMICO, 2000–present

This netsuke is compact and rounded. The simple body and the position of the duck's head are both expressive. HG

373 | **Preening Duck**

ŌHARA MITSUHIRO, Japan, 1810–1875
ivory with staining, sumi, inlays
1 3/4 x 1 1/8 x 7/8 in. (4.4 x 2.8 x 2.2 cm)
AC1998.249.82
incised and lightly stained: *Mitsuhiro*; kakihan

LITERATURE: AMICO, 2001–present; Atchley, "The Pavilion for Japanese Art in Los Angeles," p. 24; Bushell, *Collectors' Netsuke*, fig. 128, p. 97; Bushell, *An Exhibition of Netsuke*, fig. 73, p. 19

This graceful duck in smooth, lightly stained ivory is typical of the simple elegance of many of Mitsuhiro's netsuke. His lines are clean and flowing, his finish lustrous, with a warm, high polish. VA

374 | **Stylized Swimming Duck**

Illustrated on page 86
Masanobu (Adachi Tomoshichi), Japan, born 1838
ivory with staining, sumi
1 9/16 x 1 5/16 x 7/8 in. (4 x 3.3 x 2.2 cm)
M.91.250.262
incised: *Fuji Masanobu*; kakihan

LITERATURE: Bushell, *An Exhibition of Netsuke*, fig. 152, p. 45; Bushell, *Netsuke Familiar and Unfamiliar*, fig. 188, p. 124; Phillips, ed., *The Collectors' Encyclopedia of Antiques*, p. 569

The deeply recessed "inside" carving (*ana-bori*) of this netsuke reveals a tiny scene of a river, bridge, shrine gate, boat, and people—all seen through an opening in the shape of a half cherry blossom. Masanobu was a late-nineteenth-century samurai of the Owari branch of the Tokugawa house. VA

375 | **Owl**

Japan, late 18th–early 19th century
wood
2 x 1 3/16 x 1 3/8 in. (5.1 x 3 x 3.5 cm)
AC1998.249.160

LITERATURE: Bushell, *The Wonderful World of Netsuke*, fig. 21, p. 28

PROVENANCE: Abram Gercik

The Chinese and Japanese considered the owl evil, a symbol of ingratitude. Although the owl is therefore a relatively rare netsuke subject, this collection boasts an unusually broad range of examples. VA

376 | **Owl**

Ikkei Seishinsai, Japan, active late 18th–early 19th century
early 19th century
ebony; manjū type
1 11/16 x 1 5/8 x 13/16 in. (4.3 x 4.2 x 2.1 cm)
M.87.263.29
incised: *Seishinsai Ikkei*

LITERATURE: AMICO, 1999–present; Bushell, *An Exhibition of Netsuke*, fig. 235, p. 53; Bushell, *Netsuke Familiar and Unfamiliar*, fig. 474, p. 176; Hurtig, *Masterpieces of Netsuke Art*, fig. 115, p. 46

Owls were often carved from dark materials such as ebony, jet, or peat to suggest their nocturnal habits. An owl netsuke in *manjū* form associated the bird with the moon. HG

377 | **Owl and Owlets**

Style of Ikkyū, Japan, early to mid-19th century
wood with inlays
1 3/4 x 1 5/16 x 15/16 in. (4.5 x 3.4 x 2.4 cm)
M.91.250.255
incised: *Tomokazu* [added later]

PROVENANCE: Abraham Globerman

The tiny owlets, which are movable, pop up when this netsuke is handled, and their positioning reminds one of a puppet stage. An owl with autumn ivy symbolizes the melancholy aspects of fall. VA/HG

378 | **Owl**

Japan, 19th century
porcelain with celadon glaze
1 11/16 x 1 1/8 x 1 3/16 in. (4.3 x 2.8 x 3 cm)
M.87.263.55

LITERATURE: AMICO, 2001–present; Bushell, "Ceramic Netsuke," fig. 16, p. 27; Bushell, *An Exhibition of Netsuke*, fig. 415, p. 73

Because of the fragility of the material, few ceramic netsuke have survived. The simplicity of this mold-made form increased its durability. VA/HG

379 | **Stylized Owl**

Japan, 19th century
jet or peat with inlays
1 9/16 x 15/16 x 1 1/8 in. (3.9 x 2.3 x 2.8 cm)
M.91.250.148

This owl's placement on a plinth suggests that it may have been intended as a seal, although the base is not carved. HG

380 | **Owl and Bat**

Also illustrated on page 254
HŌRAKU, Japan, active early to mid-19th century
ebony with inlays
1 7/16 x 1 5/16 x 1 7/16 in. (3.6 x 3.4 x 3.6 cm)
M.90.186.3
incised in oval cartouche: *Hōraku*

LITERATURE: Bushell, *An Exhibition of Netsuke*, fig. 234, p. 22; Hill and Johnson, "The Raymond Bushell Netsuke Exhibition," fig. 234, p. 29

PROVENANCE: Archer Spence

Although the owl is a natural predator of the bat, the combination of these two animals is rare. Perhaps they offset each other—the owl a symbol of evil, the bat a symbol of happiness. VA/HG

381 | **Owl**

Illustrated on page 64
SUZUKI TŌKOKU, Japan, 1846–1913
wood with inlays, lacquer; manjū type
1 5/16 x 1/2 in. (3.4 x 1.2 cm)
M.91.250.238
seal form in gold *makie*: *Bairyū*
seal form in red lacquer: *Tōkoku*

LITERATURE: AMICO, 2001–present; Bushell, *Collectors' Netsuke*, fig. 212, p. 145; Bushell, *An Exhibition of Netsuke*, fig. 380, p. 70

This lovely *manjū* probably dates from Tōkoku's early years, when he was partial to this style. Later, he was best known for his skillful use of inlays. Tōkoku uses the manjū form to good effect, creating the impression of an owl silhouetted against the moon. VA/HG

382 | **Plover**

Japan, late 18th century
ivory with staining, sumi, inlays
1 1/8 x 1 5/8 x 1 15/16 in. (2.8 x 4.1 x 5 cm)
AC1998.249.13

LITERATURE: AMICO, 2001–present

This bird resembles a plump and truncated abstraction of the plover by Rimpa artist Ogata Kōrin (1658–1716). The so-called plump sparrow (*fukura suzume*), symbol of a good harvest, is also similar in form. HG

383 | **Stylized Plover**

SHŪCHI, Japan, active early 19th century
wood
1 7/8 x 1 7/16 x 11/16 in. (4.7 x 3.6 x 1.7 cm)
M.91.250.180
incised on inlaid mother-of-pearl plaque:
Shūchi [or *Shūji*]

LITERATURE: Hurtig, *Masterpieces of Netsuke Art*, fig. 102, p. 45

This Kōrin-style plover was a popular motif in patterned textile design, and it complemented an inrō decorated with a seaside theme. HG

384 | **Plovers**

ISHIKAWA RENSAI, Japan, active mid- to late 19th century
walrus tusk with staining, sumi, inlays; ryūsa type
1 7/16 x 1 1/4 x 7/16 in. (3.7 x 3.2 x 1.1 cm)
M.91.250.226
incised and stained: *Rensai*

LITERATURE: Bushell, *Collectors' Netsuke*, fig. 240, p. 151; Davey, *Netsuke*, fig. 537, p. 181

PROVENANCE: Mark T. Hindson; William Wilberforce Winkworth

Rensai made many *manjū-* and *ryūsa*-style netsuke, and his favorite material was stag antler. Although he signed most of his work simply "Ren," here he signed with his full signature in *tensho* script. Like Kokusai, he belonged to the popular Asakusa School. These Kōrin-style plovers are shown with curling "finger waves," a mannerism of Rimpa painting and design style. VA/HG

385 | **Double-Ended Plovers**

Japan, late 19th century
ivory with staining, sumi, inlays
1 9/16 x 15/16 x 9/16 in. (3.9 x 2.3 x 1.5 cm)
M.87.263.125

LITERATURE: AMICO, 2000–present; Bushell, *Netsuke Familiar and Unfamiliar*, fig. 633, p. 206

An identical plover is carved on each end of this piece, perhaps alluding to the belief that plovers live in pairs. The netsuke's wave shape symbolically places the subject in its natural environment, the seashore. VA/HG

386 | **Sparrow in Flight**

Japan, early 19th century
wood
1 15/16 x 1 5/16 x 1 in. (5 x 3.4 x 2.6 cm)
M.91.250.141

LITERATURE: Bushell, *An Exhibition of Netsuke*, fig. 237, p. 53; Bushell, *The Wonderful World of Netsuke*, fig. 39, p. 39

PROVENANCE: Matsubara Eizaburo

The sparrow, a harbinger of spring, was also associated with an abundant harvest. (Like the rat, the sparrow's presence in the grain fields portended a favorable crop.) In pictorial art especially, these two aspects are shown by setting a fluttering sparrow amid snow-covered bamboo, or near barley heads bending under their own weight. The back feathers of this sparrow evoke barley heads just before harvest. HG

387 | **Stylized Sparrow**

Japan, 19th century
lacquer with pigment and gold flecks
1 15/16 x 1 1/4 x 15/16 in. (4.9 x 3.2 x 2.4 cm)
M.91.250.72

LITERATURE: Bushell, *Netsuke Familiar and Unfamiliar*, fig. 261, p. 138

The lacquer design applied to the back of this sparrow shows a cloth fence, maple leaves, a banner, and a bird-form helmet, all associated both with autumn and court performances of bugaku ceremonial dance. This netsuke symbolizes a good harvest and a wealthy nation. HG

388 | **Sparrow on Tile**

Ōhara Mitsuhiro, Japan, 1810–1875
ebony with inlays
1 5/8 x 1 x 15/16 in. (4.1 x 2.6 x 2.3 cm)
M.91.250.233
incised and stained on inlaid ivory plaque: *Mitsuhiro*

LITERATURE: Bushell, *Collectors' Netsuke*, fig. 130, p. 98

In netsuke, a sparrow on a roof tile symbolizes good wishes for happiness and prosperity. The tile here has a motif of multiple chrysanthemums, perhaps suggesting a connection to the imperial palace and wishes for a prosperous reign. HG

389 TOP

389 | **Sparrow**

ISHIKAWA RENSAI, Japan, active mid- to late 19th century
stag antler with inlays
1 11/16 x 1 9/16 x 15/16 in. (4.3 x 3.9 x 2.4 cm)
M.87.263.18
seal form, incised on raised square: *Ren*

LITERATURE: AMICO, 1999–present; Bushell, *Collectors' Netsuke*, fig. 235, p. 150; Bushell, *An Exhibition of Netsuke*, fig. 351, p. 67

Like the sparrow on a roof tile, a sparrow with the character *kotobuki* (felicity) carved on its back symbolizes hope for happiness and prosperity. The bamboo may indicate that this netsuke represented good wishes for the New Year. The pierced work on the sparrow recalls the lacy center section of the stag's antler. Rensai carved numerous versions of this theme. HG

390 | **Kissing Geese**

Japan, 18th century
ivory with staining, sumi
2 3/16 x 1 11/16 x 5/8 in. (5.6 x 4.3 x 1.6 cm)
M.91.250.53

LITERATURE: Bushell, *An Exhibition of Netsuke*, fig. 236, p. 53; Bushell, *The Wonderful World of Netsuke*, fig. 77, p. 60; Hill and Johnson, "The Raymond Bushell Netsuke Exhibition," fig. 236, p. 34

PROVENANCE: Tahara Giichiro

These kissing geese symbolize wedded bliss. The design may well have been adapted from a family crest (*mon*). VA/HG

391 | **Goose in Flight**

Japan, 19th century
wood
3 x 13/16 x 7/16 in. (7.7 x 2 x 1.1 cm)
M.87.263.128

LITERATURE: AMICO, 2000–present; Bushell, *An Exhibition of Netsuke*, fig. 139, p. 44; Bushell, *Netsuke Familiar and Unfamiliar*, fig. 626, p. 206

Among the most interesting bird netsuke from the early to mid-1800s were those in which the form was simplified and abstracted (see also CATS. 383, 395–98). These were produced contemporaneously with highly naturalistic animal netsuke. This bird is a study in elegance and extreme economy of design. HG

392 | **Sea Bird in Clamshell**

NAITŌ TOYOMASA, Japan, 1773–1856
wood with inlays
1 13/16 x 1 7/16 x 1 1/8 in. (4.6 x 3.7 x 2.8 cm)
M.87.263.111
incised: *Toyomasa*

LITERATURE: Hata Akira, "Naitō Toyomasa," fig. 26, p. 36

This bird, probably a snipe, struggles from a clamshell resembling a broken egg. Toyomasa is considered one of the greatest carvers of netsuke. VA/HG

393 | **Pigeon Hawk**

Rangyoku, Japan, active early 19th century
ivory with light staining, sumi, inlays
1 1/4 x 13/16 x 1 15/16 in. (3.1 x 2 x 5 cm)
M.91.250.179
incised: *Rangyoku*

LITERATURE: Bushell, *An Exhibition of Netsuke*, fig. 137, p. 20, and front cover; Bushell, *Netsuke Familiar and Unfamiliar*, fig. 643, p. 208; Phillips, ed., *The Collectors' Encyclopedia of Antiques*, p. 566

This netsuke seems more pigeon than hawk, but in size and heft is perfectly usable. VA

394 | **Lovebirds**

Japan, 19th century
red and gold lacquer
1 3/16 x 1 5/8 x 1 1/2 in. (3 x 4.1 x 3.8 cm)
M.87.263.48

LITERATURE: AMICO, 2000–present; Hurtig, *Masterpieces of Netsuke Art*, fig. 946, p. 222

PROVENANCE: Avery Brundage

Images of lovebirds were sometimes used as talismans to attract the opposite sex. Lacquered objects require many coats, each of which must dry in a humidor before the next is applied. The lacquer treatment on this bird could have been applied long after the original form was carved. VA/HG

394 TOP

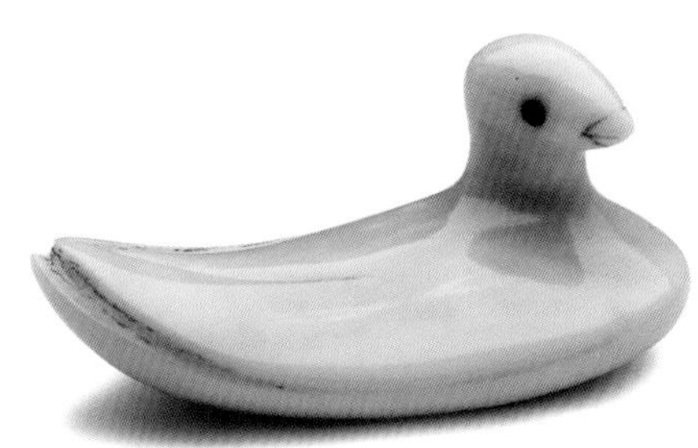

395 | **Simplified Bird**

Chingendō Hidemasa, Japan, active early 19th century
wood with inlays
$1\,{}^{5}/_{16}$ x $1\,{}^{5}/_{16}$ x $1\,{}^{3}/_{16}$ in. (3.4 x 3.3 x 3 cm)
M.91.250.333
incised: *Hidemasa*

LITERATURE: Bushell, "Questions & Answers" (1978c), figs. 6a and b, p. 14; Lazarnick, *Netsuke and Inro Artists*, vol. 1, p. 461

Although Hidemasa often followed late-eighteenth-century carving styles, this netsuke is notable for its simplicity and humor. HG

396 | **Simplified Gull**

Japan, 19th century
ivory with staining, sumi, inlays
$1\,{}^{5}/_{8}$ x 1 x ${}^{15}/_{16}$ in. (4.2 x 2.5 x 2.3 cm)
M.87.263.127

LITERATURE: AMICO, 2000–present; Bushell, *An Exhibition of Netsuke*, fig. 142, p. 20; Bushell, *Netsuke Familiar and Unfamiliar*, fig. 639, p. 207

This abstracted gull looks like a leaf-boat set upon the water. The position of the head and its wide eyes give the bird a gentle aspect. HG

397 | **Abstract Bird**

Japan, 19th century
cryptomeria or cedar wood with inlays
$2\,{}^{9}/_{16}$ x ${}^{15}/_{16}$ x ${}^{7}/_{8}$ in. (6.6 x 2.4 x 2.2 cm)
M.87.263.129

LITERATURE: AMICO, 1999–present; Bushell, "Questions & Answers" (1978d), fig. 20a, p. 44

The strong grain of this wood conveys the bird's motion and speed. HG

398 | **Simplified Quail**

Japan, early 20th century
ivory with sumi, inlays
$1\,^{13}/_{16} \times 1\,^{3}/_{8} \times {}^{15}/_{16}$ in. (4.6 x 3.4 x 2.3 cm)
M.87.263.124

LITERATURE: AMICO, 2000–present; Bushell, *An Exhibition of Netsuke*, fig. 132, p. 43; Bushell, *Netsuke Familiar and Unfamiliar*, fig. 645, p. 208

This quail's faceted surface hints that the swelling form reminded the carver of a gourd or squash. HG

399 | **Resting Swan**

Zōroku, Japan, 1822–1877
mid- to late 19th century
porcelain with celadon glaze
$1\,^{7}/_{8} \times 1 \times 1$ in. (4.8 x 2.6 x 2.5 cm)
M.87.263.54
Impressed: *Zōroku*

LITERATURE: AMICO, 2001–present; Bushell, *The Inrō Handbook*, fig. 85, p. 122

Zōroku based his technique on that used for ancient Korean pottery. VA

400 | **Lotus and Bird**

Ishikawa Rensai, Japan, active mid- to late 19th century
ivory with staining, sumi, inlays; ryūsa type
$1\,^{5}/_{8} \times {}^{1}/_{2}$ in. (4.2 x 1.3 cm)
M.91.250.225
seal form, incised and stained on raised square: *Ren*

LITERATURE: Bushell, *Collectors' Netsuke*, fig. 236, p. 151

PROVENANCE: Fred B. Thomas

Rensai created this composition from several abstractions. For the lotus blossoms, he banded the petals' outer edges in the manner seen in ancient Buddhist symbology. The bird is composed of spirals, hooks, and fragments of curves, giving it great dynamism. HG

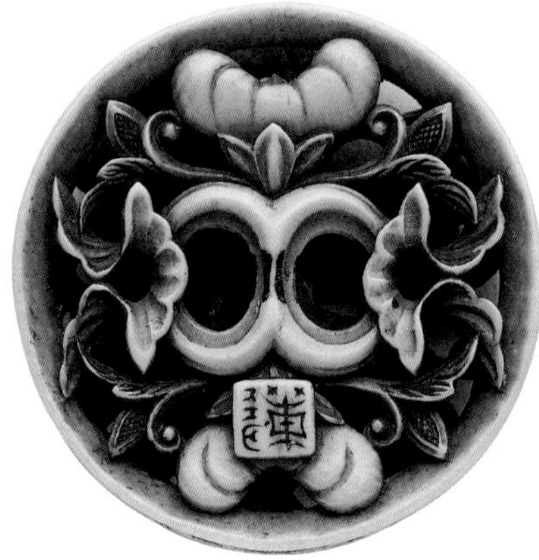

400 BACK

402 | **Head of Hawk**

Japan, late 19th–early 20th century
tiger tooth with inlays
$2\,^{7}/_{8}$ x $1\,^{9}/_{16}$ x $^{13}/_{16}$ in. (7.3 x 4 x 2 cm)
M.91.250.87

LITERATURE: Bushell, *The Wonderful World of Netsuke*, fig. 85, p. 64

PROVENANCE: Kuroda-ya

The material used for this netsuke, a tiger fang, emphasizes the hawk's strength. The unknown artist achieved a strong effect with minimal carving. VA/HG

401 | **Okimono of Falcon**

HARUMITSU, Japan, active circa 1860–1880
wood with inlays
$2\,^{1}/_{4}$ x $1\,^{3}/_{16}$ x $1\,^{1}/_{4}$ in. (5.8 x 3 x 3.1 cm)
M.91.250.178
incised: *Harumitsu*

LITERATURE: Ueda, *The Netsuke Handbook of Ueda Reikichi*, fig. 156, p. 151

Falcons were used by the samurai for hunting; for this reason, in paintings, falcons frequently symbolized the merciless warrior spirit. The branch is cut so that the piece will sit on a flat surface; the protrusions would have hampered its use as a netsuke. HG

402 BACK

403 SIDE

403 | **Cormorant and Young**

Masatoshi (Nakamura Tokisada), Japan, 1915–2001
November 1960
ebony
$1^{15}/_{16}$ x $1^{5}/_{16}$ x $^{7}/_{8}$ in. (5 x 3.3 x 2.2 cm)
M.91.250.92
incised: *Tokisada*

LITERATURE: Bushell, *Collectors' Netsuke*, fig. 349, p. 183; Bushell, *An Exhibition of Netsuke*, fig. 495, p. 81; Bushell, *Masatoshi*, fig. 58, p. 9; Masatoshi, *The Art of Netsuke Carving*, fig. 59, p. 155

The contrast of the voracious sea bird tenderly feeding her young appealed to Masatoshi. This netsuke is a study in interlocking curves, seen in the birds' bodies and beaks and the drooping fish. VA/HG

404 | **Heron**

Illustrated on page 88
Masatoshi (Nakamura Tokisada), Japan, 1915–2001
June 1974
ivory with light staining, sumi, black coral inlays
$1^{7}/_{8}$ x $1^{3}/_{16}$ x $^{7}/_{8}$ in. (4.7 x 3 x 2.2 cm)
M.91.250.89
incised: *Masatoshi*; kakihan

LITERATURE: Bushell, *An Exhibition of Netsuke*, fig. 482, p. 80; Bushell, *Netsuke Familiar and Unfamiliar*, fig. 379, p. 158; Hurtig, "Contemporary Netsuke," p. 24; Masatoshi, *The Art of Netsuke Carving*, fig. 49, p. 152

The lovely simplicity of this piece recalls Mitsuhiro's treatment of a similar subject in *Preening Duck* (CAT. 373). VA

405 | **Lizard on Acorn Branch**

Japan, 18th century
wood with inlays
$1^{1}/_{8}$ x $2^{9}/_{16}$ x $1^{5}/_{8}$ in. (2.9 x 6.5 x 4.1 cm)
M.91.250.139

LITERATURE: Bushell, *An Exhibition of Netsuke*, fig. 224, p. 51; Bushell, *Netsuke Familiar and Unfamiliar*, fig. 483, p. 177

It is said that most Japanese heartily dislike lizards, which may account for their rare appearance in netsuke. Lizards were, however, an ingredient of a popular aphrodisiac, and could be used as a talisman to increase sexual potency. VA/HG

406 | **Lizard and Centipede**

YOSHINAGA, Japan, active before 1781
wood
1 x $2^{1}/_{4}$ x $1^{1}/_{2}$ in. (2.5 x 5.7 x 3.8 cm)
AC1998.249.109
incised: *Yoshinaga*

LITERATURE: Bushell, *An Exhibition of Netsuke*, fig. 225, p. 52; Ueda, *The Netsuke Handbook of Ueda Reikichi*, fig. 109, p. 102

The pairing of a centipede and a lizard is unusual, and its meaning is not known. The centipede is a natural predator of the lizard, and the wilting lotus leaf has long been a Buddhist symbol for the ephemeral nature of existence. HG

407 | **Lizard on Chestnut**

Style of Mitani Gōhō, Japan,
late 18th–early 19th century
wood with inlays
$1^{1}/_{8}$ x $1^{9}/_{16}$ x $1^{3}/_{4}$ in. (2.8 x 3.9 x 4.4 cm)
M.91.250.14
inscription: [undecipherable]

LITERATURE: AMICO, 2001–present; Bushell, *An Exhibition of Netsuke*, fig. 223, p. 51; Bushell, *Netsuke Familiar and Unfamiliar*, fig. 485, p. 178

PROVENANCE: Fujie Tomosaburō

The lizard, whose skin texture is rendered using the "relief carving" (*ukibori*) technique, is typical of the style of Iwami carvers. Although Gōhō lived in Hiroshima, he sculpted in the Iwami manner, working mostly in wood. He was a prolific carver (see Lazarnick, *Netsuke and Inro Artists*, vol. 1, pp. 407–16). VA/HG

408 | **Snake Encircling Turtle**

Japan, early 19th century
wood with inlays
$2^{1}/_{16}$ x $1^{5}/_{8}$ x $1^{5}/_{16}$ in. (5.3 x 4.1 x 3.3 cm)
M.91.250.315

LITERATURE: Bushell, "Questions & Answers" (1976a), fig. 15f, p. 51

A snake encircling a turtle was an emblem of the guardian of the north. The turtle may be the avatar of Vishnu, which sank to the bottom of the sea and became the base of the holy mountain Meru. In the Chinese version of this legend, the turtle is female and the snake male. VA

409 | **Turtle Group**

Kano Tomokazu, Japan, circa 1764/71–circa 1830/43
early 19th century
wood with inlays
1 5/8 x 1 1/4 x 1 1/8 in. (4.1 x 3.2 x 2.9 cm)
M.91.250.254
incised in oval cartouche: *Tomokazu*

Netsuke showing young turtles swarming over their mother's back were extremely popular (cats. 409–11). These compositions could symbolize a desire for many children or a wish for happiness and longevity. Note that the more young the mother carries, the more retracted is her head. This form of self-protection was perhaps a sign of wisdom. These turtle groups are rendered in a naturalistic manner and suggest intent observation by the artists. HG

410 | **Turtle Group**

Ryōichi (or Yoshikazu), Japan, active early to mid-19th century
wood
1 1/2 x 1 5/16 x 1 1/4 in. (3.8 x 3.3 x 3.1 cm)
AC1998.249.40
incised on raised rectangular reserve: *Ryōichi*

LITERATURE: AMICO, 2001–present

See catalogue 409.

411 | **Turtle Group**

Shūkōsai Anraku, Japan, active early to mid-19th century
mid-19th century
ivory with dark staining, sumi, inlays
1 1/4 x 1 5/8 x 1 in. (3.1 x 4.1 x 2.5 cm)
AC1998.249.147
incised: *Anraku*

See catalogue 409.

412 BACK

412 | Long-Tailed Sea Turtles on Craggy Rock

HARA SHŪGETSU (or SHŪGETSU III), Japan, born 1828, active until circa 1880
wood
1 5/8 x 1 3/16 x 1 1/8 in. (4.2 x 3 x 2.8 cm)
AC1998.249.208
seal forms, carved in reserve: *Shūgetsu; Hōgen*

Turtles that had spent many years in the ocean eventually acquired barnacles on their shells. Seaweed would get stuck on the barnacles, forming a raincape-like tail, and turtles exhibiting this phenomenon were called *minogame* (raincape turtles). Minogame were popular long-life symbols in art; in China, the minogame, dragon, *hōō*, and tiger were the Four Supernatural Animals. The loose-grained wood accentuates the subject's antiquity. HG

413 | Frog on Taro Leaf

Illustrated on page 48
SEIYŌDŌ TOMIHARU, Japan, 1733–1811
1782
boxwood
2 13/16 x 1 5/16 x 15/16 in. (7.1 x 3.4 x 2.4 cm)
M.91.250.13
ukibori inscription: *Imo [no] ha kawazu [no] sekyō; Hako-ko tō Juchihō ka Seiyōdō Tomiharu Doshū Kakushi Seigen'an ka ni oite kore [o] chōkoku; Kore toki ni Tenmei mizu no e tora [no] haru nari* / "Design of a frog on a taro leaf; on a spring day of 1782, Seiyōdō Tomiharu carved this at Seigen'an at Kakushi, which is situated at the foot of Juchihō [mountain] and east of Lake Hako in the southern part of the same province"

LITERATURE: AMICO, 2001–present; Atchley, "The Pavilion for Japanese Art in Los Angeles," p. 23; Bushell, *Collectors' Netsuke*, fig. 54, p. 58; Bushell, *An Exhibition of Netsuke*, fig. 59, p. 36; Hill and Johnson, "The Raymond Bushell Netsuke Exhibition," fig. 59, p. 33; Lazarnick, *Netsuke and Inro Artists*, vol. 2, p. 1125

In Asia, frogs and toads are considered clean and wholesome; in art, they are often shown with water plants, especially the lotus. There is a famous legend about the calligrapher Ono no Tōfū and a frog (see CAT. 533), and the poet Bashō's best known haiku is *Furu ike ya / Kawazu tobikomu / Mizu no oto* (An old pond / A frog jumps in— / The sound of water). VA

414 | **Toad Crawling through Leaves**

Naitō Toyomasa, Japan, 1773–1856
wood; ryūsa type
1 5/8 x 13/16 in. (4.1 x 2.1 cm)
AC1998.249.288
incised: *Toyomasa* [altered?]

literature: Hata Akira, "Naitō Toyomasa," fig. 20, p. 35

Toyomasa typically depicted toads with the immortal Gama Sennin (cat. 52). He treats this one, however, much like his *Dragon in Clouds* (cat. 296). Here, the toad crawls through the leaves, which camouflage it. Toyomasa's distinctive stylization of this animal is evident. CD

415 | **Toads on Stone**

Ryūkōsai Jugyoku, Japan, active early to mid-19th century
ivory with staining, narwhal tusk, inlays
1 1/2 x 1 1/8 x 7/8 in. (3.8 x 2.8 x 2.2 cm)
AC1998.249.32
incised and stained: *Jugyoku*
seal form in inlaid carved red lacquer: *no saku* [?] / "made by" or *Yukizumi [?]*

literature: AMICO, 2001–present; Bushell, *Netsuke Familiar and Unfamiliar*, fig. 100, p. 108

In Japanese art, frogs and toads are often used as symbolic references or as allusions to specific legends. When depicted in a natural setting, as this pair is, there is frequently no clear distinction between frogs and toads. This colorful composition of inlaid and stained materials is typical of Jugyoku's work. While the larger toad appears to be wood, it is in fact ivory with heavy staining. CD

416 | **Frogs on Rock**

TSUKAMOTO KYOKUSAI, Japan, active 1868–1926
wood
1 3/4 x 1 1/4 x 7/8 in. (4.4 x 3.1 x 2.2 cm)
M.91.250.127
incised: *Kyokusai*

LITERATURE: Bushell, *Collectors' Netsuke*, fig. 290, p. 161

This netsuke's deep recesses and overhanging rocks are typical of Kyokusai's work. The space between the frogs is deeply carved, clearly differentiating each frog. Japan's flooded rice paddies were the perfect environment for frogs, and their presence came to signify spring rains and a bountiful harvest. CD

417 | **Frog on Well Cover**

SHIGEMASA, Japan, active 1801–1829
wood with staining
1 1/8 x 1 15/16 x 1 7/16 in. (2.8 x 4.9 x 3.7 cm)
M.91.250.45
incised: *Shigemasa*; kakihan

LITERATURE: Bushell, *Collectors' Netsuke*, fig. 103, p. 89; Bushell, *An Exhibition of Netsuke*, fig. 230, p. 52

Shigemasa's favorite subjects were frogs, shells, and snails, and he excelled at carving them. His frogs and snails are usually shown with a bucket, wooden lid, or mushrooms. This piece exemplifies the artist's brilliant use of stain and color to differentiate and emphasize textures and materials. CD

418 | **Frog on Well Cover**

SHIGEMASA, Japan, active 1801–1829
wood
1 9/16 x 1 x 1 in. (3.9 x 2.5 x 2.5 cm)
AC1998.249.26
incised: *Shigemasa*; kakihan

LITERATURE: AMICO, 2001–present; Bushell, *Collectors' Netsuke*, fig. 107, p. 90; Bushell, *An Exhibition of Netsuke*, fig. 231, p. 52

The split well cover in this and the previous piece is characteristic of Shigemasa's netsuke and lends both works an air of naturalism. To heighten the effect, he included the small holes and a broken-off peg that would have held the wooden planks together. CD

419 | **Toad on Roof Tile**

Illustrated on page 49
MATSUDA SUKENAGA, Japan, 1800–1871
mid-19th century
wood with inlays
1 1/4 x 2 x 1 1/2 in. (3.1 x 5.1 x 3.8 cm)
M.91.250.142
incised: *Hida Sukenaga* / "Sukenaga of Hida"; kakihan

LITERATURE: Bushell, "Questions & Answers" (1980a), figs. 3a and b, p. 39

Sukenaga primarily made animal netsuke, most notably snakes and frogs or toads. The latter are typically seen on roof tiles or pumpkin stems, or with a snake and snail. The three characters along this tile's edge read "Tofurō," which was a mansion in Kyūshū. Although Meinertzhagen mentions that there was only one Sukenaga netsuke with a *kakihan*, this piece makes it clear that there are at least two. CD

420 | **Frog on Mushroom**

MATSUDA SUKENAGA, Japan, 1800–1871
mid-19th century
wood with inlays
1 3/4 x 1 1/8 x 7/8 in. (4.4 x 2.8 x 2.2 cm)
AC1998.249.206
incised: *Sukenaga*

Frogs, like mushrooms, proliferate in spring rains. When someone wore a netsuke with this subject, it might convey a desire for fertility. HG

420 SIDE

421 | **Toad on Mushroom**

Japan, mid-19th century
Hirado ware; porcelain with blue and brown glazes
$1^{9}/_{16}$ x $1^{7}/_{16}$ x 1 in. (3.9 x 3.7 x 2.6 cm)
M.87.263.60

LITERATURE: AMICO, 2001–present; Bushell, "Ceramic Netsuke," fig. 2, p. 27

The toad's compact form was appreciated by netsuke artists working in fragile materials, such as porcelain. This netsuke has been hollowed out to make it less susceptible to cracking in the extremely high temperatures of the kiln. Two holes have been carved underneath for the *himotōshi*. CD

422 | **Frogs on Lotus Leaf**

SEIMIN, Japan, active mid- to late 19th century
ivory with staining, sumi
1 x $1^{5}/_{16}$ x $^{15}/_{16}$ in. (2.6 x 3.3 x 2.4 cm)
M.91.250.125
incised: *Seimin*

LITERATURE: Bushell, *An Exhibition of Netsuke*, fig. 156, p. 45

The image of a frog seated on a lotus leaf may be an allusion to a story associated with Emperor Go-Toba (r. 1183–1198), who, annoyed by frogs croaking in his pond, asked them to be quiet. From then on, the frogs in the garden remained silent. HG

423 | **Frog on Lotus Leaf**

NISAI, Japan, late 19th–early 20th century
wood with inlays
1 7/8 x 1 1/2 x 1 1/4 in. (4.7 x 3.8 x 3.1 cm)
AC1998.249.261
incised: *Nisai tō* / "carved by Nisai"

Like the previous piece, this lone frog may allude to the story of Go-Toba. Nisai's work was typically simple and bold; here, however, he has textured the leaf and carved its veins to differentiate the frog from the surface upon which it sits. CD

424 | **Frog on Pumpkin**

NOBUMASA, Japan, active mid-19th century
wood with staining, inlays
1 3/16 x 1 5/16 in. (3 x 3.3 cm)
M.91.250.151
incised on raised rectangle: *Nobumasa*

Netsuke similar to this were carved by artists from the Nagoya and Hida Schools. The small gouges and carefully applied stain used by Nobumasa are also seen in the work of Tomonobu, who is known to have favored this subject. This pumpkin is upside down, enabling Nobumasa to use the pumpkin stem for the *himotōshi*. CD

425 | **Lotus, Frog, and Bird**

ISHIKAWA RENSAI, Japan, active mid- to late 19th century
ivory with staining, inlays; ryūsa type
1 9/16 x 1 3/4 x 5/8 in. (3.9 x 4.4 x 1.6 cm)
M.87.263.38
seal form, carved on raised square: *Ren*

LITERATURE: AMICO, 2000–present; Bushell, *Collectors' Netsuke*, fig. 237, p. 151

In a scene alluding to the transience of life, the kingfisher patiently waits for its prey, in this case, the frog on the lotus leaf below. Rensai, partial to *manjū* and *ryūsa* forms, often depicted frogs amid mushrooms, gourds, or leaves. He was also known to portray religious themes. CD

426 | **Frogs in Clamshell**

Japan, late 19th century
ivory with sumi
netsuke: 7/8 x 1 7/8 x 1 5/8 in. (2.2 x 4.8 x 4.1 cm)
ojime: 13/16 x 1/2 x 1/2 in. (2 x 1.3 x 1.2 cm)
M.91.250.126a–b

LITERATURE: AMICO, 2001–present; Bushell, *Netsuke Familiar and Unfamiliar*, fig. 713, p. 220

Seimin's ivory netsuke typically depict groups of frogs, and this piece is similar in treatment to one of his signed works (CAT. 422). The positioning of the frogs and the deep recesses between them suggest that these pieces may be by Seimin or one of his followers. This netsuke is paired with a matching *ojime*. CD

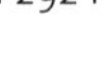

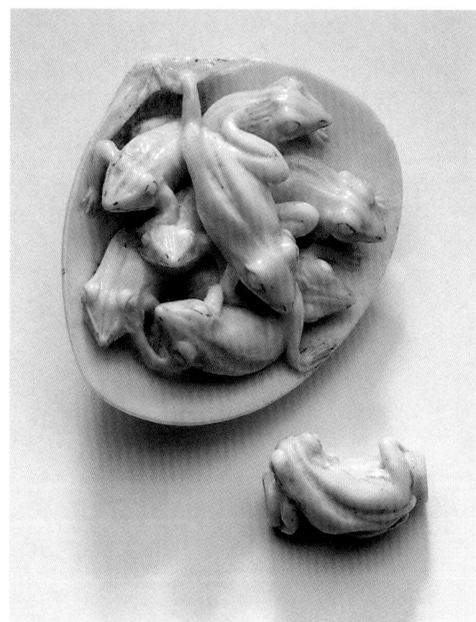

427 | **Abstract Frog**

Japan, 20th century
amber
2 x 1 7/16 x 1 3/8 in. (5.1 x 3.6 x 3.5 cm)
M.91.250.63

LITERATURE: Atchley, "The Pavilion for Japanese Art in Los Angeles," p. 23; Bushell, *An Exhibition of Netsuke*, fig. 371, p. 68; Hurtig, *Masterpieces of Netsuke Art*, fig. 123, pp. 48, 49

While frogs are particularly well suited as subjects for functional netsuke, this artist has further emphasized the creature's compact and rounded form. This treatment is similar to ancient Chinese jade carvings of highly stylized small animals. CD

429

428 | **Weird Frog**

Illustrated on page 90
MASATOSHI (NAKAMURA TOKISADA), Japan, 1915–2001
January 1976
ivory with light staining, sumi, black coral inlays
2 $^1/_4$ x 1 $^5/_{16}$ x $^{15}/_{16}$ in. (5.8 x 3.4 x 2.4 cm)
M.91.250.90
incised: *Masatoshi*

LITERATURE: Bushell, *An Exhibition of Netsuke*, fig. 490, p. 29; Bushell, *Masatoshi*, fig. 310, p. 16; Hill and Johnson, "The Raymond Bushell Netsuke Exhibition," fig. 490, p. 28; Masatoshi, *The Art of Netsuke Carving*, fig. 310, p. 213

This very bizarre frog seems to be scratching itself all over. Masatoshi made several netsuke that, like this one, can only be called weird. VA

429 | **Tadpoles**

SŌKO (MORITA KISABURŌ), Japan, 1879–1943
May 1926
wood with inlays
1 $^7/_8$ x 1 $^3/_{16}$ x $^9/_{16}$ in. (4.8 x 3 x 1.5 cm)
M.91.250.249
incised: *Sōko tō* / "carved by Sōko"
ink on box lid: *Sōko tō* / "carved by Sōko"; *Shōwa toradoshi shoka* / "Shōwa, Year of the Tiger [1926], early summer"
seal on box lid: *Sōko*

LITERATURE: Bushell, *An Exhibition of Netsuke*, fig. 427, p. 75; Bushell, *The Wonderful World of Netsuke*, fig. 87, p. 65

PROVENANCE: Nishiura Shunichi

Sōko was one of the best and most meticulous artists of the Sō School. This fluid design is both pleasing and eminently practical. Tadpoles may represent a desire for many heirs. VA/HG

430 | **Salamander**

Front illustrated on page 88
MASATOSHI (NAKAMURA TOKISADA), Japan, 1915–2001
January 1970
whale tooth with silver nitrate, sumi, black tortoiseshell inlays
2 $^1/_4$ x 1 $^1/_{16}$ x $^1/_2$ in. (5.7 x 2.7 x 1.2 cm)
AC1998.249.189
incised and stained: *Jikishiin* [Masatoshi's art name] *Masatoshi tō* / "carved by Masatoshi"

LITERATURE: Bushell, *Masatoshi*, fig. 196, p. 13; Masatoshi, *The Art of Netsuke Carving*, fig. 196, p. 187

Masatoshi individually carved each nodule of this salamander to convey the texture of the creature's hide. The giant Japanese salamander is five feet long and weighs about forty pounds; its speckled black and brown skin provides camouflage as it searches river bottoms for food. Salamanders were an important source of protein for mountain dwellers until the animals were declared endangered in 1952. VA/HG

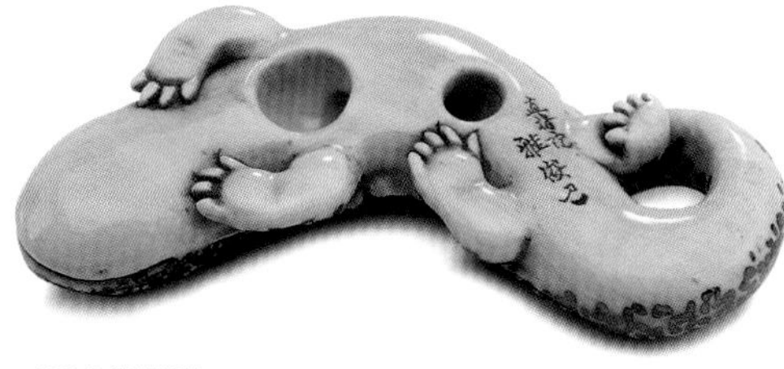

430 BOTTOM

431

431 | **Seal**

Japan (Ainu culture), 18th century
wood with inlays
3 1/2 x 1 x 1 9/16 in. (8.9 x 2.5 x 4 cm)
M.91.250.204

LITERATURE: Bushell, *An Exhibition of Netsuke*, fig. 242, p. 54; Bushell, *Netsuke Familiar and Unfamiliar*, fig. 32, p. 95

The Ainu people were traditionally hunters and gatherers, and motifs from nature are often incorporated into their carvings, textiles, and everyday objects. This carving of a seal is typical of the bold, stylized treatment seen in other Ainu woodwork. The incised lines around this seal's body are reminiscent of the decorative chain stitch often found on Ainu clothing. The linear design rings two cord holes on the seal's back, suggesting that this carving was intended as a netsuke. CD

432 | **Seal**

STYLE OF HŌRAKU, Japan, early 19th century
ebony or persimmon wood
1 3/4 x 1 1/2 x 7/8 in. (4.4 x 3.8 x 2.2 cm)
AC1998.249.23

LITERATURE: AMICO, 2001–present

This piece has characteristics often found in Hōraku's animal and bird netsuke, such as a soft, textured body, with wings or fins given an angular, bold treatment. His animals have large, black eyes and a rounded muzzle or beak, and are typically made of ebony, which works well for this subject. Hōraku is best known for his depictions of another black creature, the bat (CATS. 366, 380). CD

432

433 | **Sea Cow and Young**

Illustrated on page 21
MASATOSHI (NAKAMURA TOKISADA), Japan, 1915–2001
December 1964
boxwood with inlays
2 1/4 x 1 3/16 x 1 1/16 in. (5.8 x 3 x 2.7 cm)
M.91.250.97
incised: *Masatoshi tō* / "carved by Masatoshi"

LITERATURE: Bushell, *Collectors' Netsuke*, fig. 344, p. 182; Bushell, *An Exhibition of Netsuke*, fig. 488, p. 29; Bushell, *Masatoshi*, fig. 89, p. 23; Masatoshi, *The Art of Netsuke Carving*, fig. 89, p. 162

For this piece, Masatoshi was inspired by an illustrated article about the sea cow, or dugong. Dugongs and manatees are similar and are said to have prompted the mermaid legend. Masatoshi seems to have combined elements from the dugong, manatee, mermaid, and his own imagination in rendering this pair, hence Raymond Bushell's accurate description, "fanciful sea cow and young." A hitherto unseen subject in netsuke, this piece is evidence that artists' repertoires expanded as pictures and information became more available. This piece, like the ebony *Carp* (CAT. 437), stands upright on its own. CD

434 | **Whale**

Toshiaki, Japan, active late 19th–early 20th century
ivory with dark staining, sumi, inlays
2 9/16 x 7/8 x 3/4 in. (6.6 x 2.2 x 1.9 cm)
AC1998.249.223
incised and stained: *Toshiaki*

literature: AMICO, 2001–present; Bushell, *Netsuke Familiar and Unfamiliar*, fig. 501, p. 180; Lazarnick, *Netsuke and Inro Artists*, vol. 2, p. 1171

For centuries, whales have been a source of food, baleen combs, and oil in Japan. Whaling was so economically important to coastal Japan that it was said that one whale could save four villages. While other sea life subjects abound in netsuke, whales are far less common. The few whale netsuke that do exist are generally from the late 1800s or 1900s. CD

435 | **Blowfish**

Masanao, Japan, active before 1781
ivory with staining, sumi, inlays
1 13/16 x 1 1/8 x 1 1/8 in. (4.6 x 2.9 x 2.9 cm)
M.91.250.143
incised and stained in oval reserve cartouche: *Masanao*

literature: Bushell, *Collectors' Netsuke*, fig. 22, p. 31; Bushell, *An Exhibition of Netsuke*, fig. 31, p. 33

The globefish (*fugu*), also known as the blowfish or puffer, gets its name from its reaction to a threat: it inflates its body, which is covered with tiny spines. This ability to change form appealed to the Japanese, whose folktales often included mythical creatures with magical powers of transformation. In netsuke, the blowfish is always shown in its puffed-up state, a strikingly functional form. Here Masanao has curled the tail and flattened the fins against the fish's body to create an exceptionally compact sculpture. CD

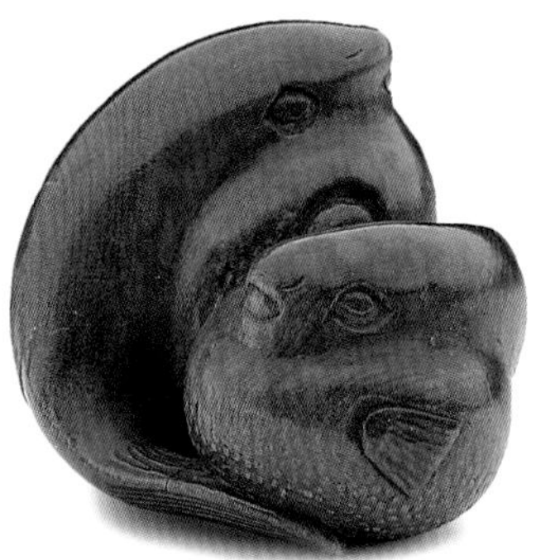

436 | **Pair of Blowfish**

Sari, Japan, active late 18th century
wood with staining
1 9/16 x 1 1/4 x 1 3/16 in. (3.9 x 3.1 x 3 cm)
AC1998.249.22
incised in oval cartouche: *Sari*

LITERATURE: AMICO, 2001–present; Bushell, *Collectors' Netsuke*, fig. 68, p. 63

Sari has combined two blowfish swimming around one another, treating the round bodies and tapering tails much like a "magic jewel" (*tomoe*) motif, which is shaped like a double comma. The expanded bellies of the fish are covered in tiny raised dots in the "relief carving" (*ukibori*) technique, and their backs are spotted with carefully applied stain. The appearance of most blowfish netsuke—the puffed-up body with tiny fins, bulging eyes, and a toothy grin—is humorous, intentionally or not. In many wood netsuke, the teeth are inlaid in ivory, enhancing the comical element. CD

437 | **Carp**

Kiyoshi, Japan, active 19th century
ebony
1 11/16 x 3 3/16 x 7/8 in. (4.3 x 8.2 x 2.2 cm)
M.91.250.34
seal form, incised: *Kiyoshi*

LITERATURE: AMICO, 2001–present; Bushell, *An Exhibition of Netsuke*, fig. 243, p. 22; Bushell, *An Introduction to Netsuke*, fig. 13, p. 48; Hill and Johnson, "The Raymond Bushell Netsuke Exhibition," fig. 243, p. 34; Lazarnick, *Netsuke and Inro Artists*, vol. 1, p. 626; Ueda, *The Netsuke Handbook of Ueda Reikichi*, fig. 191, p. 185

PROVENANCE: Otsuki Yuzuru

As in the next piece, the tail and dorsal fin of this carp have been curled around its body and rounded. This piece meets two criteria for good netsuke: it is compact and stands upright. CD

437 BACK

438 | **Carp and Young**

Masatoshi (Nakamura Tokisada), Japan, 1915–2001
May 1963
boxwood with inlays
2 9/16 x 1 1/4 x 1 1/8 in. (6.6 x 3.2 x 2.9 cm)
M.91.250.93
incised in oval reserve: *Masatoshi*

LITERATURE: Bushell, *Masatoshi*, fig. 170, p. 12; Bushell, *The Wonderful World of Netsuke*, fig. 56, p. 48; Masatoshi, *The Art of Netsuke Carving*, fig. 170, p. 182

PROVENANCE: Kubota Tatsuo

In Japanese art, the carp is often depicted swimming up a waterfall. Its perseverance and strength as it swims against the current have made it a symbol for Boys' Day (the fifth day of the fifth month). This original design by Masatoshi of an adult carp with its young is an unusual subject. The space made by the adult's curled tail makes a perfect hiding place for its offspring. CD

439 | **Catfish**

Japan, 19th century
ivory with staining, inlay; obihasami type
$3^{5}/_{8}$ x 1 x $^{3}/_{8}$ in. (9.3 x 2.5 x 1 cm)
M.90.186.7
incised on inlaid mother-of-pearl plaque:
[undecipherable]

LITERATURE: AMICO, 1999–present

PROVENANCE: Hans Conried; Ann Meselson

This catfish's twisted and curled tail suggests that it is an earthquake fish (*namazu*) in the act of shaking the earth. In a unique treatment of a common subject, this catfish has been designed as an *obihasami* netsuke, with its ends hooked to grasp the upper and lower edges of the obi. The *himotōshi* is beautifully incorporated into the final form: the corners of the fish's mouth are open, allowing the cord to pass through. CD

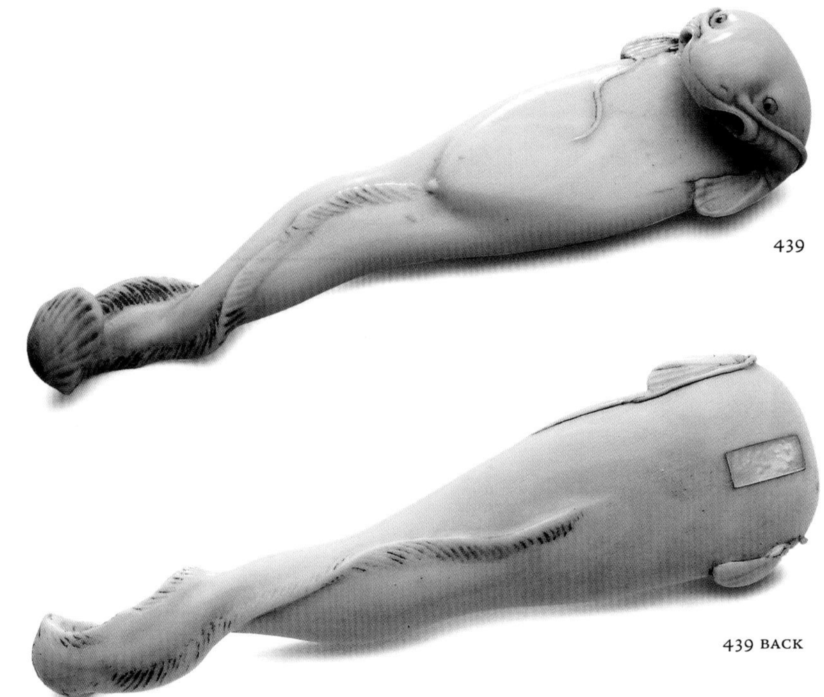

439

439 BACK

440

440 | **Catfish**

Japan, 19th century
boar tusk with staining, sumi
$2^{13}/_{16}$ x $1^{1}/_{8}$ x $^{1}/_{2}$ in. (7.1 x 2.9 x 1.3 cm)
M.91.250.35

LITERATURE: Bushell, *An Exhibition of Netsuke*, fig. 131, p. 43; Bushell, *The Wonderful World of Netsuke*, fig. 55, p. 47

PROVENANCE: Taniguchi Hideo

The form of this catfish, with distinctive barbels on its snout, was dictated by the material. The contours of a boar tusk are visible in the flattened triangular shape with a ridge on top, a curved and tapering tail, and a hollow core that serves as the fish's mouth. The use of boar tusk recalls the work of the Iwami School; however, while this school was known to carve small sea creatures, these tended to be crabs, turtles, and shells, but rarely fish. CD

441 | **Weird Fish**

Japan, 19th century
wood with staining, sumi
$1^{5}/_{8}$ x $1^{5}/_{16}$ x $^{9}/_{16}$ in. (4.1 x 3.4 x 1.5 cm)
AC1998.249.256

LITERATURE: AMICO, 2001–present; Bushell, *An Exhibition of Netsuke*, fig. 245, p. 54; Bushell, *Netsuke Familiar and Unfamiliar*, fig. 726, p. 222

This fish bears the characteristic flat form of a bottom feeder, like a catfish, and its thrashing tail suggests it may be an earthquake fish. However, it lacks the barbels seen on catfish, and its especially large pectoral fins, long dorsal fin, and stripes suggest that it may be a different variety. The nineteenth century saw a growing interest in the realistic depiction of nature, and carvers portrayed animals not seen before in netsuke. CD

442 | **Sea Horse**

Isshin (or Kazuya), Japan, active 19th century
red sandalwood
$3^{1}/_{2}$ x $^{5}/_{8}$ x 1 in. (9 x 1.6 x 2.5 cm)
M.91.250.16
incised: *Isshin* (or *Kazuya*)

LITERATURE: AMICO, 2001–present; Bushell, *An Exhibition of Netsuke*, fig. 246, p. 54; Bushell, *Netsuke Familiar and Unfamiliar*, back cover; Hill and Johnson, "The Raymond Bushell Netsuke Exhibition," fig. 246, p. 34; Ueda, *The Netsuke Handbook of Ueda Reikichi*, fig. 184, p. 181

PROVENANCE: William Wilberforce Winkworth

The sea horse is another unusual subject in netsuke, and the few that do exist are often *sashi* or *obihasami* netsuke, which take advantage of the creature's long and slender shape. This artist has created a shorter, less narrow, and more compact form, with a pair of cord holes on its reverse side. (For other sea horse netsuke, see *Female Kimono and Male Toggles*, p. 64, and Davey, *Netsuke*, fig. 1155, p. 384.) CD

443 | **Pilot Fish**

Japan, 19th century
black persimmon wood with inlays
$3^{3}/_{16}$ x 1 x $^{7}/_{8}$ in. (8.1 x 2.5 x 2.2 cm)
M.90.186.15

LITERATURE: Behrens, *Netsuke*, fig. 1768, pl. 30

PROVENANCE: Mark Severin; Walter Lionel Behrens

This artist seems to have combined elements from various fish to create a unique sea creature. Pictured from above in Behrens's *Netsuke*, this fish with its thrashing tail suggests a catfish, but its accompanying description reads, "a fish of the shark group," an attribution no doubt derived from its fierce expression and inlaid ivory teeth. CD

443

444 | **Cuttlefish**

NISAI, Japan, late 19th–early 20th century
wood
$2^{11}/_{16}$ x $1^{5}/_{8}$ x $1^{5}/_{16}$ in. (6.9 x 4.1 x 3.3 cm)
AC1998.249.279
incised: *Nisai tō* / "carved by Nisai"

LITERATURE: AMICO, 2001–present

When cuttlefish or squid sense a predator, they can camouflage their bodies to match their surroundings. Squids have ten arms, two of which are longer and used to catch prey. Here, one of these long arms is wrapped around the cuttlefish, and the opening it creates on the back serves as the *himotōshi*. (For a similar netsuke by this artist, entitled *Squid*, see Lazarnick, *Netsuke and Inro Artists*, p. 832.) CD

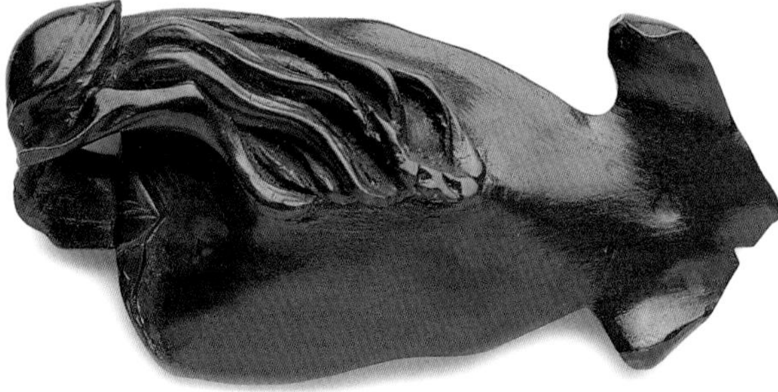

444

444 BACK

445 | Crab and Fern on Boar Tusk

Kakusen, Japan, active early 19th century
boar tusk
$2^{9}/_{16}$ x $^{11}/_{16}$ x $^{1}/_{2}$ in. (6.5 x 1.7 x 1.2 cm)
AC1998.249.204
incised and stained with sumi: *Uno* [or *Sawarano*] *sho Kakusen kore [o] kizamu* / "Kakusen carved this in Uno [or Sawarano] village"; kakihan

LITERATURE: Bushell, *Collectors' Netsuke*, fig. 65, p. 61

PROVENANCE: Imai Kenzō

Artists of the remote province of Iwami, using locally available materials and depicting subjects familiar to them, developed a style with unique characteristics and themes. Their netsuke frequently combine insects, reptiles, snails, and frogs with leaves, shells, or logs. In particular, spiders or centipedes resting on a boar tusk are favorites of Iwami School carvers, though crabs like this were carved by several artists of the school. The inscription stating the name of the carver and where the piece was made is also typical of Iwami netsuke. These inscriptions are often quite long and sometimes include the date of the carving. CD

446 | Stylized Crab

Ono Ryōmin, Japan, active late 19th century
whale tooth
$1^{5}/_{16}$ x 1 x $^{9}/_{16}$ in. (3.3 x 2.6 x 1.5 cm)
M.91.250.182
incised and stained: *Ono Ryōmin*; kakihan; *Kujira no ha o motte chūshō Heike kani* / "abstract Heike crab, [made] of whale tooth"

LITERATURE: Bushell, *An Exhibition of Netsuke*, fig. 138, p. 43; Bushell, *Netsuke Familiar and Unfamiliar*, fig. 636, p. 207; Phillips, ed., *The Collectors' Encyclopedia of Antiques*, p. 570

According to legend, Heike crabs (*Heike kani*), tiny crabs local to Honshū's west coast, are the ghosts of the Heike (Taira) warriors killed in a sea battle in 1185 by the Minamoto family. The word *kani* also means "brave and daring," and the crab became a natural symbol of the warrior class. Ryōmin produced a number of abstract netsuke, in particular a form resembling a chestnut. Numerous theories have been proposed about the subjects of Ryōmin's abstract forms; here the inscription accompanying this crab leaves no doubt. (Examples of Ryōmin's chestnut forms are in Davey, *Netsuke*, fig. 320, p. 112, and Ueda, *The Netsuke Handbook*, fig. 213, p. 196.) CD

447

447 | Octopus

GYOKUZAN, Japan, active early 19th century
red and black Negoro lacquer with inlays
$2\,^1/_4 \times 1\,^3/_4 \times ^7/_8$ in. (5.8 x 4.5 x 2.2 cm)
M.91.250.152
incised: *Gyokuzan*

LITERATURE: AMICO, 2001–present; Bushell, *An Exhibition of Netsuke*, fig. 397, p. 72; Bushell, *Netsuke Familiar and Unfamiliar*, fig. 409, p. 163; Mikoshiba and Bushell, "Netsuke and the *Sōken kishō*," p. 110

PROVENANCE: Sammy Yukuan Lee

Unlike some of the rare sea creature subjects in the Bushell collection, octopuses are common in netsuke and are often shown with their multiple arms amorously embracing a diving girl (CATS. 627–29). While other artists lavished time and effort on depicting individual tentacles and suckers, Gyokuzan embellished his octopus with color. Its smooth tentacles are tucked under its body, with simple drilled holes indicating the suckers. CD

448 | Standing Octopus

IKKYŪ, Japan, active early to mid-19th century
wood with inlays
$2\,^1/_2 \times 1\,^7/_8 \times 1\,^3/_8$ in. (6.4 x 4.7 x 3.5 cm)
M.91.250.41
incised in irregular cartouche: *Ikkyū*

LITERATURE: AMICO, 2001–present; Bushell, *An Exhibition of Netsuke*, fig. 239, p. 54; Bushell, *Netsuke Familiar and Unfamiliar*, back cover; Ueda, *The Netsuke Handbook of Ueda Reikichi*, fig. 175, p. 177

The octopus has often been anthropomorphized, its face animated by a silly, perplexed, or angry expression. This octopus scratches its head in confusion and assumes an upright posture. Though the tentacles appear fragile, Ikkyū has curled and entwined them into a rounded and compact form. CD

449 | **Baby Octopus**

Ōhara Mitsuhiro, Japan, 1810–1875
wood with inlays
$1^{7}/_{16}$ x $1^{1}/_{8}$ x $1^{1}/_{8}$ in. (3.7 x 2.9 x 2.9 cm)
M.91.250.234
incised: *Mitsuhiro*
seal form, incised: *Ōhara*

LITERATURE: Bushell, *Collectors' Netsuke*, fig. 125, p. 96; Bushell, *An Exhibition of Netsuke*, fig. 76, p. 37

PROVENANCE: Eugene Kettering

In the past, this piece was mistakenly identified as an owl; however, upon close inspection, one can see the suggestion of tentacles and suckers. Mitsuhiro made a number of octopus netsuke, usually combining the octopus with a pot or bowl. This netsuke has a playful feel, akin to his treatment of *Raconteur* (CAT. 587). Mitsuhiro described one of his octopus treatments in *Takarabukuro* (fig. 249, p. 162)—"It should be done with a spirit of laughter and humor"—which seems to be the case here. CD

450 | **Octopus**

Illustrated on pages 76 and 82
Japan, mid-19th century
ivory with staining, sumi, double inlays
$^{7}/_{8}$ x 2 x $1^{7}/_{16}$ in. (2.2 x 5.1 x 3.7 cm)
AC1998.249.92

LITERATURE: AMICO, 2001–present; Bushell, *An Exhibition of Netsuke*, fig. 238, p. 22; Phillips, ed., *The Collectors' Encyclopedia of Antiques*, p. 563

In contrast to the three previous octopuses, this example is highly realistic, reflecting the nineteenth-century interest in naturalism. Here the octopus displays no anthropomorphic qualities but rather has been closely observed and rendered with careful attention to its true form. The long, entwined tentacles are very finely executed. (For a detail of the underside, see p. 82.) CD

451 | **Sea Cucumber**

Dōraku (sai), Japan, active early 19th century
wood
$2^{1}/_{4}$ x 1 x $^{1}/_{2}$ in. (5.7 x 2.5 x 1.2 cm)
AC1998.249.28
incised on soft rectangular reserve: *Dōraku*

LITERATURE: AMICO, 2001–present; Bushell, *Netsuke Familiar and Unfamiliar*, fig. 490, p. 179

The sea cucumber, considered a gastronomic delicacy, is also called a sea slug. Dōraku shows concern for naturalism, creating an anatomical study of the creature. The sea cucumber's mouth and flexible musculature, which contracts and expands to give it movement, are all visible on the underside of this netsuke. CD

452 | **Prawn**

TETSUGEN (KYŪSAI), Japan, 1879–1938
ivory
$1^{15}/_{16} \times 1 \times {}^{9}/_{16}$ in. (5 x 2.6 x 1.5 cm)
M.87.263.130
incised in oval cartouche: *Kyūsai*
ink on box lid: *Kyūsai kore [o] kokusu* / "carved by Kyūsai"
seal on box lid: [undecipherable]

LITERATURE: AMICO, 1999–present; Bushell, *Collectors' Netsuke*, fig. 254, p. 154; Bushell, *An Exhibition of Netsuke*, fig. 247, p. 22

Because the bent or doubled-up body of the prawn is said to resemble the curved back of an aged person, this creature has come to symbolize longevity. Prawns are not uncommon in netsuke and are sometimes combined with bamboo as emblems of the New Year. Most often, the prawn is in this curled-up position, a form perfectly suited for netsuke. Kyūsai was an Osaka carver and his materials and fine carving suggest that he was influenced by the work of Kaigyokusai. CD

453

453 | **Bean Pod and Snail**

Japan, 18th century
wood
$2^{9}/_{16} \times 1^{1}/_{2} \times 1^{5}/_{16}$ in. (6.5 x 3.8 x 3.4 cm)
AC1998.249.38

LITERATURE: AMICO, 2001–present; Bushell, *An Exhibition of Netsuke*, fig. 57, p. 35

The snail and bean pod combination is unusual, and there are no known symbolic meanings or fables associated with snails, although Paul Moss refers to them as "agents of decay" (Moss, *Meetings with Remarkable Netsuke*, fig. 96). Netsuke artists found it a happy challenge to reproduce the textures of the snail's body and shell, and this netsuke is a tactile pleasure for the wearer. HG

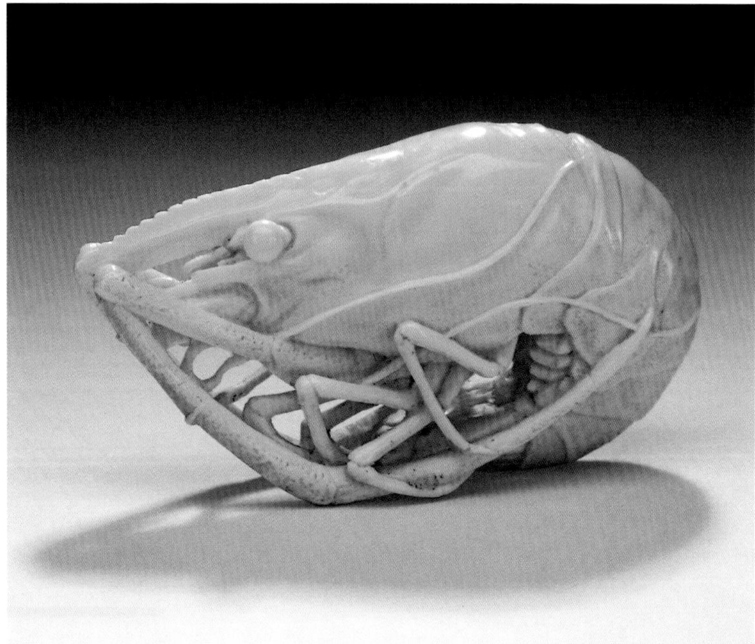

452

454 | **Snail**

Illustrated on page 82
SEIYŌDŌ TOMIHARU, Japan, 1733–1811
ivory with dark staining, sumi
$1^3/_4$ x $1^1/_8$ x $^1/_2$ in. (4.4 x 2.8 x 1.2 cm)
AC1998.249.144
incised and stained in rectangular reserve: *Kawaigawa Seiyōdō Tomiharu kokuari* / "carved by Seiyōdō Tomiharu at the Kawai River"

LITERATURE: Bushell, *Collectors' Netsuke*, fig. 52, p. 57; Hurtig, *Masterpieces of Netsuke Art*, fig. 484, p. 122; Hurtig, *The Netsuke Hall of Fame's Record Breakers*, fig. 51, p. 125; Lazarnick, *Netsuke and Inro Artists*, vol. 2, p. 1132

PROVENANCE: Robert S. Huthart; Imai Kenzō

The Iwami carvers, somewhat isolated in the northwest corner of Japan's main island of Honshū, developed their own distinctive style. They often used boar tusks and etched long inscriptions in fine-line carving (*kebori*). These carvers frequently made small animals, including snails, lizards, spiders, centipedes, and frogs. VA/HG

455

455 | **Snail on Log**

SEIYŌDŌ TOMIHARU, Japan, 1733–1811
circa 1770
wood and *umoregi* (partially fossilized wood)
overall: $2^{15}/_{16}$ x $1^5/_{16}$ x $1^1/_4$ in. (7.5 x 3.3 x 3.1 cm)
snail: $1^7/_{16}$ x $^1/_2$ x 1 in. (3.6 x 1.3 x 2.6 cm)
log: $2^{15}/_{16}$ x $1^5/_{16}$ x $^{13}/_{16}$ in. (7.5 x 3.3 x 2.1 cm)
AC1998.249.168
incised: *Nanajūnanasai Tomiharu chōkoku* / "sculpted by Tomiharu, age thirty-seven" [probably altered later to read "seventy-seven"]

Seiyōdō Tomiharu, who also carved *Snail* (CAT. 454), was prolific. He is noted for his fascination with texture, achieved in the previous piece with the "relief carving" (*ukibori*) technique and *kebori* and achieved here through the contrast of *umoregi* and wood. (For more about Seiyōdō Tomiharu, see Lazarnick, *Netsuke and Inro Artists*, vol. 2, pp. 1113–44.) VA

456 | **Snail on Log**

SHUKUTŌ ATAKANOSUKE, Japan, active late 18th–early 19th century
boar tooth
$1^{15}/_{16}$ x $^3/_4$ x $^9/_{16}$ in. (4.9 x 1.9 x 1.5 cm)
AC1998.249.187
incised and stained: *Seiyōdō Tomiharu otoko Shukutō chōkoku* / "sculpted by Shukutō, the son of Seiyōdō Tomiharu"

LITERATURE: Bushell, *Collectors' Netsuke*, fig. 55, p. 58; Lazarnick, *Netsuke and Inro Artists*, vol. 2, p. 994

This is the only published work by Tomiharu's son, and its subject is similar to those that interested Tomiharu. This netsuke does not display the father's skill in naturalism. HG

456

457 | **Snail on Boar Tusk**

Sasaki Tomiaki, Japan, 1746–after 1827
1787
boar tusk with sumi, water buffalo horn
3$\frac{1}{2}$ x $\frac{13}{16}$ x $\frac{1}{2}$ in. (9 x 2.1 x 1.3 cm)
M.91.250.15
incised and stained with sumi: *Sasaki Tomiaki chōkoku* / "sculpted by Sasaki Tomiaki"
seal form, incised and stained with sumi: *Tomiaki*
incised and stained: *Toki ni Tenmei hi no to hitsuji shoshun* / "in the Tenmei era, Younger Brother of Fire, Year of the Ram [1787], early spring"

LITERATURE: Bushell, *Collectors' Netsuke*, fig. 67, p. 62; Lazarnick, *Netsuke and Inro Artists*, vol. 2, p. 1110; Rasmussen, "Discussion of the Iwami School," front cover

Here Tomiaki has skillfully combined the lustrous materials of boar tusk and water buffalo horn. The polish on the horn emphasizes the moist surface of the snail's shell. HG

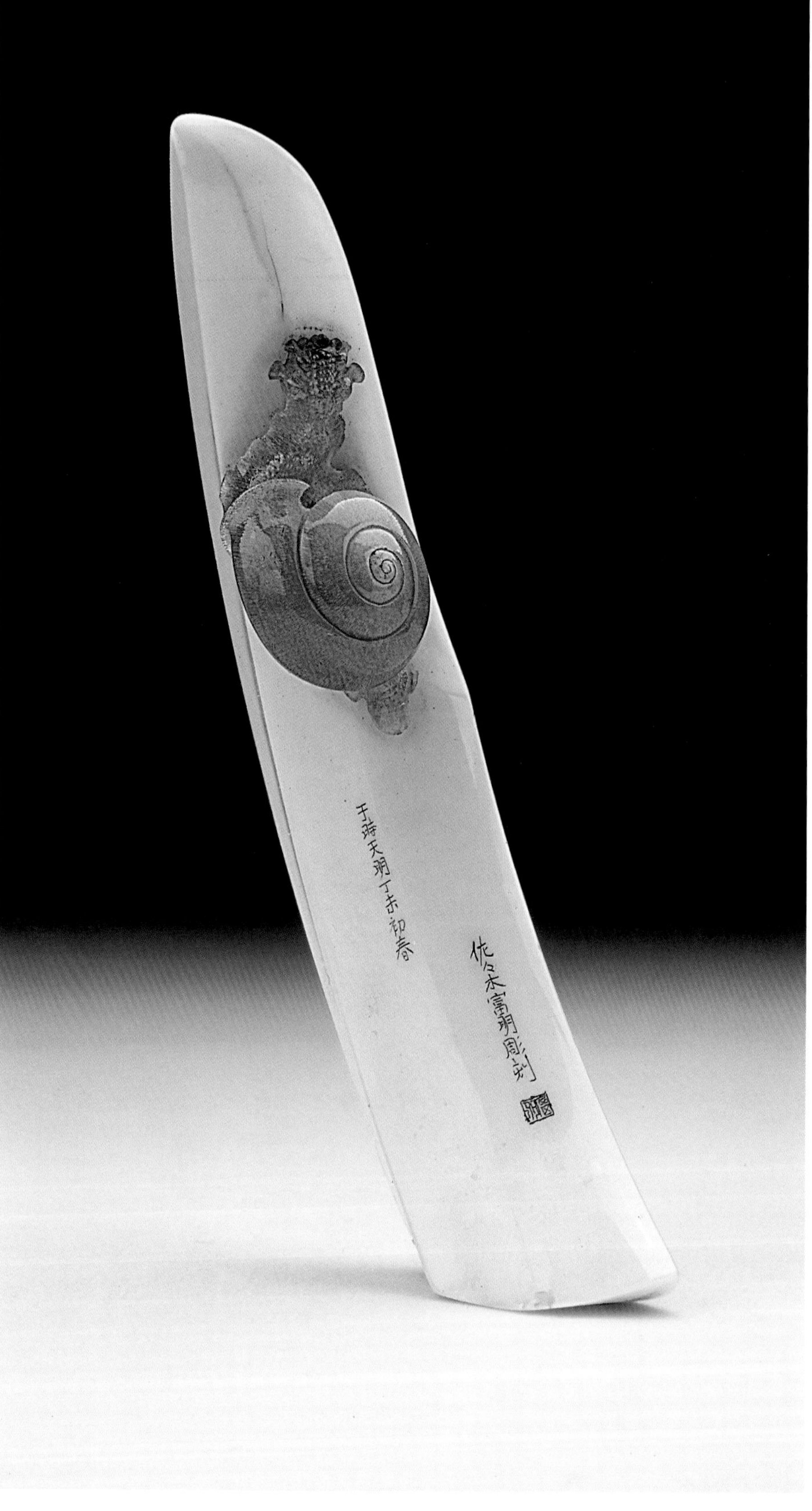

458 BOTTOM

458 | **Snail on Mushrooms**

NAITŌ TOYOMASA, Japan, 1773–1856
wood
2 x 1 7/8 x 1 1/8 in. (5.1 x 4.8 x 2.8 cm)
M.87.263.108
incised: *Toyomasa*

LITERATURE: Bushell, *An Exhibition of Netsuke*, fig. 68, p. 36

PROVENANCE: Adolph Kroch

Like *Bean Pod and Snail* (CAT. 453), the combination of snail and mushrooms could refer to the cycle of death and regeneration. The mushroom was long a symbol for fertility, while the snail aids decay. HG

459 | **Snail on Well Bucket**

Also illustrated on page 255
SHIGEMASA, Japan, active 1801–1829
wood with staining
1 5/8 x 1 5/16 x 1 3/16 in. (4.1 x 3.4 x 3 cm)
AC1998.249.127
incised: *Shigemasa*

LITERATURE: AMICO, 2001–present; Bushell, *Collectors' Netsuke*, fig. 105, p. 89; Bushell, *An Exhibition of Netsuke*, fig. 232, p. 22

Shigemasa excelled in his carving of snails; through the use of stain and color, he has made the shells of all his snails look hard while the bodies appear soft, even moist—as they should. VA

460 | **Snail**

TADATOSHI, Japan, circa 1780–1844
wood
1 5/8 x 1 3/8 x 1 3/16 in. (4.1 x 3.5 x 3 cm)
M.91.250.149
ukibori in rectangular reserve: *Tadatoshi*

LITERATURE: Ueda, *The Netsuke Handbook of Ueda Reikichi*, fig. 121, p. 132

The snail's compact form and opportunities for naturalistic detailing were of central importance to netsuke artists from Nagoya, including Tadatoshi. The snail's body shows an elongated, netlike texture commonly seen in Tadatoshi's work, and the shell was ribbed using the "relief carving" (*ukibori*) technique. HG

460 BOTTOM

461 | **Snail Group**

HIDEHARU, Japan, active late 19th century
wood
2 1/8 x 1 5/8 x 1 5/16 in. (5.4 x 4.1 x 3.4 cm)
AC1998.249.196
incised in rectangular reserve: *Hideharu*

PROVENANCE: Jacques Carré; Daniel Rouviere

Snails were commonly depicted with their bodies fully extended, enabling the artist to work with a number of textural elements and shapes. Hideharu complements the snails' rounded forms with an overall triangular composition. HG

461 SIDE

462 | **Wasp and Hive**

Naitō Toyomasa, Japan, 1773–1856
wood with inlays
1 1/2 x 1 3/8 x 1 1/2 in. (3.8 x 3.5 x 3.8 cm)
M.87.263.106
incised in oval reserve: *Toyomasa*

LITERATURE: Atchley, "The Pavilion for Japanese Art in Los Angeles," p. 23; Ueda, *The Netsuke Handbook of Ueda Reikichi*, fig. 86, p. 91

Toyomasa's mechanical skill is evident in his construction of this netsuke: the larvae are movable and loose, but securely attached. At about the time of Toyomasa's birth, Japanese intellectuals interested in Western studies began collecting specimens and copying scientific drawings of small animals and insects observed under magnification. This had become a widespread practice by the time Toyomasa reached artistic maturity, and it seems that he obtained a wasp and hive to study firsthand before rendering this piece. VA/HG

463 | **Fossilized Insects**

Also illustrated on page 32
Japan, 19th century
cloisonné with gold wire on silver ground, amber
1 11/16 x 1 3/16 x 13/16 in. (4.3 x 3 x 2 cm)
M.91.250.259
in raised metal on reverse: *Ninkan kōshun*

LITERATURE: AMICO, 2001–present; Bushell, *An Exhibition of Netsuke*, fig. 363, p. 68; Bushell, *Netsuke Familiar and Unfamiliar*, fig. 347, p. 151

This is a unique piece. The flat-lobed top surface of amber has been etched with fossilized insects. The sides of the netsuke are densely worked with fine partitions, some filled with remnants of silver leaf. Each long side has a diamond-shaped cartouche with enameled floral décor, and each short side has a solid section of silver topped with floriform partitions. The inscription on the reverse is "written" in seal script using gold wires against a silver ground. Interest in specimen collection had been growing in Japan since the late 1700s. VA/HG

464 | **Centipede**

Nagami Iwao, Japan, active late 18th–early 19th century
1810
boar tusk
$3^{5}/_{8}$ x $1^{1}/_{16}$ x $^{1}/_{2}$ in. (9.3 x 2.7 x 1.2 cm)
M.91.250.206
incised and stained: *Bunka shichi ka no e uma chūka Iwami (no) kuni Mihashi-san ka Ise Ogata be Nagami Iwao chōkoku* / "Bunka 7 [1810], Elder Brother of Metal, Year of the Horse, midsummer; carved by Nagami Iwao near Ise Ogata at the foot of Mt. Mihashi in Iwami province"
seals, incised and stained: *Ei*; *Naga*

LITERATURE: Bushell, *Collectors' Netsuke*, fig. 64, p. 61

Like Seiyōdō Tomiharu, Nagami Iwao was a carver from Iwami. (On Iwami carvers, see CAT. 454.) While most carvers used the open end and hollow core of the tusk for the *himotōshi*, this artist has carved two holes on the reverse side. CD

465 | Pumpkin Stem and Fly

MASATSUGU, Japan, active mid-19th century
boxwood
$1^{5}/_{8}$ x $1^{7}/_{16}$ x $1^{1}/_{4}$ in. (4.1 x 3.7 x 3.2 cm)
M.91.250.221
carved: *Masatsugu*

LITERATURE: AMICO, 2001–present; Atchley, "Kaigyokusai," fig. 21, p. 18; Bushell, *Collectors' Netsuke*, fig. 145, p. 104; Bushell, *An Exhibition of Netsuke*, fig. 90, p. 38; Hurtig, "Kaigyokusai Masatsugu," fig. 50, p. 21

This is possibly an early piece by Kaigyokusai, when he is said to have signed "Masatsugu," though samples of this signature style remain unpublished. It is an unusual design, but his models are seldom conventional. Another Osaka artist, Mitsuhiro, mentions in *Takara-bukuro* (Treasure bag) his idea of carving a fly resting on some vegetal mount, copied exactly from life. VA/HG

466 | Praying Mantis on Bean

BAZAN, Japan, circa 1833–circa 1897
second half of the 19th century
wood
$2^{1}/_{16}$ x $^{15}/_{16}$ x $^{11}/_{16}$ in. (5.3 x 2.4 x 1.7 cm)
AC1998.249.83
incised: *Bazan*

LITERATURE: AMICO, 2001–present; Bushell, *Collectors' Netsuke*, fig. 162, p. 109; Bushell, *An Exhibition of Netsuke*, fig. 249, p. 55

Bazan worked exclusively in wood and never made two netsuke of the same design. The Japanese were very fond of insects, including the praying mantis, which was emblematic of raw courage. However, it was rarely represented in netsuke because of the difficulty of rendering the fragile insect in a sturdy, compact form. VA

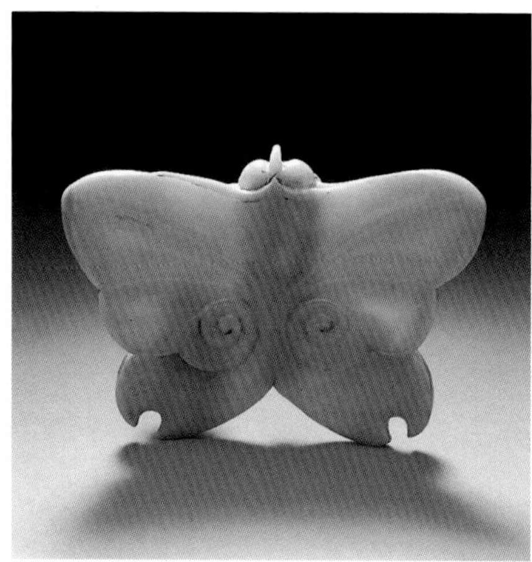

467 | **Moth**

Japan, 19th century
ivory with traces of sumi, oiled
1 3/8 x 2 1/16 x 9/16 in. (3.5 x 5.3 x 1.5 cm)
M.91.250.275

LITERATURE: Bushell, *An Exhibition of Netsuke*, fig. 248, p. 55; Bushell, *The Wonderful World of Netsuke*, fig. 29, p. 32

This unknown artist was obviously skilled in the art of burnishing ivory, here emphasizing the translucency of the material. VA

468 | **Moth**

ATTRIBUTED TO KANŌ NATSUO,
Japan, 1828–1898
gold disk, wood bowl; kagamibuta type
1 1/2 x 3/8 in. (3.8 x 1 cm)
M.87.263.76
incised: *Natsuo* [in hiragana]

LITERATURE: AMICO, 1999–present; Ueda, *The Netsuke Handbook of Ueda Reikichi*, fig. 10, p. 31

Lightly raised gold lines adumbrate the transparent wings of a moth in flight. This piece is attributed to Kanō Natsuo, the most renowned metal artist of the Meiji period. VA

469 | **Cicada on Folded Lotus Leaf**

IWAMI SCHOOL, Japan, late 18th–19th century
boar tusk
3 1/8 x 7/8 x 1/2 in. (7.9 x 2.2 x 1.2 cm)
AC1998.249.179

LITERATURE: Rasmussen, "Discussion of the Iwami School," fig. 11, p. 22

In most boar tusk netsuke from Iwami, the tusk retains its natural form. The treatment is typically an insect or small creature carved in relief upon the tusk, or an incised surface decoration such as a fern or inscription. This tusk, however, has been transformed by the carver into a rolled leaf. The cicada is often pictured in Japanese art. Its cries mostly occur during the hottest summer weather. VA/CD

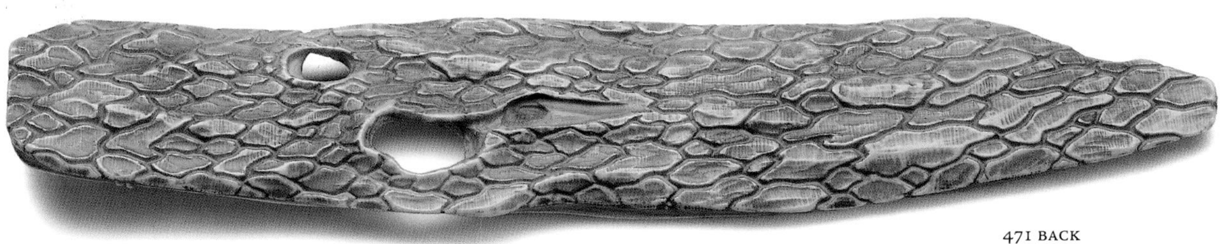

471 BACK

471 | Cicada on Pine Bark

TETSUGEN (KYŪSAI), Japan, 1879–1938
ivory with staining, sumi; sashi type
6 1/2 x 1 1/4 x 1/2 in. (16.6 x 3.1 x 1.3 cm)
M.91.250.76
incised: *Tetsugen saku* / "made by Tetsugen"
seal form, incised: *Tetsu*
ink on box lid: *Tetsugen*
seal on box lid: *Tetsugen*

LITERATURE: Bushell, *An Exhibition of Netsuke*, fig. 251, p. 55

Kyūsai was called Tetsugen until he was thirty-six, when Prince Konoe Fumimaro (1891–1945) conferred on him the name Kyūsai, which he thereafter used as his artist name (*gō*). His work often shows painstakingly accurate textures and proportions, indicating that he used insect specimens as models. VA/HG

470 | Cicada on Pine Cone

HOKUFŪ, Japan, active late 19th century
wood with staining, lacquer
2 3/16 x 1 5/16 x 7/8 in. (5.5 x 3.4 x 2.2 cm)
M.91.250.51
incised: *Hokufū saku nari* / "made by Hokufū"

LITERATURE: Bushell, *An Exhibition of Netsuke*, fig. 250, p. 23; Hurtig, *Masterpieces of Netsuke Art*, fig. 126, p. 48

The cicada, which goes through two metamorphoses in its life cycle, was a seasonal reference. Hokufū has emphasized the insect's varying textures, manipulating the surface with stain and lacquer. HG

472 | **Cicada**

Illustrated on page 7 and 73
MASATOSHI (NAKAMURA TOKISADA), Japan, 1915–2001
October 1975
hippopotamus tooth; sashi type
5 x 3/4 x 3/8 in. (12.7 x 1.9 x 1 cm)
AC1998.249.53
incised and stained: *Jikishiin* [Masatoshi's art name] *Masatoshi*

LITERATURE: AMICO, 2001–present; Bushell, *An Exhibition of Netsuke*, fig. 481, p. 80; Masatoshi, *The Art of Netsuke Carving*, figs. 70a and b, p. 158

Masatoshi deliberately elongated his cicada to make it into a *sashi* netsuke. He claimed he selected hippopotamus tooth for its greater strength in thinly carved areas (Masatoshi, *The Art of Netsuke Carving*, p. 158). VA/HG

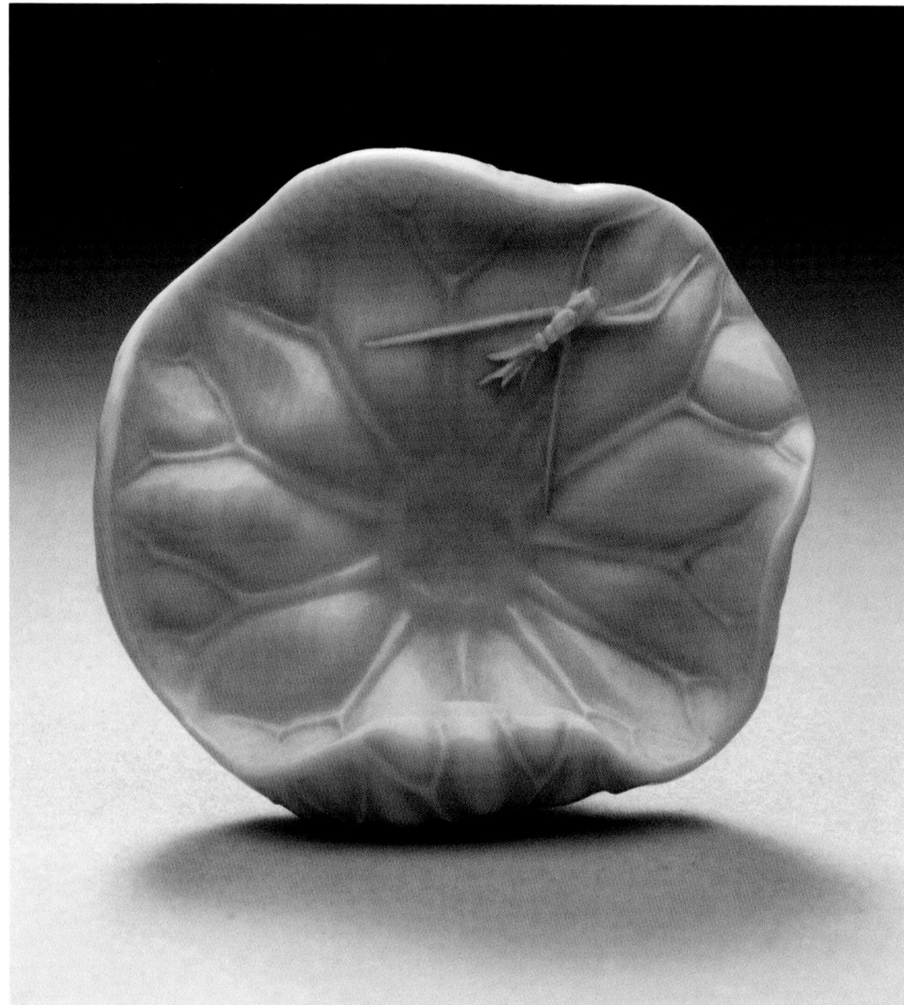

473 | **Water Bug on Lotus Leaf**

SŌKO (MORITA KISABURŌ), Japan, 1879–1943
ivory with light staining, sumi
1 1/2 x 1 5/16 x 3/4 in. (3.8 x 3.4 x 1.9 cm)
AC1998.249.95
incised: *Sōko*

LITERATURE: Bushell, *Collectors' Netsuke*, fig. 281, p. 158; Bushell, *An Exhibition of Netsuke*, fig. 431, p. 75

Flora and fauna were not often portrayed by Sōko, who preferred genre scenes and objects. His choice of a water bug is unusual, likely the result of the ever-expanding sources of information and images to which artists had access. In earlier times, a dragonfly or cricket would have been a more typical subject. CD

474 | **Cricket on Leaf**

Tetsugen (Kyūsai), Japan, 1879–1938
wood with red and black lacquer
$2^{7}/_{16}$ x $^{15}/_{16}$ x $^{7}/_{8}$ in. (6.3 x 2.3 x 2.2 cm)
AC1998.249.209
incised: *Kyūsai tō* / "carved by Kyūsai"; kakihan
ink on box lid: *Kyūsai kore o kizamu* / "Kyūsai carved this"
seal on box lid: *Kyū*

The cricket is an auspicious symbol, and its chirrups are a sign of approaching autumn and the cessation of summer's oppressive heat. VA

475 | **Spider on Boar Tusk**

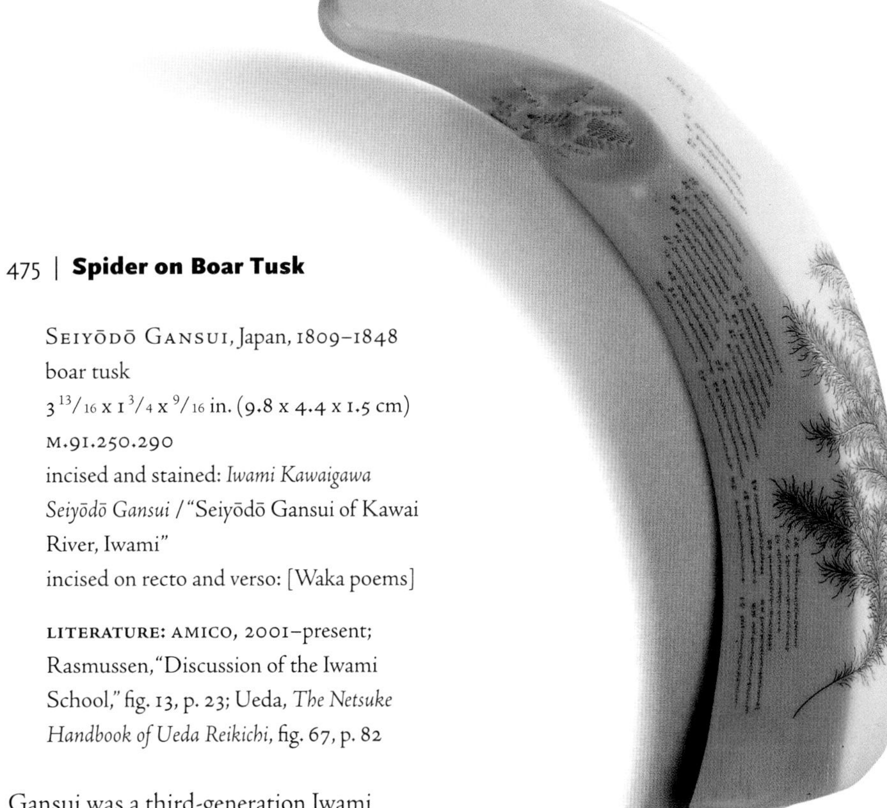

Seiyōdō Gansui, Japan, 1809–1848
boar tusk
$3^{13}/_{16}$ x $1^{3}/_{4}$ x $^{9}/_{16}$ in. (9.8 x 4.4 x 1.5 cm)
M.91.250.290
incised and stained: *Iwami Kawaigawa Seiyōdō Gansui* / "Seiyōdō Gansui of Kawai River, Iwami"
incised on recto and verso: [Waka poems]

LITERATURE: AMICO, 2001–present; Rasmussen, "Discussion of the Iwami School," fig. 13, p. 23; Ueda, *The Netsuke Handbook of Ueda Reikichi*, fig. 67, p. 82

Gansui was a third-generation Iwami carver, reputedly the grandson of Tomiharu (see CAT. 455). Because he died young, his output was limited. This netsuke is a fine example of the characteristic fine-line carving (*kebori*) inscriptions that many Iwami carvers incorporated into their designs. (A similar example by this artist, though without the inscribed poetry, is in Earle, *The Robert S. Huthart Collection of Iwami Netsuke*, pl. 138, p. 159.) VA/CD

Flowers and Other Plants

THROUGHOUT HISTORY, THE JAPANESE, like other peoples, have creatively expressed the beauty and poignancy of the cycle of birth, death, and regeneration, which is most evident during seasonal changes. In Japan, the four seasons are marked by a traditional array of flowers; for example, blossoming cherry from late March to early April and chrysanthemums in early autumn. In all East Asian countries, plants not subject to this brief seasonal efflorescence, such as pine, cedar, and bamboo, are held in special regard for their seeming invincibility to the cycle of nature.

Many plants and flowers also have deeper symbolic meanings, several of which were adopted from China. The Three Friends of Winter (pine, plum, and bamboo) represent comrades that remain faithful through turbulent times (CAT. 476). The pine and bamboo had further significance as emblems of immortality: Pinesap was an ingredient in Daoist immortality elixirs, and bamboo was resilient against variations of weather.

The chrysanthemum (*kiku*), which symbolizes long life and integrity, is in Chinese tradition associated with elderly gentlemen living in seclusion (Baird, *Symbols of Japan*, p. 75) and was adopted as an emblem of the imperial family (CATS. 478–81).

Although the cherry blossom (CAT. 482) is currently the flower most commonly identified with Japan, the blossoming plum (CAT. 485) was the favored subject in Japanese poetry from the beginning of the sixth century until the beginning of Heian period (794–1185). During the Heian period, the elite favored imagery of transient beauty. The popularity of the plum, an evergreen, waned, replaced by the more ephemeral cherry blossom, which put on a fantastic floral display for about a week in spring. This made the cherry blossom the perfect metaphor for aging and the passing of all beauty, or for the death of a beautiful young warrior.

LEFT: *Cherry Blossom and Bud* (CAT. 482); RIGHT: *Blade of Grass* (CAT. 492)

The peony (CAT. 484) was also of primary importance in East Asian art. It was considered "king of all flowers" and, when paired with the king of beasts, the Chinese lion, was considered a felicitous wish for power and wealth.

In East Asian art, gourds (CATS. 487–88) were sometimes used as symbols for fall and for fertility. They also functioned as containers, and by extension as symbols for Daoist immortals who carried immortality elixirs. According to legend, the gourds of two Daoist immortals contained a mule and an entire world, respectively (see CATS. 65, 78). Other plants with multiple seeds, such as the pomegranate (CAT. 489), also had fertility symbolism.

Scenes of famous places (*meisho-e*), one of the oldest pictorial themes in Japanese art, were rarely produced in netsuke. Of the Bushell collection's four landscape netsuke (CATS. 493–96), two portray specific sites in Japan and two depict imaginary Chinese-style mountain retreats that may represent Mt. Sumeru, the mythical Buddhist mountain atop the axis of the world. *Rakan* (the most worthy direct disciples of the historical Buddha) are often depicted in mountain retreats that represent Mt. Sumeru.

The Japanese sites are Shinto sanctuaries. Both Itsukushima and Mt. Fuji are renowned for their spectacular beauty, and this inspired the belief that *kami* (divine spirits) reside in them. Itsukushima was the family shrine of the Taira clan, which was defeated in 1185 during the great war to rule the country. Mt. Fuji, considered a smaller manifestation of Mt. Sumeru, is worshiped in both Shinto and Buddhist faiths. Pilgrims frequent its shrines and temples, and circumambulate the mountain to symbolize the path and stages to enlightenment.

476 | **Pine, Plum, and Bamboo**

Ōhara Mitsuhiro, Japan, 1810–1875
ivory with sumi; manjū type
$1^{5}/_{8}$ x $1^{1}/_{4}$ x $^{13}/_{16}$ in. (4.2 x 3.2 x 2.1 cm)
M.91.250.237
incised and stained: *Mitsuhiro*
seal form, incised and stained: *Ōhara*

LITERATURE: Bushell, *An Exhibition of Netsuke*, fig. 74, p. 37; Bushell, *The Inrō Handbook*, fig. 23, p. 41

Many symbols and design motifs found in Japanese art originated in China, including this plant grouping. The combination of pine, plum, and bamboo, known as Three Friends of Winter (*shōchikubai*), is a symbol of longevity, and it has always been highly popular in Japan. Mitsuhiro has combined the three in a unique composition with the pinecone and plum blossom nestled in a node of bamboo. This center section is removable and contains the *himotōshi*. Mitsuhiro's bamboo shoots and nodes in particular are highly realistic, and he wrote in *Takarabukuro* (Treasure bag) that he aimed to create an "exact copy." CD

477 | **Insects amid Autumn Flowers and Grasses**

Japan, mid- to late 19th century
ivory with staining, sumi; ryūsa type
$^{13}/_{16}$ x $1^{1}/_{8}$ in. (2 x 2.8 cm)
AC1998.249.301

LITERATURE: AMICO, 2001–present

The Seven Grasses of Autumn (*aki no nanakusa*) is an original Japanese grouping from the eighth century. These grasses, which include flowers as well, are often combined with other symbols of the season, such as the butterfly, dragonfly, and cricket, all of which are carved around this netsuke. Above and below this scene are highly decorative borders. The bottom is a stylized flower design with a hole through its center for the cord. The top is covered in an overall diaper pattern with a removable flower in the center that conceals the channel for the cord. CD

478 | **Chrysanthemums and Butterfly**

Japan, late 19th century
wood with ivory, tortoiseshell, mother-of-pearl inlays; manjū type
$1^{5}/_{8}$ x $^{7}/_{8}$ in. (4.1 x 2.2 cm)
M.87.263.36

LITERATURE: AMICO, 2000–present; Bushell, *Netsuke Familiar and Unfamiliar*, fig. 277, p. 141

In addition to their symbolic significance, the chrysanthemum and butterfly were always favored by the Japanese for their beauty and elegance. Depicted in a delicate, realistic manner or stylized, they are seen in paintings and other works of art and often used in a repeating pattern to decorate lacquers and textiles. Here, the chrysanthemum's beauty is enhanced by the lustrous materials and the *shibayama* technique of embellishing the surface with inlaid materials, developed by the artist Shibayama I (Ōnogi Senzō, fl. 1772–1780). Shibayama had many followers who employed this style of decoration. CD

479 | **Chrysanthemum in Flower Vase**

Japan, late 19th century
wood with gold, coral, mother-of-pearl, metal inlays; manjū type
1 9/16 x 1 1/8 in. (4 x 2.8 cm)
AC1998.249.240

LITERATURE: AMICO, 2001–present; Bushell, *Netsuke Familiar and Unfamiliar*, fig. 292, p. 143

Executed in the same inlay technique as the previous piece (CAT. 478), this stem of chrysanthemums is shown in a flower vase (*hanaire*). Containers like this were placed in the alcove (*tokonoma*) of a tea room during tea ceremonies to hold flowers appropriate for the season, in this case autumn. CD

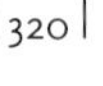

480 | **Chrysanthemum**

TSUKAMOTO KYOKUSAI, Japan, active 1868–1926
wood
1 7/16 x 7/8 in. (3.6 x 2.2 cm)
M.91.250.309
incised in oval cartouche: *Kyokusai*

LITERATURE: AMICO, 2001–present; Bushell, *Collectors' Netsuke*, fig. 291, p. 161; Bushell, *An Exhibition of Netsuke*, fig. 443, p. 76

Kyokusai created many netsuke such as flowers, birdcages, and baskets that had tiny apertures and, in some cases, thin, overlapping, or layered pieces. The multiple layers of petals on this chrysanthemum (*kiku*) blossom are finely carved, one curled atop another. Known for his painstaking realism, Kyokusai apparently favored this treatment for his flower subjects, several of which are in the Bushell collection (also CATS. 482–83). In all of these flower netsuke (CATS. 480–84), the *himotōshi* were fashioned by an opening between the stem and flower. CD

480 BACK

481 | **Chrysanthemum**

Tetsugen (Kyūsai), Japan,
1879–1938
wood
$1^{7}/_{16}$ x $^{11}/_{16}$ in. (3.6 x 1.7 cm)
AC1998.249.249
incised: *Tetsugen*

LITERATURE: Bushell, *Collectors' Netsuke*, fig. 251, p. 153

While its curling and tangled petals are reminiscent of the previous piece, this flower netsuke's more compact and less delicate structure suggests that it was intended for use, not display. Signed "Tetsugen," a signature Kyūsai used until age thirty-six, this piece dates well into the era when the functional aspects of netsuke were hardly a concern for *netsukeshi*. Foreigners were the primary netsuke market in the late 1800s and early 1900s, although netsuke were also commissioned by wealthy Japanese patrons who wore these show pieces on special occasions or to formal events. CD

482 | **Cherry Blossom and Bud**

Illustrated on page 316
Tsukamoto Kyokusai, Japan,
active 1868–1926
ivory with light staining
$1^{7}/_{16}$ x $1^{3}/_{16}$ x $^{5}/_{8}$ in. (3.6 x 3 x 1.6 cm)
M.91.250.207
incised: *Kyokusai*

LITERATURE: Bushell, *Collectors' Netsuke*, fig. 293, p. 161

Like the chrysanthemum (CAT. 480), this cherry blossom and the following camellia reiterate Kyokusai's penchant for extremely intricate carving. The blossoms of the cherry tree have long been Japan's most highly regarded flower and, also like the chrysanthemum, have been represented in art and used as a decorative motif since the Heian period (794–1185). On the tree, cherry blossoms appear in bunches and are often likened to clouds and, at the end of their short lives, to snow covering the ground. Perhaps alluding to this characteristic blooming en masse, Kyokusai has grouped a full blossom with a bud yet to open. CD

483

483 | **Camellia**

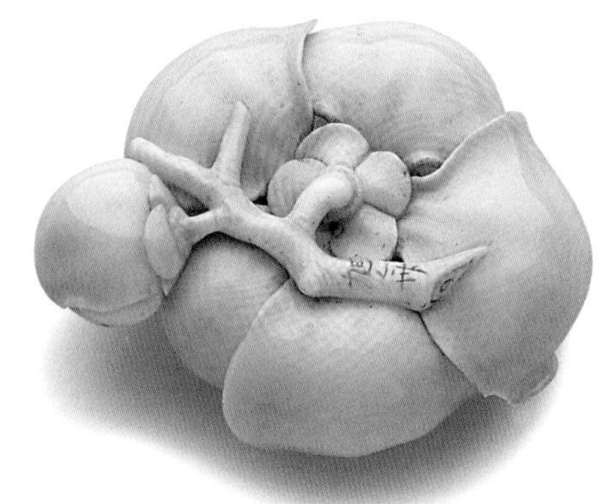

483 BACK

Tsukamoto Kyokusai, Japan, active 1868–1926
ivory with light staining, sumi
1 3/4 x 1 7/16 x 11/16 in.
(4.4 x 3.6 x 1.8 cm)
AC1998.249.86
incised and lightly stained: *Kyokusai*

LITERATURE: AMICO, 2001–present; Bushell, *An Exhibition of Netsuke*, fig. 444, p. 27; Bushell, *Netsuke Familiar and Unfamiliar*, back cover; Hill and Johnson, "The Raymond Bushell Netsuke Exhibition," fig. 444, p. 29; Ueda, *The Netsuke Handbook of Ueda Reikichi*, fig. 166, p. 156

An evergreen that blooms in winter, the camellia represents that season and, as early as the fourth and fifth century, it was considered a sacred plant. While its beautiful flower was highly admired and often incorporated into design motifs used on lacquer, ceramics, and textiles, it was not appreciated by the samurai class. The camellia's full blossoms suddenly break off at the height of its beauty—an uncomfortable suggestion of the beheading of a samurai. When this piece was carved, the samurai class no longer existed; this netsuke was likely made for the foreign market. CD

484 | **Windblown Peony**

Illustrated on page 29
Sōko (Morita Kisaburō), Japan, 1879–1943
1993
wood
1 3/4 x 1 7/16 x 7/8 in. (4.5 x 3.7 x 2.2 cm)
M.91.250.78
incised: *Sōko*
ink on box lid: *Kibori mizu no to tori aki* / "carved wood netsuke, autumn 1933"; *Sōko saku* / "made by Sōko"
seal on box lid: *Sōko*

LITERATURE: AMICO, 2001–present; Atchley, "The Pavilion for Japanese Art in Los Angeles," p. 24; Bushell, *An Exhibition of Netsuke*, fig. 430, p. 27; Hurtig, "Collecting Legends," fig. 8, p. 17

Sōko excelled at depicting this type of subject matter—flowers and other objects reproduced almost life-size. Working in the early to mid-1900s, Sōko did not concern himself a great deal with functional considerations, instead creating netsuke that were often too fragile for use. Like Kyokusai, Sōko employed deep undercutting to separate the petals and carve the stamen. CD

485 | **Plum Branch and Blossoms**

Illustrated on page 21
Sōko (Morita Kisaburō), Japan, 1879–1943
ivory with staining, lacquer inlay;
sashi type
5 5/8 x 7/8 x 7/16 in. (14.3 x 2.2 x 1.1 cm)
M.91.250.79
incised: *Sōko*
seal form in inlaid carved red lacquer: *Sō*

LITERATURE: Bushell, *Collectors' Netsuke*, fig. 277, p. 158; Bushell, *An Exhibition of Netsuke*, fig. 435, p. 75

Before the cherry blossom became the favored flower in Japanese art and poetry, that distinction belonged to the plum. A symbol of longevity, it is often grouped with the pine and bamboo (Three Friends of Winter). A flowering plum is sometimes added to a *kadomatsu*, an arrangement of specific plants used as a decoration for the New Year. This very thin *sashi* netsuke has a slight curve that could comfortably tuck into an obi. The surface is subtly carved with very shallow grooves mimicking the bark of the plum tree. CD

486 | **Pumpkin**

Illustrated on page 50
Japan, 19th century
Hirado ware; porcelain with blue glaze
1 3/4 x 1 5/16 x 1 1/4 in.
(4.4 x 3.3 x 3.1 cm)
M.87.263.59

LITERATURE: AMICO, 2001–present; Bushell, "Ceramic Netsuke," fig. 1, p. 26; Bushell, *Netsuke Familiar and Unfamiliar*, fig. 451, p. 171

Ivory and wood were by far the most commonly used materials in netsuke production. In the 1800s, however, to meet increasing demand, mask carvers and artists working in metal and ceramic also began to produce netsuke. Ceramic netsuke were made by kilns all over Japan, with most originating in the Hirado fief in Kyūshū. Porcelain, fired at a higher temperature than other ceramics, has a hard, smooth surface; when sculpted in a compact, rounded form—as is this pumpkin—it is suited for use as a netsuke. CD

487 | **Gourd**

Japan, 19th century
gourd, metal
2 3/8 x 1 x 7/8 in. (6 x 2.6 x 2.2 cm)
AC1998.249.239

LITERATURE: Bushell, *Netsuke Familiar and Unfamiliar*, fig. 169, p. 120

Before artists began carving miniature sculptures for use as netsuke, small, readily available objects such as shells, pieces of root or twigs, and gourds were used to support "hanging things" (*sagemono*). Gourds were plentiful and were of a suitable size and shape; in addition, they were useful containers for medicine or sake and considered to be talismans. It was not long before the Japanese began shaping gourds by wrapping metal bands around them as they grew. A metal cord ring was then attached to the band to complete the netsuke. This particular gourd was apparently banded twice, producing its unique shape. CD

488 | **Gooseneck Gourd**

Illustrated on page 86
Ōhara Mitsuhiro, Japan, 1810–1875
ivory with light staining, sumi
1 5/16 x 1 1/16 x 3/4 in. (3.4 x 2.7 x 1.9 cm)
AC1998.249.191
incised and stained: *Mitsuhiro*

LITERATURE: Bushell, *Netsuke Familiar and Unfamiliar*, fig. 164, p. 119; Phillips, ed., *The Collectors' Encyclopedia of Antiques*, p. 568

The gourd, a favorite of early netsuke wearers, seems to have been a preferred subject of Mitsuhiro as well, who rendered them in combination with other objects or hollowed them out like miniature cups. Here he has taken a solitary gourd and created a very simple form suggesting the shape of a goose. In his *Takarabukuro* (Treasure bag), notes by Mitsuhiro accompany several gourd netsuke. An "interesting" form and the "appropriate" staining and finishing of the surface were evidently his priorities in creating these gourd pieces. CD

489 | **Pomegranates**

Nisai, Japan, late 19th–early 20th century
wood
1 13/16 x 1 5/16 x 1 1/4 in. (4.6 x 3.3 x 3.2 cm)
AC1998.249.277
incised: *Nisai tō* / "carved by Nisai"

Owing to its numerous seeds, the pomegranate represents the wish for many offspring, and Nisai may be alluding to this symbolism. In contrast to the highly realistic pieces produced during the Meiji period (1615–1868), the carving style here is bold, more akin to early netsuke. The form is solid and the seeds inside the broken fruit are roughly carved. While perhaps not having great appeal to the export market, Nisai's simple netsuke are distinctive and remarkable during a period teeming with delicate and dainty carvings; they were likely favored by the Japanese. CD

490 | **Strung Acorns**

Sōko (Morita Kisaburō), Japan, 1879–1943
wood with staining
1 5/8 x 1 5/16 x 1/2 in. (4.1 x 3.4 x 1.3 cm)
M.91.250.251
incised: *Sōko*

LITERATURE: Bushell, *Netsuke Familiar and Unfamiliar*, fig. 547, p. 190

In stark contrast to the previous netsuke's bold carving style, this group of nuts is extremely realistic. Through the use of intricately carved textures and careful staining, Sōko has masterfully conveyed the mass and weight of the nuts, contrasting them with the thin, delicate leaves and stems. The careful finishing of every surface attests to Sōko's unparalleled attention to execution. These acorn-like nuts (*donguri*) were strung by Japanese children as beads or toys. CD

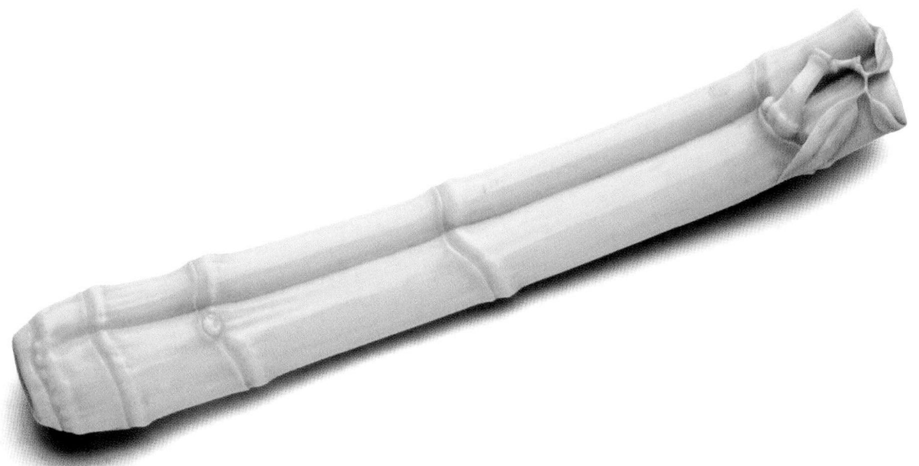

491 | **Bamboo**

Sōko (Morita Kisaburō), Japan, 1879–1943
December 1929
ivory with light staining, sumi; sashi type
$5\,^{3}/_{8}$ x $^{13}/_{16}$ x $^{7}/_{16}$ in. (13.7 x 2.1 x 1.1 cm)
M.91.250.106
incised: *Sōko tō* / "carved by Sōko"
incised: *Shōwa tsuchi no to mi gokugetsu* / "Shōwa, Younger Brother of Earth, Year of the Serpent, final month [December 1929]"

LITERATURE: Bushell, *Collectors' Netsuke*, fig. 275, p. 158

The treatment of this stalk of bamboo is much like that of *Plum Branch and Blossoms* (CAT. 485, illustrated on p. 21). The overall size and formation of the *himotōshi* are similar, and again Sōko's delicate touch is evident in the subtle depiction of the numerous nodes along the bamboo. CD

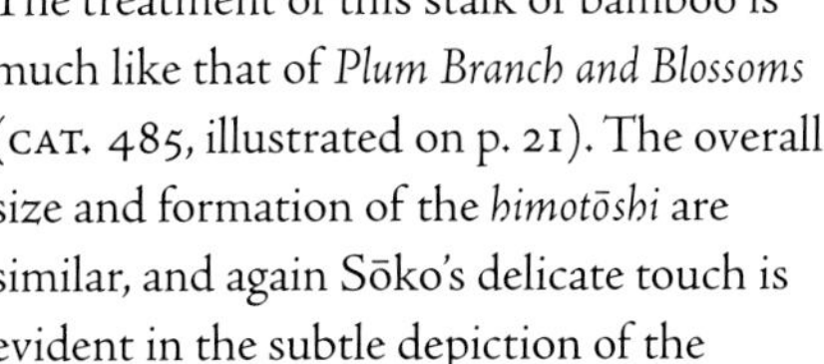

491 BACK

492 | **Blade of Grass**

Illustrated on page 317
Masatoshi (Nakamura Tokisada), Japan, 1915–2001
August 1975
ivory; sashi type
$4\,^{1}/_{2}$ x $^{13}/_{16}$ x $^{7}/_{16}$ in. (11.4 x 2 x 1.1 cm)
M.91.250.96
incised: *Masatoshi*; kakihan

LITERATURE: Bushell, *An Exhibition of Netsuke*, fig. 480, p. 80, and back cover; Bushell, *Masatoshi*, fig. 78, p. 10; Hill and Johnson, "The Raymond Bushell Netsuke Exhibition," fig. 480, p. 36; Hurtig, "Contemporary Netsuke," p. 24; Masatoshi, *The Art of Netsuke Carving*, fig. 78, p. 160

Masatoshi, struck by the simplicity of an *okimono* of a similar subject by Kaigyokusai, was inspired to create his own version. It was of utmost importance to Masatoshi that the *himotōshi* not interfere with the design and that cord holes be placed so that the netsuke was positioned correctly on the obi when worn. He preferred a natural opening through which to pass the cord. If that was not possible, he hid the holes. This piece, made of a fine, lustrous core section of ivory, was designed so that the looped end would serve as the himotōshi. CD

493 | **Pavilions in Forest Retreat**

Gotō Masayoshi, Japan, 1819–1848
wood
$2\,^{1}/_{4} \times 1\,^{11}/_{16} \times 1\,^{5}/_{8}$ in. (5.7 x 4.3 x 4.2 cm)
M.91.250.269
incised in oval cartouche: *Gotō Masayoshi*

LITERATURE: Bushell, *An Exhibition of Netsuke*, fig. 155, p. 45; Hill and Johnson, "The Raymond Bushell Netsuke Exhibition," fig. 155, p. 33; Ueda, *The Netsuke Handbook of Ueda Reikichi*, fig. 98, p. 96

This mountain villa with terraced fields is surmounted by wavelike forms that could represent either heavy mist or ocean spray. If the latter, the netsuke would be a fanciful rendition of the palace of Ryūjin, the Ruler of Seas and Tides (see CATS. 515–20). HG

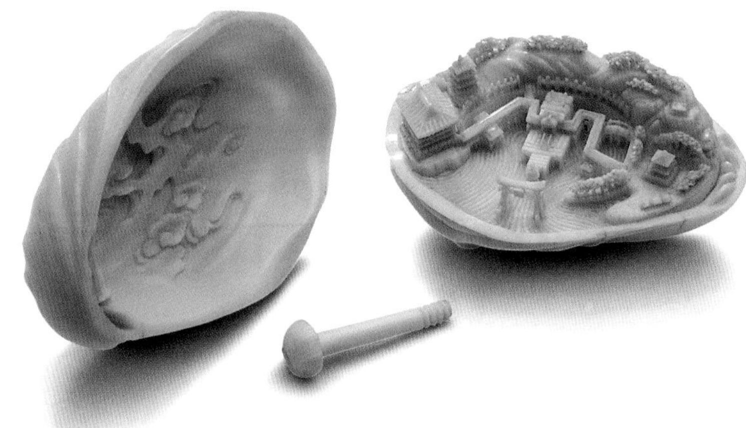

494 | **Oyster Shell with Interior Carved As View of Itsukushima Shrine**

Kaigyokusai Masatsugu, Japan, 1813–1892
ivory
$1\,^{3}/_{4} \times 1\,^{3}/_{16} \times 1\,^{1}/_{16}$ in. (4.4 x 3 x 2.7 cm)
M.91.250.220a–c
incised and lightly stained: *Kaigyokusai Masatsugu*

LITERATURE: AMICO, 2001–present; Bushell, *An Exhibition of Netsuke*, fig. 89, p. 38; Bushell, *Netsuke Familiar and Unfamiliar*, fig. 187, p. 124; Hurtig, "Kaigyokusai Masatsugu," fig. 55, p. 22; Meinertzhagen, *The Meinertzhagen Card Index*, pt. A, p. 301

PROVENANCE: Frederick M. Meinertzhagen; Sir Trevor Lawrence

Itsukushima Shrine (on the island of Itsukushima in Hiroshima prefecture) is one of the Three Famous Views of Japan (*Nihon sankei*). Kaigyokusai created a similar landscape netsuke showing Amanohashidate, another famous site, although in a clamshell (Coullery and Newstead, *The Baur Collection*, pp. 266–67), perhaps indicating that the Bushell netsuke was part of a series. These shell-landscape netsuke are a variation of an older theme called the "clam's dream," which featured Ryūjin's palace in a clamshell. Here it is evident that Kaigyokusai challenged himself to reproduce the surface details of every object. HG

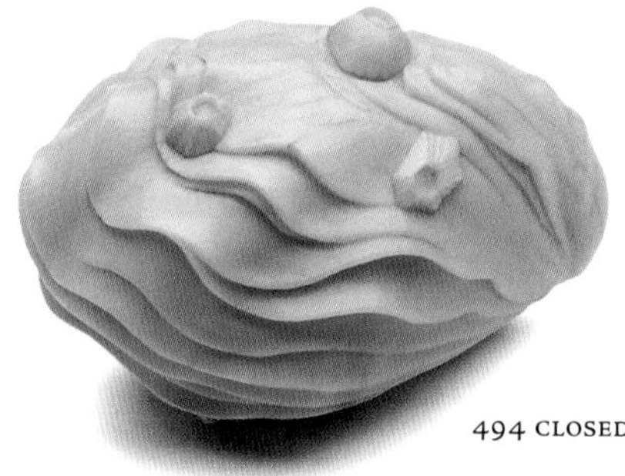

494 CLOSED

495 | **Buddhist Jewel of Wisdom Carved with Mountain Pavilions**

Illustrated on page 62
Kaigyokusai Masatsugu, Japan, 1813–1892
ivory with staining, sumi, inlays
$1\,^{5}/_{16}$ x $1\,^{3}/_{8}$ x $^{15}/_{16}$ in. (3.4 x 3.5 x 2.4 cm)
M.91.250.224
incised: *Kaigyokusai*
seal form, incised: *Masatsugu*

LITERATURE: Phillips, ed., *The Collectors' Encyclopedia of Antiques*, p. 563

With astounding precision and delicacy, Kaigyokusai has created a palatial Chinese-style mountain abode that includes bridges and covered walkways, all within the confines of a Wish-granting Jewel. He has pierced through the netsuke on both sides, breaking the walls of the jewel with cloudlike formations, to reveal the scene within. All the power of the Wish-granting Jewel and of the magical and magnificent landscape could be held in the palm of this netsuke wearer's hand. HG

496 | **Mt. Fuji and Plovers**

Ichigyoku, Japan, active late 19th–early 20th century
natural pearl, gold
$1\,^{1}/_{2}$ x 1 x $^{3}/_{4}$ in. (3.8 x 2.5 x 1.9 cm)
AC1998.249.129
incised: *Ichigyoku*

LITERATURE: Bushell, *An Exhibition of Netsuke*, fig. 368, p. 26; Bushell, *The Wonderful World of Netsuke*, fig. 22, p. 28

PROVENANCE: Frances Numano

Ichigyoku set a felicitously shaped pearl amidst fingerlike waves reminiscent of those seen in paintings by artists of the Rimpa School. Plovers, poetically associated with the shoreline, are often an animating element in Rimpa-style seaside views. Mt. Fuji is rarely shown with waves, with Hokusai's *Kanagawa oki nami ura* (The great wave off Kanagawa) from his famous series Thirty-six Views of Mt. Fuji being an exception. In the Meiji era, when Ichigyoku probably created this work, Mt. Fuji had become the primary symbol of Japanese national identity. HG

Legends

DURING THE EDO PERIOD (1615–1868), some of the best-known historical narratives and works of fiction from Ming dynasty China became widely available in Japan. These texts had a great influence on Japanese literature from the late 1700s and early 1800s (Kornicki, *The Book in Japan*, p. 299), and their settings and characters inspired printmakers, playwrights, and other artists, including netsuke carvers, who adopted several popular figures for their carvings. Peter Kornicki claims that *Shuihu zhuan* (J., *Suikoden*; Tales of the water margin) was the most influential text. From existing netsuke subjects, however, it appears that the beloved semi-historical epic *Sanguo yanyi* (J., *Sangokushi engi*; Romance of the three kingdoms), attributed to Luo Guanzhong, and the tale *Xiyouji* (J., *Saiyuki*; Journey to the west, or The monkey), attributed to Wu Cheng'en (ca. 1500–1582), had a broad readership in Japan as well.

Kan'u (cats. 497–500) is a character from *Romance of the Three Kingdoms*, a partly fictionalized account of the last years of the Han dynasty (ca. 169–234). In China, Kan'u was a symbol of unshakable loyalty who dedicated his life to supporting Gentoku (CAT. 512) and upholding the Han emperor. *Tales of the Water Margin* comprises numerous stories that are primarily concerned with the lives of violent men and women; however, most are decent individuals at heart with a strong sense of loyalty and a desire to protect the weak. *Journey to the West* is a folktale about the Monkey Songokū, who accompanied the historical monk Xuanzang to India to retrieve holy texts for use in China (CAT. 511).

Other popular legends in Edo-period Japan include the story of Shōki (Ch., Zhongkui), a T'ang dynasty doctor who committed suicide by smashing his head on the palace steps. The emperor, fearing that Shōki's angry spirit would haunt them, demanded that he have a full imperial burial, and Shōki's grateful spirit vowed

LEFT: *Kyūmonryū Shishin from the Chinese Novel* Suikoden (CAT. 508); RIGHT: *Tongue-Cut Sparrow* (CAT. 554)

to keep the palace free of demons. For an as yet undetermined reason, the Japanese adopted Shōki as a favored motif in painting, prints, and netsuke (CATS. 501–7).

For netsuke sources from Japanese legend, artists also drew upon characters from kabuki and noh theater, and figures from Japan's ancient creation myths. Myths about Ryūjin seem to have originated in the Nara period (710–794) and one appears in the *Kojiki* (Record of ancient matters, 712). In Japanese legend, Ryūjin takes the form of a wizened and bearded man, whose constant companion was a dragon (CATS. 515–20).

Semi-historical romances inspired the majority of nineteenth-century hero-themed netsuke, partly because the Tokugawa government enacted a number of reforms at the end of the eighteenth century that restricted prurient themes in art, as well as subjects related to the Tokugawa shogunate or its immediate predecessors. As a result, writers and artists turned to narratives from classical history, including *Konjaku monogatari* (Tales of times now past, ca. 1100s), a collection of more than one thousand short tales; the *Heike monogatari* (The tale of the Heike), an anonymous "war tale" about twelfth-century Japan that was probably composed, in Chinese, by a thirteenth-century court noble; and the *Taiheiki* (Chronicle of the great peace, completed ca. 1370–71). Samurai were at the center of many such legends, and an example is that of Tadamori and the oil thief (CATS. 524–26). Master archers such as Minamoto no Yorimasa (1104–1180) were also held in highest regard (CATS. 528–29).

Stories of the poetic accomplishments, aesthetic skills, and legendary romances of court nobles grew more popular around 1868. Most of these poetic immortals were drawn from the two greatest anthologies of verse, the *Kokinshū* (Collection from ancient and modern times, completed ca. 905), and the *Shin kokinshū* (New collection from ancient and modern times, officially completed 1205).

Fables and folk stories were drawn from sources such as *Konjaku monogatari* and *Uji shūi monogatari* (A collection of Uji tales, compiled ca. 1180–1220).

Chinese Legends

Netsuke artists used numerous texts from Ming dynasty China for their subjects. Kan'u, a Chinese general from *Sanguo yanyi* (J., *Sangokushi engi;* Romance of the three kingdoms), is portrayed in netsuke as he was described in that text: with "gleaming skin, glistening lips, eyes like the crimson phoenix, brows like nestling silkworms." The emperor called him "Lord of the Magnificent Beard," and he is often shown holding his beard. The warrior Gentoku escaped an assassination attempt by riding Red Hare, Kan'u's horse, across the rushing Tan River (CAT. 512), and Kan'u himself is sometimes shown astride his mount (CAT. 497).

Two characters from *Shuihu zhuan* (J., *Suikoden;* Tales of the water margin) who often appear in netsuke are Kyūmonryū Shishin and Bushō. Artist Utagawa Kuniyoshi (1797–1861) often treated the *Suikoden* series in his prints, and it is from his composition that Anraku drew his netsuke (CAT. 508) of Kyūmonryū. This type of figural group netsuke became popular around the same time that prints of the subjects began selling well, from the 1830s through the 1860s. The netsuke of Bushō (CAT. 509) depicts a scene from chapter 22, in which Bushō defeats a tiger.

The Monkey Songokū (Ch., Sunwukong), whose adventures are described in *Xiyouji* (J., *Saiyuki;* Journey to the west, or The monkey), accompanied the historical monk Xuanzang to India. A netsuke of the Monkey Songokū from the late 1800s (CAT. 511) shows the new fashion for Western-style realism current in the early Meiji era. Inlay encrustation, which became more fashionable throughout the 1800s, is also appropriate to a subject so eager to avail himself of the magical substances of heaven.

ABOVE: *Bushō the Bandit from the Chinese Novel* Suikoden (CAT. 509)

497 | **Kan'u Mounted**

Illustrated on page 33
Japan, 18th century
ivory with staining, sumi, gold-colored powder pigment
$3^{5}/_{16}$ x $1^{13}/_{16}$ x $^{15}/_{16}$ in.
(8.4 x 4.6 x 2.3 cm)
M.87.263.6

LITERATURE: AMICO, 1999–present; Bushell, *An Exhibition of Netsuke*, fig. 265, p. 57

A less common depiction of Kan'u, this is a particularly lively rendition of the celebrated Chinese general. Mounted on his great horse Red Hare and holding the halberd Blue Dragon, Kan'u is shown twisting to confront the enemy. The artist sculpted the figures with less regard for anatomical accuracy than for producing a powerful and functional netsuke. CD

498 | **Kan'u: Chinese God of War**

GENRYŌSAI MINKOKU I, Japan, active late 18th–early 19th century
wood
$3^{1}/_{8}$ x $1^{5}/_{16}$ x 1 in. (8 x 3.4 x 2.5 cm)
M.91.250.183
incised in rectangular reserve: *Minkoku*

LITERATURE: AMICO, 2001–present; Bushell, *An Exhibition of Netsuke*, fig. 266, p. 57

In his most familiar pose, Kan'u stands to face his foe, one hand grasping his slender beard, the other on his weapon. Less menacing than he is often depicted, here the general takes on an almost noble air. His beard is particularly long and lustrous, perhaps to emphasize his nickname, "Lord of the Magnificent Beard." Minkoku I worked in several styles during his career, with this finely carved, refined style probably dating from the early 1800s. CD

499 | **Kan'u: Chinese God of War**

Illustrated on page 40
Japan, early 19th century
stag antler with staining, sumi
$2^{1}/_{16}$ x $1^{3}/_{4}$ x $1^{1}/_{16}$ in. (5.2 x 4.4 x 2.7 cm)
M.87.263.15

LITERATURE: AMICO, 2000–present; Bushell, *An Exhibition of Netsuke*, fig. 349, p. 67; Bushell, *Netsuke Familiar and Unfamiliar*, fig. 683, p. 215

Kan'u, a powerful and ferocious warrior, was deified as the god of war, and Kan'u, Chōhi, and Gentoku were known as the Three Heroes of Han. Kan'u is seen here in battle, his flowing beard and robes suggesting the great force of the blow to come. CD

500 | **Kan'u: Chinese God of War**

Japan, early 19th century
wood
$3^{5}/_{16}$ x $1^{5}/_{16}$ x $^{15}/_{16}$ in. (8.5 x 3.4 x 2.3 cm)
AC1998.249.254

LITERATURE: AMICO, 2001–present

Although Kan'u is depicted in a pose almost identical to that of a previous piece (CAT. 498), the material used here entirely changes the effect. Unlike dense woods such as boxwood and cherry, coarse open-grained woods do not allow for precise carving, resulting in a bolder, less detailed sculpture. Nonetheless, we can easily identify Kan'u's costume, his trademark weapon, and his fierce visage. CD

501 | **Shōki: The Demon Queller**

Japan, 18th century
ivory with staining, sumi
$2^{3}/_{8}$ x $1^{1}/_{16}$ x $^{3}/_{4}$ in. (6.1 x 2.7 x 1.9 cm)
M.91.250.185

LITERATURE: Bushell, *The Inrō Handbook*, fig. 111, p. 149

Vowing to rid the world of demons, Shōki (Ch., Zhongkui) angrily searches for evidence of their presence. Wearing heavy boots and the robes and cap of a Chinese scholar, and carrying a long sword, he, like Kan'u, is recognizable by his beard. Unlike Kan'u, though, whose beard is long and narrow, Shōki's beard is full, flowing around his face and often tripartite. CD

502 | **Shōki: The Demon Queller**

FOLLOWER OF YOSHIMURA SHŪZAN, Japan, late 18th century
boxwood with pigments
$3^{7}/_{16}$ x 1 x $^{11}/_{16}$ in. (8.7 x 2.5 x 1.8 cm)
M.87.263.93

LITERATURE: AMICO, 1999–present; Ueda, *The Netsuke Handbook of Ueda Reikichi*, fig. 143, p. 144

Characteristics of the work of eighteenth-century artist Yoshimura Shūzan are evident in this netsuke. Depicting a subject favored by Shūzan, this wood Shōki is unsigned and painted; however, the wood used is not Shūzan's typical cypress but boxwood, and the size and proportions of the figure differ from those of other pieces attributed to this early master carver. Because his work was highly admired in his time and after, Shūzan had many followers, this piece likely carved by one of them. CD

503 | **Shōki: The Demon Queller**

YOSHINAGA, Japan, active before 1781
ivory with staining, sumi, inlays
3 5/8 x 1 3/16 x 13/16 in. (9.2 x 3 x 2 cm)
M.91.250.305
incised and stained with sumi in oval reserve: *Yoshinaga*

LITERATURE: Bushell, *An Exhibition of Netsuke*, fig. 34, p. 33; Lazarnick, *Netsuke and Inro Artists*, vol. 2, p. 1240; Mikoshiba and Bushell, "Netsuke and the *Sōken kishō*," p. 114

While many netsuke show demons hiding under Shōki's hat, here we find the Demon Queller sporting it. The hat's thin, wide shape poses a challenge in creating a compact form without exposed edges. Yoshinaga has incorporated this element well into the design of this netsuke for a very functional piece. Shōki was a favorite subject of Yoshinaga's. (Similar netsuke can be found in Ueda, *The Netsuke Handbook*, p. 200, and Davey, *Netsuke*, p. 57.) CD

504 | **Shōki: The Demon Queller**

Japan, early 19th century
ivory with staining, sumi
1 5/16 x 1 5/16 x 15/16 in. (3.3 x 3.3 x 2.4 cm)
M.91.250.136

LITERATURE: Bushell, *The Inrō Handbook*, fig. 116, p. 155

In Japanese mythology, Chinese lions (*shishi*), like Shōki, are believed to be guardians against evil, and large sculpted statues of Chinese lions often protect the entrances of temples and shrines. Here we have the two guardians in an apparently friendly exchange, reminiscent of a man with his house cat. This scene suggests collaboration between the two as protectors against demons and evil spirits. CD

505 | Painted Scroll Coming to Life: Shōki Attacking Demon

SHŪŌSAI HIDEMASA II, Japan,
active mid-19th century
ivory with staining, sumi, wood inlays
$1^{7}/_{8} \times 1^{7}/_{8} \times {}^{3}/_{4}$ in. (4.7 x 4.7 x 1.9 cm)
M.91.250.186
incised and stained with sumi: *Shūōsai*
seal form, pot-shaped, incised and stained with sumi: *Masa; Fujimoto*

LITERATURE: Bushell, *Collectors' Netsuke*, fig. 173, p. 112

PROVENANCE: Marcel Lorber

The Demon Queller was a very popular subject in painting as well as netsuke. Here, a scroll rendering of Shōki has come to life just in time to catch a demon (*oni*), which has nearly escaped the confines of the painting. Oni are often portrayed as much smaller than Shōki, seemingly no match for their giant and powerful pursuer. Hidemasa II worked in both ivory and wood, each of which he has incorporated into this piece. His works are noted for extensive surface detail, seen here on Shōki's costume and the painting's border. An almost identical piece is in the collection of the British Museum (see Barker and Smith, *Netsuke*, p. 27). CD

506 | Shōki Mounted on Chinese Lion

KIKUGAWA FAMILY, Japan,
active 1844–1867
ivory with staining, sumi; manjū type
$2 \times 1^{15}/_{16} \times {}^{13}/_{16}$ in. (5.1 x 5 x 2.1 cm)
M.87.263.28
incised and stained: *Kikugawa saku* / "made by Kikugawa"

LITERATURE: AMICO, 2000–present

Leading the way with his sword, Shōki and his companion courageously battle evil forces, in this case the terrified demon on the reverse of this *manjū*. Although the two figures are combined into one large mass, the artist has used heavy staining and carved textures to delineate each. The stippled effect on Shōki's arm, his dark hair, and his fancy robe border set him apart from the lion's lightly tinted body and curly coat. CD

507 | Shōki and Demon

Front illustrated on page 55
SCHOOL OF NAGAI RANTEI, Japan,
mid- to late 19th century
ivory with staining, sumi, inlays
$2^{9}/_{16} \times 1^{7}/_{16} \times 1$ in. (6.5 x 3.6 x 2.6 cm)
M.91.250.61
carved in oval reserve: *Rantei*

LITERATURE: AMICO, 2001–present; Bushell, *Collectors' Netsuke*, fig. 180, p. 122; Bushell, *An Exhibition of Netsuke*, fig. 264, p. 57; Hill and Johnson, "The Raymond Bushell Netsuke Exhibition," fig. 264, p. 34

While much smaller in size and strength than his hunter, the demon often gets the best of Shōki with its tricks. Here one has found a place to hide, confounding Shōki again. Nagai Rantei established a school whose primary material was ivory, often stained in places a deep, rich brown. CD

507 BACK

508 TOP

508 BACK

508 BOTTOM

508 | **Kyūmonryū Shishin from the Chinese Novel *Suikoden***

Front illustrated on page 328
Shūkōsai Anraku, Japan,
active early to mid-19th century
early 19th century
ivory with deep staining, sumi
2 3/16 x 1 15/16 x 1 1/2 in. (5.5 x 5 x 3.8 cm)
M.91.250.67
incised and lightly stained: *Anraku*

LITERATURE: AMICO, 2001–present; Bushell, *An Exhibition of Netsuke*, fig. 149, p. 45; Hurtig, *Masterpieces of Netsuke Art*, fig. 92, p. 43

Some characters from the Chinese novel *Shuihu zhuan* (Tales of the water margin; J., *Suikoden*) were famous not only for their acts of daring but for the elaborate tattoos that covered their bodies, in this case a design of dragons in clouds. The novel's outrageous adventures and eccentric personalities were popular subjects in art, primarily *ukiyo-e* and netsuke. Anraku, who was known to use multiple shades of brown to stain his netsuke, has quite literally conveyed the colorfulness of those stories in this piece. CD

509 | Bushō the Bandit from the Chinese Novel *Suikoden*

GENRYŌSAI MINKOKU I, Japan, active late 18th–early 19th century
early 19th century
ivory with staining, sumi, inlays
1 7/16 x 1 9/16 x 1 1/4 in. (3.7 x 3.9 x 3.1 cm)
M.91.250.137
incised and stained with sumi in oval cartouche: *Minkoku*

LITERATURE: AMICO, 2001–present; Bushell, *The Wonderful World of Netsuke*, fig. 23, p. 29

As one of the 108 heroes of the *Suikoden*, the strongman Bushō is commonly shown partially clothed, exposing his muscular build. He is said to have killed a tiger with a single blow of his right fist. Here his intense gaze and bared, clenched teeth suggest the great effort of this feat. CD

510 | Kōsekikō and Chōryō

Front illustrated on page 31
ONO RYŌMIN, Japan, active late 19th century
ivory with staining, sumi, inlays
1 7/8 x 1 3/4 x 1 7/16 in. (4.8 x 4.4 x 3.7 cm)
AC1998.249.88
incised: *Ono Ryōmin*; kakihan
seal form, carved and red-lacquered: [undecipherable]

LITERATURE: AMICO, 2001–present; Bushell, *An Exhibition of Netsuke*, fig. 153, p. 20; Bushell, *Netsuke Familiar and Unfamiliar*, fig. 414, p. 164

Chinese legend tells of an old man, Kōsekikō (Ch., Huang Shigong), who loses a shoe while riding horseback over a bridge. Chōryō (Ch., Zhang Liang) retrieves the shoe from the dragon-infested river below and returns it to its owner, who proves to be "The Yellow-Stone Elder." Testing Chōryō, Kōsekikō requests that they meet later so that he can properly reward him. Kōsekikō arrives at the meeting place and, finding that Chōryō is not there, leaves. Chōryō eventually arrives early, and Kōsekikō, satisfied that Chōryō is not undeserving, rewards him with a roll of manuscript containing military advice and strategies that lead to Chōryō's becoming the most powerful man in the land. The complex composition of this piece exemplifies Ryōmin's skill at carving groups of figures in forms suggestive of *okimono* rather than functional netsuke. CD

510 BACK

511 | **Monkey Songokū**

Japan, late 19th century
wood with precious and semiprecious stone inlays
4 x 1 1/2 x 1 1/2 in. (10.1 x 3.8 x 3.8 cm)
M.90.186.10

LITERATURE: AMICO, 2000–present; Bushell, *The Wonderful World of Netsuke*, fig. 7, p. 19

PROVENANCE: Cornelius Van Schaak Roosevelt

In a highly detailed and inlaid piece from the Meiji period, the Monkey Songokū (Ch., Sunwukong) stands proud, carrying many volumes of sacred text for Sanzō (Hōshi) (also Genjō, Ch., Xuanzang). Songokū was a follower of the priest Sanzō and accompanied him on his travels to India in the seventh century. They spent seventeen years collecting Buddhist books and relics and returned to China with hundreds of volumes of sacred Buddhist text. The adventures of the Monkey Songokū are told in *Xiyouji* (Journey to the west, or The monkey; J., *Saiyuki*). Monkeys appear often in Japanese art, but none is easier to identify than Songokū, as he had learned to wear the clothing of humans. His upright posture, full attire, and magical scepter clearly distinguish him. CD

512 | **Gentoku Escaping**

Kōsai Moritoshi, Japan, 1854–1911
ivory with sumi, red pigment; manjū type
2 1/16 x 1 in. (5.3 x 2.5 cm)
M.87.263.25
incised and stained with sumi on oval reserve: *Moritoshi*
kakihan, crest-shaped, incised: crane

LITERATURE: AMICO, 1999–present; Bushell, *An Exhibition of Netsuke*, fig. 92, p. 39; Bushell, *Netsuke Familiar and Unfamiliar*, fig. 293, p. 143; Davey, *Netsuke*, fig. 414, p. 139

PROVENANCE: Mark T. Hindson; William Wilberforce Winkworth

512 BACK

This scene from the fourteenth-century Chinese classic *Sanguo yanyi* (Romance of the three kingdoms; J., *Sangokushi engi*), attributed to Luo Guanzhong, displays the great storytelling possibilities of netsuke. Gentoku was a famous warrior said to have escaped capture by jumping over a massive ravine on horseback. For the netsuke carver, the *manjū* form lends itself to two-dimensional pictorial execution much like paper does for a painter. Moritoshi used his knife like a brush with ink, creating lines of varying thickness, heavily patterned areas, and rough, jagged stippling. The water in the background is deeply carved, giving the horse and rider a sculptural quality. CD

Japanese Legends

Ancient Japanese creation tales inspired many netsuke. Ryūjin, the Ruler of Seas and Tides, is an old man accompanied by a dragon, and he often holds a Tide-ruling Jewel, which controls the ebb and flow of the tides. He gave the jewel away twice: first to Ninigi no Mikoto, the grandson of Amaterasu Ōmikami, and second to his own grandchild, Emperor Ōjin, son of Emperor Chūai and Empress Jingū. One of Ryūjin's daughters married Urashima Tarō, a fisherman, whose tale was told in the *Nihon shoki* (Chronicle of Japan) (CAT. 562). In the Bushell collection, netsuke of Ryūjin and his attendants (CATS. 515–21) were produced in clusters in the eighteenth century and again at the end of the nineteenth century. During the lapse, figures of classic heroes such as samurai and master archers took center stage.

Taira no Tadamori (1096–1153) was head of the Taira clan, the father of its first great political leader Kiyomori (1118–1181), and the first samurai directly to serve an emperor. He is usually shown in netsuke with the oil thief (CATS. 524–26). One night, when he was in the emperor's presence, it was reported that a flame-spitting monster was heading toward the temple Gionji. Tadamori pursued the monster and attacked it; however, he soon discovered that the "monster" was in fact a bedraggled temple servant who went to the temple at night to pilfer oil. The "flames" were produced by the servant's torch, which he blew on to keep lit.

In a tale from *Heike monogatari* (The tale of the Heike), it is said that Emperor Konoe was tormented every evening by a black cloud that settled on the palace roof. Master archer Minamoto no Yorimasa (CATS. 528–29) soon pierced the monster within the cloud, a beast called a *nue*. His second, Ii no Hayata, stepped in to finish off the monster with his sword.

In netsuke, the gentler arts of poetry and music were celebrated (CATS. 542, 544), as well as individual poets and musicians (CATS. 550, 552).

ABOVE: *Urashima Tarō* (CAT. 562)

513 | **Tenjiku Tokubei**

Japan, early 19th century
ivory with staining, sumi
1 1/8 x 1 7/16 x 1 1/2 in. (2.8 x 3.6 x 3.8 cm)
M.91.250.21

LITERATURE: AMICO, 2001–present; Bushell, *An Exhibition of Netsuke*, fig. 147, p. 45; Bushell, *Netsuke Familiar and Unfamiliar*, figs. 764a and b, p. 227; Davey, *Netsuke*, fig. 1062, p. 353; Phillips, ed., *The Collectors' Encyclopedia of Antiques*, p. 567

PROVENANCE: Mark T. Hindson; William Wilberforce Winkworth; Frederick M. Meinertzhagen; Dr. H. A. Gunther

Due to their shapes, some subjects are easily represented within the confines of a functional netsuke. This depiction of the seventeenth-century adventurer Tenjiku Tokubei is an ideal netsuke form, compact and rounded. Legend has it that Tokubei was endowed with magical powers that enabled him to assume the form of man or toad. Here we find him in the midst of such a transformation. CD

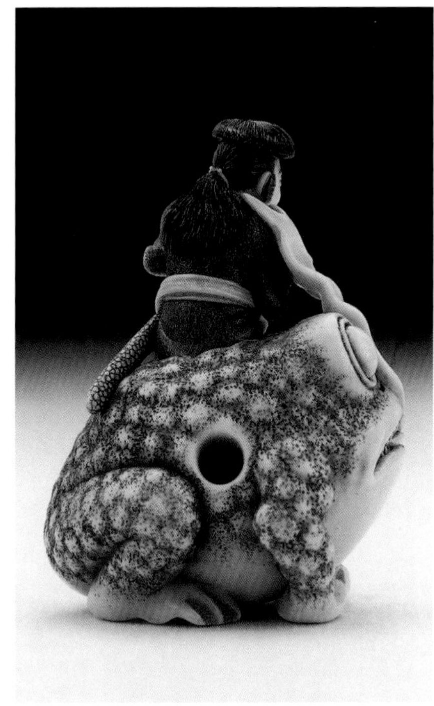

514 BACK

514 | **Frog Magic of Tenjiku Tokubei**

Masatoshi (Nakamura Tokisada), Japan, 1915–2001
May 1973
ivory with staining, sumi, hornbill inlays, red pigment
1 5/8 x 1 1/4 x 1 1/8 in. (4.2 x 3.1 x 2.9 cm)
AC1998.249.237
incised and stained: *Masatoshi tō* / "carved by Masatoshi"

LITERATURE: Bushell, *An Exhibition of Netsuke*, fig. 486, p. 29; Bushell, *Masatoshi*, fig. 14, p. 9; Bushell, "Travels by Netsuke," fig. 19, p. 108; Masatoshi, *The Art of Netsuke Carving*, fig. 14, p. 141

Kabuki theater began in the seventeenth century and quickly became a popular form of entertainment. This kabuki version of *Tenjiku Tokubei*, a mid-nineteenth-century play, shows an actor bursting from a giant frog, an allusion to his ability to change forms. The actor is costumed and made up just as one would see him at this climactic moment in the performance. CD

515 | **Ryūjin: Ruler of Seas and Tides**

Illustrated on page 36
Attributed to Yoshimura Shūzan, Japan, died 1776
wood with pigments
$3\,^1/_2 \times 1\,^1/_4 \times 1\,^3/_{16}$ in. (9 x 3.1 x 3 cm)
M.91.250.9

LITERATURE: AMICO, 2001–present; Bushell, *Collectors' Netsuke*, fig. 2, p. 25; Bushell, *An Exhibition of Netsuke*, fig. 5, p. 17; Hill and Johnson, "The Raymond Bushell Netsuke Exhibition," fig. 5, p. 31; Mikoshiba and Bushell, "Netsuke and the *Sōken kishō*," p. 106

In the majority of Ryūjin netsuke, he is shown holding the jewel by which he controls the tides, as in the numerous representations (also CATS. 516–20) in the Bushell collection. In this particular piece, however, the Dragon King holds a stem of red coral as a scepter, perhaps alluding to its association with magical powers. CD

516

516 | **Ryūjin: Ruler of Seas and Tides**

Japan, 18th century
wood
$3\,^3/_4 \times 1\,^7/_{16} \times 1\,^3/_8$ in. (9.6 x 3.7 x 3.5 cm)
M.91.250.287

LITERATURE: Bushell, *An Exhibition of Netsuke*, fig. 160, p. 46; Bushell, *The Wonderful World of Netsuke*, fig. 91, p. 67

PROVENANCE: Japan Art Center

The source for this unconventional rendition of a multi-headed Ryūjin is not clear. The extra heads could allude to Ryūjin's two attendants, or to the two instances when Ryūjin gave away the Tide-ruling Jewel, or to the tale of Hohodemi and Hoderi. The hunter, Hohodemi, and the fisherman, Hoderi, were brothers who switched occupations. Hohodemi loses Hoderi's fishhook and, in searching the sea for it, encounters the Dragon King. Ryūjin, wanting to help Hohodemi, gives him the Tide-ruling Jewel and thereby power over his brother. It is said that Hoderi's descendants later portrayed this tale in dance and may have used masks similar to the highly stylized faces carved here. CD

518 BACK

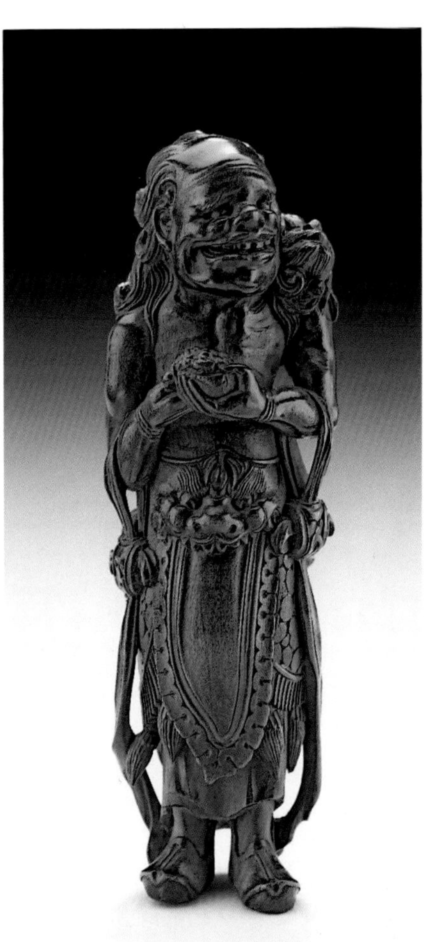

517 | **Ryūjin: Ruler of Seas and Tides**

TAMETAKA, Japan, active circa 1730–1790
wood
1 15/16 x 1 3/4 x 1 1/4 in. (4.9 x 4.4 x 3.1 cm)
AC1998.249.138
incised: *Tametaka*; kakihan

LITERATURE: Bushell, *An Exhibition of Netsuke*, fig. 19, p. 17; Ueda, *The Netsuke Handbook of Ueda Reikichi*, fig. 142, p. 143

Depicting Ryūjin in such an unconventional manner—the tall, standing representation is found much more often—is characteristic of Tametaka's work. His netsuke often show familiar models in uncommon poses. This compact form is ideally suited for use, with Ryūjin's hands and feet and the dragon's tail neatly incorporated into the design. Oddly, while wood gave artists more flexibility, Tametaka has nonetheless carved this piece in the overall triangular shape one would expect of an ivory piece. CD

517 BACK

518 | **Ryūjin: Ruler of Seas and Tides**

Japan, late 19th century
wood
3 x 1 x 7/8 in. (7.6 x 2.5 x 2.2 cm)
AC1998.249.266

LITERATURE: AMICO, 2001–present

In a less ferocious portrayal of the Dragon King, the artist here has relaxed Ryūjin's stern facial features, giving him a mischievous grin. The dragon headdress has become a dragon resting upon Ryūjin's shoulder. The imagination of the carver is also evident in the transformation of Ryūjin's sash into the face of a demon, whose long tongue forms the front panel of his costume. CD

519 | **Ryūjin: Ruler of Seas and Tides**

Japan, late 19th century
ebony, coral, ivory with staining
1 1/4 x 1 3/16 x 15/16 in. (3.1 x 3 x 2.3 cm)
AC1998.249.283

LITERATURE: AMICO, 2001–present; Behrens, *Netsuke*, fig. 3375, pl. 46

PROVENANCE: Walter Lionel Behrens

The combination of ebony with inlays of ivory and coral suggests that this unsigned netsuke may be the work of a Minkoku School carver; in particular, the relief carving on the coral inlay is a trait often found in their work. Here the coral, Ryūjin's Tide-ruling Jewel, is encircled by a dragon. (Similar compositions and treatments by Minkoku are in Meinertzhagen, *The Meinertzhagen Card Index*, p. 519, and Harris, *Netsuke*, fig. 60, p. 31.) CD

519

520 BACK

520 | **Ryūjin: Ruler of Seas and Tides**

Japan, 18th century
wood
3 11/16 x 1 1/2 x 15/16 in. (9.4 x 3.8 x 2.3 cm)
M.91.250.325

LITERATURE: Bushell, *An Exhibition of Netsuke*, fig. 58, p. 35; Bushell, *Netsuke Familiar and Unfamiliar*, fig. 762, p. 227; Hill and Johnson, "The Raymond Bushell Netsuke Exhibition," fig. 58, p. 32

Several elements from the Ryūjin legends are combined here in what seems to be a depiction of the Dragon King of the Sea literally becoming a dragon. In his hand is the Tide-ruling Jewel, but the dragon headdress has taken over his entire body. The dragon tail, clawlike hands, and scaly torso indicate his transformation from man to beast. Masatoshi created a very similar netsuke in ivory, using an older wood netsuke as a model, undoubtedly this piece. The feet here are repaired but, based on Masatoshi's rendition (*The Art of Netsuke Carving*, p. 167), we can assume that Ryūjin's feet, like his hands, have turned into claws. CD

521

521 | **Attendant to Ryūjin: Ruler of Seas and Tides**

Miura Yoshinaga, Japan, active late 19th century
ivory with staining, sumi
$3\,^{3}/_{4}$ x $1\,^{3}/_{16}$ x $^{9}/_{16}$ in. (9.6 x 3 x 1.4 cm)
M.87.263.8
incised and stained: *Yoshinaga*

LITERATURE: AMICO, 1999–present; Bushell, *Netsuke Familiar and Unfamiliar*, fig. 752, p. 225

Descriptions of Ryūjin's attendants mention curly hair and Chinese-style dress, sometimes covered with seashells or scales. Of the two assistants most commonly encountered in Japanese stories and art, one carries a dragon while the other wears an octopus headdress. This, the only ivory carving of a Ryūjin subject in the Bushell collection, is also the sole depiction of the octopus-clad attendant. CD

522 | **Takenouchi no Sukune in Korea with Baby Emperor Ōjin**

Japan, 18th century
wood
$2\,^{13}/_{16}$ x $2\,^{1}/_{4}$ x $1\,^{1}/_{8}$ in. (7.2 x 5.8 x 2.8 cm)
M.91.250.184

LITERATURE: Ueda, *The Netsuke Handbook of Ueda Reikichi*, fig. 201, p. 191

The third-century conquest of Korea by Empress Jingū is told in the *Nihon shoki* (Chronicle of Japan), Japan's earliest recorded history. Accounts of Empress Jingū's campaign to capture Korea vary. In some, she is pregnant with her son for years, waiting until after her return to Japan to give birth. In other stories, Ōjin accompanies his mother through Korea in the care of Takenouchi no Sukune, Jingū's attendant. Here Ōjin is safely tucked into the warrior's robes. CD

522 BACK

523 | **Kugatsume Kaneko Halting a Runaway Horse**

NAOMITSU, Japan, late 18th–early 19th century
ivory with staining, sumi; manjū type
$2^{1}/_{8}$ x 1 in. (5.4 x 2.5 cm)
AC1998.249.91
incised: *Ichiyūsai* [Naomitsu's art name]
seal form, carved and incised: *Naomitsu*

LITERATURE: AMICO, 2001–present; Bushell, *Collectors' Netsuke*, fig. 241, p. 152; Bushell, *An Exhibition of Netsuke*, fig. 94, p. 20; Meinertzhagen, *The Meinertzhagen Card Index*, pt. B, p. 596; Trower, *Catalogue of the H. Seymour Trower Collection of Japanese Art*, fig. 362, pl. 3

PROVENANCE: Mark T. Hindson; Dr. H. A. Gunther; Harry Seymour Trower

Numerous stories were told about Kugatsume, the fabled strongwoman. In the tale most often depicted, she stops a runaway horse by stepping on its reins. Her relaxed posture and the undisturbed basket of laundry on her hip convey the apparent ease with which she accomplishes this feat. CD

524 | **Tadamori and the Oil Thief**

Front illustrated on page 25
CHINGENDŌ HIDEMASA, Japan, active early 19th century
ivory with staining, sumi, inlays
$1^{3}/_{4}$ x $1^{1}/_{2}$ x $^{15}/_{16}$ in. (4.4 x 3.8 x 2.3 cm)
M.91.250.38
incised and stained: *Hidemasa*; kakihan

LITERATURE: AMICO, 2001–present; Bushell, *An Exhibition of Netsuke*, fig. 262, p. 23

Having heard reports of a flame-eating monster terrorizing the temple, Tadamori attempts to vanquish the creature. When he apprehends the intruder, Tadamori realizes it is merely a servant who has stolen oil for his lamp. The thief here is clearly surprised, raising his hand in protest and dropping his oil jar. Legendary and historical figures were frequent subjects for Hidemasa. The light staining and intricate design on Tadamori's robe are characteristic of Hidemasa's work. (For a similar piece, see Ueda, *The Netsuke Handbook*, p. 155.) CD

524 BACK

525 | **Tadamori and the Oil Thief**

Japan, 19th century
boxwood
$2^{1}/_{4}$ x $1^{5}/_{8}$ x $1^{7}/_{16}$ in. (5.7 x 4.1 x 3.6 cm)
M.91.250.192

LITERATURE: Bushell, *An Exhibition of Netsuke*, fig. 261, p. 57

The same scene as the previous piece is here shown in a far more caricature-like style. In an exaggerated pose, an angry and determined Tadamori holds the surprised thief, who wears a mischievous, almost demonic grin. The expressive features, flowing robes, and deep sculptural carving suggest the style of the Sō School. CD

526 | Tadamori and the Oil Thief

Illustrated on page 24
Shunkōsai Chōgetsu, Japan, 1826–1892
ivory with staining, sumi; manjū type
$2^{3}/_{8}$ x $^{7}/_{8}$ in. (6 x 2.2 cm)
M.87.263.21
incised and stained with sumi in oval cartouche: *Shunkōsai*

LITERATURE: AMICO, 2000–present; Bushell, *An Exhibition of Netsuke*, fig. 96, p. 39; Phillips, ed., *The Collectors' Encyclopedia of Antiques*, p. 569

A particularly angry Tadamori secures his victim. Shunkōsai has carefully composed the image to fit the space without the functional center plug interfering with the design. CD

527 | Oguri Hangan: The Horse Tamer

Isshū, Japan, active early 19th century
ivory with staining, sumi, inlays
$1^{3}/_{4}$ x $1^{9}/_{16}$ x $1^{3}/_{16}$ in. (4.5 x 4 x 3 cm)
M.91.250.191
incised: *Isshū*

LITERATURE: Joly, *Legend in Japanese Art*, p. 374; Ueda, *The Netsuke Handbook of Ueda Reikichi*, fig. 152, p. 148

PROVENANCE: Henri L. Joly

Oguri Hangan, celebrated for his skill as a horseman, sits astride his horse Onikage. Hangan demonstrated his extraordinary ability to tame horses by having one stand atop a *go* board. CD

528 | Yorimasa: The Master Archer

Kōryūsai (Naokazu or Naoichi), Japan, active 19th century
ivory with staining, sumi, red pigment; manjū type
$1^{5}/_{8}$ x $^{3}/_{4}$ in. (4.1 x 1.9 cm)
M.87.263.22
incised and stained with sumi on raised rectangle: *Kōryūsai*

LITERATURE: AMICO, 2000–present; Bushell, "Questions & Answers" (1980b), figs. 3a and b, p. 45

The deeply carved background of this *manjū* brings Minamoto no Yorimasa (1104–1180) to life, the figure standing well above the dark background, his arm almost completely raised from the recessed surface as he reaches for his bow and arrow. Minamoto no Yorimasa was a famous Heian-period archer who slew a *nue* that was causing the emperor to lose his sleep and his health. Each night, stormy skies signaled the arrival of the beast, until Yorimasa eventually shot it down. Before this, a nue had never been seen; it has since been described as having a monkey's head, a tiger's claws, a badger's body, and a snake for a tail. The reverse of this manjū shows lightning against a dark background, a reference to the storm clouds in which the nue took cover. CD

529 | **Yorimasa: The Master Archer**

Shūōsai Hidemasa II, Japan,
active mid-19th century
ivory with staining, sumi
$2^{3}/_{16}$ x $1^{1}/_{8}$ x 1 in. (5.5 x 2.9 x 2.5 cm)
M.87.263.114
incised and stained: *Shūōsai*; kakihan
seal form, incised and stained: *Fujimoto*

LITERATURE: AMICO, 1999–present; Bushell, *Collectors' Netsuke*, fig. 172, p. 112; Bushell, *An Exhibition of Netsuke*, fig. 269, p. 57, and front cover; Hill and Johnson, "The Raymond Bushell Netsuke Exhibition," fig. 269, p. 34

The figure's posture, the position of his hands and bow, and the motion of his full sleeve let us know that Yorimasa has just released his arrow. The famous archer watches intently as his arrow finds the monstrous *nue*. Hidemasa's characteristic surface decoration is especially evident here. CD

530 | **Asahina Saburō and Demon**

Matsushita Otoman, Japan,
active early to mid-19th century
ivory with dark staining, sumi
$2^{1}/_{4}$ x $1^{7}/_{16}$ x $1^{1}/_{8}$ in. (5.7 x 3.7 x 2.8 cm)
AC1998.249.5
incised and stained: *Matsushita Otoman*

LITERATURE: Ueda, *The Netsuke Handbook of Ueda Reikichi*, fig. 190, p. 184

While Asahina Saburō is a historical figure, legendary stories about his superhuman strength include him subduing a giant carp or a group of crocodiles, and wrestling with demons. He is so strong that this tug-of-war with a demon is merely an effortless game. CD

531 | **Ariōmaru and the Octopus**

RYŪKŌSAI JUGYOKU, Japan, active early to mid-19th century
wood with inlays
1 5/8 x 1 1/8 x 1 1/16 in. (4.1 x 2.8 x 2.7 cm)
AC1998.249.20
incised: *Jugyoku*

LITERATURE: AMICO, 2001–present; Ueda, *The Netsuke Handbook of Ueda Reikichi*, fig. 155, p. 150

Ariōmaru comes from the story of Shunkan, a priest exiled for his role in a conspiracy against Taira no Kiyomori. Shunkan is sometimes shown as a desperate old man at the seashore, begging for forgiveness as his condemners leave him behind. Here, in his final days, Shunkan is visited by his servant, Ariōmaru, who fights off an octopus that has attacked his master. Apparently a favorite subject of Jugyoku's, several of these netsuke from his hand exist, as do similar pieces by numerous other artists. CD

532 | **Mitsunaka Killing a Demon**

KAZUSHIGE, Japan, active mid-19th century
ivory with staining, sumi, inlays
2 1/4 x 1 5/16 x 1 1/8 in. (5.7 x 3.4 x 2.8 cm)
AC1998.249.139
incised in oval cartouche: *Kazushige*

LITERATURE: AMICO, 2001–present; Bushell, *An Exhibition of Netsuke*, fig. 263, p. 57; Bushell, *The Inrō Handbook*, fig. 36, p. 59

The tenth-century noble and general Mitsunaka was also known as an avid and skillful hunter. The common images of him subduing a demon are likely a reference to this. The motion of these figures, shown by the large, flowing sleeves and extensive surface decoration, suggest the influence of the school of Hidemasa. CD

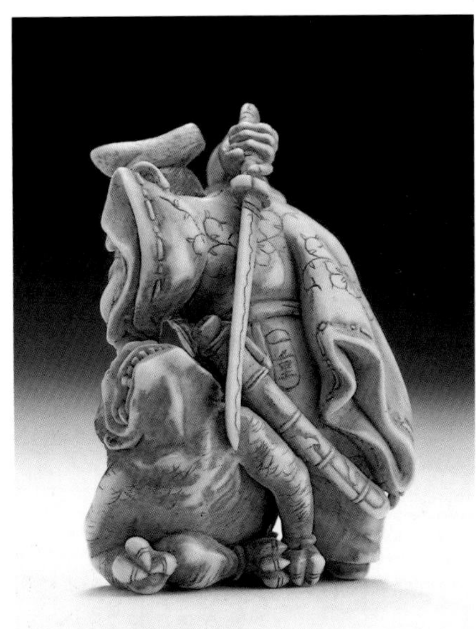

532 BACK

533 | **Ono no Tōfū**

Japan, 18th–19th century
wood with lacquer, double inlays
3 1/8 x 1 1/16 x 1 1/4 in. (7.9 x 2.7 x 3.1 cm)
AC1998.249.72
incised: *Garaku* [spurious]

LITERATURE: AMICO, 2001–present; Bushell, *An Exhibition of Netsuke*, fig. 268, p. 23; Bushell, *Netsuke Familiar and Unfamiliar*, fig. 741, p. 224

The Western adage "if at first you don't succeed, try, try again" has a Japanese equivalent dating back a thousand years. The Heian-period calligrapher Ono no Tōfū sought to gain a higher post. After his seventh unsuccessful attempt, as he was about to give up, he spied a frog desperately trying to reach a low-hanging leaf on a willow branch. On its eighth attempt, it finally secured the leaf. Ono no Tōfū took this as a sign and continued his quest, this time succeeding. A frog dressed as the calligrapher is emblematic of this lesson of perseverance. (A very similar piece appears in Earle, *Netsuke*, p. 174.) CD

534 BACK

534 | **Kojima no Takanori Inscribing the Cherry Bark**

HASEGAWA IKKO, Japan, mid- to late 19th century
late 19th century
ivory with staining, sumi, inlays
1 15/16 x 1 9/16 x 1 1/8 in. (4.9 x 3.9 x 2.8 cm)
AC1998.249.211
incised and stained in irregular oval reserve: *Ikko*

LITERATURE: AMICO, 2001–present; Bushell, *The Wonderful World of Netsuke*, fig. 84, p. 63

PROVENANCE: William Wilberforce Winkworth

Kojima no Takanori inscribes a short verse on a cherry tree—a hidden message to the exiled emperor vowing his continued loyalty and intentions of rescuing him. In this *okimono*-like netsuke, a style typical of Meiji-era work, the artist has painstakingly included every element of the story, including the tiny portable ink well (*yatate*) in Takanori's hand and the miniscule characters on the tree. CD

535 | **Abe no Seimei**

Suzuki Masanao, Japan, 1815–1890
mid-19th century
boxwood
1 15/16 x 1 1/16 x 1 1/2 in. (5 x 2.7 x 3.8 cm)
AC1998.249.58
incised: *Masanao*

LITERATURE: AMICO, 2001–present; Bushell, *Collectors' Netsuke*, fig. 120, p. 94; Bushell, *An Exhibition of Netsuke*, fig. 270, p. 57; Davey, *Netsuke*, fig. 686, p. 223

PROVENANCE: Mark T. Hindson; Guest collection; Gilbertson

This scene, probably from kabuki theater, shows the Heian-period court wizard and astrologer Abe no Seimei (921–1005). Said to have conjured mice from an empty box as part of a wizard's competition, here he performs his magic under the scrutinizing eye of what appears to be a judge. According to legend, Abe no Seimei's powers came from his mother, Kazunoha, who was a fox (see CAT. 246). Designed with little regard for function, the *himotōshi* consists of a very small hole between the standing figure's feet. CD

535

536

536 | **Benkei**

Morikawa Toen, Japan, 1820–1894
wood with gold pigment
2 1/8 x 1 9/16 x 15/16 in. (5.4 x 3.9 x 2.4 cm)
M.91.250.56
incised: *Toen*

LITERATURE: AMICO, 2001–present; Bushell, *Collectors' Netsuke*, fig. 155, p. 107; Bushell, *An Exhibition of Netsuke*, fig. 271, p. 23

In addition to creating netsuke, Morikawa Toen was considered the foremost of the Nara doll (*ningyō*) carvers. The flat planes of Benkei's robes are characteristic of the "single-knife carving" (*ittōbori*) technique employed in creating ningyō. While the only color added to this particular piece is in the eyes, many of Toen's netsuke were colorfully painted, like ningyō. Toen's work also reflects his interest in the noh theater—he was an accomplished noh performer. The features of this masklike face, with its wide, tightly closed mouth and bulging eyes, are reminiscent of a traditional noh Beshimi mask. CD

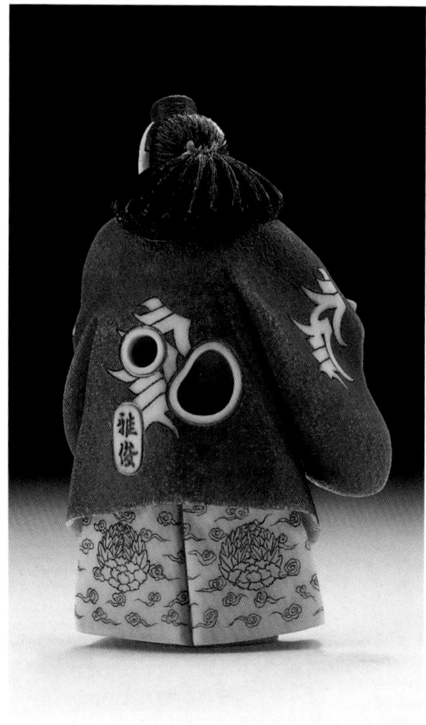

537 BACK

537 | **Benkei Reading List, from *Kanjinchō***

MASATOSHI (NAKAMURA TOKISADA), Japan, 1915–2001
January 1953
ivory with staining, sumi, red and gold pigments
2 1/16 x 1 1/4 x 1 in. (5.2 x 3.1 x 2.5 cm)
AC1998.249.207
incised and stained with vermilion: *Masatoshi*
ink on box lid: *Isshunsai Masatoshi*; kakihan
seals on box lid: *Isshunsai*; *Masatoshi*

LITERATURE: Bushell, *Masatoshi*, fig. 12, p. 18; Masatoshi, *The Art of Netsuke Carving*, fig. 12, p. 141

Benkei was a warrior-ascetic (*yamabushi*) of such cunning, strength, skill, and loyalty that the high-ranking warrior Minamoto no Yoshitsune (1159–1189) made him his retainer for life. When Yoshitsune's brother turned against him, he and Benkei fled and went into hiding; as Yoshitsune was surrounded by enemies, Benkei alone fought to his death to give his beloved master the time to commit an honorable suicide. Stories about Benkei's cleverness and courage were very popular, and several were depicted in noh and kabuki. In this netsuke, Masatoshi has shown Benkei in a scene from the play *Kanjinchō* (The subscription list). CD

538 | **Yasumasa and Kidomaro**

ŌYAMA MOTOZANE IV, Japan, died 1916
gold, mixed-metal disk, ivory bowl; kagamibuta type
1 3/4 x 9/16 in. (4.4 x 1.5 cm)
M.87.263.73
incised: *Taizan Motozane*; kakihan

LITERATURE: AMICO, 2000–present; Bushell, *An Exhibition of Netsuke*, fig. 420, p. 74; Bushell, *Netsuke Familiar and Unfamiliar*, fig. 218, p. 131

In Japanese tradition, the music from a flute is credited with the ability to pacify beasts—a concept familiar in the West as well. The story of Yasumasa is one allusion to this belief. Yasumasa's brother Kidomaro was a villain who sought to kill his brother. Just as he was about to attack, Yasumasa began to play his flute, and its melody dispelled Kidomaro's anger. CD

539 BACK

539 | **Yasumasa and Kidomaro**

School of Jugyoku, Japan,
Meiji period (1868–1912)
ivory with dark staining, sumi
1 9/16 x 1 1/4 x 1 in. (3.9 x 3.2 x 2.5 cm)
AC1998.249.164

This depiction of the brothers Yasumasa and Kidomaro was created in the fashion of the late 1800s, when functional considerations were no longer a factor and the foreign market was the greatest influence on netsuke production. While an obvious attempt has been made to create a compact form with no protruding elements, the flat bottom and lack of cord holes—though there are natural openings through which a cord could be threaded—make it more suited as an *okimono* than a netsuke. CD

540 | **Kuranosuke Feigning Leisure**

Ueda Kōhōsai, Japan, died circa 1907
ivory with light staining, sumi
1 3/4 x 1 11/16 x 1 1/4 in. (4.4 x 4.3 x 3.1 cm)
M.91.250.284
incised and lightly stained: *Kōhōsai*

LITERATURE: AMICO, 2001–present; Bushell, *Collectors' Netsuke*, fig. 208, p. 128; Bushell, *An Exhibition of Netsuke*, fig. 296, p. 60

Having drawn his sword against Kira Kozuke no Suke Yoshinaka in Edo castle, a capital offence, Asano Takumi no Kami is sentenced to commit seppuku. Though law dictated that both parties were to be punished equally, Kira walked free. Now masterless (*rōnin*), Ōishi Kuranosuke and the dead lord's other retainers vow one day to exact fair punishment on Kira. For years they pretend to live in unaffected leisure, lulling Kira into complacency. Finally, the time for revenge arrives. (Although netsuke portrayals of Kuranosuke are not common, there is an almost identical rendition by Rantei in Hurtig, *Masterpieces*, p. 76.) CD

541 | **Soga no Gorō**

Illustrated on page 70
Ōuchi Sōsui, Japan, 1911–1972
ivory with staining, sumi
1 11/16 x 1 9/16 x 1 5/16 in. (4.3 x 4 x 3.3 cm)
M.91.250.211
incised and stained with sumi: *Sōsui*

LITERATURE: Bushell, *Collectors' Netsuke*, fig. 323, p. 176; Bushell, *An Exhibition of Netsuke*, fig. 449, p. 77; Bushell, "Questions & Answers" (1977), fig. 19f, p. 47

Some mythological and historical characters appear frequently in Japanese art, usually in a familiar and often repeated scene. In netsuke, Soga no Gorō is usually shown on horseback, riding furiously to be by his brother's side in battle. Here, however, he is uprooting a bamboo stalk, an image likely based on the eighteenth-century print by Torii Kiyomasu I. Sōsui wrote to Raymond Bushell in July 1953, saying that he was working on some *ukiyo-e* subjects for netsuke; this was probably one of the pieces. CD

542 BACK

542 | **Narihira Eloping with Takako**

Shōminsai, Japan, active early 20th century
ivory with staining, sumi, lacquer details
1 9/16 x 1 3/8 x 1 in. (3.9 x 3.5 x 2.5 cm)
M.91.250.314
incised and stained with sumi: *Shōminsai*

LITERATURE: Bushell, *The Inrō Handbook*, fig. 56, p. 85

Much of the tenth-century *Ise monogatari* (Tales of Ise) recounts the romantic affairs of a character who is unidentified but assumed to be Ariwara no Narihira (825–880). Although in love with Narihira, Takako obeys her father's wishes that she marry Emperor Seiwa. Narihira is shown here stealing her away, an act for which he was later exiled. Narihira was one of the Six Immortal Poets (*Rokkasen*) and in netsuke is commonly represented with the other five poets. CD

543 | **The Courtesan Eguchi no Kimi As Fugen, Bodhisattva of Universal Wisdom**

Front illustrated on page 68
Ōuchi Gyokusō, Japan, 1879–1944
ivory with light staining, sumi
1 7/16 x 1 7/16 x 15/16 in. (3.6 x 3.6 x 2.3 cm)
M.91.250.80
incised: *Gyokusō*

LITERATURE: Bushell, *An Exhibition of Netsuke*, fig. 439, p. 27; Bushell, *Netsuke Familiar and Unfamiliar*, back cover; Ueda, *The Netsuke Handbook of Ueda Reikichi*, fig. 211, p. 195

The bodhisattva Fugen, the god of compassion who dispenses wisdom, sits on a white elephant to the right of the Buddha, usually with a scroll in hand. He is shown here in a common depiction that alludes to the story of Saigyō Hōshi. With darkness falling, and having no other accommodations, Saigyō is forced to spend the night at the home of Eguchi no Kimi, a courtesan. During the night, he is awakened by a vision of Fugen, who tells Saigyō that he has been reincarnated as Eguchi, who is much learned in the sutras. CD

543 BACK

544 BACK

544 | **Nakakuni and Kogō no Tsubone**

Ōuchi Sōsui, Japan, 1911–1972
wood
1 7/8 x 1 1/4 x 1 1/16 in. (4.7 x 3.2 x 2.7 cm)
M.91.250.83
incised: *Sōsui*
ink on box lid: *Heike monogatari ni yoru Daihitsu Minamoto Nakakuni senji o tamawatte Kogō no Tsubone o tazunaru no zu* / "The scene from *The Tale of the Heike* in which Daihitsu Minamoto Nakakuni, under orders from the emperor, searches for Kogō no Tsubone"
ink on box lid: *Ōuchi Sōsui koku* / "carved by Ōuchi Sōsui"
seal on box lid: [undecipherable]

LITERATURE: Bushell, *An Exhibition of Netsuke*, fig. 448, p. 77; Bushell, "Questions & Answers" (1978a), figs. 17c and d, p. 44

In this tale from *Heike monogatari* (The tale of the Heike), Kogō no Tsubone was the mistress of Emperor Takakura, whose wife schemed to have her poisoned. Kogō learned of the plot and went into hiding, and the emperor searched for her unsuccessfully for years. Eventually, Minamoto Nakakuni, a courtier and musician, volunteered to look for her, claiming that her *koto* music was so beautiful he could recognize it anywhere. One day, hearing the enchanting melody of her koto, he found her. Here, he answers her music with his own. This netsuke showcases Sōsui's unsurpassed ability with the tools of his trade. While likely not intended for use, the netsuke's composition is nonetheless compact and rounded. All views have been detailed and finished; the gate even opens. CD

545 BACK

545 | Ōkubo Hikozaemon

Dōkei, Japan, active early to mid-20th century
1951
ivory with staining, sumi
$2^{1}/_{8}$ x $1^{3}/_{16}$ x 1 in. (5.4 x 3 x 2.5 cm)
M.91.250.328
incised and lightly stained with sumi: *Dōkei*
incised: *Hōgachō* / "subscription list"
ink on box lid: *Dōkei saku, Shōwa nijūrokunen jūichigatsu* / "made by Dōkei, Shōwa 26 [1951], November"; *Shimotsuki Hōgachō* / "Hōga ward, Shimotsuki"
seal on box lid: *Dōkei*

LITERATURE: Bushell, "Questions & Answers" (1978a), fig. 3, p. 44; Bushell, "Questions & Answers" (1991), figs. 2a and b, p. 9; Bushell, "Questions & Answers" (1996), p. 49

Ōkubo Hikozaemon (1560–1639) was retainer to several Tokugawa shogun and famous for his loyalty, military ability, and sage advice. Tales about him, however, more often detail his strong personality and eccentric behavior, and he is a favorite subject in romance stories of the time. He is shown here carrying his notebook of duties, a reference to his steadfast sense of duty to the shogun. Dōkei was a contemporary of Sōko, Sōsui, and Shōko, although he never worked with them. Though greatly interested in netsuke, he produced very few himself. CD

546 | Benten Kozō

Also illustrated on pages 72 and 81
Masatoshi (Nakamura Tokisada), Japan, 1915–2001
July 1957
ivory with staining, sumi, red and gold pigments
$1^{9}/_{16}$ x $1^{7}/_{16}$ x $1^{1}/_{4}$ in. (3.9 x 3.7 x 3.2 cm)
M.91.250.98
incised and stained with sumi in oval reserve cartouche: *Masatoshi*

LITERATURE: Bushell, *Collectors' Netsuke*, fig. 345, p. 182; Bushell, *Masatoshi*, fig. 29, p. 9; Masatoshi, *The Art of Netsuke Carving*, fig. 29, p. 146

Masatoshi's repertoire of subjects was fueled by many sources, one of his favorites being the theater, from which he draws this depiction of Benten Kozō. Dressed in women's clothing and a wig, Benten Kozō and his cohorts carry out an elaborate plot to swindle a shopkeeper. Tattoos, most common on firemen and the lower classes of Edo society of the mid-1800s, were an emblem of vanity and tolerance to pain appropriate for Benten Kozō. Clearly, his tattoos, theatrical makeup, and costumes are colorful and complex elements relished by Masatoshi. CD

546 BOTTOM

547 | **Moritō and Kesa**

Illustrated on page 75
MEIKEI, Japan, born 1932
wood
$2\,^{9}/_{16}$ x 1 x $^{15}/_{16}$ in. (6.6 x 2.5 x 2.3 cm)
AC1998.249.89
incised: *Meikei*

Meikei has captured the horrible moment when Moritō discovers his mistake: The life he has just taken is that of his beloved Kesa. Moritō, in love with Kesa, a married woman, threatens her family if she does not yield to him. Finally, Kesa accedes to his plan to kill her husband. At the arranged time, Moritō enters Kesa's home and beheads the man sleeping there, unaware that Kesa has taken the place of her husband to save his life and her honor. The tragedy of Moritō and Kesa is not a unique subject in netsuke, with Kesa sometimes portrayed as a ghost haunting Moritō. (An almost identical piece is pictured in Kinsey, *Living Masters of Netsuke*, p. 175.) CD

548 BACK

548 | **Komachi Clears Her Name**

MASATAMI, Japan, circa 1850–1890
late 19th century
wood
$1\,^{13}/_{16}$ x $1\,^{1}/_{8}$ x $^{7}/_{8}$ in. (4.6 x 2.8 x 2.2 cm)
AC1998.249.197
incised in rectangular cartouche: *Masatami tō* / "carved by Masatami"

LITERATURE: AMICO, 2001–present; Ueda, *The Netsuke Handbook of Ueda Reikichi*, fig. 174, p. 176

The sole woman among the Six Immortal Poets (*Rokkasen*) was Ono no Komachi, famed poetess of the ninth century. As a young woman, she was a beauty with many suitors, whom she spurned one after another. Eventually, her looks abandoned her and she became a ragged and lonely old woman. In "Sōshi arai Komachi" (Book-washing Komachi), represented in this netsuke, Komachi has recited one of her poems at court, only to be accused by her rival, Ōtomo no Kuronushi, of having stolen it from the eighth-century poetry anthology *Man'yōshū* (Collection of ten thousand leaves), a copy of which he produces. With water, Komachi wipes away the fresh ink that Kuronushi has written into the book. Earlier he had heard her reciting the poem aloud and copied it into the book in an attempt to ruin Komachi's reputation. CD

549 | **Komachi on Grave Post**

TAMETAKA, Japan, active circa 1730–1790
wood
$2\,^{3}/_{16}$ x $1\,^{7}/_{16}$ x 1 in. (5.5 x 3.6 x 2.5 cm)
AC1998.249.181
incised: *Tametaka*; kakihan

In contrast to the previous piece (CAT. 548) and in a far more familiar representation, we have the famous poetess shown here in her later years, destitute and alone. This depiction, known as "Sotoba Komachi" (Grave-post Komachi), shows her reflecting on her wasted youth. She rests upon a fallen grave marker (*sotoba*), which were found in Buddhist cemeteries and had one end carved with shapes representing the five elements. CD

550 | **Hitomaro: The Classic Poet**

Illustrated on page 24
OZAWA SHŪRAKU, Japan, 1830–after 1878
early 19th century
mixed-metal disk, ivory bowl; kagamibuta type
$1\,^{7}/_{8}$ x $^{5}/_{8}$ in. (4.7 x 1.6 cm)
M.91.250.69
incised: *Shūraku*; kakihan

LITERATURE: AMICO, 2001–present; Bushell, *An Exhibition of Netsuke*, fig. 419, p. 74; Bushell, *Netsuke Familiar and Unfamiliar*, fig. 229, p. 133

As one of the Three Gods of Poetry (*Waka sanjin*), along with Akahito and Sōtori Hime, Hitomaro (fl. ca. 685–705) was celebrated as one of Japan's greatest poets. So revered was his writing that even a normally ill-behaved demon is on his best behavior, apparently inspired to mix the poet's ink. The poet can be identified by the writing brush in his hand, a clue invariably present in representations of him. CD

551 | **Six Poetic Immortals**

HŌSHUNSAI MASAYUKI, Japan, active mid- to late 19th century
mid-19th century
wood with inlays
$1\frac{5}{16}$ x $1\frac{1}{4}$ x $1\frac{1}{4}$ in. (3.3 x 3.1 x 3.1 cm)
AC1998.249.255
incised and stained on inlaid bone or antler plaque: *Masayuki*

LITERATURE: AMICO, 2001–present; Ueda, *The Netsuke Handbook of Ueda Reikichi*, fig. 183, p. 180

551 BACK

The Six Immortal Poets (*Rokkasen*) lived in the ninth century and were considered the best of Japan's classical poets. They are most commonly seen in prints and paintings, often each poet shown in tandem with a poem. In netsuke, the poets are most often seen solo, the most popular being Ono no Komachi (CATS. 548–49), but are sometimes grouped in the manner seen here. Masayuki often created humorous pieces and here has piled up the poets, each with brush in hand, writing on one another. CD

552 | **Ueda Akinari**

MASATOSHI (NAKAMURA TOKISADA), Japan, 1915–2001
September 1976
ivory with staining, sumi
$2\frac{7}{8}$ x 1 x 1 in. (7.3 x 2.5 x 2.5 cm)
AC1998.249.212
incised and stained: *Masatoshi*

LITERATURE: Bushell, *Masatoshi*, fig. 129, p. 27; Masatoshi, *The Art of Netsuke Carving*, fig. 129, p. 172

To carve this netsuke of the scholar and novelist Ueda Akinari (1734–1809), Masatoshi modeled the figure after a painting executed during Akinari's lifetime. Masatoshi used a "roughening-up" technique called *arashi* to create the surface of the figure's robe, in this case silk crepe roughening (*chirimen arashi*). The subtle texture and delicate staining very convincingly convey the soft, flowing fabric. CD

553 | **Horse in Gourd**

Naitō Toyomasa, Japan, 1773–1856
wood with inlays
1 13/16 x 1 5/8 x 1 in. (4.6 x 4.2 x 2.5 cm)
M.91.250.135
incised: *Toyomasa*

LITERATURE: AMICO, 2001–present; Dee, "Toyomasa," fig. 2, p. 30

While animal subjects in netsuke are plentiful, those by Toyomasa stand out for their original interpretations and playful quality. Toyomasa often grouped animals and objects in unexpected combinations and produced a body of work depicting various creatures bursting from fruits, nuts, and shells, as exemplified here. Like this smiling horse, Toyomasa's animal and figurative subjects have a characteristic cartoonlike quality, giving them a humorous feel. This netsuke refers to the proverb "The Horse from a Gourd" (*Hyōtan kara koma*), warning that even the most unexpected things are possible. CD

554 | **Tongue-Cut Sparrow**

Also illustrated on page 329
Chingendō Hidemasa, Japan, active early 19th century
wood with double inlays
1 1/2 x 1 5/16 x 1 1/16 in. (3.8 x 3.4 x 2.7 cm)
M.91.250.337
incised: *Hidemasa*

LITERATURE: Bushell, *Collectors' Netsuke*, fig. 167, p. 110; Hurtig, "Collecting Legends," p. 7; Hurtig, *Masterpieces of Netsuke Art*, fig. 456, p. 118

PROVENANCE: Imai Kenzō

"The Tongue-Cut Sparrow" is one of the many tales commonly referenced in netsuke. In this warning against greed, Nasakeji returns home to find Bidori, his beloved pet sparrow, missing. He questions the old woman next door, who tells him that she caught the bird eating from her garden and cut its tongue. Horrified, Nasakeji searches for the bird which, grateful for the old man's care, lets him choose one of two boxes. Nasakeji, old and frail, chooses the smaller. Once home, he discovers that the box is filled with treasure. The old woman, hearing of Nasakeji's fortune, looks for Bidori. The bird also offers her two boxes, and the greedy old woman chooses the larger one. When she opens the box, out come ghosts and monsters that haunt her for the rest of her days. CD

554 BOTTOM

555 | **Tongue-Cut Sparrow**

MASATOSHI (NAKAMURA TOKISADA), Japan, 1915–2001
August 1972
ivory with staining, sumi, and white tortoiseshell and lampblack inlays
1 1/16 x 1 5/8 x 1 7/16 in. (2.7 x 4.2 x 3.6 cm)
AC1998.249.215
incised and stained: *Hidemasa netsuke yori Masatoshi sha* / "copied by Masatoshi from a netsuke by Hidemasa"

LITERATURE: Bushell, *Masatoshi*, fig. 238, p. 33; Masatoshi, *The Art of Netsuke Carving*, fig. 238, p. 197

This netsuke and the preceding one depict the story of the tongue-cut sparrow in remarkably similar fashion. Hidemasa's carving (CAT. 554) was in fact the model for Masatoshi's version. While none of the story's numerous variations tells of an old woman riding on the back of Bidori, it is not an unusual design in netsuke. Masatoshi describes this scene as the sparrow carrying the old woman to his home in the forest. CD

556 | **Tiny Man on Monkey's Back**

SHŪZAN, Japan, active early to mid-19th century
ivory with staining, sumi, inlays
1 7/8 x 1 13/16 x 15/16 in. (4.8 x 4.6 x 2.4 cm)
M.91.250.291
incised and stained with sumi on raised oval reserve: *Shūzan*

LITERATURE: Bushell, *An Exhibition of Netsuke*, fig. 256, p. 23; Bushell, "Questions & Answers" (1978a), fig. 7, p. 45

PROVENANCE: Naitō Haruo

Unexpected, clever, and imaginative portrayals in art and netsuke appealed to the Japanese sense of humor. *Netsukeshi* played with odd combinations of subjects, altered their sizes, or reversed their roles for comic or surprise effect. Here the "monkey trainer with monkey" theme has been reinterpreted, with the tiny trainer now in the role of performer resting on his giant master's shoulder. CD

557 | **Priest and Teakettle**

SHŪKŌSAI ANRAKU, Japan, active early to mid-19th century
mid-19th century
ivory with staining, sumi, inlays
1 5/8 x 1 7/16 x 1 in. (4.1 x 3.6 x 2.5 cm)
AC1998.249.171
incised and stained in reserve cartouche: *Anraku*

LITERATURE: AMICO, 2001–present

In Japanese folklore, the raccoon-dog (*tanuki*) is credited with the ability to take the form of other beings and objects. In the tale "The Enchanted Teakettle" (*Bunbuku chagama*), of which there are numerous versions, a priest, heating his water for tea, sees that his teakettle has turned into a tanuki. Finding later that the creature has resumed its teakettle shape, the priest sells it to a poor junk dealer who, with his new "trick" kettle, sets out entertaining audiences and soon becomes a rich man. In this rendition of the tale, Anraku seems to be playing with the popular "frustrated rat-catcher" form, creating one of his typically spirited or humorous pieces. The incised and stained line work, found in this figure's body hair and facial features, is characteristic of Anraku. CD

558 | **Tanuki Teakettle**

Ōhara Mitsuhiro, Japan, 1810–1875
ebony with double inlays, metal
1 3/4 x 1 3/16 x 1 1/8 in. (4.4 x 3 x 2.9 cm)
M.91.250.236
incised in oval reserve: *Mitsuhiro*

LITERATURE: AMICO, 2001–present; Ueda, *The Netsuke Handbook of Ueda Reikichi*, fig. 106, p. 100

Mitsuhiro excelled at miniature studies of ordinary objects, flowers, and fruit. His skill at carving different textures gave his ivory or wood netsuke the convincing appearance of stone, hair, pottery, or in this case metal. One of Mitsuhiro's commonly used techniques was *ishime*, where tiny gouges cover the surface, giving it a rough, pitted finish. He also used this technique effectively in rendering the surfaces of tea bowls, tangerines, and loquats. The combination of the black ebony and the ishime technique perfectly mimics the black metal teakettles of the time. The lid is removable, with the cord channel on its underside. CD

559 | **Kintarō**

Kōgetsusai Naomasa, Japan, active 1830–1850
ivory with staining, sumi, red pigment; manjū type
1 7/8 x 13/16 in. (4.8 x 2.1 cm)
M.87.263.24
incised and stained: *Kōgetsusai*
seal form, incised and stained: *Naomasa*

LITERATURE: AMICO, 1999–present; Bushell, *Collectors' Netsuke*, back of slipcase; Davey, *Netsuke*, fig. 82, p. 40

PROVENANCE: Mark T. Hindson; Guest collection; Rev. L. B. Cholmondeley

The pairing of the "strong boy" and the carp, found on the reverse side of this *manjū*, refers to the story of Kintarō, who was raised by the mountain woman Yamanba (or Yamauba) and showed evidence of his great strength at an early age. The legend of Kintarō may have been based on Sakata no Kintoki, a samurai under Minamoto no Yorimitsu (944/948–1021). Japanese legend includes several boys known for their exceptional strength, all of whom are shown struggling with carp. CD

560 | **Fox and Drum**

Illustrated on page 64
KAIGYOKUSAI MASATSUGU,
Japan, 1813–1892
ivory with sumi, inlays
$1^{1}/_{4} \times 1^{5}/_{16} \times {}^{13}/_{16}$ in. (3.2 x 3.4 x 2.1 cm)
M.91.250.218
incised in oval reserve: *Kaigyoku*

LITERATURE: Atchley, "Kaigyokusai," fig. 18, p. 18; Bushell, *Collectors' Netsuke*, fig. 150, p. 106; Bushell, *An Exhibition of Netsuke*, fig. 84, p. 38; Hurtig, "Kaigyokusai Masatsugu," fig. 53, p. 21

The legend of Kitsune Tadanobu has many variations. In some, Tadanobu is a man-fox who transforms into a fox to steal the drum (*tsuzumi*) made from his mother's hide. Another version says that a fox—the pup of the vixen whose skin was used in making the drum—takes on Tadanobu's likeness to get back the relic of its mother. This netsuke depicts the former, which is most commonly seen in allusions to this tale. Kaigyokusai's influence on Gyokusō is evident when this piece is compared with Gyokusō's almost identical version in the Baur collection (Coullery and Newstead, *The Baur Collection*, fig. 1061, p. 339). CD

561 BOTTOM

561 | **"No Evil" Monkey**

KAIGYOKUSAI MASATSUGU,
Japan, 1813–1892
wine-colored amber
$1^{5}/_{16} \times 1^{5}/_{16} \times 1^{1}/_{4}$ in. (3.3 x 3.3 x 3.1 cm)
AC1998.249.87
incised: *Kaigyoku*
seal form, incised: *Masatsugu*

LITERATURE: AMICO, 2001–present; Bushell, *An Exhibition of Netsuke*, fig. 372, p. 68; Ueda, *The Netsuke Handbook of Ueda Reikichi*, fig. 146, p. 145

PROVENANCE: Tomita Kumasaku

This lone monkey representation of the "Three Wise Apes" (*Sambiki saru*) was apparently a favorite of Kaigyokusai, who produced numerous netsuke of this model. Most, however, are of ivory or wood rather than expensive and rare amber. Meinertzhagen mentions this particular netsuke form executed in all three materials in his *Card Index*. Kaigyokusai was known for his use of the finest materials, as exemplified in this amber of exceptional color and clarity. CD

562 | **Urashima Tarō**

Ozawa Shūraku, Japan, 1830–after 1878
gold disk, water buffalo horn bowl; kagamibuta type
$1^{5}/_{8}$ x $^{9}/_{16}$ in. (4.1 x 1.4 cm)
M.87.263.74
incised: *Shūraku*; kakihan

LITERATURE: AMICO, 1999–present; Bushell, *An Exhibition of Netsuke*, fig. 422, p. 74; Bushell, *Netsuke Familiar and Unfamiliar*, fig. 245, p. 135

PROVENANCE: Fred B. Thomas

The tale of the fisherman Urashima Tarō dates from 478 A.D., when he encounters a turtle who reveals herself to be the daughter of Ryūjin. She takes him to the undersea palace, where they are married. Eventually, Urashima tells his wife that he must go home to see his family. Reluctantly, she allows him to leave, giving him a box that she cautions him not to open until he returns to her. Urashima goes home to find that hundreds of years have passed and his family has long since died. In his desperation, he opens the box, and all the past centuries waft out of it, consuming Urashima, who ages and dies. Here Urashima is being taken home on the back of the turtle, holding his wife's gift in his left hand. CD

563 | **Issun Bōshi: The Legendary Tiny Man**

Masatoshi (Nakamura Tokisada), Japan, 1915–2001
February 1955
ivory with staining, sumi, red pigment
$1^{1}/_{16}$ x 1 x $^{13}/_{16}$ in. (2.7 x 2.6 x 2 cm)
M.91.250.214
incised and stained with sumi: *Masatoshi tō* / "carved by Masatoshi"

LITERATURE: Bushell, *An Exhibition of Netsuke*, fig. 491, p. 80; Bushell, *Masatoshi*, fig. 236, p. 14; Bushell, *Netsuke Familiar and Unfamiliar*, fig. 428, p. 168; Bushell, "Travels by Netsuke," 104–9 fig. 20, p. 108; Masatoshi, *The Art of Netsuke Carving*, fig. 236, p. 196

Netsukeshi who used ivory were always careful to avoid waste, designing and carving the material to its fullest. Left with an especially tiny remnant of fine ivory, Masatoshi cleverly chose a perfect subject—the tiny man, Issun Bōshi. Here he is shown in the "boat" he used on his river journey to Kyoto. In subsequent stories, Issun Bōshi shows his great courage and, with the help of a lucky mallet, becomes a handsome, life-size samurai. The magic mallet is incised on the side of this bowl. CD

564 | **Catfish and Gourd**

Masatoshi (Nakamura Tokisada), Japan, 1915–2001
November 1964
ivory with staining, sumi, inlays
$2^{3}/_{4}$ x 1 x $^{13}/_{16}$ in. (7 x 2.5 x 2 cm)
M.91.250.94
incised: *Masatoshi tō* / "carved by Masatoshi"

LITERATURE: Bushell, *Collectors' Netsuke*, fig. 346, p. 183; Bushell, *Masatoshi*, fig. 184, p. 29; Masatoshi, *The Art of Netsuke Carving*, fig. 184, p. 185

According to Japanese legend, the earthquake fish (*namazu*) lives deep underground, and its movement causes the earth to tremble. The form of this mythical creature is based on catfish found in Japanese waters. The theme of gourd and catfish (*hyōtan namazu*) is seen in Zen paintings to illustrate the Zen conundrum or cryptic saying "to catch a catfish with a gourd," a seemingly impossible task. CD

Genre

Genre details (scenes of daily life) appear in paintings throughout the history of Japanese art, and genre scenes became an independent subject in screen paintings during the sixteenth century. There was no full-sized sculptural category that prefigured genre netsuke. When netsuke carvers wanted to use a genre subject, they could look to many sources, one of which was *ukiyo-e* (pictures of the floating world), the dominant genre painting and print medium of the Edo period (1615–1868). Ukiyo-e themes featured denizens of the "floating world," or entertainment quarter, such as actors and courtesans; however, figural netsuke did not usually follow this example. Netsuke carvers more often looked to Kano School artists such as Hanabusa Itchō (1652–1724) and Kusumi Morikage (ca. 1620–1690), both from Edo, and to the later artists Katsushika Hokusai (1760–1849) and Utagawa Hiroshige (1797–1858), who were inspired by the lives of all classes and types of people. Itchō and Morikage often depicted scenes from peasant life, while Hokusai, born and raised in Edo, chose more urban themes such as street vendors and performers. Maruyama-Shijō School painters who lived in Edo, including Watanabe Nangaku (1767–1813), Suzuki Nanrei (1775–1844), and Ōnishi Chinnen (1792–1851), depicted the daily activities of average citizens, and their paintings also served as models for netsuke artists. Later netsuke carvers used a figural style that enlarged the head so that the facial expression was easily readable, and this style was employed in genre netsuke, the majority of which were produced in Edo.

LEFT: *Servant and Young Mistress* (CAT. 665); RIGHT: *Bundle of Firewood* (CAT. 760)

The theme of genre in netsuke is by definition large and unwieldy because it encompasses all the commonplace details of life, from activities (cooking and getting dressed) to occupations (egg tester and parasol bearer) to objects (toys and incense burners), and more. For this reason, genre netsuke have been loosely grouped into three subsections. Dancers, characters from noh drama, performers such as acrobats and contortionists, and figures associated with New Year's festivities can be found in Entertainers and Celebrations (CATS. 565–97). Daily Life (CATS. 598–690) includes comic figures, women and children, laborers and samurai, and ghosts. Domestic Implements (CATS. 691–761) includes scholars' objects such as seals, items for tea ceremony, utensils for eating and drinking, food, dolls, toys, and things seen every day such as scarecrows, coins, firewood, and bridge posts.

Entertainers and Celebrations

The yearly cycle of celebrations, from New Year's Day through the end of the twelfth lunar month, served not only many practical functions but also provided the populace of all classes with a constant round of entertainment, for nearly all of these festivities were occasions for song, dance, and dramatic performances. In the imperial palace, there were both stately dances of Pan-Asian origin (CAT. 566) and boisterous masked chases meant to rid the precinct of demons. Within the ramparts of the shogun's castle, as well as in the gardens of the military elite, noh plays were performed, to which a select audience of commoners might also be admitted. In the countryside, local deities would be propitiated with food, drink, dance, and mime—especially at planting and harvesttime—and the peasants, too, would participate. In the cities, every neighborhood had its shrine where the guardian deity was similarly feted. Nor were the sources of entertainment limited to the annual festivities. More than a million people lived in Edo, creating a vast potential audience both for performers and for the artists who depicted them. The kabuki and puppet theaters offered constantly changing programs of full-scale dramatic productions. In smaller theaters, party venues, and even on street corners, a vast variety of talent was on display: storytellers, comic raconteurs, slapstick comedians, jugglers, acrobats (CATS. 578–90).

ABOVE: *Hostess* (CAT. 584)

565 | **Crane Dancer**

Gesshō (or Gessei), Japan, active late 18th–early 19th century
late 18th century
wood with inlay
2 7/16 x 1 1/16 x 15/16 in.
(6.3 x 2.7 x 2.3 cm)
AC1998.249.199
incised: *Gesshō [?]* [partially effaced]

LITERATURE: Bushell, *Collectors' Netsuke*, fig. 80, p. 65

The dancer postures on one leg and holds a closed fan over his head, simulating the appearance of a crane. In a real performance, he would have stood behind a paper screen, upon which his silhouette was projected. Gesshō lived in Edo and was one of several netsuke carvers who apparently worked entirely in wood, producing figural netsuke of legendary or genre subjects. NKD

566 BACK

566 | **Shinto Priest Dancing**

Japan, early 19th century
wood with lacquer; sashi type
5 1/8 x 1 5/16 x 3/4 in. (13 x 3.3 x 1.9 cm)
M.91.250.311

LITERATURE: Bushell, *An Exhibition of Netsuke*, fig. 298, p. 60; Bushell, *Netsuke Familiar and Unfamiliar*, fig. 577, p. 196

This Shinto priest performs a *kagura*, a ritual dance accompanied by music that culminates in a trancelike state. It was believed that, through the dancer, the voice of the deities could be heard. Across his back he holds *gohei*—strips of paper hanging from a sacred staff that are used to ward off evil and invite the spirit of the deity. This *sashi* netsuke is flat, allowing it to tuck comfortably into the obi. The cord passes through the natural openings in the wood around the figure's right wrist. CD

567 | **Sparrow Dance**

MINKOKU II or MINKOKU III, Japan, 19th–early 20th century
late 19th century
ivory with light staining, sumi
$1^{11}/_{16} \times 1^{5}/_{16} \times {}^{7}/_{8}$ in. (4.3 x 3.4 x 2.2 cm)
M.91.250.199
incised and stained: *Minkoku*

LITERATURE: AMICO, 2001–present; Ueda, *The Netsuke Handbook of Ueda Reikichi*, fig. 185, p. 182

In this late netsuke, two performers enact the sparrow dance (*suzume odori*), in which they flutter about as though they were flying up the walls of houses. They wear broad hats adorned with rosettes and perform with their backs to the audience. The maker is probably a distant follower of Genryōsai Minkoku II, working in the Meiji period (1868–1912) and producing netsuke for foreigners who traveled to Asia, particularly Japan, at that time. NKD

567 SIDE

568 BACK

568 | **Wisteria Maiden**

CHIKU'UNSAI, Japan, active late 19th–early 20th century
ivory with deep staining
$2^{7}/_{16} \times 1^{1}/_{8} \times 1$ in. (6.3 x 2.8 x 2.5 cm)
AC1998.249.170
incised in oval reserve: *Chiku'unsai*

The Wisteria Maiden, also known as Princess Fuji (Fujimusume), is a divinity inhabiting Mt. Fuji. She wears a broad hat and carries a spray of wisteria. Her name is a play on the similar pronunciation of the words "Fuji," for the mountain, and *fuji*, meaning "wisteria." Chiku'unsai produced figural subjects in a neat style and employed clever staining techniques. In this example, he stained the maiden's hat, hair, and robes but left her face and hands unstained for contrast. NKD

569 | **Kagura Dance**

Shōgetsu, Japan, 1888–1953
ivory with staining, sumi
$3\frac{3}{16}$ x $1\frac{7}{16}$ x $1\frac{3}{16}$ in. (8.2 x 3.6 x 3 cm)
AC1998.249.284
incised and stained: *Shōgetsu*

This dancer wears a lion-head mask and holds *gohei* to perform the Shinto ritual lion dance (*shishi kagura*). The theater was one of Shōgetsu's favorite themes, particularly plays that involved actors changing roles, and therefore masks, throughout the performance. Shōgetsu's fascination with the idea of role changing led him to create many netsuke of performers, usually wearing masks, and ultimately to develop the rotating-face technique used in this netsuke. (Unfortunately the movable face, which originally could be rotated to reveal two more faces, no longer turns.) CD

570 BACK

570 | **Scene from the Noh Play *Dōjōji***

Attributed to Tametaka, Japan, active circa 1730–1790
wood with inlays
$1\frac{3}{4}$ x $1\frac{1}{2}$ x $1\frac{1}{4}$ in. (4.4 x 3.8 x 3.2 cm)
M.91.250.25

LITERATURE: Bushell, *An Exhibition of Netsuke*, fig. 20, p. 32; Bushell, *Netsuke Familiar and Unfamiliar*, fig. 753, p. 226

The legend of the bell of Dōjōji was dramatized as a noh play and other works for the stage. In the story, a beautiful girl, Kiyohime, fell in love with Anchin, a priest at the temple Dōjōji. Because he was a devout priest, Anchin could not return her love. Enraged, she followed him to his temple, where he had hidden from her under a temple bell. She turned herself into a dragon, wound herself around the outside, heated the metal, and burned the priest to death. The work is similar in style to *Komachi on Grave Post* (CAT. 549) by Tametaka of Nagoya. NKD

571 BACK

571 | Scene from the Noh Play *Dōjōji*

TANAKA MINKŌ, Japan, 1735–1816
boxwood
$1\frac{7}{16} \times 1\frac{1}{16} \times \frac{15}{16}$ in. (3.7 x 2.7 x 2.3 cm)
AC1998.249.12
incised and red-lacquered: *Minkō*; kakihan

LITERATURE: AMICO, 2001–present

The legend of Kiyohime (CAT. 570) and her unrequited love for the priest Anchin is well represented in this example by the Minkō School. Here, the young woman is unrecognizable, as she furiously coils her serpent's body around the bell of Dōjōji, in which Anchin burns alive. NKD

572 | Scene from the Kyōgen Play *Obagasake*

FUKUMOTO HŌMIN, Japan, active mid- to late 19th century
wood, ivory with staining, sumi, red pigment
$1\frac{5}{8} \times 1\frac{1}{4} \times 1$ in. (4.1 x 3.1 x 2.5 cm)
AC1998.249.146
incised in reserve cartouche: *Hōmin*

LITERATURE: AMICO, 2001–present

PROVENANCE: Ann Meselson

After countless unsuccessful requests for a taste of the sake made by his aunt, Tarō Kaja, the main character of the kyōgen farce *Obagasake* (The aunt's sake), devises a trick. He appears at his aunt's door in the guise of a devil, demanding access to the storeroom. The frightened aunt obliges and leaves the devil alone with her sake. Tarō removes his mask to drink and soon falls into a drunken sleep. The scene ends when Tarō's aunt discovers her nephew's duplicity and chases him out of the storeroom. CD

573 | Noh Actor in a Shishiguchi Role

Illustrated on page 51
School of Koma Bunsai, Japan, 19th century
gold and colored lacquer
1 1/2 x 1 x 1 7/8 in. (3.8 x 2.5 x 4.7 cm)
M.87.263.43
makie inscription: *Koma Bunsai*

LITERATURE: AMICO, 2000–present; Bushell, *An Exhibition of Netsuke*, fig. 398, p. 72; Bushell, *Netsuke Familiar and Unfamiliar*, back cover; Bushell, *Netsuke Masks*, fig. 344; Ueda, *The Netsuke Handbook of Ueda Reikichi*, fig. 119, p. 131

The shakkyō dance, seen here, was first used in the noh play *Shakkyō* (The stone bridge), and it eventually became an intermission performance of noh plays. The formal robes, long red wig, and ferocious lion mask (*shishiguchi*) are typically used in the dance. Koma Bunsai, a member of the Koma family of lacquerers, was the second son of Koma Kansai I (d. 1792). This example is probably by a follower, working in the late 1800s. This is a faithful representation of the formalized posture and dress, with fine lacquered details. NKD

574 | Noh Actor in the Role of Hakuzōsu

Morikawa Toen, Japan, 1820–1894
wood with pigments
3 7/16 x 1 1/8 x 1 in. (8.7 x 2.9 x 2.6 cm)
AC1998.249.159
incised: *To [?]*; kakihan

LITERATURE: Bushell, *Collectors' Netsuke*, fig. 156, p. 107; Bushell, *Netsuke Masks*, fig. 347

PROVENANCE: Akai Shiro

The actor is performing the role of the fox in the play *Tsurigitsune* (Trapping of the fox). In the play, the performers don masks in sequence: one portrays the priest Hakuzōsu while the other portrays the fox. Morikawa Toen was born in Nara. He made a number of netsuke and *okimono*, always in wood, often painted, and generally in the *ittōbori* (single-knife) style of carving. NKD

575 | Noh Actor in a Shishiguchi Role

Kagawa Katsuhiro, Japan, 1853–1917
gold, mixed-metal disk, wood bowl; kagamibuta type
1 11/16 x 9/16 in. (4.3 x 1.5 cm)
M.87.263.78
incised on raised gold plaque: *Katsuhiro*

LITERATURE: AMICO, 1999–present; Bushell, *An Exhibition of Netsuke*, fig. 421, p. 74; Bushell, *Netsuke Familiar and Unfamiliar*, fig. 238, p. 134

On the gold disk, cast in fine relief, is a dancer from the noh play *Shakkyō* (The stone bridge). In the play, the performer wears a lion mask (*shishiguchi*) and dances among red and white peonies. Kagawa Katsuhiro, a sword-fitting maker from Tokyo, was an accomplished and versatile artist. He studied carving under the noh mask maker Ariyoshi, painting under Shibata Zeshin, and metalworking under Kanō Natsuo. NKD

576

577 | **Noh Actor in the Role of Hannya**

Illustrated on page 52
Matsuki Hōkei, Japan, active Meiji period (1868–1912)
late 19th century
carved red lacquer
2 1/4 x 1 1/8 x 15/16 in. (5.7 x 2.8 x 2.3 cm)
M.87.263.47
incised: *Hōkei*

LITERATURE: AMICO, 2000–present; Bushell, *Netsuke Familiar and Unfamiliar*, fig. 258, p. 137; Phillips, ed., *The Collectors' Encyclopedia of Antiques*, p. 570

The actor is playing a Hannya role of a demonized aggrieved female. Matsuki Hōkei was a fine lacquerer who specialized in the *tsuishu* (carved red lacquer) technique, which derived from China but was treated with much sophistication by Hōkei and his pupils on netsuke, inrō, and pipe cases. He became a professor at the Tokyo School of Fine Arts in 1887. NKD

576 | **Noh Dancer in the Role of Shōjō**

Koma Bunsai, Japan, active 19th century
late 19th century
lacquer with inlay
1 3/4 x 15/16 x 13/16 in. (4.4 x 2.4 x 2.1 cm)
AC1998.249.241
gold *makie* inscription: *Koma Bunsai*

LITERATURE: AMICO, 2001–present; Bushell, *Netsuke Familiar and Unfamiliar*, fig. 256, p. 137

The actor plays the role of a legendary shōjō, the water sprite, a small, chubby, red-haired creature who drinks sake. The character appears in only one play, *Shōjō* (The dancing water sprite), a comic depiction of a drunken creature reeling about on the stage. NKD

578 | **Acrobat**

Illustrated on page 53
Japan, 18th century
wood with inlays
$2\,^{1}/_{16}$ x $1\,^{1}/_{8}$ x $1\,^{3}/_{4}$ in. (5.3 x 2.9 x 4.4 cm)
M.91.250.128

LITERATURE: AMICO, 2001–present; Bushell, *An Exhibition of Netsuke*, fig. 311, p. 62; Bushell, *Netsuke Familiar and Unfamiliar*, fig. 141, p. 115

This street performer, an acrobat, contorts his body backward on a small drum to entertain his roadside audience. *Contortionist* (CAT. 579) is probably by the same hand. NKD

579 | **Contortionist**

Japan, 18th century
wood
$1\,^{3}/_{8}$ x $1\,^{7}/_{16}$ x $1\,^{5}/_{16}$ in. (3.5 x 3.7 x 3.4 cm)
M.91.250.129

LITERATURE: AMICO, 2001–present; Hurtig, *Masterpieces of Netsuke Art*, fig. 112, p. 46

An entertainer amuses the revelers in the streets of Edo by bending his body into a seemingly impossible position. This netsuke is similar to *Acrobat*, suggesting that it might be one of a series of entertainers by a single artist. NKD

579

580

580 | **Contortionist**

Japan, 19th century
ivory with staining, sumi
$1\,^{1}/_{2}$ x $1\,^{1}/_{8}$ x $1\,^{9}/_{16}$ in. (3.8 x 2.9 x 3.9 cm)
M.91.250.130

LITERATURE: AMICO, 2001–present; Bushell, *An Exhibition of Netsuke*, fig. 117, p. 41

A performer entertains the crowds in Edo by contorting himself on the ground. To capture the reality of this difficult position, the carver probably began with a life drawing before converting it into a three-dimensional sculpture. NKD

581 | **Wrestler**

Japan, 18th century
wood
$3^{7}/_{16}$ x $1^{3}/_{8}$ x 1 in. (8.7 x 3.5 x 2.5 cm)
M.91.250.54

LITERATURE: AMICO, 2001–present; Bushell, *Collectors' Netsuke*, front of slipcase; Bushell, *An Exhibition of Netsuke*, fig. 278, p. 58; Bushell, *Netsuke Familiar and Unfamiliar*, fig. 371, p. 156; Bushell, "Questions & Answers" (1983), figs. 2d, e, and f, p. 48

This is a somewhat simplified depiction of a sumo wrestler, who stands in a defiant attitude and glares at his opponent, presumably to break down the other's reserve. NKD

582 SIDE

582 BACK

581

582 | **Wrestler**

ITTOKUSAI, Japan, active mid-19th century
wood with sumi, inlays
$2^{7}/_{16}$ x $1^{3}/_{4}$ x $1^{1}/_{16}$ in. (6.3 x 4.4 x 2.7 cm)
AC1998.249.131
incised: *Ittokusai*

LITERATURE: Bushell, *An Exhibition of Netsuke*, fig. 279, p. 9; Bushell, *The Wonderful World of Netsuke*, fig. 44, p. 41; Meinertzhagen, *The Meinertzhagen Card Index*, pt. A, p. 253

PROVENANCE: Marcel Lorber

The posture of this unusually cheerful-looking wrestler indicates that he is performing a series of ceremonial gestures meant to express his power. The archaic characters on his decorative loincloth (*keshō mawashi*) read *Nihon dai ichi* ("number one in Japan"). Little is known about Ittokusai. Only a few of his netsuke exist, many in richly stained wood and on a variety of subjects. From the style, he probably worked during the mid-1800s. NKD

583 | **Entertainer**

TOMOTADA, Japan, active 18th century
ivory with staining, sumi
1 1/2 x 1 1/8 x 15/16 in. (3.8 x 2.8 x 2.4 cm)
M.91.250.188
incised and stained: *Tomotada*

LITERATURE: Bushell, "Questions & Answers" (1981), fig. 3, p. 40

Storytellers numbered among the various performers who frequented the urban centers of eighteenth-century Japan. This artist is not the well-known carver from Kyoto, but another of the same name who also worked in the eighteenth century. NKD

584 | **Hostess**

Japan, 19th century
wood with pigments
2 1/8 x 1 5/16 x 3/4 in. (5.4 x 3.3 x 1.9 cm)
AC1998.249.293

LITERATURE: AMICO, 2001–present; Phillips, ed., *The Collectors' Encyclopedia of Antiques*, p. 563

This elderly hostess of a tea house extends her arm in greeting to guests, her face wreathed in smiles. Hair, dress, and makeup were telling signs of a woman's social status. Her profession is indicated by bare feet and the front-facing knot of her obi. Red is not a color worn by honorable woman of her age, but she wears it to her advantage, the bright color no doubt catching the eye of potential customers. CD

585 | **Fukusuke**

TŌCHINSAI, Japan, active 19th century
mid-19th century
wood with inlays
2 11/16 x 1 5/16 x 1 1/4 in. (6.8 x 3.4 x 3.2 cm)
M.91.250.288
incised: *Tōchinsai*

LITERATURE: Bushell, *An Exhibition of Netsuke*, fig. 285, p. 59; Bushell, *An Introduction to Netsuke*, fig. 27, p. 72

PROVENANCE: Kotera Kazuo

Fukusuke has been variously described as a raconteur, a children's toy, and a fatuous, stupid creature. He is shown here as a macrocephalic dwarf who brings good luck. NKD

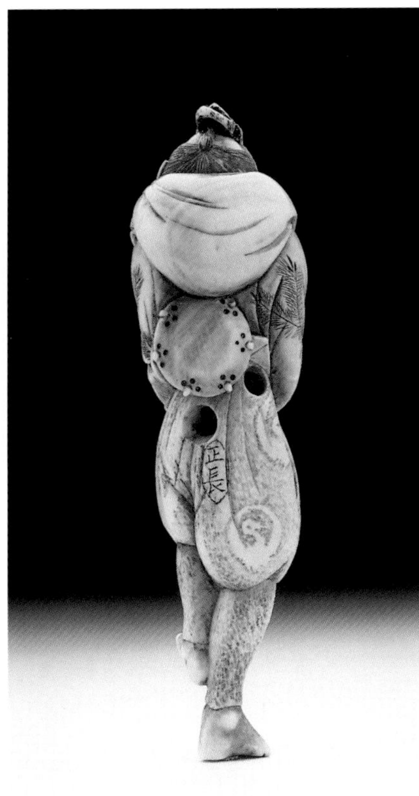

586 BACK

586 | **Manzai: Comic Actor**

Japan, mid-19th century
ivory with staining, sumi, red pigment
3 1/8 x 7/8 x 7/8 in. (7.9 x 2.2 x 2.2 cm)
AC1998.249.233
incised and stained in oval cartouche:
Masanaga [added later]

LITERATURE: AMICO, 2001–present; Bushell, *An Exhibition of Netsuke*, fig. 292, p. 59

Manzai would perform for private parties at the homes of the wealthy. Manzai dancers are generally shown as a pair (CATS. 588–89), one dancing while the other plays the hand drum (*ōtsuzumi*). Here, the drummer is depicted alone, laughing uproariously to entertain New Year's revelers. NKD

587 | **Raconteur**

ŌHARA MITSUHIRO, Japan, 1810–1875
wood with inlays
1 1/4 x 1 1/4 x 1 in. (3.2 x 3.2 x 2.5 cm)
M.90.186.14
incised and stained with sumi: *Mitsuhiro*; kakihan

LITERATURE: AMICO, 2001–present; Meinertzhagen, *The Meinertzhagen Card Index*, pt. A, p. 544

PROVENANCE: Eric R. Levett; Dr. H. A. Gunther

Raconteurs performed in smaller, sometimes temporary theaters in Edo. In this humorous representation, the raconteur illustrates the tale for his audience through his exaggerated facial expressions. The subject and treatment are unusual for Ōhara Mitsuhiro, whose work was generally of ivory. However, as seen in his book *Takarabukuro* (Treasure bag), he was not averse to using wood and liked to bring humor into his creations. NKD

588 | **Itinerant Entertainers**

Front illustrated on page 53
School of Nagai Rantei, Japan, mid- to late 19th century
ivory with staining, sumi
1 5/16 x 1 3/8 x 13/16 in. (3.4 x 3.5 x 2 cm)
M.87.263.123
incised in oval cartouche: *Rantei*

LITERATURE: AMICO, 1999–present; Bushell, *The Inrō Handbook*, fig. 98, p. 135

The two performers are Manzai dancers, singing and playing to entertain crowds at the New Year's celebration (see also CATS. 586, 589). NKD

588 BACK

589 | **Entertainers**

Meikeisai Hōjitsu, Japan, died 1872
ivory with staining, sumi
1 1/2 x 1 5/16 x 3/4 in. (3.8 x 3.4 x 1.9 cm)
AC1998.249.75
incised and lightly stained: *Meikeisai*

LITERATURE: AMICO, 2001–present; Bushell, *An Exhibition of Netsuke*, fig. 291, p. 59; Bushell, "Travels by Netsuke," fig. 12, p. 107; Ueda, *The Netsuke Handbook of Ueda Reikichi*, fig. 101, p. 97

The two entertainers represented here are Manzai dancers, performing their ancient dance to celebrate the New Year. One wields a fan while singing, accompanied by his companion, who beats a hand drum (*ōtsuzumi*). Meikeisai Hōjitsu was a prolific carver from Edo who worked mainly in ivory. He excelled in the portrayal of genre figures, either as *katabori* netsuke or in relief on *manjū*. NKD

590 | **Entertainer Playing Turtle**

Illustrated on page 17
Kokeisai Sanshō, Japan, 1871–1936
boxwood, ivory with staining, sumi
2 3/8 x 1 13/16 x 15/16 in. (6 x 4.6 x 2.3 cm)
AC1998.249.234
incised: *Sanshō*; kakihan

PROVENANCE: Betty Jahss

This is a typically comic creation by one of the most inventive artists of the late 1800s. The entertainer is inside a turtle-shaped basket, which is tied at the sides, with holes for his head, hands, and feet. The basket is of pale, lightly stained boxwood; the man's limbs are of ivory with slight sumi details. Kokeisai Sanshō lived in Osaka and produced a number of amusing and expressive figural netsuke mainly in boxwood, although he occasionally used fine-quality ivory. NKD

591 | **Kabuki Actor Nakajima Wadaemon in the Role of Tambaya Hachiemon**

Ōuchi Sōsui, Japan, 1911–1972
wood with ivory inlay
1 1/2 x 1 1/4 x 1 1/4 in. (3.8 x 3.1 x 3.1 cm)
AC1998.249.43
incised and stained with sumi on oval reserve cartouche: *Sōsui*

LITERATURE: AMICO, 2001–present; Bushell, *Collectors' Netsuke*, fig. 325, p. 177; Bushell, *An Exhibition of Netsuke*, fig. 459, p. 28

Ōuchi Sōsui has taken his design from a woodblock print of *hosoban* format by Tōshūsai Sharaku (active 1794/95), who was renowned for his portraits of kabuki actors. He has cleverly converted the two-dimensional print into a three-dimensional miniature sculpture, retaining all the implied strength and power of the original. NKD

592 | **First Cooking of the New Year**

School of Katsura Mitsunaga, Japan, mid- to late 19th century
gold disk, ivory bowl; kagamibuta type
1 3/4 x 7/16 in. (4.5 x 1.1 cm)
AC1998.249.232
incised: *Mitsunaga*; kakihan

LITERATURE: Bushell, *Netsuke Familiar and Unfamiliar*, fig. 229, p. 133

This *kagamibuta* is made of conventional materials; it has a bowl of ivory and a disk of gold. It is cast with an image of a chef who wears formal attire while ceremonially preparing food for the New Year's celebration. Katsura Mitsunaga, from Murakami in Echizen province, was a maker of sword fittings. Because he died in 1825, the present example was almost certainly made by a follower. NKD

593 | **Picking the New Year's Pine**

Toshiyama Sōkō, Japan, 1868–1935
wood disk, ivory bowl; kagamibuta type
1 3/8 x 9/16 in. (3.5 x 1.4 cm)
AC1998.249.220
incised: *Sōkō saku* / "made by Sōkō"

LITERATURE: Bushell, *Collectors' Netsuke*, fig. 284, p. 159

This *kagamibuta* is unusual in that the disk is of wood rather than the more typical metal. The carving is of a seated young girl who smiles as she picks a branch of the young pine to add to the New Year's arrangement of plum, pine, and bamboo (*kadomatsu*) for the entrance to her home. Toshiyama Sōkō was a fringe member of the Sō School, working in Osaka, and he studied under Gyokkin, Mondō, and Tessai. NKD

595 | **Boy behind Chinese Lion Mask**

Ishikawa Kōmei, Japan,
circa 1848/52–1913
ivory
$1\frac{3}{16} \times 1\frac{3}{16} \times 1$ in. (3 x 3 x 2.5 cm)
M.91.250.313
incised: *Kōmei*

LITERATURE: AMICO, 2001–present

A small boy holds the huge lion mask over his head and manipulates the lower jaw with both hands. The work is rendered in the typically realistic style of Ishikawa Kōmei, one of the founders of the Tokyo School of Fine Arts who was better known for his large *okimono*. NKD

594 | **Chinese Lion Dance**

Nobumasa, Japan, active
early 19th century
ivory with staining, sumi, inlays
$2 \times 1\frac{1}{8} \times \frac{11}{16}$ in. (5.1 x 2.9 x 1.7 cm)
AC1998.249.10
incised and stained with sumi in oval cartouche: *Nobumasa*

LITERATURE: AMICO, 2001–present; Bushell, *Netsuke Familiar and Unfamiliar*, back cover; Bushell, *Netsuke Masks*, fig. 350; Ueda, *The Netsuke Handbook of Ueda Reikichi*, fig. 189, p. 184

The dancer stands, looking up to the right, and holds a Buddhist rattle (*shakujō*). He wears the typically large lion mask (*shishiguchi*), and his robe is gathered around his shoulders. From the style of the netsuke, Nobumasa probably lived in Kyoto during the early 1800s. NKD

596 BACK

596 | Chinese Lion Dance

Takehara Chikkō, Japan, active late 19th–mid-20th century
wood
$2^{3}/_{8}$ x 1 x 1 in. (6 x 2.6 x 2.5 cm)
M.91.250.279
incised: *Chikkō*

LITERATURE: Bushell, *Collectors' Netsuke*, fig. 305, p. 164; Bushell, *An Exhibition of Netsuke*, fig. 479, p. 79

The lion dancer (*shishimai*) sings to his own accompaniment as he beats out the rhythm on a double-ended hand drum (*ōtsuzumi*). His lion mask is tipped to the back of his head, its retaining cord caught beneath his nose. Takehara Chikkō lived in Osaka and studied under Kaigyokusai Masatsugu (1813–1892). Although he is recorded as having carved "tirelessly," his work is rarely seen. NKD

597 | Chinese Lion Dance

Front illustrated on page 21
Ōuchi Sōsui, Japan, 1911–1972
wood
$1^{15}/_{16}$ x $1^{1}/_{8}$ x $1^{1}/_{8}$ in. (5 x 2.8 x 2.8 cm)
AC1998.249.98
incised: *Sōsui*

LITERATURE: Bushell, *Collectors' Netsuke*, fig. 313, p. 175; Bushell, *An Exhibition of Netsuke*, fig. 461, p. 78; Bushell, "Travels by Netsuke," fig. 11, p. 106

In this unusually elaborate and complex depiction of a lion dancer, the figure wears the typical mask and cloak over his street clothes, which he vainly attempts to keep dry beneath a very tattered umbrella. NKD

597 BACK

Daily Life

The minutiae of daily life were a rich source of subject matter for netsuke carvers. Many of the pieces in this section—for example, a man pulling on his loincloth or a priest distracted by a fly—focus on a moment of humor in the passing panorama because patrons of netsuke carvers in Edo often requested comical subjects. Other *netsukeshi* were inspired by quite mundane activities, yet observed them so closely and executed them so exquisitely that the carvers seem to capture something timeless in the instant they depict—a man and wife quarreling, an egg tester squinting to verify the fertility of an egg, a beautiful woman caught in a moment of reflection. Netsuke of women also included the blatantly and the subtly erotic; the latter is exemplified here by numerous netsuke of diving girls (*ama*) with octopuses (CATS. 627–29).

Since the thirteenth century, scrolls and later, screens, showed artisans engaged in their trades. The growing awareness of the artisans' role in the early Edo period stimulated the development of a new painting subject called "pictures of all the craftsmen" (*shokunin zukushie*) and craftspeople became a subject of interest to carvers as well.

Ghost stories were popular in late-eighteenth- and early-nineteenth-century literature and theater, and netsuke of ghosts can sometimes be related to contemporary plays (CAT. 681). The Japanese ghost, usually female, is typically shown without feet, and with bedraggled hair and beckoning hands (CATS. 674–82). Skeletons were associated with the dead, but they were also interesting to people fascinated by science and anatomy, and in netsuke they tend to be carved fairly realistically (CATS. 683–87).

ABOVE: *Child Drying Herself* (CAT. 643)

598 BACK

598 | **Blind Man**

Japan, 18th century
ivory with staining, sumi
3 7/16 x 1 1/8 x 1 in. (8.8 x 2.9 x 2.5 cm)
M.87.263.4

LITERATURE: AMICO, 2000–present; Bushell, *An Exhibition of Netsuke*, fig. 276, p. 58

This is an elegant representation of a blind man. His expression suggests that he may have been a survivor of one of Japan's smallpox epidemics, as the disease is known to distort the features and cause blindness. NKD

599 | **Blind Men Fighting**

ZEMIN, Japan, active mid-19th century
ivory with staining, sumi, red and white pigments; manjū type
1 3/4 x 1 in. (4.5 x 2.6 cm)
M.87.263.31
incised and stained: *Zemin*; kakihan

LITERATURE: AMICO, 2000–present; Bushell, *An Exhibition of Netsuke*, fig. 93, p. 39; Bushell, *Netsuke Familiar and Unfamiliar*, fig. 286, p. 142; Davey, *Netsuke*, fig. 313, p. 110; Lazarnick, *Netsuke and Inro Artists*, vol. 2, p. 1258

PROVENANCE: Mark T. Hindson

The blind were often used as comic subjects, particularly in netsuke. Here, several blind men have bumped into each other in the street, each believing that he is being attacked. Zemin was one of a number of fine *netsukeshi* working in Edo during the mid-1800s. His output was mainly of figural subjects and *manjū*. NKD

599 BACK

600 | **Blind Man with Stone in Clog**

Illustrated on page 54
Suganoya Shōko, Japan,
active circa 1840–1880
wood
$2\,^{3}/_{16} \times {}^{15}/_{16} \times 1\,^{3}/_{16}$ in. (5.5 x 2.4 x 3 cm)
M.91.250.160
incised: *Shōko*

LITERATURE: Bushell, *An Exhibition of Netsuke*, fig. 277, p. 58; Ueda, *The Netsuke Handbook of Ueda Reikichi*, fig. 81, p. 89

The blind man has stopped to remove a stone from his clog (*geta*). Suganoya Shōko worked in Takayama in Hida province and should not be confused with Shōko (Nishino Shōtarō), the twentieth-century carver. NKD

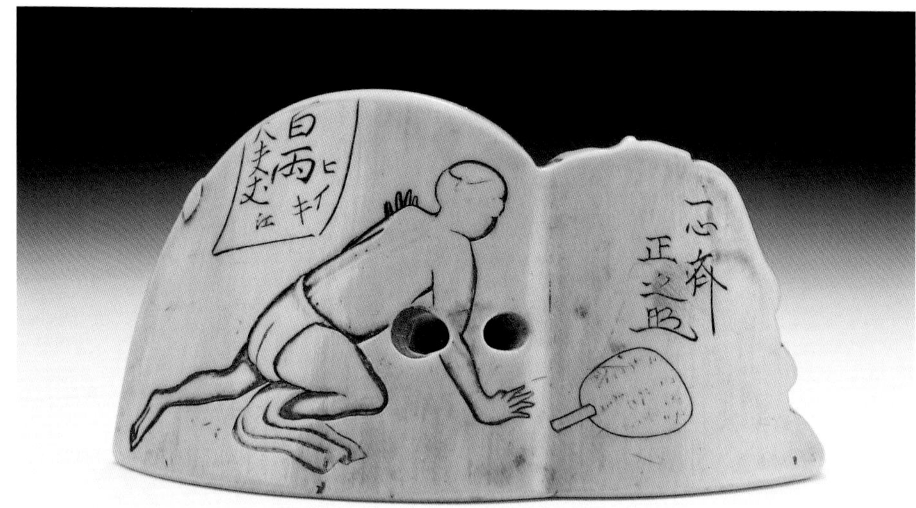

601 BACK

601 | **Voyeur Watching Scene in House of Pleasure**

Isshinsai Masayuki, Japan,
active late 18th–early 19th century
late 18th century
ivory with sumi, red pigment
$1\,^{5}/_{8} \times 3\,^{1}/_{8} \times 1\,^{1}/_{8}$ in. (4.1 x 7.9 x 2.9 cm)
AC1998.249.262
incised and stained: *Isshinsai Masayuki*; kakihan; [various graffiti: for example, *Hyakuryō daijōbu* / "a hundred ryō is okay"]

The setting is a house of pleasure in the Yoshiwara district of Edo. A geisha is singing, accompanying herself on the *shamisen*, while her gentleman client tries to keep up, reading from a songbook and beating a rhythm. Between them, at the back, is the face of a voyeur, who looks in with little expression. Voyeurism had been a common theme in Japanese erotic prints of the *ukiyo-e* style from the earliest days of woodblock printing, in the late 1600s. NKD

602 | **Female Daruma Doll**

Japan, 18th century, with 20th-century additions
ivory with sumi, red pigment
1 5/16 x 1 1/4 x 1 5/16 in. (3.3 x 3.1 x 3.3 cm)
AC1998.249.275

The roly-poly doll is in the form of Daruma, the patriarch of Zen Buddhism, but with a beauty's face. Daruma of this type are called *onna Daruma* (female Daruma). The work is reminiscent of that created by Ogasawara Issai, who worked in the mid- to late 1700s. The face was later recarved and tinted details were added. NKD

602 BACK

603 | **Female Daruma Doll**

Japan, 19th century
gold lacquer
1 1/2 x 1 1/4 x 1 1/16 in. (3.8 x 3.1 x 2.7 cm)
M.87.263.45

LITERATURE: AMICO, 2000–present; Bushell, *An Exhibition of Netsuke*, fig. 404, p. 26; Bushell, *Netsuke Familiar and Unfamiliar*, fig. 251, p. 136

PROVENANCE: Sam Broadbent

This is a lacquered depiction of a subject popular with children. The Zen patriarch is shown here with the face of Okame, the boisterous and lustful goddess of mirth. NKD

604 | **Losing a Tooth while Pounding Rice**

JOBUN, Japan, active late 18th–early 19th century
boxwood with inlays
1 5/8 x 1 1/4 x 1 1/4 in. (4.1 x 3.1 x 3.2 cm)
M.91.250.157
incised: *Jobun*

LITERATURE: AMICO, 2001–present; Bushell, *Collectors' Netsuke*, fig. 74, p. 64; Bushell, *An Exhibition of Netsuke*, fig. 102, p. 40; Hill and Johnson, "The Raymond Bushell Netsuke Exhibition," fig. 102, p. 32; Stratos, "The Netsuke Carvings of Jobun," fig. 24, p. 19

The peasant looks up with an expression of discomfort as he realizes that one of his few remaining teeth has worked itself loose, due to his enthusiastic pounding of the rice. Jobun's work is often very expressive, a trait shown to great advantage in this example. NKD

605 | **Strength Stone Contest**

Illustrated on page 54
JOBUN, Japan, active late 18th–
early 19th century
boxwood
$1^{5}/_{8}$ x $1^{5}/_{16}$ x $^{15}/_{16}$ in. (4.1 x 3.4 x 2.4 cm)
M.91.250.168
incised: *Jobun*

LITERATURE: Bushell, *Collectors' Netsuke*, fig. 75, p. 64; Bushell, *An Exhibition of Netsuke*, fig. 103, p. 40; Stratos, "The Netsuke Carvings of Jobun," fig. 12, p. 18

A blind man, probably a masseur, shows the effort on his face as he tries to lift a large boulder. This common subject has also been described as a blind man trying to rise beneath the weight of a hugely distended scrotum, but this idea has been generally discounted. Little is known of Jobun and his life, except that he lived in Edo at the end of the eighteenth century and produced a comparatively small number of netsuke, mostly of expressive figural subjects. NKD

606 | **Master and Hungry Dog**

JOBUN, Japan, active late 18th–
early 19th century
late 18th century
wood
$1^{5}/_{8}$ x $1^{3}/_{8}$ x $1^{1}/_{4}$ in. (4.1 x 3.5 x 3.2 cm)
AC1998.249.156
incised and stained: *Jobun*

LITERATURE: AMICO, 2001–present; Bushell, *Collectors' Netsuke*, fig. 76, p. 64; Bushell, *An Exhibition of Netsuke*, fig. 101, p. 40; Stratos, "The Netsuke Carvings of Jobun," fig. 20, p. 19

The dog sits at his master's side, looking up longingly as the man greedily eats a biscuit. NKD

607 | **Peasant Trying to Lift Himself**

Japan, 19th century
ivory with staining, sumi
$2^{1}/_{16}$ x $^{3}/_{4}$ x $^{5}/_{8}$ in. (5.2 x 1.9 x 1.6 cm)
M.91.250.155

LITERATURE: Bushell, *Netsuke Familiar and Unfamiliar*, figs. 175a and b, p. 121

Here, a peasant is attempting the impossible: By grabbing his neck and the back of his loincloth (*fundoshi*), he is trying to lift himself from the ground. This netsuke probably depicts a comic performer who entertained crowds in eighteenth-century Edo. NKD

609 BACK

608 | **Man Pulling on Loincloth**

Japan, 19th century
ivory with sumi
2 13/16 x 1 1/4 x 11/16 in. (7.2 x 3.2 x 1.8 cm)
M.91.250.167

PROVENANCE: Adolph Kroch

In this comic netsuke, the man holds the front of his loincloth (*fundoshi*) with his chin as he yanks the rest of it tightly behind him. NKD

609 | **Man Tying Loincloth**

Tokyo School of Fine Arts,
Japan, created 1887
circa 1890
ivory with light staining
2 3/16 x 1 x 9/16 in. (5.6 x 2.5 x 1.5 cm)
M.90.186.18

LITERATURE: AMICO, 2000–present

PROVENANCE: Denis Szeszler

A man looks down in concentration as he starts the process of tying his loincloth (*fundoshi*). The work is in the style of the Tokyo School of Fine Arts, which opened in 1887. Its members excelled in ivory and wood carving and bronze casting, bringing a previously unseen realism to their sculptures. NKD

610 | **Man with Exaggerated Topknot**

Illustrated on page 51
Japan, early 19th century
wood
2 x 15/16 x 1 in. (5.1 x 2.4 x 2.5 cm)
M.91.250.163

LITERATURE: Bushell, *An Exhibition of Netsuke*, fig. 110, p. 40; Bushell, *Netsuke Familiar and Unfamiliar*, fig. 180, p. 122

Throughout the Edo period (1615–1868), Japanese art increasingly incorporated political and social themes. A fashionable hairstyle for men in the late Edo period is rendered here with exaggeration and humor. The attention lavished on one's hair seemed ludicrous to some, a sentiment obviously shared by this *netsukeshi*, who pokes fun at those who slavishly adhere to fashion trends. CD

611 | **Cooper with Tub**

Japan, early 19th century
wood
2 1/4 x 1 1/4 x 1 1/4 in. (5.7 x 3.2 x 3.2 cm)
AC1998.249.135

LITERATURE: AMICO, 2001–present; Bushell, "Questions & Answers" (1978c), fig. 5, p. 14

This craftsman, probably having just completed this tub, has devised an ingenious method by which to transport it. While coopers are not uncommon subjects in netsuke, they are usually shown making the barrel. This portrayal is unique. CD

612 | **Meditating Priest with Buzzing Fly**

Ōhara Mitsusada, Japan, active 19th century
ivory with staining, sumi, inlays
1 9/16 x 1 1/4 x 15/16 in. (4 x 3.1 x 2.4 cm)
M.91.250.159
seal form, incised and stained in oval cartouche: *Mitsusada*

LITERATURE: Bushell, *An Exhibition of Netsuke*, fig. 118, p. 41; Hurtig, *Masterpieces of Netsuke Art*, fig. 127, p. 48

Daruma was often portrayed with a fly whisk, a symbol of his preparedness to fight off all distractions to his meditations. The priest here, however, is less prepared; his concentration has been broken by a buzzing fly that alights on his head, which indicates his lack of purposefulness. The netsuke was made by Ōhara Mitsusada (a contemporary of Ōhara Mitsuhiro of Osaka) in the mid-1800s. NKD

613 | **Frustrated Rat Catcher**

Illustrated on page 26
ITTAN, Japan, circa 1820–1877
wood
$1^{9}/_{16}$ x $1^{1}/_{16}$ x $^{13}/_{16}$ in. (4 x 2.7 x 2.1 cm)
M.91.250.166
incised: *Ittan gi [?]* / "playfully carved [?] by Ittan"

LITERATURE: AMICO, 2001–present; Bushell, *Collectors' Netsuke*, fig. 111, p. 91

The rat catcher presses down on his trap, yelling in anger as the rat escapes over his back. This particular subject was often treated in netsuke. Ittan was one of several artists working in nineteenth-century Nagoya. His work was invariably in wood, the carving extremely neat and well detailed. NKD

614 | **Frustrated Rat Catcher**

ITTAN, Japan, circa 1820–1877
wood
$1^{1}/_{2}$ x $1^{1}/_{4}$ x 1 in. (3.8 x 3.1 x 2.5 cm)
AC1998.249.17
incised: *Ittan*; kakihan

While slightly smaller than the previous piece, this and most of Ittan's rat catchers are nearly identical in design and treatment. (See Meinertzhagen, *The Meinertzhagen Card Index*, p. 250, for a comparable netsuke.) CD

615 SIDE

615 | **Frustrated Rat Catcher**

SHŌAI, Japan, active late 19th century
ivory with staining, sumi
2 x $1^{7}/_{8}$ x $1^{1}/_{4}$ in. (5.1 x 4.7 x 3.2 cm)
AC1998.249.151
incised and stained: *Shōai tō* / "carved by Shōai"

LITERATURE: AMICO, 2001–present

This is a fine example of a commonly treated subject that was more frequently carved in wood by a number of Nagoya artists (CATS. 613–14). The work is in the style of Kihōdō Masaka, who made similar examples toward the end of the nineteenth century. The carver of this example may be another member of the Kihōdō family. NKD

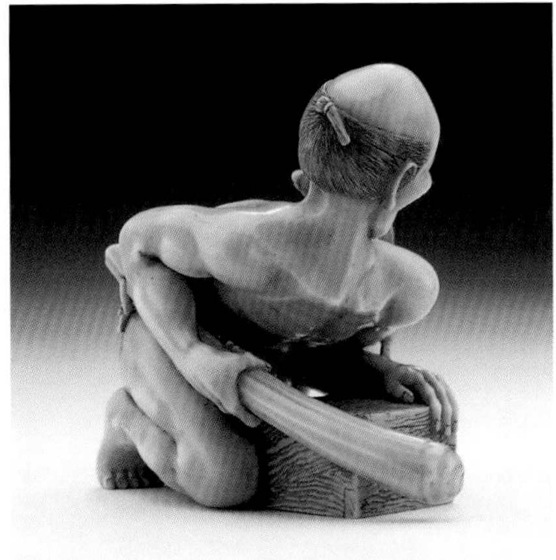

615 SIDE

616 | Townsman Holding Long Pipe with Lip

HŌSHUNSAI MASAYUKI, Japan,
active mid- to late 19th century
wood
1 7/16 x 1 7/16 x 1 in. (3.6 x 3.6 x 2.5 cm)
M.91.250.156
incised in irregular reserve: *Masayuki*; kakihan

LITERATURE: AMICO, 2001–present; Bushell, *An Exhibition of Netsuke*, fig. 111, p. 40; Bushell, *Netsuke Familiar and Unfamiliar*, fig. 177, p. 122; Phillips, ed., *The Collectors' Encyclopedia of Antiques*, p. 568

Hōshunsai Masayuki worked in Asakusa, Tokyo, during the late 1800s, and had two distinctly different styles. One style was favored by other members of his group, such as Ozaki Kokusai and Ishikawa Rensai, who made a variety of netsuke in stag antler or ivory. The other style, shown here, comprised neat, naturalistic figural images, mostly of genre subjects and perhaps copied from life. In this netsuke, the man holding his pipe with his lower lip is probably taking part in a party trick or game. NKD

617 | Moxibustion Patient in Agony

HARA SHŪGETSU (or SHŪGETSU III), Japan, born 1828, active until circa 1880
wood with inlays
1 5/16 x 1 1/16 x 1 3/8 in. (3.4 x 2.7 x 3.5 cm)
M.91.250.161
incised: *Shūgetsu*

LITERATURE: AMICO, 2001–present; Bushell, *An Exhibition of Netsuke*, fig. 36, p. 33; Hurtig, *Masterpieces of Netsuke Art*, fig. 108, p. 45; Mikoshiba and Bushell, "Netsuke and the *Sōken kishō*," p. 113

In moxibustion, a technique used in traditional Chinese medicine, a heated stick or pellet of mugwort is placed on an acupuncture point to strengthen and stimulate the blood and life energy. In this netsuke, the patient reels back in agony as he applies a burning pellet to his leg. Hara Shūgetsu worked in Edo. His work closely follows that of Shūgetsu I and Shūgetsu II, the first of whom produced netsuke in the late 1700s. NKD

618 | Man with Hangover Sawing Sake Gourd

SCHOOL OF MIWA, Japan,
late 18th–19th century
wood
1 5/16 x 1 5/8 x 1 1/8 in. (3.3 x 4.2 x 2.8 cm)
M.91.250.162
incised: *Miwa*; kakihan

LITERATURE: AMICO, 2001–present; Bushell, *An Exhibition of Netsuke*, fig. 109, p. 40; Bushell, *Netsuke Familiar and Unfamiliar*, fig. 176, p. 122

This expressive rendition depicts a peasant who, having imbibed too much sake the previous day, has decided to destroy his very large gourd flask. NKD

619 | **Inebriated Laborer**

Kokeisai Sanshō, Japan, 1871–1936
boxwood with traces of sumi, red and white pigments
$3^{7}/_{8}$ x $1^{1}/_{2}$ x $1^{3}/_{16}$ in. (9.9 x 3.8 x 3 cm)
M.91.250.68
incised: *Sanshō*; kakihan

LITERATURE: Atchley, "The Pavilion for Japanese Art in Los Angeles," p. 25; Bushell, *Collectors' Netsuke*, fig. 244, p. 152; Davey, *Netsuke*, fig. 69, p. 36; Meinertzhagen, *The Meinertzhagen Card Index*, pt. B, p. 697; Trower, *Catalogue of the H. Seymour Trower Collection of Japanese Art*, fig. 205, pl. 6

PROVENANCE: Mark T. Hindson; Guest collection; Colonel J. B. Gaskell; Harry Seymour Trower

Kokeisai Sanshō was adept at portraying ordinary people in a highly amusing manner (see CATS. 620–21). Here, the laborer holds his sake flask and grimaces as he feels the intoxicating effect of the liquor. As with most of Sanshō's work, the carving is executed in fine, pale boxwood, which is lightly stained. NKD

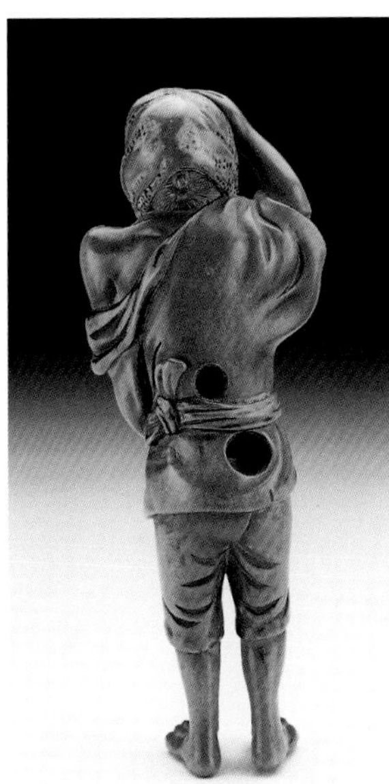

619 BACK

620 | **Inebriated Laborer**

Kokeisai Sanshō, Japan, 1871–1936
boxwood with inlays
$1^{15}/_{16}$ x $1^{1}/_{4}$ x 1 in. (4.9 x 3.1 x 2.5 cm)
M.91.250.164
incised on inlaid lacquered wood plaque: *Sanshō*; kakihan

LITERATURE: AMICO, 2001–present; Bushell, *Collectors' Netsuke*, fig. 246, p. 152; Bushell, *An Exhibition of Netsuke*, fig. 104, p. 40; Davey, *Netsuke*, fig. 68, p. 36; Meinertzhagen, *The Meinertzhagen Card Index*, pt. B, p. 698

PROVENANCE: Geoffrey Duveen; Mark T. Hindson; Harry Seymour Trower

Kokeisai Sanshō carved excellent caricatures as well as distortions of ordinary facial features (see CATS. 821–25). Here, he has created an amusing portrait of a workingman holding his sake flask and cup. His happy smile and glazed expression is heightened by the use of double inlaid eyes. NKD

621 | **Contestant in Ugly Faces Competition**

Kokeisai Sanshō, Japan, 1871–1936
wood
$1\frac{7}{16} \times 1\frac{5}{16} \times \frac{15}{16}$ in. (3.7 x 3.4 x 2.4 cm)
M.91.250.165
incised: *Sanshō*; kakihan

LITERATURE: Bushell, *Collectors' Netsuke*, fig. 242, p. 152; Bushell, *An Exhibition of Netsuke*, fig. 105, p. 40

The "ugly faces competition" theme was tailor-made for Kokeisai Sanshō, who excelled in portraying ordinary people doing silly things. NKD

622 | **Woman Blackening Teeth**

Kawahara Ryō, Japan, died circa 1942
ivory with staining, sumi
1921
$1\frac{5}{16} \times 1\frac{1}{4} \times 1$ in. (3.3 x 3.2 x 2.6 cm)
M.91.250.81
incised and stained with sumi: *Ryō*
ink on box lid: *Ka no to tori tōhi* / "winter day, 1921"; *Ryō tō* / "carved by Ryō"
seal on box lid: *Ryō*

LITERATURE: Bushell, *An Exhibition of Netsuke*, fig. 476, p. 28; Ueda, *The Netsuke Handbook of Ueda Reikichi*, fig. 192, p. 186

The custom of women blackening their teeth (*ohaguro*), which can be traced back to Heian-period (794–1185) aristocracy, was most popular around the 1700s. A woman would stain her teeth with iron filings and shave her eyebrows to look elegant. In the Edo period, married women were required to blacken their teeth. NKD

622 SIDE

623 BACK

623 | Maid Carrying Tai Fish in Basket

KAWAHARA RYŌ, Japan, died circa 1942
ivory with staining, sumi, red pigment
1 7/16 x 1 3/16 x 1 1/16 in. (4.7 x 3 x 2.7 cm)
AC1998.249.296
incised and stained with sumi: *Ryō*
incised and stained with vermilion:
kakihan

LITERATURE: AMICO, 2001–present

The young woman with elaborately coiffed hair is wearing traditional dress engraved with fan-shaped designs. She looks around in bemusement as the fish in her basket tries to escape. At the same time, she grasps her unraveling obi with her right hand. The work is typical of Kawahara Ryō, who produced fine figural netsuke of everyday life. NKD

624 | Maid Making Up

SŌKO (MORITA KISABURŌ), Japan, 1879–1943
wood with inlays, metal
1 7/16 x 1 1/8 x 1 1/16 in. (3.6 x 2.8 x 2.7 cm)
M.91.250.248
incised: *Sōko tō*/"carved by Sōko"; *Chikushō me gejo shishippana shiro botan* / "Beastly ugly maid: / Powders her pug nose to look like / A white peony"

LITERATURE: Bushell, *Netsuke Familiar and Unfamiliar*, fig. 758, p. 226; Hurtig, "Collecting Legends," fig. 2, p. 17

PROVENANCE: Julius Katchen

A maid kneels before an old iron stove, looking into a mirror as she applies makeup to her face. A pouch of white face powder sits to her right, and a shovel, fan, kindling, and straw ring are underneath the stove. Engraved on the stove is a poem, translated above. Sōko was one of the finest artists of the Sō School. He was equally adept when working in wood or ivory, although he apparently favored boxwood as a medium. NKD

626

625 | **Pregnant Woman**

Japan, early 18th century
wood
$3\,^1/_2$ x $1\,^7/_{16}$ x 1 in. (8.9 x 3.7 x 2.5 cm)
M.91.250.154

LITERATURE: Ueda, *The Netsuke Handbook of Ueda Reikichi*, fig. 132, p. 138

PROVENANCE: Ruth Schneidman

This is a caricature of a profligate farm girl, her hands and feet exaggerated in size to emphasize her homeliness and low station in life. HG

626 | **Diving Girl**

Japan, 18th century
ivory with sumi
$1\,^1/_2$ x $1\,^3/_4$ x $1\,^5/_{16}$ in. (3.8 x 4.5 x 3.3 cm)
M.91.250.18

LITERATURE: Bushell, *An Exhibition of Netsuke*, fig. 288, p. 59

Diving girls (*ama*) appear in many genres of Japanese art, including woodblock prints, often in an erotic attitude. Here, the girl is shown in a somewhat suggestive pose, because the clam was a common symbol for female genitalia. She holds a clam digger in her other hand. NKD

626 BACK

627 | **Diving Girl and Octopus**

Illustrated on page 58
GENRYŌSAI MINKOKU II, Japan,
active early to mid-19th century
early 19th century
ivory with staining, sumi, lacquer, crystal inlays
1 15/16 x 1 x 3/4 in. (5 x 2.5 x 1.9 cm)
M.90.186.13
incised and stained: *Minkoku*

LITERATURE: AMICO, 2000–present; Davey, *Netsuke*, fig. 294, p. 104

PROVENANCE: Michael Birch; Mark T. Hindson

Among the most common representations of *ama* is that of a girl in the clutches of an amorous octopus. In this example, carved in great detail in flawless ivory, the girl's hair is lacquered a lustrous black. Genryōsai Minkoku II, who worked in Edo, was a direct follower of Minkoku I. He created a number of fine figure netsuke as well as *manjū*. NKD

628 | **Diving Girl and Octopus**

KIKUGAWA FAMILY, Japan, active 1844–1867
ivory with staining, sumi, red pigment
1 1/2 x 1 1/4 x 1 in. (3.8 x 3.2 x 2.6 cm)
M.91.250.62
incised and lightly stained: *Kikugawa*

LITERATURE: Bushell, *An Exhibition of Netsuke*, fig. 289, p. 24; Hurtig, *Masterpieces of Netsuke Art*, fig. 105, p. 45; Lazarnick, *Netsuke and Inro Artists*, vol. 1, p. 615

The diving girl here also enjoys the passionate advances of an octopus. The Kikugawa family worked in Edo, producing a large number of *katabori* figure netsuke and *manjū*. NKD

629 | **Diving Girl and Octopus**

MIYAGI CHOKUSAI (MASANOSUKE), Japan, born 1877
ivory with staining, sumi, mother-of-pearl inlays
1 15/16 x 1 1/8 x 13/16 in. (5 x 2.8 x 2.1 cm)
M.91.250.138
seal form, carved: *Chokusai*

LITERATURE: AMICO, 2001–present; Ueda, *The Netsuke Handbook of Ueda Reikichi*, fig. 134, p. 140

In this example, unlike others in the collection, the octopus has been caught and is trapped in a jar. The diving girl seems amused that the creature persists in its caresses. Miyagi Chokusai was born in Osaka and carved in wood and ivory, although he appears to have preferred the latter. His work is generally small and exhibits a high degree of detail, and he often used pigment or inlay to enhance specific areas. NKD

630 | **Diving Girl**

Yūkoku, Japan, active late 19th–early 20th century
ivory with sumi, wood, metal inlay
$2\,^1/_4$ x $^{11}/_{16}$ x $^9/_{16}$ in. (5.7 x 1.7 x 1.4 cm)
AC1998.249.39
incised on inlaid gold plaque: *Yūkoku*

LITERATURE: AMICO, 2001–present; Ueda, *The Netsuke Handbook of Ueda Reikichi*, fig. 66, p. 82

This girl—unlike many depicted in netsuke—is simple and innocent, drying off after a dive. Her skirt is of finely polished wood, while the remainder of the carving is executed in flawless ivory. Yūkoku has been recorded as a possible follower of Tōkoku, although he was more likely a contemporary of Hōshu (Yoshihide), whose work is remarkably similar. NKD

631 | **Diving Girl Sleeping on Dried Bonito**

Ōuchi Gyokusō, Japan, 1879–1944
wood, ivory with staining, loose pearl, inlays
$2\,^5/_8$ x $^7/_8$ x $^7/_8$ in. (6.7 x 2.2 x 2.2 cm)
AC1998.249.107
incised: *Gyokusō*

LITERATURE: Bushell, *An Exhibition of Netsuke*, fig. 441, p. 76; Hill and Johnson, "The Raymond Bushell Netsuke Exhibition," fig. 441, p. 30; Ueda, *The Netsuke Handbook of Ueda Reikichi*, fig. 77, p. 87

A diving girl sleeps against a huge, desiccated fish and holds a large abalone. Here, the bonito with the white pearl in its mouth is a phallic symbol, while the abalone, like the clam, signifies female genitalia. Ōuchi Gyokusō was one of the foremost members of the Sō School. He was equally adept working in wood or ivory and his subject matter was varied. He was the teacher of Ōuchi Sōsui (whose works are also in the Bushell collection), among others. NKD

632 | After the Bath

Japan, late 18th–early 19th century
wood
$3\frac{3}{4}$ x $1\frac{1}{4}$ x 1 in. (9.5 x 3.1 x 2.5 cm)
AC1998.249.59

LITERATURE: AMICO, 2001–present

With feet together and toes turned inward, a woman holds a loose robe around her as she uses a mirror to inspect her coiffure, a section of her obi held in her mouth. The carving is a great exhibition of understated elegance, the woman having been caught in a very private moment. NKD

633 | Female Traveler

MINKOKU III, Japan, active late 19th–early 20th century
ivory with dark staining, sumi
$2\frac{3}{8}$ x $\frac{15}{16}$ x $\frac{7}{8}$ in. (6.1 x 2.4 x 2.2 cm)
M.91.250.277
incised in rectangular reserve: *Minkoku*

LITERATURE: AMICO, 2001–present; Bushell, *An Exhibition of Netsuke*, fig. 299, p. 60; Bushell, "Travels by Netsuke," fig. 2, p. 105; Ueda, *The Netsuke Handbook of Ueda Reikichi*, fig. 186, p. 182

Dressed for traveling, the young woman holds a bamboo cane and broad sun hat, her clothing stained to contrast with her pale face. The artist, a distant follower of Genryōsai Minkoku I and II, made netsuke and *okimono* mainly for export to the West. NKD

634 | Beauty Contemplating Love Letter

BUNGA, Japan, active early 20th century
ivory with dark staining, sumi
$1\frac{9}{16}$ x $1\frac{3}{16}$ x $1\frac{1}{8}$ in. (3.9 x 3 x 2.8 cm)
AC1998.249.289
incised and stained with sumi: *Bunga* [or *Bunya*]

A beautiful young woman (*bijin*) leans on a small cabinet, lost in thought, having just received a letter from her lover. This is a wonderfully contemplative study by an artist who is apparently hitherto unrecorded. NKD

635 | Beauty Reading Love Letter

INADA ICHIRŌ, Japan, 1891–1979
wood with pigments
2 3/16 x 1 x 7/8 in. (5.5 x 2.5 x 2.2 cm)
M.91.250.210
incised: *Ichirō*

LITERATURE: Bushell, *Collectors' Netsuke*, fig. 312, p. 174; Bushell, *An Exhibition of Netsuke*, fig. 478, p. 79

PROVENANCE: Horie Zenshiro

Holding her robe around her, a beautiful young woman (*bijin*) reads a letter from her lover. The work is expressively rendered in wood, with the elegant dress designs created from various pigments. Inada Ichirō lived in Tokyo. His work was almost always figural, with genre subjects being his specialty. He found commercial success working with ivory, but he preferred wood as his medium. NKD

636 | Mother and Child

Also illustrated on page 71
ŌUCHI SŌSUI, Japan, 1911–1972
wood
2 7/16 x 15/16 x 15/16 in. (6.2 x 2.3 x 2.3 cm)
M.91.250.212
incised: *Sōsui*
ink on box lid: *Sōsui saku* / "made by Sōsui"
seal on box lid: *Sōsui*

LITERATURE: Bushell, *Collectors' Netsuke*, fig. 324, p. 177; Hurtig, "Collecting Legends," p. 14

This netsuke is similar to the pencil sketch of a work titled *Mother and Son* that Masatoshi made in 1955 while attending an exhibition of Mexican art at the Tokyo National Museum. Masatoshi's netsuke based on that sketch is very similar to this netsuke by Sōsui. Raymond Bushell felt that this simple composition might have been made in response to books on Mexican art that he loaned to Sōsui. He also encouraged Sōsui to simplify his style, which Sōsui did for about two years before returning to more complex, inlaid works (CAT. 637). HG

636 BACK

637

637 | **Beauty**

Ōuchi Sōsui, Japan, 1911–1972
wood with inlays
1 1/2 x 1 1/4 x 1 in. (3.8 x 3.2 x 2.6 cm)
M.91.250.228
incised: *Sōsui tō* / "carved by Sōsui"
ink on box: *Bijin yosegi shō kan netsuke* / "joined and inlaid netsuke of a beauty"
ink on box lid: *Sōsui saku* / "made by Sōsui"
incised on inlaid tortoiseshell plaque in box: *Bijin yosegi shōkan netsuke* / "joined and inlaid wood portrait of a beauty" / face, hands, and feet: *zōge* / "ivory"; eyebrows: *kai* / "shell"; clothes: *byakudan* / "white sandalwood"; eyes: *umimatsu* / "black coral"; belt: *hizakura* / "scarlet cherry wood"; mouth: *hōten* / "hornbill ivory"; hair: *suigyū* / "water buffalo horn"; sash bustle: *kai* / "shell"; hair cord: *zōgehi* / "ivory bark"; hairpin: *aotsuno* / "green horn"; hair ornament: *tsuishu* / "red lacquer"; sleeve band: *tsuge* / "boxwood"; comb: *bekkō* / "tortoiseshell"; book: *hinoki* / "cypress"; pages of book: *yōkaku* / "goat horn"; face in book illustration: *zōge* / "ivory"; hair: *umimatsu* / "black coral"; kimono: *aogai* and *tsuge* / "green shell" and "boxwood"; seal: *aotsuno* / "green horn"
seal on box lid: *Sōsui*

LITERATURE: Bushell, *An Exhibition of Netsuke*, fig. 462, p. 78; Bushell, *Netsuke Familiar and Unfamiliar*, fig. 190, p. 124; Hill and Johnson, "The Raymond Bushell Netsuke Exhibition," fig. 462, p. 36; Hurtig, "Collecting Legends," p. 18

This girl is probably a young apprentice geisha (*maiko*). She half kneels, reading from an illustrated novel while adjusting her elaborate coiffure, as she prepares for work. Her face, with its tinted details, and her hands and feet are of flawless ivory, while her loose robe is of sandalwood, carved in relief with intricate designs and numerous inlays. NKD

638 | **Nude**

Susumu, Japan, active mid-20th century
wood
2 7/16 x 1 7/8 x 1 1/2 in. (6.2 x 4.7 x 3.8 cm)
M.91.250.203
incised in circular cartouche: *Susumu*

LITERATURE: Bushell, *An Exhibition of Netsuke*, fig. 328, p. 64; Bushell, *Netsuke Familiar and Unfamiliar*, fig. 378, p. 158; Lazarnick, *Netsuke and Inro Artists*, vol. 2, p. 1053

The influence of twentieth-century European art is evident in this miniature sculpture. Very simplified, almost abstract treatments of figures were being done by artists and sculptors such as Aristide Maillol (1861–1944) and Henri Matisse (1869–1954), and the form of this reclining nude is reminiscent of works by both of these artists. CD

638

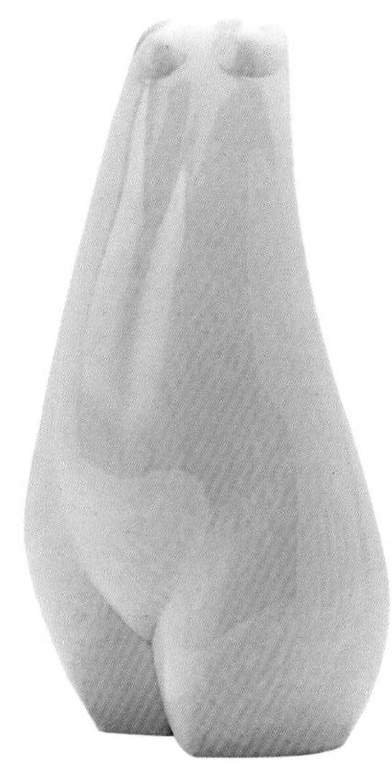

639 | **Female Torso**

Michael Birch, England, born 1926
ivory, gold inlay
2 7/16 x 1 7/16 x 15/16 in. (6.2 x 3.7 x 2.3 cm)
M.90.186.6
incised on inlaid gold plaque: *MB*

LITERATURE: AMICO, 2000–present

The study is a stylized piece by the English writer, sculptor, and netsuke artist Michael Birch. He works with equal dexterity in ivory, mammoth tusk, wood, stag antler, and black coral (*umimatsu*), producing a wide range of subjects in varying styles. NKD

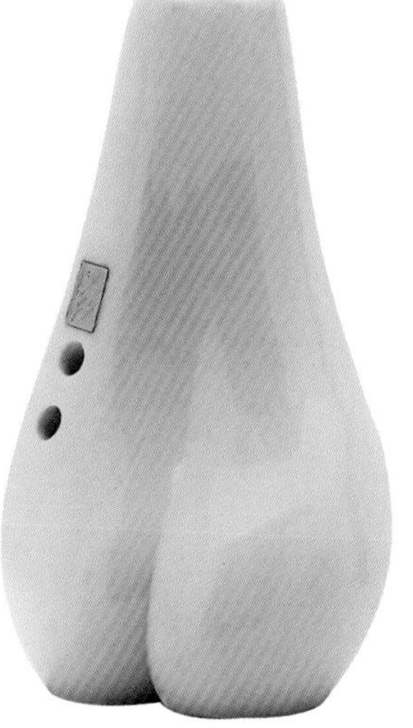

639 BACK

640 | **Boy Sounding Conch Shell**

SHUNKŌSAI CHŌGETSU, Japan, 1826–1892
mid-19th century
wood
1 5/8 x 1 5/16 x 3/16 in. (4.1 x 3.3 x 0.4 cm)
AC1998.249.140
incised in oval cartouche: *Shunkōsai*

LITERATURE: Bushell, *An Exhibition of Netsuke*, fig. 283, p. 24; Bushell, *Netsuke Familiar and Unfamiliar*, fig. 738, p. 223

This small boy's cheeks are puffed out with the exertion of sounding a conch-shell horn. Shunkōsai Chōgetsu worked in Edo in the mid-1800s. He appears to have been equally comfortable working in wood or ivory and made netsuke of figure and animal subjects, as well as *manjū*. NKD

641 | **Simplified Child**

Japan, mid-19th century
wood
1 3/4 x 1 1/4 x 3/4 in. (4.5 x 3.1 x 1.9 cm)
M.91.250.327

LITERATURE: Bushell, *An Exhibition of Netsuke*, fig. 144, p. 44; Bushell, *The Wonderful World of Netsuke*, fig. 76, p. 59

PROVENANCE: Ōno Yoshiaki

Toba Sōjō (1053–1140) was a distinguished Buddhist priest as well as a painter, primarily of Buddhist images. Also known to paint non-Buddhist works, he developed a style that subsequently came to be known as *Toba-e* (Toba pictures). His Toba-e figures were rendered humorously, with little regard for anatomical accuracy. Composed of flowing lines and few details, his figures were abbreviated and cartoonlike, often lacking toes and fingers. While the simple form of this netsuke perhaps suggests folk art, the smooth, polished finish belies the hand of an experienced *netsukeshi* who may have intentionally carved it in a Toba-e manner. CD

642 | **Twin Sisters Viewing Flowers**

Kawahara Ryō, Japan, died circa 1942
ivory with sumi
1 11/16 x 1 5/16 x 15/16 in. (4.3 x 3.4 x 2.3 cm)
M.91.250.260
seal form, carved: *Ryō [?]*

LITERATURE: Bushell, *An Exhibition of Netsuke*, fig. 475, p. 79; Bushell, "Travels by Netsuke," fig. 15, p. 107

Identical twins dressed in kimono, their hair adorned with cherry blossoms, laugh together as they gaze upon the flowers during the cherry blossom festival. Kawahara Ryō lived in Tokyo and made amusing figural netsuke, invariably in fine-quality ivory. NKD

643 | **Child Drying Herself**

Ōuchi Sōsui, Japan, 1911–1972
ivory with staining, sumi, red pigment
1 1/4 x 15/16 x 13/16 in. (3.2 x 2.4 x 2.1 cm)
M.91.250.213
incised: *Sōsui*

This charming rendition of a child is carved in a simple manner. The figure is unstained except for the lips, which are colored with red pigment, and the towel, which is deeply stained and embellished with designs enhanced with sumi. When Raymond Bushell lived in Japan, he befriended and became a patron of Ōuchi Sōsui. Sōsui's work in ivory is comparatively rare, and this example was probably produced toward the end of his life. NKD

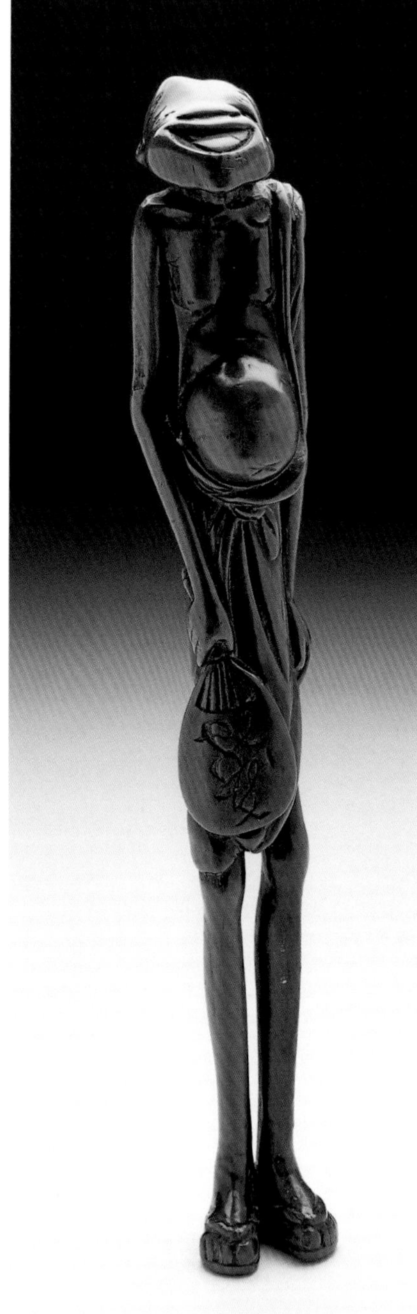

644

645 SIDE

644 | **Peasant**

Japan, 18th century
wood
$6^{5}/_{16} \times 1 \times ^{7}/_{8}$ in. (16.1 x 2.6 x 2.2 cm)
M.91.250.19

Named after its purported originator, the Buddhist priest Toba Sōjō, the *Toba-e* style of painting was humorous and simplistic. A particular mannerism found in Toba-e figures is the open, half-moon-shaped mouth seen here and on *Simplified Child* (CAT. 641). CD

645 | **Pepper Peddler**

JOBUN, Japan, active late 18th–early 19th century
wood with inlays
$2^{1}/_{8} \times ^{3}/_{4} \times 1^{1}/_{8}$ in. (5.4 x 1.9 x 2.9 cm)
AC1998.249.34
incised: *Jobun*

LITERATURE: AMICO, 2001–present; Bushell, *Collectors' Netsuke*, fig. 73, p. 64; Chappell, "Stylistic Developments in the Tokyo (Edo) School," fig. 7, p. 24; Stratos, "The Netsuke Carvings of Jobun," fig. 32, p. 22

The stance of this peddler is reminiscent of netsuke that depicted figures burdened under exaggerated loads. Here, Jobun has slightly enlarged the pepper in a similar play on size. These netsuke were admired for their ability to remain upright despite the figures' imbalanced proportions. CD

646 BACK

646 | **Peddler**

GESSEN, Japan, late 18th–early 19th century
wood
$2^{9}/_{16} \times 1^{1}/_{4} \times {}^{7}/_{8}$ in. (6.6 x 3.1 x 2.2 cm)
AC1998.249.175
incised: *Gessen*

Yawning and stretching, this peddler has apparently had a long, hard day. Characteristic of the work of Gessen and other followers of Shūgetsu I, this figure wears a robe with an abundance of folds. The modeling of his hands, feet, and facial features, as well as the overall bold carving, is also typical of these artists. CD

647 | **Peddler**

Japan, early 19th century
wood
$3^{3}/_{16} \times 1 \times {}^{11}/_{16}$ in. (8.1 x 2.5 x 1.7 cm)
M.91.250.55

LITERATURE: AMICO, 2001–present; Bushell, *An Exhibition of Netsuke*, fig. 275, p. 58

PROVENANCE: Marcel Lorber

This peddler uses a noisemaker and calls out to attract customers. The long string of coins he carries (see also CAT. 761) suggests a profitable day of sales. Laborers often wore specific attire, including headbands, the style of which would indicate their particular trade. The typical fisherman's costume included the type of grass skirt seen here. CD

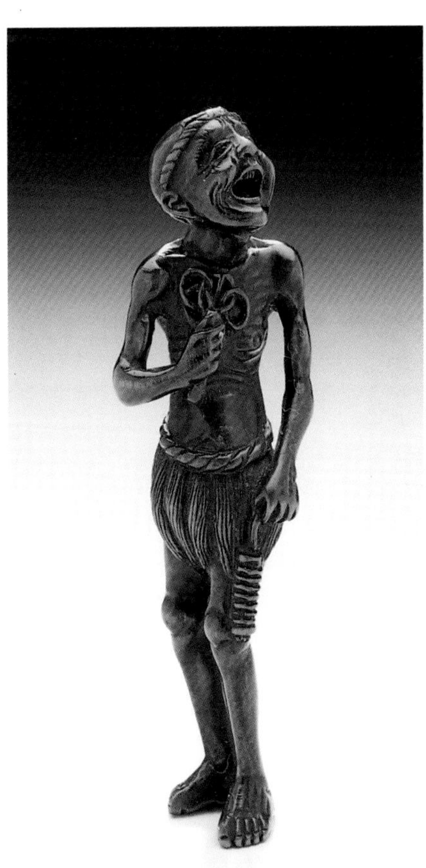

648 | **Peddler**

Ryūkei II, Japan, active mid- to late 19th century
ivory with staining, sumi
$2\,^1/_4 \times 1 \times {}^{11}/_{16}$ in. (5.8 x 2.5 x 1.7 cm)
M.91.250.316
incised and stained with sumi in oval reserve cartouche: *Ryūkei*

LITERATURE: AMICO, 2001–present

The numerous representations of peddlers in the Bushell collection (CATS. 645–48) rightly suggest that they were a common sight on the streets of major urban centers in the Edo period (1615–1868). These street vendors sold a wide variety of items, including toys, sweets, household objects, and, in this case, sake. This piece varies from most other depictions of the subject in that it is ivory instead of wood. While most peddlers and laborers are shown wearing very simple clothes, the robe of this figure is covered in elaborate surface carving. CD

649 | **Kumosuke**

Japan, 18th century
wood
$3\,^1/_4 \times 1\,^1/_2 \times 1$ in. (8.3 x 3.8 x 2.5 cm)
AC1998.249.35

LITERATURE: AMICO, 2001–present; Bushell, *Netsuke Familiar and Unfamiliar*, fig. 556, p. 191

Travelers in premodern Japan could hire road porters (*kumosuke*) to carry their loads, or even themselves, a long distance. As travel increased, so did the need for porters. As their name implies, kumosuke (literally, "cloud men") were drifters with no permanent home. Stories about these men often recounted their unruly behavior, drinking, and generally boisterous nature. In netsuke, they are often depicted dancing or singing, a reference to their carefree, unattached life. CD

650 | **Hunter and Prey**

Japan, late 18th century
ivory with staining, sumi, inlays
$2\,^5/_8 \times 1 \times {}^{13}/_{16}$ in. (6.7 x 2.5 x 2 cm)
M.91.250.190

LITERATURE: AMICO, 2001–present; Bushell, *An Exhibition of Netsuke*, fig. 297, p. 60

Hunter subjects in netsuke are identifiable by their dress and features. Fur leggings, sandals, and woven head coverings are invariably found on these pieces. Hunters are also generally unshaven and wild in appearance and are usually shown with either a weapon or a dog, which was occasionally used in the hunt. This hunter also carries his catch, a hare. CD

651 | **Laborer with Sake Gourd**

DŌRAKU (SAI), Japan, active early 19th century
boxwood
1 5/16 x 1 1/4 x 1 1/16 in. (3.4 x 3.1 x 2.7 cm)
M.91.250.302
incised: *Dōraku*

LITERATURE: Bushell, *An Exhibition of Netsuke*, fig. 116, p. 41

As evident from several netsuke in the Bushell collection (CATS. 618–20, 652), laborers frequently enjoyed sake. This figure seems particularly fond of his sake gourd, which has likely just been drained by the grinning workman. CD

652 | **Laborer Enjoying Sake**

DŌRAKU (SAI), Japan, active early 19th century
ivory with staining, sumi
1 9/16 x 1 9/16 x 1 in. (3.9 x 3.9 x 2.6 cm)
M.91.250.331
incised and stained in irregular cartouche: *Dōrakusai*

LITERATURE: AMICO, 2001–present

Through the use of surface textures and careful staining, Dōraku has effectively created depth and contrast in areas such as the smooth white loincloth (*fundoshi*) and the rough, dark sake flask. Upon studying the underside of this piece, it becomes evident that this workman is not grinning in drunken bliss but grimacing in pain: he has caught some very delicate parts of his anatomy in his fundoshi. CD

652 BACK

653 | **Laborer Smoking**

GYOKURIN, Japan, active early to mid-19th century
wood
1 1/4 x 1 3/16 x 15/16 in. (3.1 x 3 x 2.3 cm)
AC1998.249.42
incised: *Gyokurin*

LITERATURE: AMICO, 2001–present; Bushell, *An Exhibition of Netsuke*, fig. 119, p. 41

Tobacco was introduced to Japan by the Portuguese in the late sixteenth century and quickly became popular. Its great appeal is evidenced by Hokusai's *Manga* (circa 1814), a multivolume compilation of sketches of Japanese life and lore, in which Hokusai has shown a variety of people smoking, including workmen such as this (Michener, *The Hokusai Sketchbooks*, pp. 5, 176, 257). CD

654 | **Fireguard**

Japan, 19th century
wood
1 7/16 x 1 1/16 x 15/16 in. (3.6 x 2.7 x 2.3 cm)
AC1998.249.11
incised: [various graffiti: for example, *jūichinichi ban* / "evening on the eleventh day"; *Nakamura Utaemon* [name]; *nichōme* / [an address]; etc.]

LITERATURE: Bushell, *Netsuke Familiar and Unfamiliar*, fig. 383, p. 159; Davey, *Netsuke*, fig. 928, p. 305

PROVENANCE: Mark T. Hindson; William Wilberforce Winkworth; Dr. H. A. Gunther

In the Edo period (1615–1868), official firefighters primarily protected Edo Castle, residences of high-ranking citizenry, shrines, and temples. In 1718, a volunteer squad was organized to serve the general population of Edo. Each fire brigade had lookouts who sounded alarms on their drums when they spotted a fire. This lookout dons ordinary attire and occupies a graffiti-covered guard station. CD

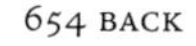

654 BACK

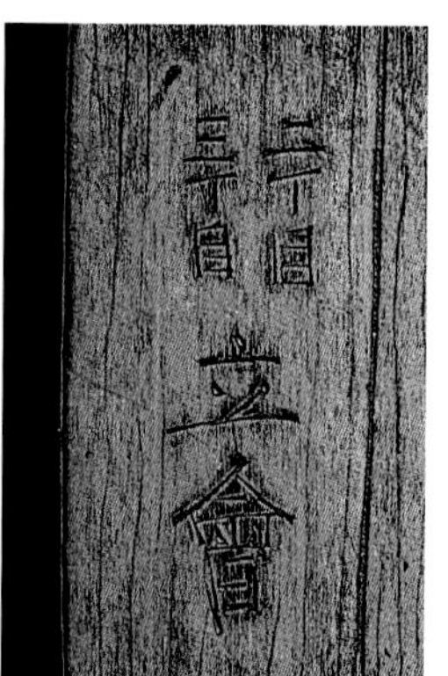

SIDE

SIDE

655 | **Kimono Blood Seal**

Hōkyūdō Itsumin, Japan, active circa 1830–1870
wood with inlays
$1^{15}/_{16} \times 1^{1}/_{8} \times 1^{1}/_{8}$ in. (4.9 x 2.8 x 2.8 cm)
AC1998.249.29
incised on inlaid mother-of-pearl plaque: *Itsuō tō* / "carved by Itsuō"

Although the subject of this netsuke has not yet been confirmed, it was Raymond Bushell's opinion that the man was a samurai marking his kimono with his own blood, an act that symbolized his promise of loyalty and his willingness to die for his master. The underside of this netsuke, however, shows the folded fabric and sleeves of a plain garment, and there is no evidence that the figure is a samurai. This netsuke probably depicts a man cleaning his robe. CD

656 | **Quarreling Couple**

Meikeisai Hōjitsu, Japan, died 1872
wood
$^{7}/_{8} \times 2^{1}/_{4} \times {}^{3}/_{4}$ in. (2.2 x 5.7 x 1.9 cm)
AC1998.249.158
incised: *Hōjitsu*

LITERATURE: AMICO, 2001–present

In the midst of an argument, this couple sits back to back, neither seeming ready to budge. The man has a pipe and tobacco pouch on his lap, and has tucked his arms deep into his sleeves. The woman tries to hide her smirk behind one hand, and she holds a paint brush in her other hand. The compact composition and expressive Okame- and *usofuki*-like faces of this pair are characteristic of theatrical satire. CD

657 | **Passengers in Ferry Boat**

Keisai, Japan, active mid- to late 19th century
late 19th century
wood
$1\,^1/_8 \times 1\,^{15}/_{16} \times 1\,^3/_{16}$ in. (2.8 x 4.9 x 3 cm)
M.91.250.195
incised in raised rectangle: *Keisai*

LITERATURE: AMICO, 2001–present; Bushell, *An Exhibition of Netsuke*, fig. 148, p. 45; Bushell, "Travels by Netsuke," fig. 5, p. 106

Travelers used ferryboats in Edo-period (1615–1868) Japan to cross rivers that did not have bridges, and people from all classes of society would be forced to share a ride. This theme was also extremely popular among painters and printmakers. Keisei has collected an assortment of travelers, including a samurai, a monkey trainer, a farmer, a pair of entertainers, a child, and the ferryman. CD

658 | **Paper-Blowing Game: Kamifuki**

Hōshunsai Masayuki, Japan, active mid- to late 19th century
mid-19th century
wood
$1\,^7/_8 \times 1\,^1/_2 \times 1\,^1/_8$ in. (4.7 x 3.8 x 2.8 cm)
AC1998.249.51
incised in irregular cartouche: *Hōshun* [reads right, left, center]; kakihan

LITERATURE: AMICO, 2001–present; Bushell, *An Exhibition of Netsuke*, fig. 108, p. 40

Games have been recorded in Japanese culture since the Heian period (794–1185), including some adopted from China or other countries. The objective of many of these games was to make the opposing player laugh; hence, they often involved wordplay or humorous contortions of the body or face. In *kamifuki* (paper blowing), two opponents faced one another and alternately tried to blow pieces of paper off their own foreheads. The first person to laugh at the silly facial expressions that ensued was the loser. CD

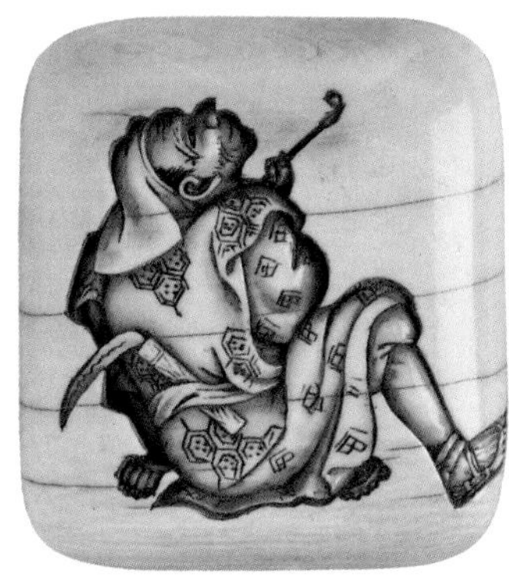

659 | **Paper-Blowing Game: Kamifuki**

GASHŌ, Japan, active mid- to late 19th century
late 19th century
ivory with staining, sumi; manjū type
1 11/16 x 1 7/16 x 1/4 in. (4.3 x 3.7 x 0.6 cm)
AC1998.249.149
incised and stained: *Gashō*

This close-up view of a *kamifuki* player emphasizes his contorted mouth and crossed eyes as he attempts to dislodge the strip of paper from his forehead. Gashō uses tiny lines to indicate the figure's body and facial hair. CD

660 | **Peasant Viewing Moonrise**

KISHŌSAI, Japan, active late 19th century
ivory with staining, sumi, red pigment; manjū type
1 5/8 x 1 5/16 x 9/16 in. (4.1 x 3.4 x 1.5 cm)
M.87.263.23
incised and stained: *Kishōsai*

LITERATURE: AMICO, 2000–present; Bushell, *Netsuke Familiar and Unfamiliar*, fig. 285, p. 142

For farmers, the autumn moon would have been a sign of the approaching harvest season, and gazing at the moon was an autumnal Japanese custom. This farmer's cutting tool indicates his readiness to reap his crops. (A similar piece is in Coullery and Newstead, *The Baur Collection*, fig. c603, p. 223.) CD

661 | **Basket Weaver**

TSUKAMOTO KYOKUSAI, Japan, active 1868–1926
wood
1 5/16 x 1 3/8 x 1 in. (3.3 x 3.5 x 2.6 cm)
M.91.250.208
incised: *Kyokusai*

LITERATURE: Bushell, *Collectors' Netsuke*, fig. 292, p. 161; Bushell, *An Exhibition of Netsuke*, fig. 446, p. 76

Kyokusai carved intricately detailed objects, particularly those with tiny openings or deep recesses such as flowers, birdcages, and baskets. While he is best known for these carvings, he also portrayed figures making, using, or carrying baskets. His penchant for this subject matter is here emphasized by the disproportionately large basket. CD

662 | **Parasol Bearer**

Tōkoku II or Tōkoku III, Japan, late 19th–early 20th century
wood
$2\,^{1}/_{4}$ x $^{7}/_{8}$ x $^{11}/_{16}$ in. (5.8 x 2.2 x 1.7 cm)
M.91.250.244
incised: *Tōko*
seal form, incised and lacquered in green: *Suzuki*

LITERATURE: Bushell, *An Exhibition of Netsuke*, fig. 378, p. 70

The high-ranking citizenry of Japan were accompanied by a variety of porters and servants. Here, a parasol bearer is ready to shield his master from the elements. This type of netsuke appealed to the foreign market, which exercised great influence on netsuke carvers of the Meiji period (1868–1912). CD

663 BACK

663 | **Workman and Daruma Doll**

Kokeisai Sanshō, Japan, 1871–1936
wood with sumi, pigments, inlays
$1\,^{15}/_{16}$ x $1\,^{5}/_{16}$ x 1 in. (5 x 3.4 x 2.5 cm)
AC1998.249.169
incised: *Sanshō*; kakihan

LITERATURE: Bushell, *Collectors' Netsuke*, fig. 243, p. 152; Bushell, *An Exhibition of Netsuke*, fig. 107, p. 40; Hill and Johnson, "The Raymond Bushell Netsuke Exhibition," fig. 107, p. 33

PROVENANCE: Cornelius Van Schaak Roosevelt

Sanshō was inspired by the local population and its activities, and he invariably depicted any situation with humor. This netsuke displays characteristics typical of Sanshō's work (CATS. 619–21), such as the contorted face, the selected use of color and inlay, and the lightly carved repeating patterns on the clothes. Although this figure does not have a sake bottle, his expression suggests he is drunk. Sanshō may have favored drunken subjects because they offered him the opportunity to exaggerate facial expressions to the fullest. Some of Sanshō's figures hold sake flasks, rice cakes, or fly whisks. He also carved a number of figures with Daruma dolls. CD

664 | **Egg Tester**

Shō (or Noboru), Japan, active early 20th century
ivory with dark staining, sumi, lacquer inlay
1 1/2 x 1 1/8 x 13/16 in. (3.8 x 2.8 x 2 cm)
AC1998.249.290
seal form, carved and lacquered in red: *Shō*

LITERATURE: AMICO, 2001–present

While the egg tester is a common subject in netsuke, this late work is different from most earlier representations. The figure, typically shown carrying a basket of eggs over his shoulder, has long, curly hair and attire indicative of South Seas islanders. The medium was usually wood, with the egg invariably inlaid in ivory. This piece, however, is made entirely of ivory and heavily stained, including the eggs. The naturalistic rendering of the facial features as the tester squints to see through the egg, as well as the style of clothing and treatment of the fabric, brings this subject solidly into the Meiji period (1868–1912). CD

665 | **Servant and Young Mistress**

Yasumichi, Japan, active early 20th century
boxwood
1 3/4 x 1 5/16 x 1 1/4 in. (4.4 x 3.4 x 3.1 cm)
AC1998.249.101
incised in rectangular cartouche: *Yasumichi*

LITERATURE: AMICO, 2001–present; Bushell, *An Exhibition of Netsuke*, fig. 295, p. 60; Hurtig, *Masterpieces of Netsuke Art*, fig. 125, p. 48

Netsuke styles changed dramatically in the Meiji period (1868–1912). The introduction of Western-style dress all but eliminated the need for netsuke as functional toggles, and the Western taste for delicate sculpture for display (*okimono*) became the prevailing force in netsuke production. As a result, *netsukeshi* had greater flexibility, producing forms that were more complex and compositions that were more intricate. This carving represents a touching moment in the life of an aristocratic child and her servant. CD

666 | **Genroku-Era Urban Sophisticate**

Illustrated on page 29
Ōuchi Gyokusō, Japan, 1879–1944
wood
2 1/8 x 1 1/8 x 1 in. (5.4 x 2.8 x 2.5 cm)
AC1998.249.79
incised in oval reserve cartouche: *Gyokusō*

LITERATURE: AMICO, 2001–present; Ueda, *The Netsuke Handbook of Ueda Reikichi*, fig. 148, p. 146

The efflorescence of arts and entertainment reached its height during the Genroku era (1688–1703). This period was marked by a cultured and wealthy society, unimpeded by heavy government regulations, that placed great emphasis on fashion and high style. This elaborately coiffed figure exemplifies the importance of the outward display of elegance and opulence. Gyokusō frequently suspended inrō from his figures' sashes. However, here the inrō ensemble lies at the figure's feet, perhaps a commentary on his feigned disdain for material wealth. CD

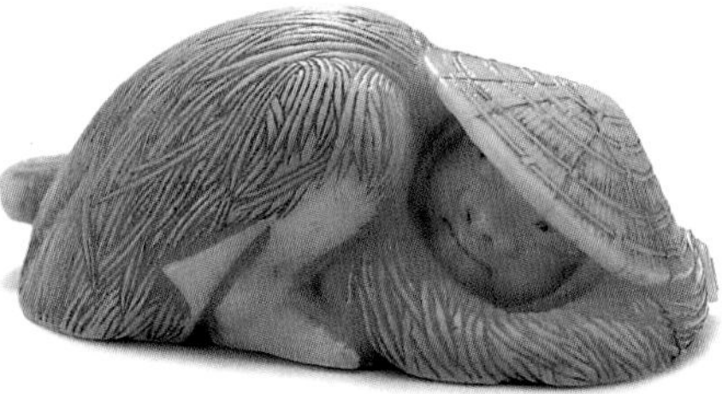

667 | **Lying in Wait**

Attributed to Ogasawara Issai, Japan, active second half of the 18th century
narwhal tusk with sumi, red pigment
$2\,^{3}/_{16}$ x $1\,^{5}/_{16}$ x $^{7}/_{8}$ in. (5.6 x 3.3 x 2.2 cm)
M.91.250.289

Literature: AMICO, 2001–present; Ueda, *The Netsuke Handbook of Ueda Reikichi*, fig. 80, p. 88

The figure twists his head to one side as he listens intently for footsteps, holding a large club at his side. To avoid detection, he has hidden himself beneath his broad hat and rice-straw cape (*mino*). This example also appears as a line drawing in Inaba Tsūryū's *Sōken kishō*, published in Osaka in 1781. The drawing is entitled "actor," indicating that the netsuke represents a climactic moment in a popular play from that time. NKD/HG

667 bottom

668 | **Masterless Samurai**

Japan, early 19th century
ivory with staining, sumi
$1\,^{1}/_{2}$ x $1\,^{1}/_{4}$ x $^{11}/_{16}$ in. (3.8 x 3.2 x 1.7 cm)
M.91.250.20

Literature: AMICO, 2001–present; Bushell, *An Exhibition of Netsuke*, fig. 286, p. 59; Bushell, *Netsuke Familiar and Unfamiliar*, fig. 549, p. 191

Provenance: Douglas Cullison

A samurai who had lost his master—for example, by being dismissed from his post or through the death of his lord—was called a *rōnin*. Some rōnin became farmers, merchants, and craftsmen, others opened schools, and a few became mercenaries. NKD

668 back

669 | **Gun**

Murasada, Japan, early 19th century
iron, wood
2 7/8 x 15/16 x 3/4 in. (7.4 x 2.3 x 1.9 cm)
M.87.263.87
incised: *Murasada*

LITERATURE: AMICO, 2001–present; Atchley, "The Pavilion for Japanese Art in Los Angeles," p. 23; Ueda, *The Netsuke Handbook of Ueda Reikichi*, fig. 95, p. 95

A simplified copy of a *tanegashima* gun, this netsuke has a stock made of wood and a barrel made of iron, with a dragon and cloud design executed in inlaid gold. The fittings are of soft metal. The term derives from the island of Tanegashima, where the Portuguese first introduced firearms to Japan in the 1500s. NKD

670 | **Samurai Armor**

Japan, 19th century
ivory with staining, sumi, thread, inlays
2 1/8 x 1 1/8 x 13/16 in. (5.4 x 2.9 x 2.1 cm)
M.91.250.308

LITERATURE: AMICO, 2001–present; Bushell, *Netsuke Familiar and Unfamiliar*, fig. 544, p. 190; Davey, *Netsuke*, fig. 1114, p. 372

PROVENANCE: Mark T. Hindson

This complete suit of armor is mounted on a stand. It is supported on its own storage box, the sides of which are engraved with a wood-grain pattern (*mokume*). All parts of the armor are shown, somewhat simplified and carved in stained ivory, with highlights in sumi. The helmet and face protector are joined by threads. NKD

671 BOTTOM

671 | **Stirrup for Samurai Horseman**

Japan, mid-19th century
gilt bronze with gold stone-ground lining
$1\,{}^{1}/_{2}$ x 1 x ${}^{11}/_{16}$ in. (3.8 x 2.5 x 1.8 cm)
M.87.263.84

LITERATURE: AMICO, 2000–present; Bushell, *Netsuke Familiar and Unfamiliar*, fig. 362, p. 154

PROVENANCE: Alice Boney

The elegantly formed stirrup was used by samurai and other mounted warriors from early times. The design of trailing foliage, executed in flat gold inlay, is a pastiche of those created in Kaga in the 1500s and 1600s. NKD

672 | **Face Protector**

Japan, mid-19th century
wood
$2\,^{3}/_{16} \times 1\,^{7}/_{8} \times 1\,^{9}/_{16}$ in. (5.5 x 4.8 x 4 cm)
M.91.250.330

LITERATURE: Bushell, *Netsuke Familiar and Unfamiliar*, fig. 537, p. 189; Bushell, *Netsuke Masks*, fig. 313

This netsuke is a model, possibly from life, of a samurai's face protector. Face protectors were generally made of iron and sometimes lacquered at the back. The nose section was often detachable and could be fastened with pegs. NKD

673 | **Family Crests**

Front illustrated on page 87
Japan, late 19th century
ivory with staining, sumi; ryūsa type
$1\,^{5}/_{8} \times 1\,^{5}/_{8} \times\,^{9}/_{16}$ in. (4.2 x 4.2 x 1.5 cm)
M.87.263.40

LITERATURE: AMICO, 2000–present; Bushell, *An Exhibition of Netsuke*, fig. 99, p. 39; Bushell, *Netsuke Familiar and Unfamiliar*, back cover; Ueda, *The Netsuke Handbook of Ueda Reikichi*, fig. 16, p. 34

Carved and pierced with a symmetrical arrangement of family crests (*mon*) in the style favored by the Edo netsuke artist Ozaki Kokusai (whose works are also in the Bushell collection), this is an unusually fine *ryūsa*-style *manjū* netsuke. The term comes from the netsuke carver Ryūsa, who lived in Edo from the early to mid-1800s and produced carved and pierced manjū as well as elaborately detailed *katabori* netsuke. NKD

673 BACK

674 | **Ghost**

Japan, late 18th century
wood
3 3/16 x 7/8 x 7/8 in. (8.2 x 2.2 x 2.2 cm)
AC1998.249.96

LITERATURE: Bushell, *An Exhibition of Netsuke*, fig. 129, p. 20; Bushell, *The Wonderful World of Netsuke*, fig. 25, p. 30

PROVENANCE: Kaneko Sukeichi

Ghost characters appeared in Japanese legends and folklore before they became popular subjects for artists in the Edo period (1615–1868). The artistic convention for these Edo-period depictions derived from a work by Maruyama Ōkyo (1733–1795), founder of the Maruyama-Shijō School. His painting *The Ghost of Oyuki* shows a haunting female with long hair and a simple robe. Ōkyo alludes to the ghost's phantasmal quality by depicting only the upper half of the body. As exemplified by many netsuke from the Bushell collection (also CATS. 675–82), the common representation of a female ghost had disheveled long hair, ragged clothes, a bony torso, and no feet. CD

674

675 | **Ghost Caring for Her Child**

SCHOOL OF CHIKUYŌSAI TOMOCHIKA, Japan, late 19th century
ivory with staining, sumi
2 3/8 x 1 x 13/16 in. (6 x 2.6 x 2 cm)
M.91.250.124
incised and stained with sumi: *Tomochika*

LITERATURE: AMICO, 2001–present

There are many popular folktales about women coming back from the dead to care for their children. One of the most famous, treated by Utagawa Kuniyoshi (1797–1861) in a woodblock print, was the story titled "The Nightly Weeping Rock." A pregnant woman, traveling to meet her husband, is murdered by a thief. Her ghost appears to her husband, who takes their baby from her and avenges her death. Chikuyōsai Tomochika was one of a number of Edo artists working mainly in ivory during the mid- to late 1800s. This netsuke is probably by a follower, working in the Meiji period (1868–1912). NKD

676

676 | **Ghost**

Ittan, Japan, circa 1820–1877
wood
$3^{9}/_{16}$ x $^{11}/_{16}$ x $^{9}/_{16}$ in. (9.1 x 1.7 x 1.4 cm)
M.91.250.123
incised: *Ittan*; kakihan

LITERATURE: Bushell, *Collectors' Netsuke*, fig. 109, p. 91; Bushell, *An Exhibition of Netsuke*, fig. 128, p. 42; Hill and Johnson, "The Raymond Bushell Netsuke Exhibition," fig. 128, p. 33

A number of stories feature female ghosts, and it is often difficult to ascertain who is represented in netsuke. This is probably Okiku, the ghost of the well, from the play known as *Banchō sarayashiki* (literally, "the 'dish mansion' of Banchō"). According to one version of the story, Okiku, a maid, is given a valuable set of ten plates by her master for safekeeping. When she refuses his advances, he asks her to return the plates (one of which he has already removed). He tells her he will disregard her "carelessness" if she will have him as a lover. She again refuses, and he kills her and throws her body into a well. She haunts the well from then on, always counting to nine but never reaching ten. Ittan was a carver from Nagoya. He worked in wood, mostly from fruit trees. NKD

677 | **Ghost**

Nanmusai, Japan, active mid- to late 19th century
late 19th century
ivory with staining, sumi
$2^{9}/_{16}$ x $^{9}/_{16}$ x $^{1}/_{2}$ in. (6.6 x 1.4 x 1.2 cm)
AC1998.249.225
incised: *Onoe Kikugorō shozō zu* / "portrait of Onoe Kikugorō"
incised: *Nanmusai tō* / "carved by Nanmusai"

LITERATURE: AMICO, 2001–present; Davey, *Netsuke*, fig. 912, p. 300

PROVENANCE: Mark T. Hindson; Sir Francis Oppenheimer; Onoe Kikugorō IV

The ghost of Okiku (see also CAT. 676) is shown in a typical attitude, her emaciated body rising on a vapor cloud, one arm across her chest. This is one of a series of similar netsuke made by Nanmusai for the kabuki actor Onoe Kikugorō IV (1808–1860), who was well known for his portrayal of ghostly females, particularly Okiku. NKD

678 | **Ghost**

Takeshi, Japan, active 19th century
late 19th century
boxwood
$7\,^{1}/_{16}$ x $1\,^{1}/_{2}$ x $1\,^{7}/_{16}$ in. (18.1 x 3.8 x 3.7 cm)
M.91.250.303
incised and stained: *Takeshi* [or *Bu*]

LITERATURE: AMICO, 2001–present; Bushell, *Netsuke Familiar and Unfamiliar*, fig. 418, p. 166; Lazarnick, *Netsuke and Inro Artists*, vol. 2, p. 1070

The ghost shown here is almost certainly that of Okiku, the ghost of the well. This netsuke is extraordinarily large, heavy, and impressive. Little is known of Takeshi, who signed, unusually, with a single character in a fine, flowing script. NKD

678

679 | **Ghost Terrorizing Her Murderer**

Suzuki Tōkoku, Japan, 1846–1913
wood with inlays
$2\,^{7}/_{8}$ x $^{11}/_{16}$ x $^{9}/_{16}$ in. (7.3 x 1.7 x 1.4 cm)
M.91.250.239
incised: *Tōkoku Fūzui*
seal form, incised and lacquered: *Bairyū*
ink on box lid: *Tōkoku Fūzui*
seal on box lid: *Bairyū*

LITERATURE: AMICO, 2001–present; Bushell, *Collectors' Netsuke*, fig. 222, p. 147

The dreadful apparition shown here is perhaps the ghost of Oiwa, who haunted her adulterous and cruel husband. (For a fuller version of the story, see CAT. 680.) Suzuki Tōkoku lived in Tokyo, and his life spanned the entire Meiji period (1868–1912). His early work was of ivory or stag antler, in the manner of Asakusa artists Ozaki Kokusai, Ishikawa Rensai, and Hōshunsai Masayuki (all of whose works are represented in the Bushell collection). Later, he developed his own style, creating a number of distinctive netsuke and pipe cases from wood and ivory, often inlaid with various materials. NKD

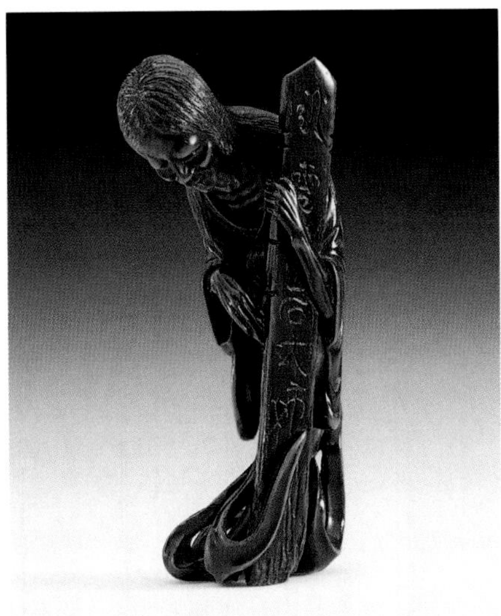

680 | **Ghost Oiwa and Posthumous Name Tablet**

Japan, late 19th century
ivory with dark staining, sumi
2 3/8 x 1 3/8 x 3/4 in. (6 x 3.5 x 1.9 cm)
AC1998.249.33

LITERATURE: AMICO, 2001–present

The ghostly figure of Oiwa rises amid flames beside a grave post engraved with a posthumous Buddhist name. According to one version of the story, Oiwa, with her infant child, was hounded from the home of her husband, a samurai named Tamiya Iemon, who was in love with Osoda, a doctor's daughter. The doctor gave Iemon a so-called medicine (in fact, poison) to give to Oiwa. After her death, Iemon married Osoda, but he was haunted forever by Oiwa's ghost. NKD

681 | **Ghosts of Oiwa and Kohei**

Also illustrated on page 71
Shōko (Nishino Shōtarō),
Japan, 1915–1969
1959
boxwood
2 1/2 x 1 5/16 x 1 1/16 in. (6.4 x 3.4 x 2.7 cm)
M.91.250.84
incised: *Shōko*
ink on box lid: *Hokusōjin Shōko saku* / "made by Hokusōjin Shōko" [exterior and interior]
seals on box lid: *Nishino*; *Shōko* [interior and exterior]; [abstracted seal script?]

LITERATURE: Bushell, *Collectors' Netsuke*, fig. 338, p. 180; Bushell, *An Exhibition of Netsuke*, fig. 468, p. 79; Bushell, "Shōko," p. 58

Shōko based his netsuke on yet another version of the Oiwa story, in which Oiwa's husband poisons her and kills Kobotoke Kohei, the servant who obtained the poison. He then ties their bodies to a door, which he throws into a river. Their spirits come back to haunt him. Shōko became a pupil of Sōko (Morita Kisaburō). He was an intensely individual artist, producing a number of fine, elaborately carved netsuke, chiefly of boxwood. He stopped carving netsuke in 1963 and focused on Buddhist sculpture. NKD

681 ALTERNATE VIEW

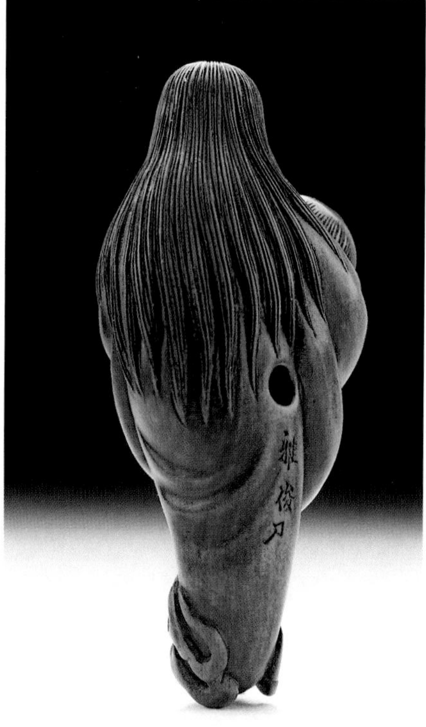

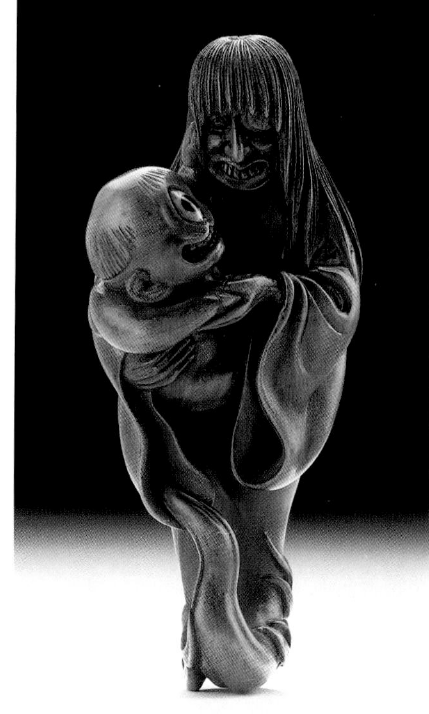

682 BACK

682 | Ghost and Baby Demon

Masatoshi (Nakamura Tokisada), Japan, 1915–2001
July 1963
boxwood with double inlays
$2\frac{9}{16} \times 1\frac{1}{16} \times 1\frac{1}{4}$ in. (6.5 x 2.7 x 3.1 cm)
AC1998.249.246
incised: *Masatoshi tō* / "carved by Masatoshi"

LITERATURE: Bushell, *Masatoshi*, fig. 325, p. 38; Bushell, *The Wonderful World of Netsuke*, fig. 26, p. 30; Masatoshi, *The Art of Netsuke Carving*, fig. 325, p. 216

PROVENANCE: Yonemasa

Masatoshi was a great innovator, and this subject may have come from his own imagination. Hitotsu-me Kozō, the one-eyed priest, was one of Japan's myriad goblins (*bakemono*). Here, Masatoshi may have been depicting the priest as a one-eyed child. NKD

683 | Walking Skeleton

Japan, early 19th century
narwhal tusk with staining, sumi
$3\frac{5}{8} \times 1\frac{1}{4} \times \frac{13}{16}$ in. (9.2 x 3.1 x 2 cm)
M.91.250.119

LITERATURE: AMICO, 2001–present; Behrens, *Netsuke*, fig. 4253, pl. 56; Bushell, *An Exhibition of Netsuke*, fig. 127, p. 42; Davey, *Netsuke*, fig. 1089, p. 362

PROVENANCE: Mark T. Hindson; William Wilberforce Winkworth; M. Isobel Sharpe; Walter Lionel Behrens

A human skeleton, or soldier-ghost, leans slightly forward, its skull turned to one side. This netsuke is based on the tenth-century story of Mitsukuni, a soldier sent to the haunted palace at Sōma. There, Princess Takiyasha, daughter of Heian-period warrior Taira no Masakado (d. 940), used witchcraft to raise an army of soldier-ghosts, which Mitsukuni defeated with his bravery. NKD

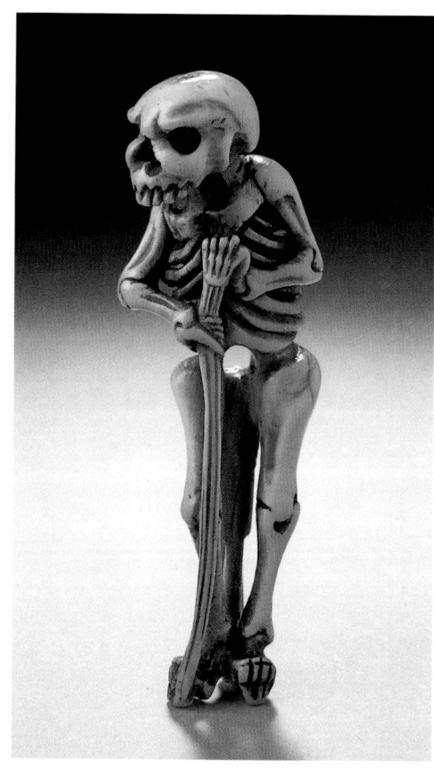

684 | **Skeleton**

Japan, 19th century
ivory with staining, sumi
1 13/16 x 1 x 15/16 in. (4.6 x 2.5 x 2.3 cm)
M.91.250.120

LITERATURE: AMICO, 2001–present; Bushell, *An Exhibition of Netsuke*, fig. 126, p. 42; Bushell, *The Wonderful World of Netsuke*, fig. 28, p. 31; Ueda, *The Netsuke Handbook of Ueda Reikichi*, fig. 64, p. 81

PROVENANCE: Joseph U. Seo

This skeleton is curled into a fetal position for burial. Its anatomy is precisely rendered, and it may have been based on an actual skeleton. HG

684

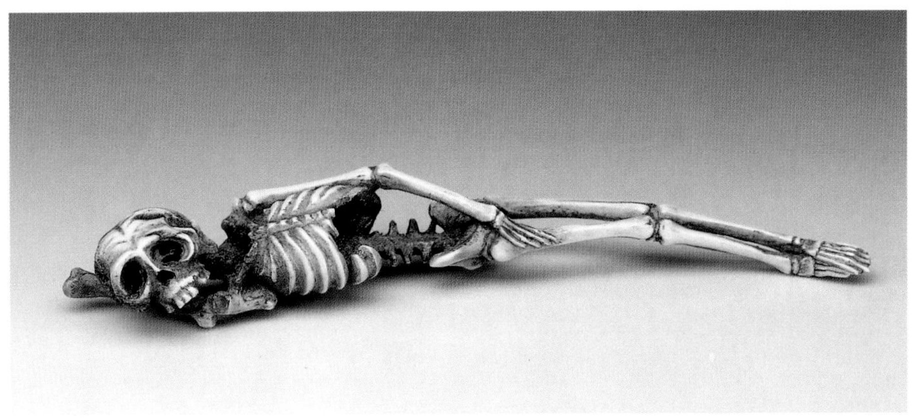

685

685 | **Skeleton**

Hokkyō Sessai, Japan, 1820–1879
stag antler with staining; sashi type
4 13/16 x 15/16 x 11/16 in.
(12.2 x 2.3 x 1.7 cm)
M.87.263.11
incised and stained: *Sessai*

LITERATURE: AMICO, 1999–present; Bushell, *Collectors' Netsuke*, fig. 160, p. 108; Hillier, "*Sessai Unkin zu fu* (Book of designs) by Sessai Unkin," fig. 14, p. 258

The skeleton of a man reclines, the bone structure well defined in lightly stained stag antler. Hokkyō Sessai lived in Mikuni, Echizen province, and was an innovative artist who made comparatively few netsuke. He worked mainly in wood, thus this rendition is quite unusual. He was one of a few *netsukeshi* who created netsuke for the daimyo, and he was awarded the Buddhist title of Hokkyō. NKD

686 | **Wolf and Skeleton**

SUGANOYA SHŌKO, Japan, active circa 1840–1880
wood with inlays
3 x 1 1/2 x 15/16 in. (7.7 x 3.8 x 2.3 cm)
AC1998.249.281
incised: *Shōko*

The skeleton fighting a wolf was apparently a favorite subject of Suganoya Shōko. A number of similar examples have been recorded, and all exhibit a remarkable degree of delicate craftsmanship. Suganoya Shōko worked in Takayama in Hida province. He produced a number of netsuke as well as *okimono*, all treated in the same refined manner. NKD

687 | **Standing Skeleton**

Japan, late 19th–early 20th century
wood
2 1/8 x 11/16 x 11/16 in. (5.4 x 1.7 x 1.7 cm)
AC1998.249.16

LITERATURE: Bushell, *Netsuke Familiar and Unfamiliar*, fig. 662, p. 211

PROVENANCE: Tsuruoka Tokutarō

The skeleton shown here is almost certainly the same character that confronted Mitsukuni at the palace at Sōma (see CAT. 683). NKD

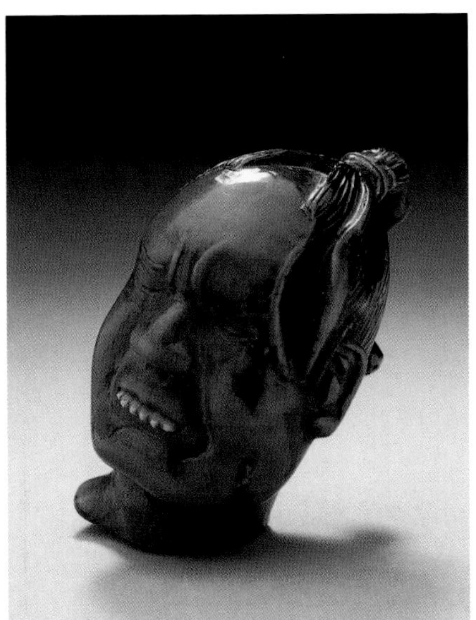

688 | Head of Nitta Yoshisada

Japan, 19th century
wood with pigment, inlay
1 3/4 x 1 5/8 x 1 1/4 in. (4.5 x 4.1 x 3.2 cm)
AC1998.249.119

LITERATURE: Bushell, *An Exhibition of Netsuke*, fig. 123, p. 20; Bushell, *The Wonderful World of Netsuke*, fig. 27, p. 31

PROVENANCE: Michael Braun

Nitta Yoshisada (1301–1338) was a legendary fourteenth-century warrior of Japan. After a short lifetime of glorious battles, his final days were spent fighting against Shiba Takatsune, the ally of an old enemy, at Echizen. During the battle, he was shot between the eyes with an arrow. His head was taken to Kyoto for public display. NKD

689 | Decapitated Woman's Head

Illustrated on page 17
Japan, 19th century
boxwood with inlays
1 9/16 x 1 9/16 x 1 1/4 in. (4 x 4 x 3.2 cm)
AC1998.249.123

LITERATURE: AMICO, 2001–present; Bushell, *An Exhibition of Netsuke*, fig. 124, p. 42; Bushell, *Netsuke Familiar and Unfamiliar*, fig. 521, p. 185

PROVENANCE: Eric R. Levett

The severed head of a woman rests on the ground. Her mouth is wide open and one eye is closed while maggots crawl around it. Here, the phases of decomposition illustrate the Buddhist idea of transitoriness. The netsuke's surface is covered with raised bumps formed by the *ukibori* technique, in use since the eighteenth century. In this technique, the area to be raised is first impressed into the wood, and the entire surface of the piece is shaved down to the bottom of the impression. The wood is then soaked overnight in water, causing bumps to rise above the new surface. NKD

690 | Severed Head of Samurai

SHŌKO (NISHINO SHŌTARŌ), Japan, 1915–1969
1955
wood
1 7/8 x 1 3/8 x 1 7/16 in. (4.8 x 3.5 x 3.6 cm)
M.91.250.85
incised: *Shōko*
ink on box lid: *Hokusōjin Shōko saku* / "made by Hokusōjin Shōko"
seals on box lid: *Nishino; Shōko*

LITERATURE: Bushell, *Collectors' Netsuke*, fig. 330, p. 178; Bushell, *An Exhibition of Netsuke*, fig. 470, p. 28; Bushell, "Shōko," p. 58

Shōko was a master of grotesque reality, a facet of his work that is exhibited to a high degree in this grim portrayal of a severed head. This netsuke may have been intended to depict the head of Nitta Yoshisada (see CAT. 688). NKD

Domestic Implements

The objects that played such an integral part in everyday human lives—carpenter's tools, the cups and bowls and chopsticks of mealtime, a child's toys and dolls, and even the tiles of a temple roof—were fascinating to some netsuke carvers. These subjects might be chosen for the intrinsic interest of the object itself, as with the simple but effective bird scare, hung out at harvesttime to protect the crop from birds. Others, such as the tea whisk or birdcage, might offer an ideal opportunity for the display of a carver's virtuosity.

Some netsuke had functions in addition to their use as counterweights, and these are primarily seen in personal seals, which, as in other countries, were used to certify writings or transactions. Seal netsuke were generally vertical, so that they could be easily grasped (CATS. 691–98, 700).

When re-created as netsuke, items such as incense implements and tea ceremony bowls, kettles, and whisks could inform those around the wearer of his deeper interests (CATS. 704, 706). Netsuke that realistically reproduced food items appear to have been carved mostly from the mid-nineteenth to twentieth centuries. Because of their delicacy and tiny cord holes, they may have been made for display, or for only occasional use (CATS. 719–25). Netsuke of dolls and toys also showed an evolution from usable to more decorative forms.

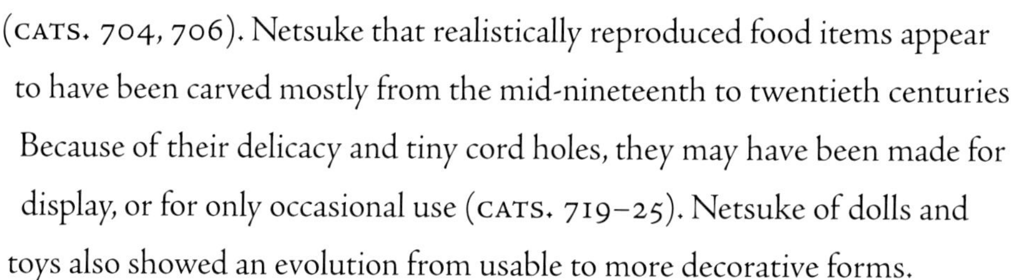

ABOVE: *Teakettle* (CAT. 708)

691 | **Seal Carved As Southeast Asian–Style Lion**

Illustrated on page 30
Japan, 17th century
ivory with dark staining, red seal pigment
1 7/16 x 15/16 x 9/16 in. (3.6 x 2.4 x 1.5 cm)
M.91.250.201
seal, carved on base: *Fuku* / "good fortune" [read in reverse]

LITERATURE: Bushell, *Netsuke Familiar and Unfamiliar*, fig. 601, p. 201; Hurtig, *Masterpieces of Netsuke Art*, fig. 109, p. 45

The earliest netsuke were often of foreign origin, many deriving from items brought to Japan and later altered for this use. Seals, being of small size and compact form, were ideally suited for use as netsuke. Occasionally, a *himotōshi* would be added, but in this case the numerous natural openings made that unnecessary. CD

691 SEAL

692 | **Seal Carved As Kirin**

Illustrated on page 31
Japan, 18th century
ivory with staining, sumi, red pigment, inlays
3 1/8 x 1 1/8 x 1 in. (8 x 2.9 x 2.5 cm)
M.87.263.5
seal, carved on base: *Suimei* / "bright water" [read in reverse]

LITERATURE: AMICO, 2000–present

In contrast to *Seal Carved As Southeast Asian–Style Lion*, this netsuke has a cord hole through its base. The inferior quality of the carved characters on the seal base suggests that they may have been added later by a different carver. The hole and seal characters were carved to accomodate each other, suggesting that they were added at the same time. CD

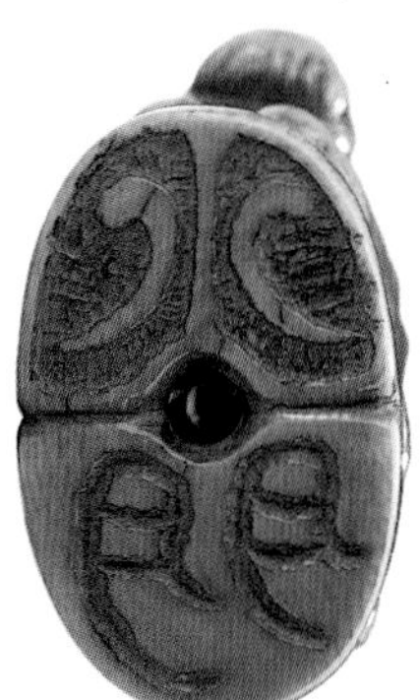

692 SEAL

693 ALTERNATE VIEW

693 | **Dragon Seal**

Japan, 18th century
wood
$2\,^{15}/_{16} \times 1\,^{5}/_{8} \times 1\,^{3}/_{16}$ in. (7.5 x 4.2 x 3 cm)
M.91.250.23
seal, carved on base: *Fuji [?]* or *tomi [?]*

LITERATURE: AMICO, 2001–present; Bushell, *An Exhibition of Netsuke*, fig. 39, p. 34; Bushell, *Netsuke Familiar and Unfamiliar*, fig. 598, p. 200

PROVENANCE: Florence Marsh

This example is a departure from the majority of seal netsuke, which are usually simple in design with minimal surface decoration. This embellished form is nonetheless functional. Compact and rounded, it is suitable for use as a netsuke while being strong enough to withstand use as a seal. Symmetry was an essential element in Chinese design from ancient times, and both the dragons and the composition of this seal strongly suggest Chinese influence. CD

693 SEAL

694 | Seal Carved As Temple Servant

Japan, 18th century
rhinoceros horn
$2^{7}/_{16}$ x $^{9}/_{16}$ x $1^{3}/_{16}$ in. (6.2 x 1.5 x 3 cm)
M.91.250.258
seal, carved on base: [undecipherable]

LITERATURE: Bushell, *An Exhibition of Netsuke*, fig. 43, p. 34; Bushell, *Netsuke Familiar and Unfamiliar*, fig. 674, p. 213

The material and features of this figure suggest African or Indonesian influence. The seal's sides are slightly indented, allowing for a firm, comfortable grip. The large hole in the upper half of the figure was once two smaller holes, but the partition between them has long since broken away. A small channel has been drilled between the figure's feet just above the base. CD

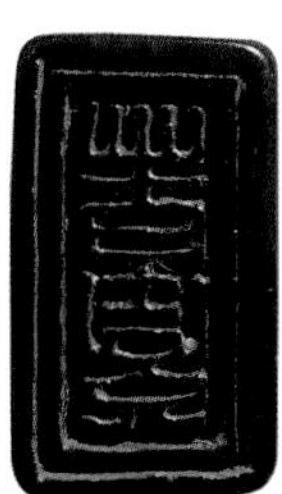

694 SEAL

695 | Stag-Shaped Seal

Japan, 19th century
stag antler
$1^{3}/_{4}$ x $^{7}/_{8}$ x $^{1}/_{2}$ in. (4.4 x 2.2 x 1.2 cm)
M.87.263.20
seal, carved on base: *Rihaku* [Li Bai, the Chinese poet, 701–762]

LITERATURE: AMICO, 2000–present; Bushell, *An Exhibition of Netsuke*, fig. 350, p. 67; Bushell, *Netsuke Familiar and Unfamiliar*, fig. 595, p. 200

The base on this seal reads "Rihaku," the Japanese name for Li Bai (701–762), considered by the Japanese to be one of the most important Chinese poets of the T'ang dynasty. Li Bai's poem *Tienmu Mountain Ascended in a Dream: A Farewell Song* ends with a reference to a white deer and mountains, the two elements that compose this netsuke. Appropriately carved of stag antler, this simple, elegant form is functional as both a seal and netsuke. CD

695 SEAL

696 | Seal Carved As Circus Impresario

Japan, 19th century
wood
3 3/16 x 1 3/16 x 1 3/16 in. (8.2 x 3 x 3 cm)
M.91.250.31
seal, carved on base: [undecipherable]

LITERATURE: Bushell, *An Exhibition of Netsuke*, fig. 310, p. 62; Bushell, *Netsuke Familiar and Unfamiliar*, fig. 154, p. 117; Hill and Johnson, "The Raymond Bushell Netsuke Exhibition," fig. 310, p. 35

PROVENANCE: Avery Brundage

Mustaches and hats of this style were common among Westerners in the 1800s, and would be adopted by Japanese men of the early Meiji period. The oversize top hat suggests that this foreigner may be a circus barker; it also serves as a handle for the seal. The cord channel runs through the hat just above the hatband, not the ideal place from which to hang a netsuke. The hole was likely added later, when the seal was retrofitted as a netsuke. CD

696 SEAL

697 | Frog-Shaped Seal

Illustrated on page 59
ŌHARA MITSUHIRO, Japan, 1810–1875
ivory with staining, red seal pigment
1 1/8 x 3/4 x 1 1/8 in. (2.8 x 1.9 x 2.8 cm)
M.91.250.44
incised and stained with sumi: *Mitsuhiro*
seal form, carved on base: [undecipherable]

LITERATURE: Bushell, *Collectors' Netsuke*, fig. 124, p. 96; Bushell, *An Exhibition of Netsuke*, fig. 79, p. 37; Mitsuhiro, *Takarabukuro*, p. 99

This stylized frog recalls many of Mitsuhiro's simple, almost abstract designs, which he more frequently modeled as birds. In his *Takarabukuro* (Treasure bag), he describes his seal forms but does not mention carving the seal bases; it is likely that his customers had them added later. Here, the two cord holes on the underside of the base cut through the characters, indicating that this piece was not originally intended for use as a netsuke. Mitsuhiro applied finishes to certain pieces that made them look antique, as seems to be the case with this netsuke. CD

698 | Seal Carved As Chinese Lion

Japan, late 19th century
boxwood
2 3/8 x 1 3/16 x 1 1/8 in. (6 x 3 x 2.8 cm)
AC1998.249.167
seal, carved on base: [undecipherable]

LITERATURE: Bushell, *Netsuke Familiar and Unfamiliar*, fig. 596, p. 200

PROVENANCE: Hazama Shigeo

It is likely that this netsuke, the base of which is in the shape of a gourd, was intended for use as a seal. The subject of this piece reflects the ancient Chinese origins of the seal form, and the delicate carving indicates its late date. CD

698 SEAL

699 BACK

699 | Seal Group

Front illustrated on page 65
SUZUKI TŌKOKU, Japan, 1846–1913
wood, ivory with staining
1 3/16 x 1 x 13/16 in. (3 x 2.5 x 2.1 cm)
M.91.250.240
seal forms, carved: *Bairyū*, *Tōkoku*, and *Fūzui*

LITERATURE: AMICO, 2001–present; Bushell, *Collectors' Netsuke*, fig. 217, p. 146

Unlike the functional seals in the Bushell collection (CATS. 691–98), this seal netsuke was meant as a still life. The combination of forms, materials, and carving treatments highlights Tōkoku's skillful coloring and inlay work. Tōkoku signed his work with a variety of names, and he has carved three of them here in seal script. CD

699 SEAL

700 | Seal Carved As One-Horned Chinese Lion

SUZUKI TŌKOKU, Japan, 1846–1913
ebony with inlays
1 15/16 x 13/16 x 11/16 in. (5 x 2 x 1.8 cm)
M.91.250.243
carved on base: *Tōkoku Fūzui*
ink on box lid: *Tōkoku Fūzui*
seal on box lid: *Bairyū*

LITERATURE: Bushell, *Collectors' Netsuke*, fig. 218, p. 146

Here, as in *Seal Group*, Tōkoku has carved the seal base with his signature, suggesting that this netsuke was not meant for practical use. (In most cases, functional seals were not signed by the carver.) The characters are also in regular order rather than reversed, as would be expected in a seal. While Tōkoku's later work was often heavily inlaid, the inlay here is limited to the gold pupils of the lion's eyes. Tōkoku's refined form and subject appealed to the antiquarian market of his time. CD

701 | ***Kokinshū*: Anthology of Classic Japanese Poetry**

Japan, 18th century
wood
1 9/16 x 1 3/8 x 9/16 in. (3.9 x 3.5 x 1.5 cm)
M.91.250.332

LITERATURE: AMICO, 2001–present; Bushell, *Netsuke Familiar and Unfamiliar*, fig. 538, p. 189

PROVENANCE: William Wilberforce Winkworth

The *Kokinshū*, compiled in the early tenth century, is a collection of more than one thousand court poems. As suggested by the decorative grasses and butterflies on the covers of these books, the *Kokinshū* reflected the Heian-period (794–1185) emphasis on the passage of time and change of seasons. Although simple in form, the subtle relief carving of the title and surface decoration, as well as the careful rendering of the binding, attests to the skill of the artist. CD

702 BACK

702 | **Calligraphy**

SEIYŌDŌ TOMIHARU, Japan, 1733–1811
1793
ivory with staining
3 3/16 x 2 1/4 x 5/16 in. (8.2 x 5.7 x 0.7 cm)
AC1998.249.201
inscribed [recto]: *Kaeri michi au kōji kuruma kuchi nagare yodare* / "Returning, I meet / a sake cart on the road / and my mouth waters"
inscribed [verso]: *Kansei mizu no to ushi haru rokujūichiō Seiyōdō Tomiharu chōkoku* / "sculpted in the spring of 1793 by sixty-one-year-old Seiyōdō Tomiharu"

LITERATURE: Bushell, *Collectors' Netsuke*, fig. 53, p. 57; Lazarnick, *Netsuke and Inro Artists*, vol. 2, p. 1139

A cross section of ivory, with its Shreger pattern and cracking, can resemble a slice of a tree trunk. Tomiharu has taken advantage of this association by staining the ivory and using a resist medium to create calligraphy. The ivory simulates the type of plaque that might be placed under the eaves or above the door of a scholar's retreat. HG

703 | **Chinese Lion Incense Burner**

Ryūgyoku, Japan, active 1789–1829
wood
$1^5/_8$ x $1^5/_{16}$ x $1^1/_4$ in. (4.1 x 3.4 x 3.1 cm)
AC1998.249.128
incised: *Ryūgyoku*

LITERATURE: Bushell, *An Exhibition of Netsuke*, fig. 319, p. 63; Bushell, *Netsuke Familiar and Unfamiliar*, fig. 616, p. 203; Lazarnick, *Netsuke and Inro Artists*, vol. 2, p. 890

Ryūgyoku and Rensai (CAT. 704) have ingeniously used two types of Chinese lion-form incense burners as models for their netsuke. Rensai's is clearly intended to represent an antique bronze censer on raised legs. On the base, he has simulated three holes where heat would have worn through the bronze. Employing narwhal tusk for his carving, he situates the spiraling patterns of the material front and center, giving an impression of patina on metal. The Ryūgyoku burner is more softly modeled and seems to approximate a stoneware lion-form censer. Members of the Raku family of potters in Kyoto—and later other kilns like Seto and Bizen—created small lion-form burners to place below special paintings in *tokonoma* during a tea ceremony. HG

704 | **Chinese Lion Incense Burner**

Illustrated on page 57
Ishikawa Rensai, Japan, active mid- to late 19th century
narwhal tusk with inlays
$1^5/_8$ x $1^9/_{16}$ x 1 in. (4.1 x 3.9 x 2.5 cm)
M.91.250.66
incised: *Rensai*

LITERATURE: AMICO, 2001–present

See catalogue 703.

705 | **Hawk Stylized As Chinese Bronze**

Illustrated on page 70
Ōuchi Sōsui, Japan, 1911–1972
ebony with inlays
$1^5/_{16}$ x $2^1/_8$ x $^{13}/_{16}$ in. (3.4 x 5.4 x 2 cm)
M.91.250.227
incised: *Sōsui*

LITERATURE: Bushell, *Collectors' Netsuke*, fig. 319, p. 176; Bushell, *An Exhibition of Netsuke*, fig. 456, p. 27

Sōsui created a netsuke for antiquarian taste by modeling this figure on a Ming (1368–1644) or Qing (1644–1911) dynasty Chinese wine vessel. The form had been adapted from an ancient Eastern or Western Zhou dynasty (ca. 1050–222 B.C.) container for ritual wine service. Sōsui's simplification of the surface lines indicates his source was a seventeenth- or eighteenth-century decorative bronze. HG

706 | **Tea Bowl and Whisk**

Illustrated on page 59
Ōhara Mitsuhiro, Japan, 1810–1875
wood with lacquer, ivory
$1\frac{1}{2} \times 1\frac{1}{2} \times 1\frac{1}{4}$ in. (3.8 x 3.9 x 3.1 cm)
M.91.250.323
incised: *Mitsuhiro*

LITERATURE: AMICO, 2001–present; Bushell, *Collectors' Netsuke*, fig. 131, p. 98

Twice in his *Takarabukuro* (Treasure bag), Mitsuhiro mentions modeling tea bowls after those made by Ryōnyū (1756–1834), the ninth-generation head of the Raku family. This bowl shape had been a standard form since the time of the family's founder, Chōjirō (d. 1592/1589). The tea whisk is carved with extreme care to simulate bamboo. Mitsuhiro has disguised the wood of the bowl under stains and lacquer, but he left the tea whisk in plain ivory with a delicate sumi stain. The artist carved a Raku stamp on the bottom as part of his design. HG

707 | **Tea Bowl**

Ueda Kōhōsai, Japan, died circa 1907
late 19th century
ivory with staining, sumi, lacquer
$1\frac{9}{16} \times 1\frac{9}{16} \times 1\frac{3}{16}$ in. (4 x 4 x 3 cm)
M.91.250.265
incised and stained with sumi: *Kōhōsai*

LITERATURE: AMICO, 2001–present; Bushell, *Collectors' Netsuke*, fig. 210, p. 128

Ueda Kōhōsai carved a Raku stamp under the base of this tea bowl, indicating that he has simulated a standard Raku family type of bowl for powdered tea. The glossy surface, however, more resembles the wares of the offshoot Ōhi School of potters. Based in Kanazawa, the school is renowned for an amber glaze that resembles melted caramel, and Kōhōsai has closely approximated that glaze here. Kōhōsai left a light patch on one side to indicate the "front" of the bowl, or the part that faced the guest during the tea ceremony. HG

708 | **Teakettle**

After Ōhara Mitsuhiro, Japan, late 19th century
ebony, ivory inlays
$1\frac{5}{8} \times 1\frac{1}{8} \times 1\frac{1}{2}$ in. (4.1 x 2.8 x 3.8 cm)
M.91.250.232
incised: *Mitsuhiro*

LITERATURE: AMICO, 2001–present; Bushell, *Collectors' Netsuke*, fig. 132, p. 99

Using the "hag's mouth" form of teakettle, this artist has painstakingly replicated the texture of cast iron. The lotus-bud knop and five bosses on the lid duplicate those on an original kettle, and ivory loops are attached to lug handles on each side. HG

709 | **Kettle with Pine Design and Lion-Head Handles**

KIYOKATSU, Japan, active early to mid-19th century
early 19th century
ivory with staining, sumi
1 1/2 x 1 3/8 x 1 in. (3.8 x 3.5 x 2.6 cm)
AC1998.249.272a–b
incised: *Kiyokatsu*
incised and stained in irregular reserve: *Rakutō kakō jūnin* / "man living in eastern Kyoto"

Kiyokatsu has pitted and stained ivory in his "stretched hip" form kettle, the model for which was used to heat water for powdered tea. Lion-head lugs and five groups of stylized pine fronds indicate a heavily elaborated metal surface. A kettle with these motifs might have been used for tea ceremonies that took place at the New Year. HG

710 | **Box with Teakettle Design**

Illustrated on page 64
SHIBATA ZESHIN, Japan, 1807–1891
bamboo, lacquer
1 5/16 x 1 5/16 x 7/16 in. (3.3 x 3.4 x 1.1 cm)
M.87.263.49
incised: *Zeshin*

LITERATURE: AMICO, 1999–present; Bushell, *An Exhibition of Netsuke*, fig. 405, p. 72; Bushell, *Netsuke Familiar and Unfamiliar*, fig. 252, p. 137; Hurtig, "Shibata Zeshin," fig. 8, p. 25

Shibata Zeshin was a renowned painter and lacquer artist who is best known for his inrō and lacquer boxes. He also used his exceptional lacquer skills to produce netsuke in primarily *manjū* or box forms. The iron kettle design is done in the *sabiji* lacquer technique, which is used to imitate the surface of old metal, particularly iron. The box netsuke produced by Zeshin and others of his school were often made of bamboo or lacquer; here, Zeshin has used both materials. The raised outer edge on the box lid is characteristic of Zeshin and his followers. CD

711 | **Charcoal and Feather for Use in Tea**

ATTRIBUTED TO KAIGYOKUSAI MASATSUGU, Japan, 1813–1892
late 19th century
ebony, ivory with staining, sumi
1 1/2 x 7/8 x 7/8 in. (3.8 x 2.2 x 2.2 cm)
AC1998.249.185
incised in rectangular reserve: *Kaigyokusai*

LITERATURE: Hurtig, "Kaigyokusai Masatsugu," fig. 63, p. 22

Kaigyokusai, or a follower, has paired two elements used when making tea. A specially prepared charcoal stick is placed inside a brazier in the tea room, and a large feather is used to dust the brazier's edges before the kettle is put on its holder over the charcoal. The charcoal stick and feather provide a dramatic contrast of color, texture, weight, and relative delicacy. Minutely detailed and elegant, this work conveys the clean refinement of the tea aesthetic. HG

712 | **Sake Cup Shaped Like Buddhist Gong**

Japan, 19th century
bamboo
$1\frac{11}{16} \times 1\frac{5}{8} \times 1\frac{1}{16}$ in. (4.3 x 4.1 x 2.7 cm)
AC1998.249.8

LITERATURE: AMICO, 2001–present

Often, the handles of rounded wooden gongs (*mokugyo*) were carved as a pair of animals facing one another. The most common handle design featured two dragons that held a sacred jewel between them. Here the handle functions as the *himotōshi*. Bamboo's hollow core makes it a difficult material to carve and limits the design options for a netsuke. The form and grain direction of this piece suggest that it was carved from a solid section of bamboo, most likely a root. As the availability of sake increased, and with it social drinking, this dual-purpose netsuke no doubt proved quite useful. CD

713 | **Gourd-Shaped Sake Cup**

Illustrated on page 16
Ōhara Mitsuhiro, Japan, 1810–1875
ivory with light staining, sumi
$1\frac{1}{2} \times 1\frac{1}{4} \times 1$ in. (3.8 x 3.1 x 2.5 cm)
AC1998.249.81
incised and stained: *Mitsuhiro*
seal form, incised and stained: *Ōhara*

LITERATURE: AMICO, 2001–present; Bushell, *An Exhibition of Netsuke*, fig. 75, p. 37; Mitsuhiro, *Takarabukuro*, p. 121

In the Edo period (1615–1868), elaborately patterned clothing and highly decorated functional objects such as combs, inrō, and household items became much more common. The lips of both this and the following gourd-shaped sake cup are ornamented with a decoration reminiscent of ancient Chinese border designs and reflect a trend toward ornate and embellished surfaces. Each netsuke features a small gourd resting against the back of a larger one, leaving an opening for the cord. CD

714

714 | **Gourd-Shaped Sake Cup**

Ōhara Mitsuhiro, Japan, 1810–1875
ivory with staining, sumi
$1\frac{9}{16} \times 1\frac{1}{4} \times 1\frac{1}{16}$ in. (3.9 x 3.1 x 2.7 cm)
AC1998.249.219
incised and stained: *Mitsuhiro*
seal form, incised and stained: *Ōhara*

LITERATURE: Bushell, *Collectors' Netsuke*, fig. 133, p. 99

Chinese artisans, believing that empty space looked unfinished and that border designs added a sense of completeness, have traditionally used a variety of overall patterns to decorate objects. The lip of this cup is decorated with patterning similar to the "thunder" or "key" pattern frequently seen in Chinese art. CD

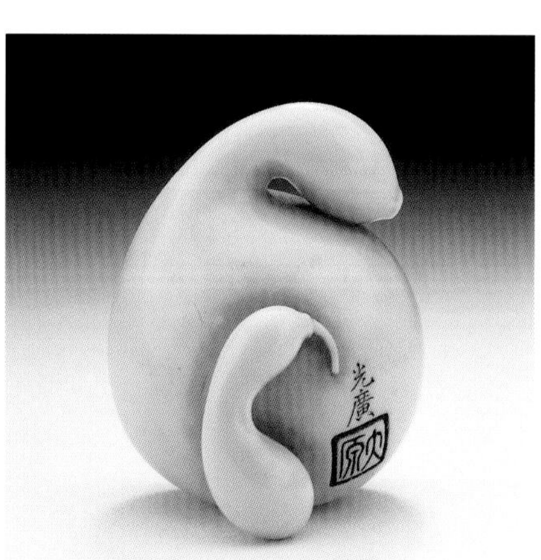

714 BACK

715 | **Gourd**

Japan, 19th century
Satsuma glass, metal
2 11/16 x 1 x 1 in. (6.9 x 2.5 x 2.5 cm)
AC1998.249.112

LITERATURE: Bushell, *An Exhibition of Netsuke*, fig. 366, p. 26; Bushell, *The Wonderful World of Netsuke*, fig. 99, p. 71

PROVENANCE: Tsuruki Yoshimatsu

Glass netsuke are extremely rare, due to their fragility. The example here forms a miniature bottle with a metal-chained stopper. In the mid-1800s, a number of feudal lords began experimenting with glass-making techniques in their own domains. The Satsuma workshop, Shūseikan, was particularly outstanding among these kilns, and its works in glass became famous. NKD

716 | **Gourd in String Bag**

SUZUKI TŌKOKU, Japan, 1846–1913
wood, metal, glass, inlays
2 1/16 x 15/16 x 15/16 in. (5.3 x 2.3 x 2.3 cm)
AC1998.249.48
incised: *Tōkoku*
seal form, incised in inlaid gold plaque: *Bairyū*
ink on box lid: *Tōkoku Fūzui*
seal on box lid: *Bairyū*

LITERATURE: AMICO, 2001–present; Ueda, *The Netsuke Handbook of Ueda Reikichi*, fig. 50, p. 49

PROVENANCE: Anne Hull Grundy; Tomkinson collection

Large gourds, carried in a string bag, were used to hold liquids such as water and sake, while smaller gourds, often hung from the obi, served as scent bottles and sometimes doubled as netsuke. Here Tōkoku combined a variety of materials and colors with remarkable virtuosity. (See also Bushell, *Collectors' Netsuke*, fig. 221, and Barker and Smith, *Netsuke*, fig. 146.) CD

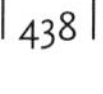

717 | **Sake Cup**

Ōuchi Sōsui, Japan, 1911–1972
ivory with light staining
$1\,^1/_2$ x $^{13}/_{16}$ in. (3.8 x 2 cm)
M.87.263.131
incised: *Sōsui*
ink on box lid: *Sōsui saku* / "made by Sōsui"
seal on box lid: *Sōsui*

LITERATURE: AMICO, 2000–present

When he was in his late forties and in poor health, Sōsui focused on forms that were simpler and ostensibly less labor intensive. The resulting body of work was inspired by archaic burial objects and Chinese and pre-Columbian artifacts (see also CAT. 705). This netsuke, based on a Song dynasty (960–1279) Chinese porcelain bowl in the shape of an open flower, is deceptively simple in appearance; Sōsui saved neither time nor labor in its production. He eventually returned to the complex and highly intricate compositions that highlighted his exceptional talents. CD

718 | **Dried Fish**

Japan, 18th century
root wood
$5\,^1/_4$ x $1\,^9/_{16}$ x $^{13}/_{16}$ in. (13.4 x 3.9 x 2 cm)
M.91.250.109

LITERATURE: Bushell, *Netsuke Familiar and Unfamiliar*, fig. 20, p. 93

The earliest netsuke were typically gourds, shells, pieces of wood, or other found objects. Sometimes the object's original shape suggested a recognizable form, and a few carefully placed knife cuts could transform it, for example, into an animal. Here the addition of eyes, mouth, and *himotōshi* has turned a piece of root into this "dried fish" netsuke. Dried fish are used in soups or as snacks to accompany sake. CD

719 | Sea Cucumber and Chestnut: Edible Treasures

Ōhara Mitsuhiro, Japan, 1810–1875
ebony, stained boxwood, ivory with sumi
2 3/16 x 13/16 x 13/16 in. (5.6 x 2 x 2 cm)
AC1998.249.157
incised and stained on inlaid ivory plaque: *Mitsuhiro*

LITERATURE: Davey, *Netsuke*, fig. 99, p. 45; Mitsuhiro, *Takarabukuro*, p. 85

PROVENANCE: Guest collection

Listed in Mitsuhiro's *Takarabukuro* (Treasure bag), this netsuke was once apparently accompanied by an ivory *ojime* in the form of a taro root. Mitsuhiro remarked in his notes that "these things of the sea, mountain, and field are for celebrating the New Year." He produced a number of similar netsuke in ebony and boxwood, and at least one in stained ivory and boxwood. CD

720 | Gingko Nut

Illustrated on page 10
Ōhara Mitsuhiro, Japan, 1810–1875
ivory with sumi
1 13/16 x 1 3/8 x 1 1/16 in. (4.6 x 3.5 x 2.7 cm)
AC1998.249.305
incised and stained: *Mitsuhiro*
seal form, incised and stained: *Ōhara*

LITERATURE: Bushell, "Questions & Answers" (1988), figs. 1 and 2, p. 5; Mitsuhiro, *Takarabukuro*, p. 95

Mitsuhiro's simple forms are no less compelling than his intricately detailed works, each netsuke combining thoughtful design, careful carving, and flawless finishing. While his *Takarabukuro* (Treasure bag) contains notes about the carving of numerous pieces, he says little of his finishing and polishing techniques. The yellowish color of many of his works, however, suggests the use of the dye *kuchinashi* (also known as gamboge), made from gardenia berries. This gingko nut is an ideal form for highlighting Mitsuhiro's exemplary finishing and polishing skills. CD

721 | **Whitebait Group**

Illustrated on page 83
Ryūkōsai Jugyoku II, Japan,
circa 1815–1877
ivory with sumi, double inlays
$1^{7}/_{8}$ x $1^{1}/_{4}$ x $^{9}/_{16}$ in. (4.7 x 3.1 x 1.5 cm)
AC1998.249.55
incised and lightly stained: *Jugyoku*

LITERATURE: AMICO, 2001–present

Whitebait are small fish—not much bigger than those in this netsuke—that when alive are almost transparent but become opaque white when dead. The size and color of this netsuke, in addition to the double-inlaid eyes, make it a perfect facsimile of nature. This subject has been carved countless times by *netsukeshi* with few variations from the treatment seen here. Ryūkōsai has rendered the seven fish with minimal surface details, emphasizing their glassy eyes. CD

722 | **Bowl with Pomegranates**

School of Kaigyokusai, Japan,
mid-19th–early 20th century
ivory with sumi
fruit: $1^{3}/_{8}$ x $1^{5}/_{16}$ x $^{15}/_{16}$ in.
(3.5 x 3.4 x 2.3 cm)
bowl: $1^{3}/_{16}$ x $1^{1}/_{4}$ in. (3 x 3.2 cm)
AC1998.249.178a–b
incised: *Masatsugu*

LITERATURE: Bushell, *Netsuke Familiar and Unfamiliar*, fig. 754, p. 226

When broken open, the pomegranate exposes innumerable seeds and for that reason is an appropriate symbol for a desire for numerous offspring. This netsuke was carved in two parts, the bowl being separate from the fruit cluster. The cord enters a hole on the bowl's base and is looped around a hook on the bottom of the fruit. The underside of the pomegranates consists of leaves and stems modeled in a fashion similar to some of the flower netsuke in the Bushell collection (CATS. 480–84), all of which were produced in the late 1800s or early 1900s. CD

723 | **String Bag of Clams**

Kayama (or Kōzan), Japan,
active late 19th century
wood
$1^{1}/_{2}$ x $1^{1}/_{4}$ x 1 in. (3.8 x 3.1 x 2.5 cm)
AC1998.249.177
incised: *Kayama* (or *Kōzan*)

LITERATURE: AMICO, 2001–present; Bushell, *Netsuke Familiar and Unfamiliar*, fig. 200, p. 126

The bag of collected clams is intricately carved in great detail although still quite functional. The name Kayama (or Kōzan) has been recorded on several wood netsuke, each of which exhibits the same degree of virtuosity. NKD

724

724 BACK

724 | **Basket of Fish**

Shinshinsai Mitsutoshi, Japan, active late 19th century
ivory with staining, sumi, inlays
$2\,^{1}/_{16}$ x $1\,^{1}/_{4}$ x $^{15}/_{16}$ in. (5.2 x 3.1 x 2.3 cm)
M.91.250.181
incised and stained with sumi in oval reserve: *Mitsutoshi*

LITERATURE: Bushell, *An Exhibition of Netsuke*, fig. 244, p. 54; Bushell, *Netsuke Familiar and Unfamiliar*, back cover; Ueda, *The Netsuke Handbook of Ueda Reikichi*, fig. 188, p. 183

The subject of fish being prepared for a meal is popular among netsuke carvers. The two shown here, trout and catfish (*masu* and *namazu*), are popular delicacies depicted to great effect. Shinshinsai Mitsutoshi lived in Asakusa, Tokyo, and specialized in the carving of intricate netsuke in ivory. NKD

725 | **Ming Bowl with Fish**

Illustrated on page 87
Masatoshi (Nakamura Tokisada), Japan, 1915–2001
January 1957
ivory with staining, sumi, inlays, red lacquer
$1\,^{1}/_{2}$ x $^{1}/_{4}$ in. (3.8 x 0.6 cm)
AC1998.249.56
incised in raised cartouche and lacquered in red: *Masatoshi*

LITERATURE: AMICO, 2001–present; Atchley, "The Pavilion for Japanese Art in Los Angeles," p. 25; Bushell, *An Exhibition of Netsuke*, fig. 499, p. 81; Bushell, *Masatoshi*, fig. 189, p. 29; Masatoshi, *The Art of Netsuke Carving*, fig. 189, p. 186

This is a remarkable work by Masatoshi, and in many ways quite unlike his general style. The bowl is a faithful copy of a Chinese piece made in the later Ming dynasty (1500s–early 1600s). It contains a bamboo branch over a large number of writhing whitebait, their eyes inlaid. Masatoshi is well known for his bold and innovative works, which are not at all similar to the highly detailed carving exhibited here. NKD

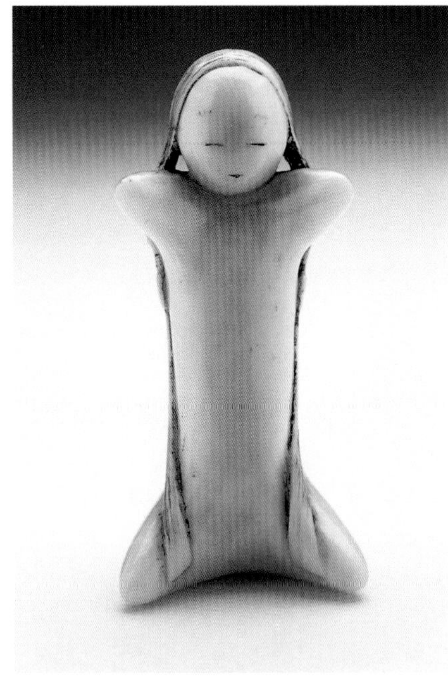

726 | **Substitute Doll**

SCHOOL OF MASANAO, Japan,
late 18th–19th century
late 18th century
ivory with staining, sumi
$2^{3}/_{16}$ x $1^{1}/_{16}$ x $^{11}/_{16}$ in. (5.5 x 2.7 x 1.8 cm)
M.91.250.22
incised in oval cartouche: *Masanao*

LITERATURE: AMICO, 2001–present; Bushell, *An Exhibition of Netsuke*, fig. 32, p. 17; Bushell, *Netsuke Familiar and Unfamiliar*, fig. 123, p. 111; Hurtig, "Masanao," fig. 29, p. 37; Mikoshiba and Bushell, "Netsuke and the *Sōken kishō*," p. 114

Known as *amagatsu*, dolls in ancient times were fashioned from paper and placed at the head of the bed of a newborn child. It was believed that demons of disease or bad luck were transferred to the doll, thereby protecting the child. NKD

727 | **Bird Whistle**

Japan, 19th century
narwhal tusk with staining, sumi, inlays
$2^{9}/_{16}$ x $1^{3}/_{8}$ x $^{13}/_{16}$ in. (6.5 x 3.5 x 2.1 cm)
M.91.250.24
incised and stained with sumi: *Okatomo*
[added later]

LITERATURE: AMICO, 2001–present; Bushell, *Collectors' Netsuke*, fig. 23, p. 32; Bushell, *An Exhibition of Netsuke*, fig. 30, p. 33; Hill and Johnson, "The Raymond Bushell Netsuke Exhibition," fig. 30, p. 32; Mikoshiba and Bushell, "Netsuke and the *Sōken kishō*," p. 114

This charming netsuke of a functional bird-shaped whistle was made by an anonymous nineteenth-century carver. The signature of Okatomo was probably added at a later date, as the work bears no relation to those created by Yamaguchi Okatomo of Kyoto. NKD

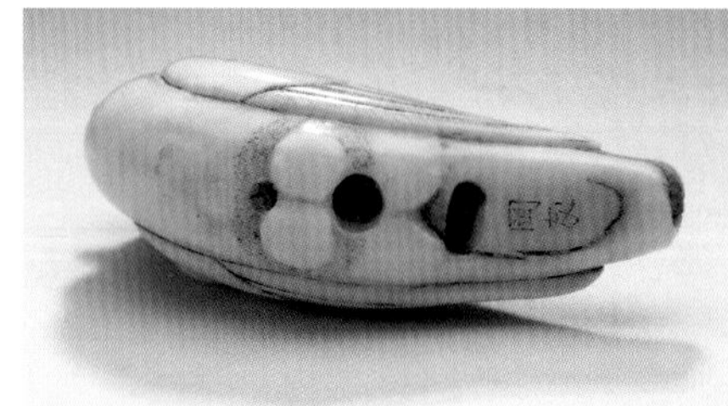

727 BOTTOM

728 | **Toy Dog**

FOLLOWER OF KENZAN, Japan,
18th–20th century
19th century
pottery with colored and crackled glazes
$1\,^{5}/_{16}$ x $1\,^{7}/_{16}$ x $^{13}/_{16}$ in. (3.3 x 3.6 x 2.1 cm)
M.87.263.64
black glaze: *Kenzan*

LITERATURE: Bushell, "Ceramic Netsuke," fig. 48, p. 31

Toy dogs were popular during the Edo period. When in the form of a box, they are known as *inu hako* or *inu hariko*. Kenzan was the name given to a number of potters from the late 1600s through the 1900s. The first Kenzan (Ogata, 1663–1743) was one of the most celebrated potters of his era and the brother of the painter Ogata Kōrin (1658–1716). He had a number of direct followers, and his name has been taken as an honorific title by many generations of potters since his death. NKD

729 | **Toy Dog**

Japan, 19th century
carved red lacquer
$1\,^{3}/_{8}$ x $^{11}/_{16}$ x $^{3}/_{4}$ in. (3.5 x 1.8 x 1.9 cm)
M.87.263.44

LITERATURE: AMICO, 2001–present; Ueda, *The Netsuke Handbook of Ueda Reikichi*, fig. 169, p. 158, and front cover

Toy dogs, constructed of papier-mâché, were popular during the Edo period (1615–1868) as talismans for safe childbirth and the protection of children. This netsuke was created using lacquer in the *tsuishu* method. Originating in China, this method came to Japan in the Muromachi period (1336–1568) and utilized a wood form under many layers of carved vermilion lacquer. CD

730 | **Dog-Shaped Box**

Illustrated on page 50
KENYA, Japan, active 1825–1889
pottery with glazes and overglaze enamels
$1\,^{7}/_{16}$ x 1 x $^{15}/_{16}$ in. (3.7 x 2.6 x 2.3 cm)
M.87.263.63
black glaze: *Kenya*

LITERATURE: AMICO, 2001–present

A lidded box for children's toys or clothes made in the shape of a dog is called an *inu hako* or *inu hariko*. These toys were brightly decorated, and had faces modeled after those of cheerful children. CD

731 | **Birdcage**

Gyokusensai Tomochika, Japan, active early 19th century
boxwood
$1^1/_2 \times 1^5/_{16} \times 1$ in. (3.8 x 3.3 x 2.5 cm)
M.91.250.263
incised: *Hokkyō Gyokusensai*; kakihan

LITERATURE: AMICO, 2001–present; Bushell, *An Exhibition of Netsuke*, fig. 151, p. 45; Bushell, *Netsuke Familiar and Unfamiliar*, fig. 202, p. 127; Lazarnick, *Netsuke and Inro Artists*, vol. 2, p. 1151

This finely carved model of a birdcage, with a small bird on a perch, is made from pale boxwood. It is surprisingly solid, belying its delicate appearance. Gyokusensai Tomochika apparently lived in Osaka at the beginning of the nineteenth century. He worked only in wood. There is no known record of his receiving the Buddhist title Hokkyō, and this is apparently the only known example of him using the title in his signature. NKD

732 | **Roly-Poly Daruma**

Hidari Issan, Japan, active late 18th–early 19th century
early 19th century
wood with inlays
$1^9/_{16} \times 1^3/_{16} \times 1^3/_{16}$ in. (4 x 3 x 3 cm)
M.91.250.271
incised: *Hidari Issan*

LITERATURE: Bushell, *An Exhibition of Netsuke*, fig. 323, p. 64; Ueda, *The Netsuke Handbook of Ueda Reikichi*, fig. 128, p. 136

In Japan, artists have often portrayed their deities and other religious figures in a comical manner, and Daruma is the most common subject of this style of parody. Hidari Issan hailed from Aizu and had a comparatively small output of netsuke of varied subject matter, usually of wood. He also produced a few inrō and pipe cases. NKD

733 | **Roly-Poly Daruma**

Japan, 19th century
Seto ware; glazed stoneware
$1^1/_8 \times 1^1/_8 \times 1^1/_8$ in. (2.8 x 2.8 x 2.8 cm)
M.87.263.67

LITERATURE: AMICO, 2000–present; Bushell, "Ceramic Netsuke," fig. 42, p. 31; Bushell, *An Exhibition of Netsuke*, fig. 414, p. 73; Bushell, *Netsuke Familiar and Unfamiliar*, fig. 445, p. 170

The Zen patriarch Daruma, who endured years of pain meditating until he achieved enlightenment, is a popular symbol of the virtue of endurance. This type of rounded Daruma is traditionally made of papier-mâché and weighted on the bottom. Japanese toys derived from ancient beliefs, prayers, and superstitions are called *engimono*. CD

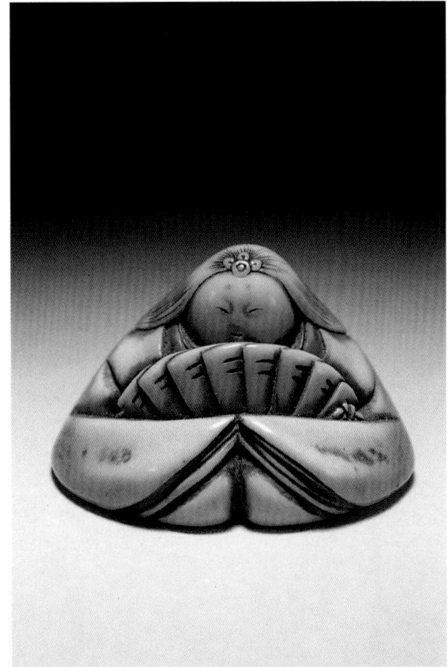

734 | **Seated Doll**

Japan, 18th century
ivory or tooth with staining, sumi
$1\,^1/_4$ x $1\,^1/_4$ x $^{13}/_{16}$ in. (3.1 x 3.1 x 2 cm)
M.91.250.194

LITERATURE: Bushell, *Netsuke Familiar and Unfamiliar*, fig. 116, p. 110

The seated doll shown here is a *dairibina*, or a doll that represents the emperor or empress. Dolls representing the court and their appurtenances are exhibited during the Doll Festival (Hina Matsuri), which is celebrated on Girls' Day (the third day of the third month). NKD

735 | **Standing Doll**

Hō, Japan, active 19th century
carved red lacquer
$1\,^3/_4$ x $^{13}/_{16}$ x $^9/_{16}$ in. (4.4 x 2 x 1.5 cm)
M.87.263.50
carved: *Hō*

LITERATURE: AMICO, 2000–present; Baten, *Japanese Dolls*, p. 104; Bushell, *The Wonderful World of Netsuke*, fig. 67, p. 55

PROVENANCE: Itō Kazuo

The first Japanese dolls, made more than two thousand years ago, were not children's toys; rather, they were used in dedications and religious ceremonies. Dolls eventually became symbols for the well being, good health, and protection of children. This *tachibina* (standing hina doll) is female and traditionally would be accompanied by a male doll (CAT. 737, illustrated on p. 59). These dolls were usually made of paper, cloth, or wood; however, this netsuke was produced using the *tsuishu* technique (for more on tsuishu, see CAT. 729). CD

736 BACK

737 | **Standing Dolls**

Illustrated on page 59
NAOAKI, Japan, active late 19th–early 20th century
ivory with light staining, sumi; manjū type
$1^{5}/_{16}$ x $^{7}/_{16}$ in. (3.4 x 1.1 cm)
M.87.263.32
incised: *Naoaki*

LITERATURE: AMICO, 2000–present; Bushell, *An Exhibition of Netsuke*, fig. 97, p. 39

These dolls stand next to one another, overlapping slightly in a typical representation of the emperor and empress. Here the artist has framed the dolls within a flower. The Doll Festival, or Girls' Day, is also known as the "Peach Blossom Festival," celebrated during the third month of the lunar calendar, the time of peach blossoms. CD

736 | **Seated Doll**

Japan, 19th century
gold lacquer, ivory with staining, sumi
$1^{1}/_{8}$ x $1^{13}/_{16}$ x $1^{1}/_{2}$ in. (2.8 x 4.6 x 3.8 cm)
M.87.263.51

LITERATURE: AMICO, 2000–present; Baten, *Japanese Dolls*, p. 105; Bushell, *Netsuke Familiar and Unfamiliar*, fig. 115, p. 110

Dolls representing the emperor and his court are displayed during the Doll Festival (Hina Matsuri), celebrated on Girls' Day (the third day of the third month). A family's collection of dolls is a prized possession, often handed down through generations. They are ceremonial, and are usually displayed in a special shelved case once a year. The lustrous gold lacquer and intricately detailed surface decoration on this netsuke reflect the importance ascribed to dolls such as this. CD

739 | **Kite in the Form of a Footman: Yakko**

Illustrated on page 58
Hōboku, Japan, active 19th century
gold and colored lacquer
1 15/16 x 1 7/16 x 1/2 in. (4.9 x 3.6 x 1.2 cm)
M.87.263.53
gold *makie* on black lacquer: *Hōboku*

LITERATURE: AMICO, 2000–present; Bushell, *Netsuke Familiar and Unfamiliar*, fig. 253, p. 137; Lazarnick, *Netsuke and Inro Artists*, vol. 1, p. 491

Many Japanese dolls and toys were not only enjoyed by children but also greatly appreciated by adults for their fine craftsmanship and artistry. Flown by boys in the New Year, kites of various shapes were made of paper over a bamboo frame and often decorated with images of strong men or legendary heroes. Yakko were lowly servants of samurai. In the Edo period (1615–1868), they were known as ruffians, constantly tormenting the local inhabitants. Placement of the image of this despised character on kites was seen as mocking retribution. CD

738 | **Fukusuke Doll**

Japan, late 19th century
lacquer with mother-of-pearl inlays
2 1/16 x 1 1/2 x 1 1/4 in. (5.3 x 3.8 x 3.1 cm)
M.91.250.296

LITERATURE: AMICO, 2001–present; Bushell, *Netsuke Familiar and Unfamiliar*, fig. 111, p. 109

PROVENANCE: Ruth Schneidman

Fukusuke ("good-fortune" boy) dolls are usually chubby, with unusually large heads and sumptuous robes. Said to bring prosperity, they were often displayed by shopkeepers. Here the doll holds in his hands a lacquer document box. As in *Seated Doll* (CAT. 736), the use of gold lacquer and inlays on the doll's clothing suggests its fine quality. The artist very carefully considered the *himotōshi* in the design of this netsuke: The doll's own netsuke and pouch are removable and serve as a peg with a hole for the cord. CD

740 | **Pigeon Toy on Wheels**

Japan, 19th century
ivory with sumi, red pigment
$1\,^3/_4$ x $1\,^1/_4$ x $^{15}/_{16}$ in. (4.5 x 3.2 x 2.4 cm)
M.91.250.338

LITERATURE: AMICO, 2001–present; Hurtig, *Masterpieces of Netsuke Art*, fig. 449, p. 117

PROVENANCE: Imai Kenzō

A mother pigeon carries her offspring in a display that idealizes the care parents show for their children. Doves or pigeons were credited with the ability to prevent children from choking on their food. Similar netsuke exist and, unlike this example, some have movable wheels. Wooden toys with wheels were famous products of Kyūshū. CD

741 | **Toy Ox**

Ōhara Mitsusada, Japan,
active 19th century
ivory with staining, sumi
$1\,^5/_8$ x 1 x $^{11}/_{16}$ in. (4.2 x 2.6 x 1.7 cm)
M.91.250.47
seal form, incised and stained: *Mitsusada*

LITERATURE: Bushell, *An Exhibition of Netsuke*, fig. 188, p. 21; Bushell, *Netsuke Familiar and Unfamiliar*, back cover; Ueda, *The Netsuke Handbook of Ueda Reikichi*, fig. 187, p. 183

Doll making reached its height in the Edo period (1615–1868). *Tsuchiningyō*—clay figures of religious or folktale characters, legendary heroes, and animals—were covered with powdered oyster shell and then brightly colored. These popular dolls were available at shrines and temples. Netsuke depictions invariably included the protruding seam that joined the two halves of the clay mold. Oxen were thought to protect health. CD

741 BACK

742 | **Toy Monkey Doll**

Suzuki Masanao, Japan, 1815–1890
wood
1 5/8 x 1 5/16 x 1 1/4 in. (4.1 x 3.4 x 3.1 cm)
AC1998.249.190
incised: *Masanao*

LITERATURE: Baten, *Japanese Dolls*, p. 104; Bushell, *Collectors' Netsuke*, fig. 114, p. 92

Simple *saru ningyō* (monkey dolls), made of cloth and stuffed with cotton, were often sewn onto children's clothing. Monkeys supposedly repelled the demons of disease, but these talismans later served as general good-luck charms. Masanao has taken advantage of this ideally suited form for a netsuke, even using the natural openings to serve as a *himotōshi*. CD

743 | **Tiger Doll**

Hōichi, Japan, 1829–1879
bone with staining, sumi, red pigment, double inlays
2 1/4 x 1 3/16 x 3/4 in. (5.7 x 3 x 1.9 cm)
M.91.250.261
incised: *Hōichi*

LITERATURE: AMICO, 2001–present; Bushell, *The Wonderful World of Netsuke*, fig. 40, p. 39

PROVENANCE: Frances Numano

Hōichi used round eyes and boldly applied sumi and red pigment to capture the feel of a true tiger doll. These toys were most often constructed of papier-mâché; their swiveling heads made them a favorite of children. Hōichi added a special feature: the tiger's tail is also movable. CD

744 | **Pigeon-Shaped Toy**

Ōhara Mitsuhiro, Japan, 1810–1875
ivory with staining, sumi
1 9/16 x 1 1/8 x 3/4 in. (4 x 2.8 x 1.9 cm)
M.91.250.235
incised and stained: *Mitsuhiro saku* / "made by Mitsuhiro"

LITERATURE: Bushell, *Collectors' Netsuke*, fig. 129, p. 97; Bushell, *An Exhibition of Netsuke*, fig. 77, p. 37; Mitsuhiro, *Takarabukuro*, p. 111

One of Mitsuhiro's greatest talents was his ability to copy objects, creating miniatures that were virtually identical to the originals. His surface treatments, staining, and polishing techniques carefully simulated various textures such as iron (CAT. 558), glazed ceramics (CAT. 706), and clay. In *Takarabukuro* (Treasure bag), Mitsuhiro described his goal: "Make an exact copy of a toy clay pigeon." Netsuke of this subject by other carvers are usually modeled as whistles. CD

745 | **Cricket Cage**

Tsukamoto Kyokusai, Japan, active 1868–1926
wood
15/16 x 15/16 x 13/16 in. (2.3 x 2.3 x 2 cm)
AC1998.249.292
incised in irregular reserve: *Kyokusai*

LITERATURE: AMICO, 2001–present

Crickets were popular pets in Japan. Inside this miniature cage, a cricket sits on a small eggplant. Like his netsuke of flowers (CATS. 480, 482–83) and baskets (CAT. 661), this piece exemplifies Kyokusai's deep undercutting and skillful rendering of narrow openings. (See also Hurtig, *Masterpieces of Netsuke Art*, fig. 280, p. 83.) CD

746 | Fushimi Fox Doll Representing Messenger of God of Rice

Kyokusō, Japan, active late 19th–early 20th century
ivory with staining, sumi
$2^{3}/_{16}$ x $^{13}/_{16}$ x $^{15}/_{16}$ in. (5.5 x 2 x 2.3 cm)
M.91.250.274
seal form, carved: *Kyokusō*

PROVENANCE: Nakajima Meiken

This netsuke is representative of fox dolls from the Fushimi Inari Shrine near Kyoto, reputed to be the earliest of the *tsuchiningyō* figures to be produced. Inari is the god of rice and could provide an abundant harvest. His messengers were foxes, and thus the fox image became symbolic for wishes of prosperity and plenty. Inari foxes are the most prevalent of the clay figures. As in *Toy Ox* (CAT. 741), the carver here has rendered the pottery mold seam. CD

747 | Fukusuke As a Jumping Jack

Miyagi Chokusai (Masanosuke), Japan, born 1877
wood, ivory with sumi, inlay
$1^{9}/_{16}$ x $1^{7}/_{16}$ x 1 in. (4 x 3.7 x 2.5 cm)
M.91.250.264
incised and stained: *Chokusai*

LITERATURE: Bushell, *An Exhibition of Netsuke*, fig. 325, p. 64; Bushell, *Netsuke Familiar and Unfamiliar*, fig. 541, p. 189

This raconteur was named after Fukusuke because of the disproportionate size of his head. The bobbing head suggests the exaggerated movements and facial expressions with which he animates his tales; the fan was used to keep the audience's attention and to emphasize parts of the story. Chokusai's fine inlay work is evident here, as is his tendency to produce nonfunctional pieces. An actual jumping jack toy had a small stick with a rubber band underneath the bamboo section. CD

748 | Toy Box

Illustrated on page 67
Sōko (Morita Kisaburō), Japan, 1879–1943
wood
1932
$1^{5}/_{8}$ x $1^{1}/_{4}$ x $^{7}/_{8}$ in. (4.1 x 3.1 x 2.2 cm)
AC1998.249.85
incised: *Sōko*
ink on box lid: *Kibori netsuke Shōwa kōnen haru* / "carved wood netsuke, spring 1932"; *Sōko saku* / "made by Sōko"
seal on box lid: *Sōko*

LITERATURE: AMICO, 2001–present; Bushell, *Collectors' Netsuke*, fig. 266, p. 156; Bushell, *An Exhibition of Netsuke*, fig. 426, p. 75; Hill and Johnson, "The Raymond Bushell Netsuke Exhibition," p. 35

Sōko often created netsuke inspired by household items (also CATS. 751, 760–61). This toy box is filled with traditional children's toys—a balancing mat, model dog, roly-poly Daruma, and carp—that might amuse children on special occasions such as Boys' Day and Girls' Day. The wooden box rests upon a Sanbasō hat, drum, and drum sticks, with an Okame mask to one side. NKD

749 | **Scarecrow**

Ōmiya Kahei, Japan, active 18th century
wood
$3\,^{13}/_{16}$ x $1\,^{5}/_{16}$ x $1\,^{3}/_{16}$ in. (9.8 x 3.4 x 3 cm)
M.91.250.286
incised: *Kahei*

LITERATURE: AMICO, 2001–present; Bushell, *An Exhibition of Netsuke*, fig. 322, p. 64; Bushell, "Questions & Answers" (1978a), fig. 8, p. 45; Mikoshiba and Bushell, "Netsuke and the *Sōken kishō*," p. 116

PROVENANCE: Atsumi Aoi

Scarecrows in Japan come in various forms. Those shaped like humans are said to possess the divine spirit of the god of the fields who protects the crops. This scarecrow, made of straw mats and covered with tattered rags, wears an *usofuki* (twisted mouth) mask. Kahei is one of the fifty-seven *netsukeshi* mentioned in the *Sōken kishō*. CD

750 | **Scarecrow**

Masatoshi (Nakamura Tokisada), Japan, 1915–2001
May 1962
ivory with staining, sumi, teak
$2\,^{7}/_{8}$ x $2\,^{9}/_{16}$ x $^{13}/_{16}$ in. (7.4 x 6.5 x 2 cm)
AC1998.249.214
incised: *Tokisada tō* / "carved by Tokisada"

LITERATURE: Bushell, *Collectors' Netsuke*, fig. 342, p. 181; Bushell, *Masatoshi*, fig. 219, p. 13; Masatoshi, *The Art of Netsuke Carving*, fig. 219, p. 192

Masatoshi seized the opportunity to have some fun with this netsuke. Copying a popular Japanese doodle, he has formed the scarecrow's facial features using symbols from *hiragana* (a Japanese syllabary). When strung together, these syllables create nonsense words: "heno heno mohe." Other than this unique element, Masatoshi's scarecrow includes typical clothing such as a straw hat and rope-tied robe. CD

751 | **Bird Scare**

Illustrated on page 67
Sōko (Morita Kisaburō), Japan, 1879–1943
wood
$1\frac{3}{4}$ x $1\frac{1}{4}$ x $\frac{1}{2}$ in. (4.4 x 3.1 x 1.2 cm)
AC1998.249.120
incised: *Sōko tō* / "carved by Sōko"

LITERATURE: AMICO, 2001–present; Bushell, *Collectors' Netsuke*, fig. 264, p. 156; Bushell, *An Exhibition of Netsuke*, fig. 432, p. 75; Hill and Johnson, "The Raymond Bushell Netsuke Exhibition," p. 36

Many netsuke artists used simple household utensils or farmyard implements as their inspiration. Sōko has created a faithful depiction of a wooden bird scare (*naruko*), with hanging bamboo pipes that rattle in the wind. NKD

752 | **Bizen Pottery Sherd**

Gechū, Japan, active 18th century
wood
$1\frac{15}{16}$ x $1\frac{5}{8}$ x $\frac{7}{16}$ in. (5 x 4.1 x 1.1 cm)
M.91.250.205
incised: *Gechū*

LITERATURE: Bushell, *Netsuke Familiar and Unfamiliar*, fig. 508, p. 182; Lazarnick, *Netsuke and Inro Artists*, vol. 1, p. 399; Mikoshiba and Bushell, "Netsuke and the *Sōken kishō*," p. 115

The pottery, or more accurately stoneware of Bizen province was manufactured in large amounts during the 1700s and 1800s. The hard base was covered with a reddish brown glaze. The wares were used as household utensils, and one of the most popular was the sake bottle (*tokuri*) of dimpled shape with a molded figure of Hotei in the depression, as shown on this broken sherd. NKD

753 | **Tile-End Mask**

Ryūkōsai Jugyoku, Japan, active early to mid-19th century
wood with gold leaf
$2\frac{9}{16}$ x $1\frac{7}{8}$ x $\frac{7}{8}$ in. (6.6 x 4.7 x 2.2 cm)
AC1998.249.152
incised: *Jugyoku*

Roof-tile ends are used to finish the tiles at roof corners, where the gargoyle-like images seem to ogle passersby. Roof-tile ends in the form of demon masks were popular netsuke subjects, and Jugyoku carved several versions (also CAT. 754) in different materials. Jugyoku worked in Edo, creating netsuke of varying subject matter; however, from the large number of works bearing his signature, it is probable that he had pupils or apprentices who assisted him. NKD

754

755 BACK

754 | **Tile-End Mask**

RYŪKŌSAI JUGYOKU, Japan, active early to mid-19th century
stag antler
$2\,^{1}/_{4}$ x $1\,^{5}/_{8}$ x 1 in. (5.7 x 4.2 x 2.5 cm)
AC1998.249.203
incised: *Jugyoku*
seal form, inlaid and carved in red lacquer: *Jugyoku*

See catalogue 753.

755 | **Bridge Post**

SŌKO (MORITA KISABURŌ), Japan, 1879–1943
May 1923
wood with staining
$2\,^{7}/_{16}$ x $^{7}/_{8}$ x $^{7}/_{8}$ in. (6.3 x 2.2 x 2.2 cm)
M.91.250.245
incised: *Taishō mizu no to i gogatsu Sōko koku* / "Taishō era [1923], Younger Brother of Fire, Year of the Boar, carved by Sōko"
incised: *Nihonbashi ondaiku Shiina Hyōgo Manji gansai kugatsu kichinichi* / "Master builder of the Nihonbashi bridge, Shiina Hyōgo; Manji 1 [1658], ninth month, auspicious day" [on collar]

LITERATURE: Bushell, *Collectors' Netsuke*, fig. 274, p. 157

According to the inscription, in 1658 a master carpenter reconstructed Nihonbashi (Bridge of Japan), which had been destroyed in the Great Meireki Fire that leveled most of Edo in 1657. The starting point for all five of Japan's major highways, Nihonbashi appears in a number of prints by Utagawa Hiroshige (1797–1858). This type of bridge post can be seen in the prints. Like other examples of Sōko's work (see CATS. 760–61), this netsuke attests to the carver's love of detail and quest for perfection. All three netsuke are marvels of surface texture and staining. CD

756 | **Pigeon-Shaped Box**

Japan, 19th century
gold lacquer
$^{7}/_{8}$ x 1 $^{3}/_{4}$ x $^{3}/_{4}$ in. (2.2 x 4.5 x 1.9 cm)
M.87.263.42a–b

LITERATURE: Bushell, *An Exhibition of Netsuke*, fig. 407, p. 72; Bushell, *The Inrō Handbook*, fig. 73, p. 107

This box netsuke (*hako*) is in the form of a resting pigeon, its plumage delineated in gold relief lacquer (*takamakie*). The interior of the box is finished with sprinkled gold powder (*nashiji*). Due to their fragility, lacquer netsuke of this type are relatively uncommon. They were produced mostly during the mid- to late 1800s. NKD

757 | **Elephant-Shaped Box**

Japan, 19th century
dry lacquer
1 $^{3}/_{16}$ x 2 $^{3}/_{16}$ x 2 $^{1}/_{16}$ in. (3 x 5.6 x 5.2 cm)
M.87.263.46

LITERATURE: AMICO, 2001–present; Bushell, *Netsuke Familiar and Unfamiliar*, fig. 109, p. 109

This is a primitive model of a pottery storage vessel, with a clamped lid, in the form of a standing elephant. It is fashioned from "dry" lacquer (*kanshitsu*) in a technique introduced to Japan from China at an early date. The earliest known Japanese examples are two Buddhist statues dedicated by Emperor Tenji (662–671). The base material is hemp or linen, soaked in lacquer, which is formed before it dries and becomes hard. Once it has hardened it is again lacquered and then decorated. NKD

758 | **Haniwa Horse**

TOSHITSUGU, Japan, active late 19th–early 20th century
ivory with staining, sumi
1 $^{7}/_{16}$ x 1 $^{3}/_{16}$ x $^{3}/_{4}$ in. (3.6 x 3 x 1.9 cm)
AC1998.249.287
incised and painted: *Toshitsugu*

Horses of the *haniwa* type were made in the Kofun period (250–552). This is a reasonably faithful representation. Originally fashioned from coarse red pottery and fired at low temperature, the various, somewhat primitive figures and animals were built up using hollow cylinders. Toshitsugu was a commercial carver who worked into the twentieth century. NKD

759 | **Sculling Oar for Small Boat**

Kokeisai Sanshō, Japan, 1871–1936
ivory with staining, sumi; sashi type
7 9/16 x 7/16 x 1/8 in. (19.3 x 1.1 x 0.3 cm)
AC1998.249.231
incised and stained: *Sanshō; Kōzan fūgetsu ikkan nari "Nandai [?]"* / "Rivers and mountain, wind and moon afford tranquility 'Nandai [?]'"
ink on inside box lid: *Kokeisai Sanshō saku kore* / "Kokeisai Sanshō made this" [interior]; *Zōge bori, ro sashi netsuke* / "Ivory carving, boat oar sashi netsuke" [exterior]
seal on box lid: *Sanshō*

This ivory carving of an oar is highly unusual for Sanshō, who is known for his boxwood netsuke of humorous, almost grotesque figures, in particular of drunken workmen (see cats. 619–20). Its inscription suggests that it was made in a poetic context. cd

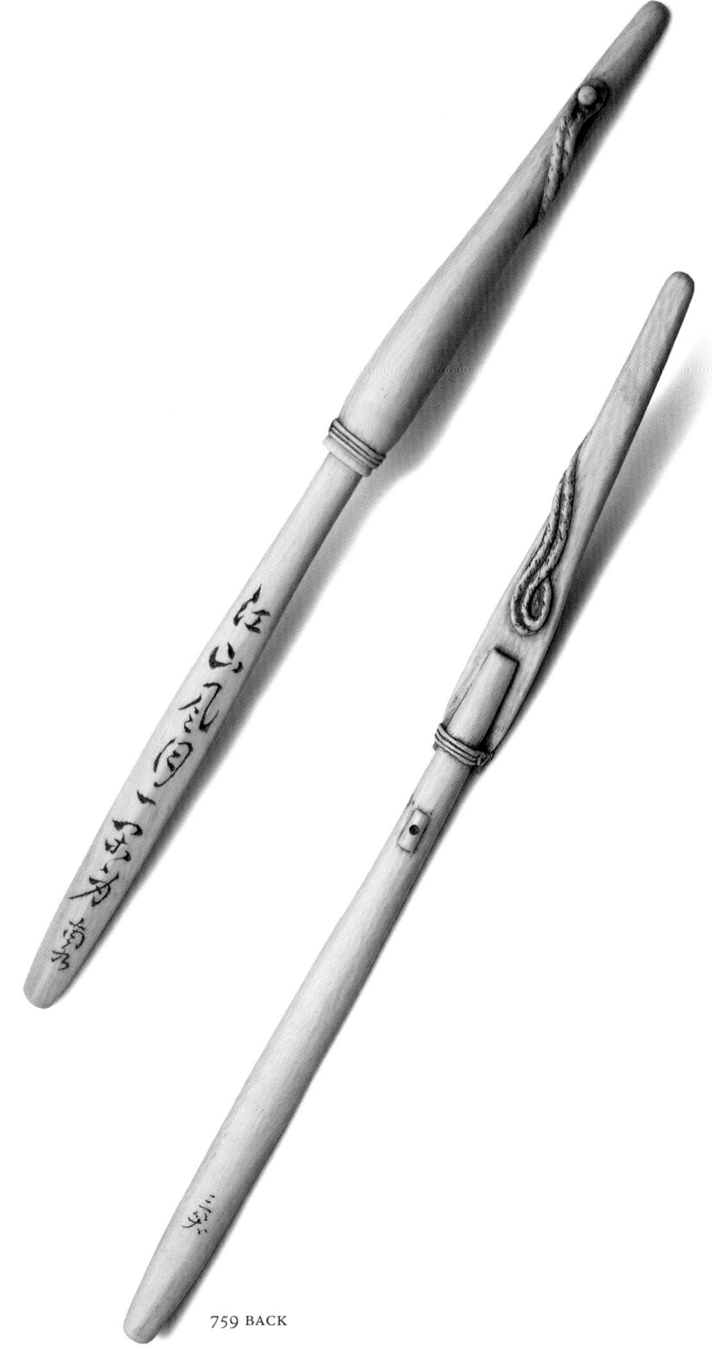

759 back

760 | **Bundle of Firewood**

Sōko (Morita Kisaburō), Japan, 1879–1943
wood with staining, sumi
$1^{15}/_{16} \times 1^{1}/_{4} \times 1$ in. (4.9 x 3.2 x 2.5 cm)
M.90.186.12
incised and stained on inlaid ivory plaque: *Sōko*

LITERATURE: Lazarnick, *Netsuke and Inro Artists*, vol. 2, p. 1026; London Netsuke Committee, *Contrasting Styles*, fig. 97, p. 43

PROVENANCE: Mark Severin

In Japanese art, a bundle of cut wood often alludes to the tale of Kosage, the poor woodcutter who could not afford sake for his parents, but whose filial love so impressed the gods that they made a waterfall flow with sake. Cut twigs with their bark are also considered to have protective powers. Sōko seems to have favored common wood items as subjects. He occasionally added colored stains or inlays, and here he inlaid an ivory plaque for his signature. CD

760 BOTTOM

761 | **Coins on String**

Sōko (Morita Kisaburō), Japan, 1879–1943
wood with staining, sumi
$1^{3}/_{4} \times {}^{15}/_{16} \times {}^{15}/_{16}$ in. (4.5 x 2.3 x 2.3 cm)
M.91.250.246
incised: *Sōko*

LITERATURE: Bushell, *Collectors' Netsuke*, fig. 269, p. 157

The last coin on the string (next to the small knot at the bottom) is a Kan'ei *tsūhō* (Kan'ei-era coin), which was minted in Japan from 1636 and officially designated as the national currency. While coin clusters are not uncommon in netsuke, few compare to the quality of this piece. Each of these seven coins is individually carved, with characters in relief on both sides, and each differs slightly in size and color. Surface textures and subtle staining suggest different metals. Netsuke also show coin groupings in piles or stacks, but stringing coins on a cord was an easy way to carry them, as seen in *Peddler* (CAT. 647). CD

Masks

MASKS WERE USED IN A VARIETY of performance arts, folk dances, and rituals during the Edo period (1615–1868). Carvers of netsuke masks adhered to or diverged from full-size models, depending upon the level of orthodoxy that had been used in the making of full-size masks. For example, netsuke carvers had a fair range of artistic license when approaching a mask used for New Year (CAT. 819) or harvest rituals—such as those of demons (CAT. 773), Chinese lions, or Okame—while they restrained their inventiveness with masks that followed exacting formulas for specific character types, such as those that would be worn for noh or kyōgen performances.

For replicas of noh masks that were made as netsuke, a carver could emulate requirements that called for cheeks that were full or emaciated; eyes that protruded, receded, or were carved out; brows that peaked, stretched across the forehead, or furrowed in anger; lips that stretched or puckered; and hair that was straight, disheveled, elaborately coiffed, or swirled. Combinations of these features defined the role types for which these masks were appropriate.

Certain subtleties very important to connoisseurship of full-size masks cannot be transferred to their miniature forms. The authentic noh mask was deliberately colored and distressed or aged by the carver to imbue it with a patina appropriate to a role type. The back of each mask was carved as carefully as the front, and much material was removed for the wearer's comfort. If netsuke masks had been carved with this degree of exactness, they would have been too fragile to perform their function as toggles. Also, the full-size noh mask conveyed a range of emotions depending on the position of the actor's head. This extreme level of sensitivity was virtually impossible to capture in a miniature model. For the noh aficionado, however, there could be no better netsuke than one showing a specific type of noh mask, especially if it were part of noh-themed inrō ensemble.

LEFT: *Demon Mask* (CAT. 773); RIGHT: *Fox Mask: Kitsune* (CAT. 817)

If a carver preferred more creative freedom, he could draw on themes from his imagination. Portraits of people (CAT. 820), Sanshō's outrageously exaggerated comic masks (CATS. 821–25), and masks of ancient worthies such as *rakan* (CAT. 826) showed artists taking the mask format as a blank canvas on which to convey their artistic priorities.

Whether they followed formulas or an artist's whim, mask netsuke were made to suit their function. Their small size was a format distinctly well suited to inrō ensembles. Also, they exuded a concentrated expression or emotion that could aptly express the wearer's attitude on a particular day.

762 | **Chinese Lion Mask**

Japan, 18th century
wood with red and black Negoro lacquer
1 3/8 x 1 3/8 x 1 1/16 in. (3.4 x 3.4 x 2.7 cm)
AC1998.249.295

The Chinese lion dance (*shishimai*) is a festival component conducted especially at New Year to rid an area of demons. Masks made for this celebration did not conform to strict conventions of shape and composition. These four masks (CATS. 762–65), with their variously proportioned snouts, foreheads, and jaws, and varying levels of embellishment, display the freedom available to the carvers. Yūtoku's mask (CAT. 763) is unique in this group for having a hinged, movable jaw. HG

763 | **Chinese Lion Mask**

YŪTOKU, Japan, active late 18th century
wood
1 7/8 x 1 9/16 x 1 9/16 in. (4.7 x 3.9 x 3.9 cm)
AC1998.249.226
incised: *Yūtoku*

LITERATURE: AMICO, 2001–present; Bushell, *Netsuke Masks*, figs. 58a and b

See catalogue 762.

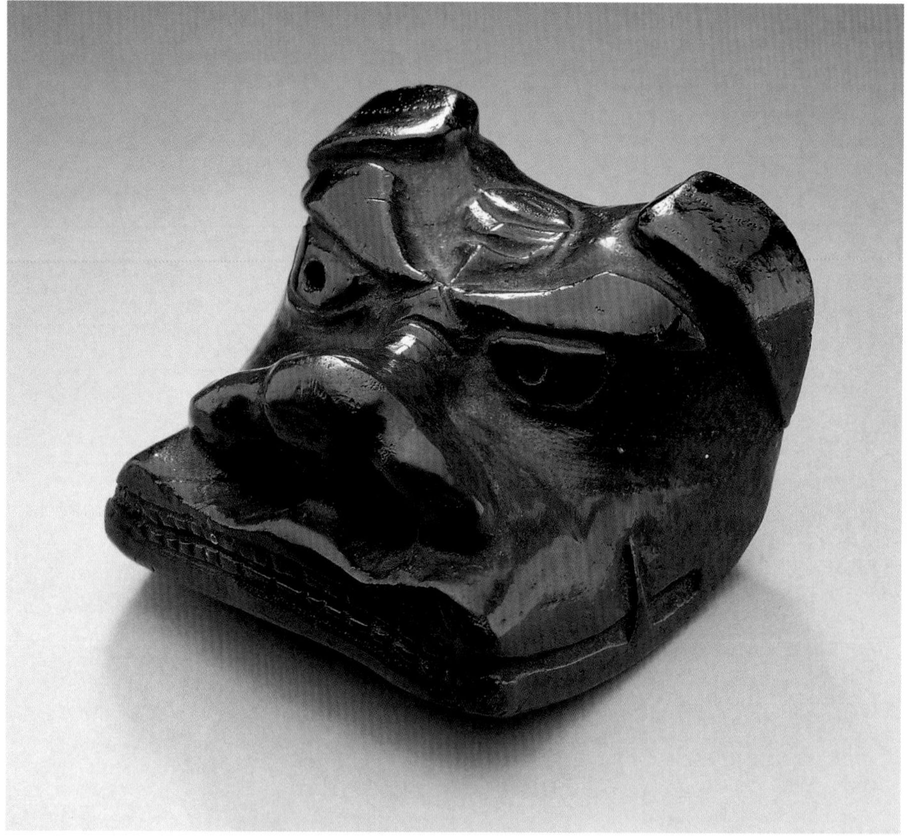

764

764 | **Chinese Lion Mask**

Japan, late 18th–early 19th century
wood with Negoro lacquer
$2\,^{7}/_{16}$ x $2\,^{5}/_{16}$ x $1\,^{5}/_{8}$ in. (6.3 x 5.9 x 4.2 cm)
M.91.250.319

LITERATURE: Bushell, *Netsuke Familiar and Unfamiliar*, fig. 368, p. 155; Bushell, *Netsuke Masks*, fig. 57

PROVENANCE: Walter Belanger

See catalogue 762.

765 | **Chinese Lion Mask**

Yūsō, Japan, active late 19th century
wood with red and gold lacquer, inlays
$1\,^{1}/_{8}$ x $1\,^{3}/_{8}$ x $1\,^{5}/_{8}$ in. (2.8 x 3.5 x 4.1 cm)
AC1998.249.227
incised on inlaid green-stained plaque: *Yūsō*

LITERATURE: AMICO, 2001–present; Bushell, *Netsuke Familiar and Unfamiliar*, fig. 613, p. 203; Bushell, *Netsuke Masks*, fig. 59; Lazarnick, *Netsuke and Inro Artists*, vol. 2, p. 1256

See catalogue 762.

765

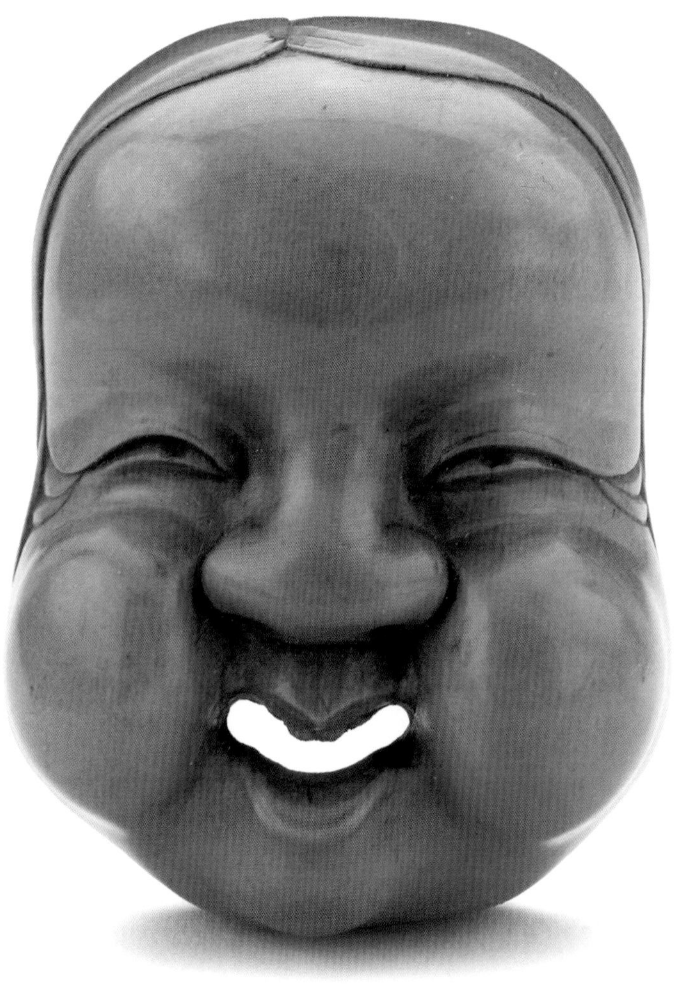

766 | **Okame Mask**

Japan, 19th century
boxwood
1 15/16 x 1 5/8 x 15/16 in. (5 x 4.1 x 2.3 cm)
AC1998.249.229

LITERATURE: AMICO, 2001–present

Humorous roles in provincial, amateur folk plays (*sato kagura*) were sometimes loosely based on standardized characters from kyōgen, the light-hearted plays performed in the interval between noh plays. The Okame character, called Oto in kyōgen and often Otafuku in folk plays, originated from the goddess of mirth, Ame no Uzume no Mikoto. The example by Yamaji Mitsuyuki (CAT. 767) appears as the face of Uzume engaged in a ribald song, when her performance draws the sun goddess, Amaterasu no Ōmikami, from her hiding place in a cave. Ōuchi Sōsui's subtle rendering (CAT. 769) is closest to the standardized Oto mask worn in kyōgen. By comparison, the two remaining Okame masks (one shown here and the other in CAT. 768) are exaggerated depictions of the bawdy character represented in provincial folk plays. HG

767 | **Okame Mask**

YAMAJI MITSUYUKI, Japan, active 19th century
ivory with staining, sumi
1 5/16 x 1 1/4 x 9/16 in. (3.4 x 3.1 x 1.5 cm)
AC1998.249.257
incised and stained: *Mitsuyuki*

LITERATURE: AMICO, 2001–present

See catalogue 766.

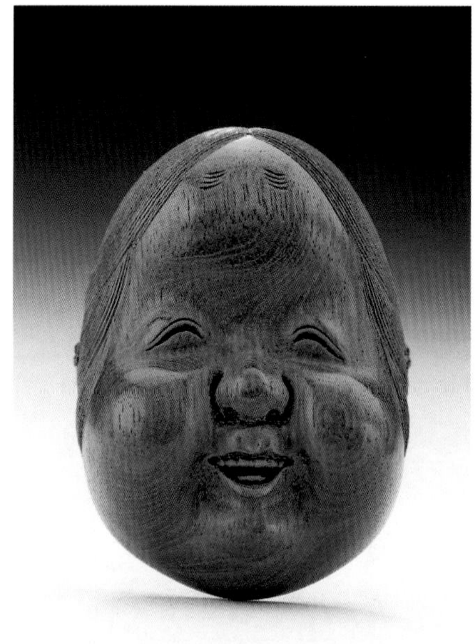

768 | **Okame Mask**

Japan, late 19th century
ivory with staining, sumi
1 1/2 x 1 1/2 x 9/16 in. (3.8 x 3.8 x 1.5 cm)
M.91.250.1

LITERATURE: AMICO, 2001–present; Bushell, *Collectors' Netsuke*, back of slipcase; Bushell, *An Exhibition of Netsuke*, fig. 385, p. 71; Bushell, *Netsuke Masks*, fig. 250

See catalogue 766.

769 | **Okame Mask**

Ōuchi Sōsui, Japan, 1911–1972
1926
wood
1 5/16 x 1 x 1/2 in. (3.4 x 2.5 x 1.2 cm)
AC1998.249.230
incised: *Sōsui tō*/ "carved by Sōsui"
ink on box lid: *Taishō hi no e tora natsu, Sōsui* / "summer 1926, Sōsui"
seal on box lid: *Sōsui*

LITERATURE: AMICO, 2001–present

See catalogue 766.

770 | **Laughing Demon Mask**

Japan, 18th century
wood with sumi
2 7/16 x 1 7/8 x 1 5/16 in. (6.2 x 4.7 x 3.4 cm)
M.91.250.5

LITERATURE: AMICO, 2001–present; Bushell, *Collectors' Netsuke*, back of slipcase; Bushell, *An Exhibition of Netsuke*, fig. 386, p. 71; Bushell, *Netsuke Familiar and Unfamiliar*, fig. 372, p. 156; Bushell, *Netsuke Masks*, fig. 34

Tsuina, a dance rite performed to dispel demons, was widespread in Japan from the country's earliest history. Like costume for folk plays, these tsuina masks (CATS. 770–73) were carved freely from the artist's imagination, though sometimes they were inspired by conventional masks for ritual performances. The laughing demon mask shown here, for example, though roughly conceived, has a passing resemblance to a Namanari mask for noh theater (see CAT. 793), with its huge grin and the eyebrows drawn together and peaked over the nose bridge. HG

771 | **Demon Mask**

Japan, 18th century
wood with sumi
2 3/4 x 1 7/8 x 1 3/16 in. (7 x 4.7 x 3 cm)
M.91.250.7

LITERATURE: AMICO, 2001–present; Bushell, *An Exhibition of Netsuke*, fig. 395, p. 71; Bushell, *Netsuke Masks*, fig. 38 and front of slipcase; Bushell, *The Wonderful World of Netsuke*, fig. 82, p. 62

PROVENANCE: William Wilberforce Winkworth

This mask retains the thick, ropelike eyebrows and broad nose of the standardized *tsuina* masks stored in Hōryūji, Nara (Bushell, *Netsuke Masks*, pp. 20, 78, pls. 31–32). The artist has skewed the face further, however, to show the demon's true ugliness and evil. HG

772 | **Mask of Demon of Ōeyama**

Japan, 18th century
wood with inlays
2 13/16 x 1 1/4 x 15/16 in. (7.2 x 3.1 x 2.4 cm)
M.91.250.324
incised: *Ōeyama* [reads center, right, left]

LITERATURE: Bushell, *An Exhibition of Netsuke*, fig. 390, p. 71; Bushell, *Netsuke Familiar and Unfamiliar*, fig. 296, p. 144; Bushell, *Netsuke Masks*, fig. 312; Lazarnick, *Netsuke and Inro Artists*, vol. 2, p. 1300

This *tsuina* mask resembles a horizontally elongated carving or painting that would have been installed above a doorway to deflect evil. Its inscription, however, refers to the story of the legendary demon of Ōeyama, named Shuten dōji, who kidnapped women from the capital and was eventually defeated by Minamoto no Raikō. HG

773 | **Demon Mask**

Illustrated on page 458
MASATOSHI (NAKAMURA TOKISADA), Japan, 1915–2001
April 1972
hornbill
1 9/16 x 1 5/16 x 9/16 in. (4 x 3.3 x 1.5 cm)
M.91.250.3
incised: *Masatoshi tō gojitsunyūmei* / "carved by Masatoshi, signed later"

LITERATURE: Bushell, *An Exhibition of Netsuke*, fig. 396, p. 71; Bushell, *Masatoshi*, fig. 154, p. 11; Bushell, *Netsuke Familiar and Unfamiliar*, fig. 350, p. 151; Bushell, *Netsuke Masks*, fig. 197 and back of slipcase; Masatoshi, *The Art of Netsuke Carving*, fig. 154, p. 178

Masatoshi's demon seems to be loosely based on the Ko-Beshimi mask for noh (CAT. 798). For this carving, he used rare hornbill material, with red layers concentrated in the carved area to indicate the strength and fury of the character portrayed. HG

774 | **Weird Face**

Japan, 19th century
gourd with lacquer, metal and other inlays
1 15/16 x 1 5/16 x 1 1/2 in. (4.9 x 3.3 x 3.8 cm)
AC1998.249.248

LITERATURE: AMICO, 2001–present; Bushell, *Netsuke Familiar and Unfamiliar*, fig. 160, p. 118

The carver of this netsuke chanced upon a gourd that resembled a silly face, akin to finding a "face rock" while hiking. With inlay and slight carving, he made the gourd into a mask of the *hyottoko* or *usofuki* type: a foolish bumpkin frequently paired with Otafuku in folk plays (CATS. 766–69). HG

775 | **Karasu Tengu Mask**

Japan, late 18th–early 19th century
wood
1 3/4 x 2 1/4 x 2 1/4 in. (4.5 x 5.7 x 5.7 cm)
M.91.250.326

LITERATURE: Bushell, *Netsuke Familiar and Unfamiliar*, fig. 297, p. 144; Bushell, *Netsuke Masks*, fig. 309; Hurtig, *Masterpieces of Netsuke Art*, fig. 950, p. 222

PROVENANCE: Jeffrey Moy; Asian Art Museum of San Francisco; Avery Brundage

Masks of the crow mountain goblin (*karasu tengu*) were worn by kyōgen performers. This mask may represent a type used in provincial festivals to stave off the ill effects of the malevolent *tengu*. HG

776 | **Gigaku Buddhist Guardian Mask**

RYŪKŌ, Japan, active early 19th century
wood
2 1/4 x 1 1/4 x 1 3/8 in. (5.7 x 3.2 x 3.5 cm)
AC1998.249.36
incised: *Ryūkō*

LITERATURE: AMICO, 2001–present; Bushell, *Netsuke Familiar and Unfamiliar*, fig. 301, p. 145; Bushell, *Netsuke Masks*, fig. 4; Lazarnick, *Netsuke and Inro Artists*, vol. 2, p. 892

Gigaku was the earliest recorded formalized performance type practiced in Japan. Imported from the Asian mainland with the dramatic form in the seventh century, gigaku masks represent caricatures of all the groups visiting T'ang China (618–907) via the Silk Road. Gigaku performances were held in the midst of celebrating crowds, and thus there was no need for subtlety of characterization. This mask represents a guardian king, Kongō Rikishi, whose fixed glare was a warning to trespassing demons and those who would trammel upon Buddhist law. A gigaku netsuke would be based upon formulas derived from standard original masks. HG

777 | **Buaku Mask**

Illustrated on page 52
Japan, 18th–19th century
ivory with staining, sumi
1 3/4 x 1 9/16 x 1 3/16 in. (4.5 x 4 x 3 cm)
M.91.250.6

LITERATURE: AMICO, 2001–present; Bushell, *Collectors' Netsuke*, front of slipcase; Bushell, *An Exhibition of Netsuke*, fig. 394, p. 71; Bushell, *Netsuke Masks*, fig. 331

Buaku is a standardized kyōgen mask type, recognized by its large, often golden eyes, broad nose, protruding cheeks, and upper teeth clamping down over the lower lip. This mask could have been used for multiple roles, but it always represented a frightening god or demon such as Raijin, god of thunder. Rather than showing pure ferocity, the character exhibits a bit of reticence and indecision, allowing for comic relief. HG

778 | **Mask Group**

NAITŌ TOYOMASA, Japan, 1773–1856
wood
2 1/16 x 1 1/2 x 1 1/4 in. (5.2 x 3.8 x 3.2 cm)
M.91.250.322
incised: *Toyomasa saku* / "made by Toyomasa"

LITERATURE: Bushell, *Netsuke Masks*, figs. 273a and b; Hata Akira, "Naitō Toyomasa," figs. 31a and b, p. 37

Naitō Toyomasa combines four noh masks into a group—that of Oto (or Okame); Hannya, the jealous female demon; Shikami, a vicious and destructive demon; and Ebisu, a god of good luck. Toyomasa's masks—though each contains the required elements of the sanctioned mask type—diverge from standard depictions in their wild expressions and proportions. These masks seem almost lifelike, rather than copies of conventional masks. HG

779 | **Usofuki**

Japan, 19th century
stag antler
1 9/16 x 1 1/4 x 15/16 in. (3.9 x 3.2 x 2.3 cm)
M.91.250.8

LITERATURE: AMICO, 2001–present; Bushell, *Netsuke Masks*, fig. 225

PROVENANCE: Tsurata

The *usofuki* (twisted mouth) mask could be used in kyōgen in the roles of an insect, scarecrow, or root vegetable. The carver used pits in the stag antler surface to convey unshaven facial and head hair, contributing to the unkempt appearance of the character. HG

780 | **Kappa Mask**

Illustrated on page 33
FUKUMOTO HŌMIN, Japan, active mid- to late 19th century
stag antler with hide, inlays
1 7/16 x 1 5/16 x 1 1/8 in. (3.7 x 3.4 x 2.8 cm)
M.91.250.215
incised and stained: *Hōmin*; kakihan [in shape of Buddhist jewel]

LITERATURE: AMICO, 2001–present; Bushell, *Collectors' Netsuke*, fig. 234, p. 150; Bushell, *An Exhibition of Netsuke*, fig. 348, p. 25; Bushell, *Netsuke Masks*, fig. 295

This *kappa* (water spirit), with a hinged jaw and hair made from deer's fur, does not represent a mask type for performance. Instead, it depicts the entire head of this creature in a portraitlike rendering. HG

781 | **Okina (Hakushiki-jō)**

KIMURA RYŪMIN, Japan, active mid- to late 19th century
wood
1 7/8 x 1 3/8 x 3/4 in. (4.8 x 3.5 x 1.9 cm)
M.91.250.361
incised: *Ryūmin saku* / "made by Ryūmin"

LITERATURE: Bushell, *Netsuke Masks*, fig. 67

Ryūmin created thirty-six masks (CATS. 781–816), an auspicious number used famously by Hokusai in his print series of Mt. Fuji. The total number of noh and kyōgen mask types exceeds three hundred, with more than eighty basic categories, each having innumerable permutations. For the sake of durability, Ryūmin left the masks unpainted, though this might obscure exact identification of some characters. The Okina mask is used in an auspicious dance performed at New Year or during certain special occasions. Although it predates noh, it is often danced on noh stages. The actor brings the mask to the stage in a special lacquer box and dons it in front of the audience. In the noh repertoire, this mask is unique for its jaw that appears to be hinged, a stylistic carryover from earlier hinged types, and for the circular eyebrows. HG

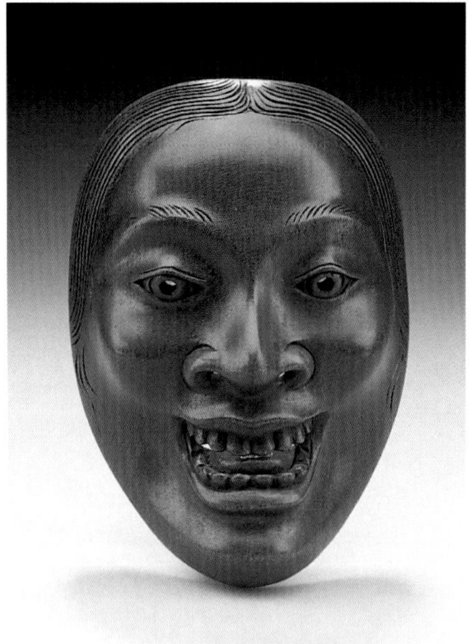

782 | **Yamanba (Yamauba)**

Kimura Ryūmin, Japan, active mid- to late 19th century
wood
2 x 1 7/16 x 15/16 in. (5.1 x 3.7 x 2.3 cm)
M.91.250.368
incised: *Ryūmin saku* / "made by Ryūmin"

LITERATURE: Bushell, *Netsuke Masks*, fig. 76

Unlike most other noh masks that represent general types, these netsuke (also CATS. 783–86) depict individual characters. Yamanba is a protagonist in *Yamanba* (also *Yamauba*; The mountain witch). Endowed with special powers, she has round pupils surrounded by gilded irises (in the performance mask) and eyebrows that splay upward. Her hair is drawn as parallel lines, except for a few stray hairs to indicate her madness, and both rows of teeth form a malicious grin. HG

783 | **Shōjō**

Kimura Ryūmin, Japan, active mid- to late 19th century
wood
1 15/16 x 1 3/8 x 15/16 in. (4.9 x 3.5 x 2.4 cm)
M.91.250.366
incised: *Ryūmin saku* / "made by Ryūmin"

LITERATURE: Bushell, *Netsuke Masks*, fig. 77

Shōjō, the water sprite, is shown with the features of a young boy, with only upper teeth exposed, dimpled cheeks, and hair falling in loose fringe along his forehead. Ryūmin sacrifices some detail in his use of plain wood, as the shōjō's hair and skin would usually be a reddish hue. HG

784 | **Yorimasa**

Kimura Ryūmin, Japan, active mid- to late 19th century
wood
1 7/8 x 1 7/16 x 1 in. (4.8 x 3.7 x 2.5 cm)
M.91.250.371
incised: *Ryūmin saku* / "made by Ryūmin"

LITERATURE: Bushell, *Netsuke Masks*, fig. 80

The tragic hero of *Uji Yorimasa* (Yorimasa at Uji) appears in this mask during the second act as the ghost of the great warrior Minamoto no Yorimasa, who committed suicide after defeat in a catastrophic battle. The Yorimasa mask features rounded eyes and sunken cheeks, which are strongly lined under the eyes and around the jowls. The eyebrows are drawn together in consternation. HG

785 | **Kagekiyo**

Kimura Ryūmin, Japan, active mid- to late 19th century
wood
2 x 1 1/2 x 15/16 in. (5.1 x 3.8 x 2.4 cm)
M.91.250.355
incised: *Ryūmin saku* / "made by Ryūmin"

LITERATURE: Bushell, *Netsuke Masks*, fig. 82

Kagekiyo represents another tragic hero. He blinded himself rather than watch his enemies claim victory. For the play *Kagekiyo*, the mask's eyes are hollowed out as slits and the beard is formed with horsehair. Both rows of teeth appear beneath sunken cheeks and his brow is furrowed. The effect is intended to be one of dignity despite grief. HG

786 | **Fudō**

Kimura Ryūmin, Japan, active mid- to late 19th century
wood
1 7/8 x 1 1/2 x 1 in. (4.8 x 3.8 x 2.5 cm)
M.91.250.349
incised: *Ryūmin saku* / "made by Ryūmin"

LITERATURE: Bushell, *Netsuke Masks*, fig. 87

The godly protector of Buddhist law, Fudō the immovable, appears in the play *Chōbuku Soga* (The curse of the Soga). Unusual for a mask, Fudō has tightly curled hair and wears a crown. His square, strong features are punctuated by a snarl exposing all his teeth, upward-flowing eyebrows, and gilded eyes without irises. HG

787 | **Kasshiki**

Kimura Ryūmin, Japan, active mid- to late 19th century
wood
1 15/16 x 1 5/16 x 15/16 in. (4.9 x 3.4 x 2.4 cm)
M.91.250.356
incised: *Ryūmin saku* / "made by Ryūmin"

LITERATURE: Bushell, *Netsuke Masks*, fig. 75

Kasshiki represents a young religious acolyte entering temple training and austerities. The dimpled features and fan-shaped arrangement of hair on the forehead distinguish this mask. HG

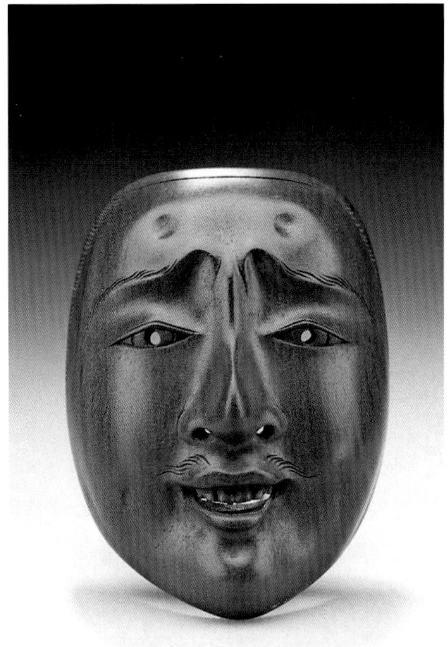

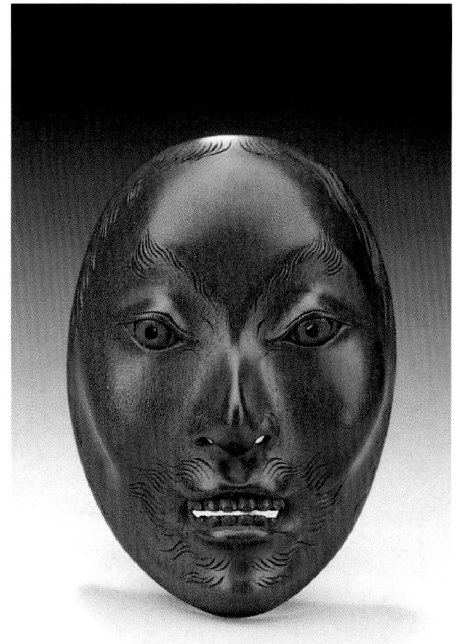

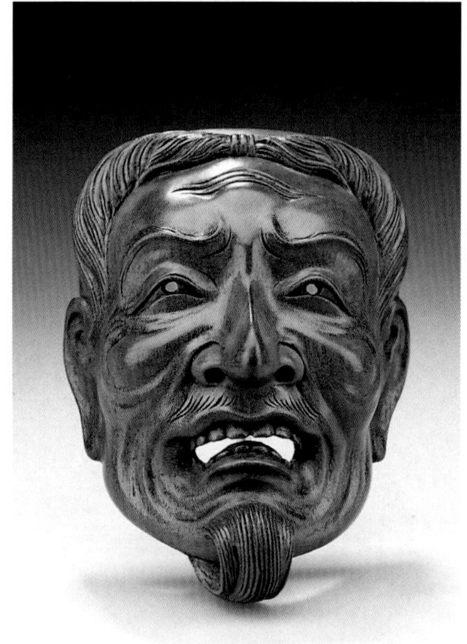

788 | **Chūjō**

KIMURA RYŪMIN, Japan, active
mid- to late 19th century
wood
1 15/16 x 1 7/16 x 15/16 in. (4.9 x 3.7 x 2.3 cm)
M.91.250.347
incised: *Ryūmin saku* / "made by Ryūmin"

LITERATURE: Bushell, *Netsuke Masks*, fig. 89

Chūjō is a person of middle rank in the military. Unlike Kasshiki (CAT. 787), who shows both rows of teeth, Chūjō is somewhat more serious, showing only his upper teeth, knitting his brow, and sporting a slight mustache. HG

789 | **Heita**

KIMURA RYŪMIN, Japan, active
mid- to late 19th century
wood
1 15/16 x 1 7/16 x 15/16 in.
(4.9 x 3.7 x 2.4 cm)
M.91.250.353
incised: *Ryūmin saku* / "made by Ryūmin"

LITERATURE: Bushell, *Netsuke Masks*, fig. 91

Heita is hirsute and has both rows of teeth set in a scowl. His eyebrows are arched while the hairs of his brows stand vertically. Incised lines are an indicator of age. A character wearing the Heita mask would be a member of the Heike warrior clan. HG

790 | **Asakura-jō**

KIMURA RYŪMIN, Japan, active
mid- to late 19th century
wood
2 1/16 x 1 7/16 x 1 in. (5.2 x 3.7 x 2.5 cm)
M.91.250.345
incised: *Ryūmin saku* / "made by Ryūmin"

LITERATURE: Bushell, *Netsuke Masks*, fig. 94

The netsuke of Asakura-jō is the sole representative in Ryūmin's set of a mask of an older human male. This class of masks is made distinctive by the styling of hair, with locks from each side of the forehead tied together over the center. Several performance masks of the *jō* ("old man") type have beards made from applied horsehair and either painted or applied mustaches. Those features are carved on this netsuke. Asakura-jō represents a friendly older man. HG

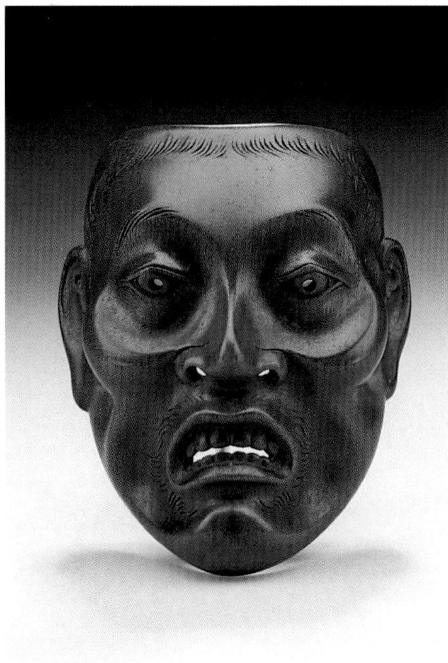

791 | **Yase-Otoko**

KIMURA RYŪMIN, Japan, active mid- to late 19th century
wood
1 7/8 x 1 1/2 x 1 in. (4.8 x 3.8 x 2.5 cm)
M.91.250.370
incised: *Ryūmin saku* / "made by Ryūmin"

LITERATURE: Bushell, *Netsuke Masks*, fig. 100

Only one mask in the Ryūmin set shows the face of a ghostly male. Yase-Otoko, the emaciated man, has hollowed eyes and sunken cheeks, with both rows of teeth set in a mouth that conveys suffering. It embodies the ghost of an individual who has been wrongly treated in life. Mustache and beard hairs carved askew indicate a character tormented nearly to madness. HG

792 | **Hannya**

KIMURA RYŪMIN, Japan, active mid- to late 19th century
wood
1 7/8 x 1 3/8 x 3/4 in. (4.8 x 3.5 x 1.9 cm)
M.91.250.351
incised: *Ryūmin saku* / "made by Ryūmin"

LITERATURE: Bushell, *Netsuke Masks*, fig. 71

Noh masks of female spirits and supernatural beings are some of the best known of the genre. Hannya, shown here, is one of the most recognizable masks. It is the ghost or spirit of a woman overcome with jealousy and rage who nonetheless retains a possibility for redemption. On performance masks, tall horns protrude from the brow. In netsuke, these horns were made smaller and the tips were attached to the skull. Hannya's fanged leer is enhanced by sunken cheeks and lowered brows, her hair disheveled to indicate madness. HG

793 | **Namanari**

KIMURA RYŪMIN, Japan, active mid- to late 19th century
wood
1 7/8 x 1 3/8 x 1 in. (4.8 x 3.5 x 2.5 cm)
M.91.250.359
incised: *Ryūmin saku* / "made by Ryūmin"

LITERATURE: Bushell, *Netsuke Masks*, fig. 103

Another female spirit, although more implacable than Hannya, Namanari is insane with jealousy. Her eyes are angled down at the outer corners, and her lips open around her elongated fangs. Her irreconcilable anger makes her terrifying. HG

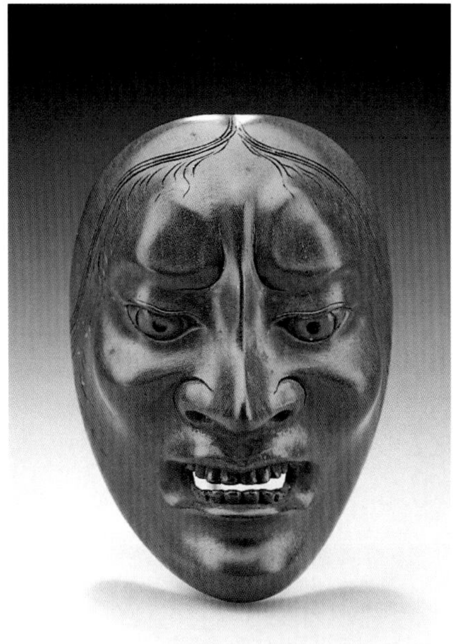

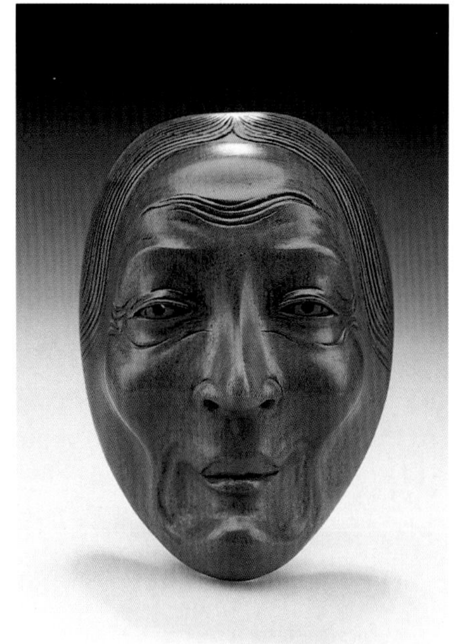

794 | **Hashihime**

KIMURA RYŪMIN, Japan, active
mid- to late 19th century
wood
1 15/16 x 1 3/8 x 1 in. (4.9 x 3.5 x 2.5 cm)
M.91.250.352
incised: *Ryūmin saku* / "made by Ryūmin"

LITERATURE: Bushell, *Netsuke Masks*, fig. 104

Hashihime is a ghost possessed by a seething fury, and her state of mind is best conveyed by tousled hair, lowered eyes, and a scowl exposing both rows of teeth. HG

795 | **Yase-Onna**

KIMURA RYŪMIN, Japan, active
mid- to late 19th century
wood
2 x 1 7/16 x 15/16 in. (5.1 x 3.7 x 2.3 cm)
M.91.250.369
incised: *Ryūmin saku* / "made by Ryūmin"

LITERATURE: Bushell, *Netsuke Masks*, fig. 105

Least virulent of the female ghosts, Yase-Onna can play the role of a remorseful ghost whose soul must gain release through prayer. Emaciated features, horizontal lines on the forehead, and a deeply creased face define this mask type. The performance mask would be a deathly white. HG

796 | **Ō-Tobide**

KIMURA RYŪMIN, Japan, active
mid- to late 19th century
wood
1 15/16 x 1 1/2 x 1 1/8 in. (4.9 x 3.8 x 2.8 cm)
M.91.250.363
incised: *Ryūmin saku* / "made by Ryūmin"

LITERATURE: Bushell, *Netsuke Masks*, fig. 107

One-third of Ryūmin's set of thirty-six netsuke is dedicated to male demons and deities (CATS. 796–807). If full-size, these masks would be outfitted with painted or inset metal eyeballs to convey the characters' supernatural state. Many of these would have extra coloration on the face as well, either metallic, red, gray, ivory, or white to emphasize their otherworldly origins. Ō-Tobide, one of the many open-mouthed masks in this group, is noted for his popping eyes and the upward-flying hairs of his eyebrows, mustache, and beard, indications of his power. The Ō-Tobide mask represents the protective aspect of a fox deity. HG

797 | **Ō-Beshimi**

Kimura Ryūmin, Japan, active
mid- to late 19th century
wood
1 13/16 x 1 7/16 x 1 in. (4.6 x 3.7 x 2.5 cm)
M.91.250.360
incised: *Ryūmin saku* / "made by Ryūmin"

LITERATURE: Bushell, *Netsuke Masks*, fig. 115

Ō-Beshimi and Ko-Beshimi (CAT. 798), forms of the same mask with greater or lesser power, compress their lips to be intimidating. Ō-Beshimi can represent a possibly malevolent magical beast like the *tengu* (mountain goblin), while the Ko-Beshimi mask would signify either a neutral or helpful being. HG

798 | **Ko-Beshimi**

Kimura Ryūmin, Japan, active
mid- to late 19th century
wood
1 3/4 x 1 1/2 x 15/16 in. (4.4 x 3.8 x 2.3 cm)
M.91.250.357
incised: *Ryūmin saku* / "made by Ryūmin"

LITERATURE: Bushell, *Netsuke Masks*, fig. 116

See catalogue 797.

799

799 | **Kurohige**

Kimura Ryūmin, Japan, active
mid- to late 19th century
wood
$1^{15}/_{16}$ x $1^{1}/_{2}$ x 1 in. (4.9 x 3.8 x 2.5 cm)
M.91.250.358
incised: *Ryūmin saku* / "made by Ryūmin"

LITERATURE: Bushell, *Netsuke Masks*, fig. 118

Kurohige, or Black Whiskers, with his long, sharp chin, red tongue, and earless head, represents a powerful god with the ability to do good or evil. The Dragon King of the Sea, Ryūjin, is outfitted with this mask. HG

800 | **Tenjin**

Kimura Ryūmin, Japan, active
mid- to late 19th century
wood
$1^{13}/_{16}$ x $1^{1}/_{2}$ x 1 in. (4.6 x 3.8 x 2.5 cm)
M.91.250.367
incised: *Ryūmin saku* / "made by Ryūmin"

LITERATURE: Bushell, *Netsuke Masks*, fig. 119

Tenjin, the deified form of the unfairly exiled ninth-century court official Sugawara Michizane, is worshiped as the patron deity of learning. His angry spirit was believed to have wreaked havoc in Kyoto after his death. HG

800

801 | **Shishiguchi**

KIMURA RYŪMIN, Japan, active mid- to late 19th century
wood
$1^{5}/_{8}$ x $1^{1}/_{2}$ x 1 in. (4.2 x 3.8 x 2.5 cm)
M.91.250.365
incised: *Ryūmin saku* / "made by Ryūmin"

LITERATURE: Bushell, *Netsuke Masks*, fig. 121

Masks of Shishiguchi and Ikazuchi (CAT. 802) were worn by different noh schools in the roles of a Chinese lion (*shishi*) or other powerful animals. HG

802 | **Ikazuchi**

KIMURA RYŪMIN, Japan, active mid- to late 19th century
wood
$1^{7}/_{8}$ x $1^{1}/_{2}$ x $^{15}/_{16}$ in. (4.7 x 3.8 x 2.3 cm)
M.91.250.354
incised: *Ryūmin saku* / "made by Ryūmin"

LITERATURE: Bushell, *Netsuke Masks*, fig. 123

See catalogue 801.

803 | **Shikami**

KIMURA RYŪMIN, Japan, active mid- to late 19th century
wood
$1^{7}/_{8}$ x $1^{1}/_{2}$ x 1 in. (4.8 x 3.8 x 2.5 cm)
M.91.250.364
incised: *Ryūmin saku* / "made by Ryūmin"

LITERATURE: Bushell, *Netsuke Masks*, fig. 125

Shikami and Deija (CAT. 804), both with open mouths and scowling expressions, are used in roles for spirits bent on evil. Shikami could represent an earth spider ready to attack a valiant warrior. Deija's prominent forehead veins heighten a sense of malevolent concentration. It may be substituted for the female Hannya mask, although it has a mustache. HG

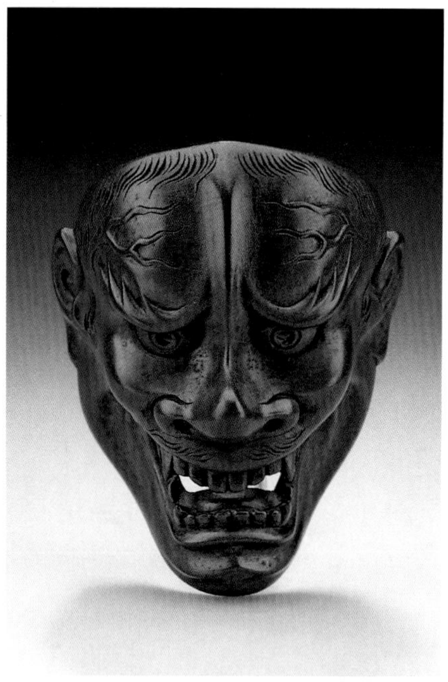

804 | **Deija**

Kimura Ryūmin, Japan, active mid- to late 19th century
wood
2 x 1 9/16 x 1 in. (5.1 x 4 x 2.5 cm)
M.91.250.348
incised: *Ryūmin saku* / "made by Ryūmin"

LITERATURE: Bushell, *Netsuke Masks*, fig. 128

See catalogue 803.

805 | **Hanakobu Akujō**

Kimura Ryūmin, Japan, active mid- to late 19th century
wood
1 7/8 x 1 1/2 x 1 in. (4.8 x 3.8 x 2.5 cm)
M.91.250.350
incised: *Ryūmin saku* / "made by Ryūmin"

LITERATURE: Bushell, *Netsuke Masks*, fig. 131

The Akujō masks, here represented by Hanakobu Akujō, Omoni Akujō, and Beshimi Akujō (CATS. 805–7), all depict fearsome male demons or spirits. Hanakobu, or Lump Nose, is named for the distinguishing characteristic of an enlarged proboscis. Omoni Akujō is lovelorn, shown by his raised brows and wrinkled forehead. Beshimi Akujō, with teeth clamping down on his lower lip, is filled with magical power of a negative sort. Akujō performance masks always have round, gilt eyes and often have protruding veins around the forehead. HG

806 | **Omoni Akujō**

Kimura Ryūmin, Japan, active mid- to late 19th century
wood
2 x 1 1/2 x 1 in. (5.1 x 3.8 x 2.5 cm)
M.91.250.362
incised: *Ryūmin saku* / "made by Ryūmin"

LITERATURE: Bushell, *Netsuke Masks*, fig. 132

See catalogue 805.

807

807 | **Beshimi Akujō**

Kimura Ryūmin, Japan, active mid- to late 19th century
wood
2 x $1^{1}/_{2}$ x 1 in. (5.1 x 3.8 x 2.5 cm)
M.91.250.346
incised: *Ryūmin saku* / "made by Ryūmin"

LITERATURE: Bushell, *Netsuke Masks*, fig. 133

See catalogue 805.

808 | **Daikoku**

Kimura Ryūmin, Japan, active mid- to late 19th century
wood
$1^{3}/_{4}$ x $1^{5}/_{8}$ x $^{15}/_{16}$ in. (4.4 x 4.2 x 2.3 cm)
M.91.250.373
incised: *Ryūmin saku* / "made by Ryūmin"

LITERATURE: Bushell, *Netsuke Masks*, fig. 149

Used in farcical plays, kyōgen masks do not require the subtle, versatile qualities of noh masks. The expression is usually fixed and does not appear to vary when the mask is held at different angles. The Gods of Good Fortune appear in kyōgen, often represented by the most popular of the group, Daikoku and Ebisu (CATS. 808–9). The two have similarly curved and crinkled eyes, but Ebisu's mouth is more open. He has fewer forehead wrinkles, and unlike Daikoku, who is clean shaven, has both beard and mustache. HG

808

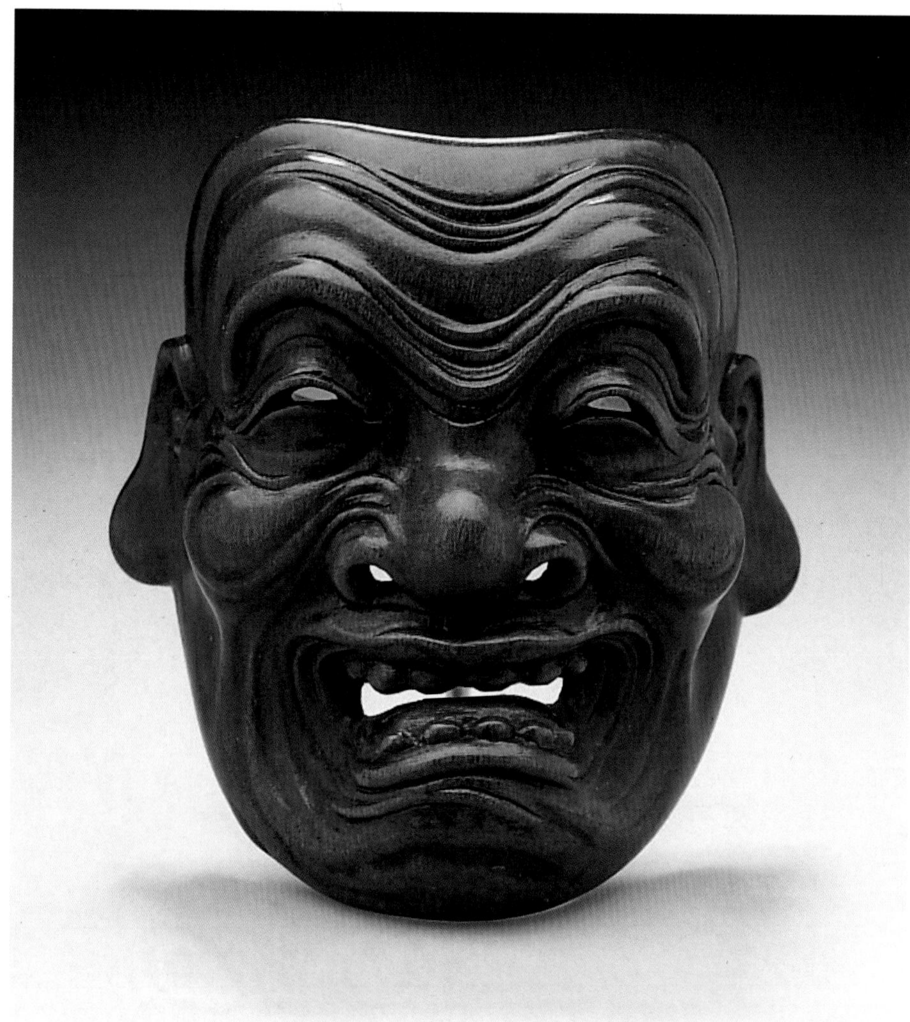

809 | **Ebisu**

Kimura Ryūmin, Japan, active mid- to late 19th century
wood
1 7/8 x 1 9/16 x 1 in. (4.8 x 4 x 2.5 cm)
M.91.250.374
incised: *Ryūmin saku* / "made by Ryūmin"

LITERATURE: Bushell, *Netsuke Masks*, fig. 150

See catalogue 808.

810 | **Ōji**

Kimura Ryūmin, Japan, active mid- to late 19th century
wood
1 3/4 x 1 5/8 x 1 in. (4.4 x 4.2 x 2.5 cm)
M.91.250.377
incised: *Ryūmin saku* / "made by Ryūmin"

LITERATURE: Bushell, *Netsuke Masks*, fig. 155

Fixed in a perpetual chuckle, this mask depicts an ordinary older gentleman with a comical side. Oddly, he has elongated ears, which are normally associated with the Gods of Good Fortune. HG

811 | **Buaku**

Kimura Ryūmin, Japan, active mid- to late 19th century
wood
1 7/8 x 1 7/16 x 1 in. (4.8 x 3.7 x 2.5 cm)
M.91.250.372
incised: *Ryūmin saku* / "made by Ryūmin"

LITERATURE: Bushell, *Netsuke Masks*, fig. 158

Buaku can represent either a demon or a frightening god. The lower half of his face appears determined and scowling, while brows and eyes, in contrast, seem frozen in terror. This ambivalence gives the mask its humor. HG

812 | **Kentoku**

Kimura Ryūmin, Japan, active mid- to late 19th century
wood
1 3/4 x 1 1/2 x 15/16 in. (4.4 x 3.8 x 2.3 cm)
M.91.250.376
incised: *Ryūmin saku* / "made by Ryūmin"

LITERATURE: Bushell, *Netsuke Masks*, fig. 166

Kentoku, Usofuki, and Saru (CATS. 812–14) masks signify odd creatures. The shocked, round-eyed expression of the Kentoku mask makes it suitable for use as an octopus or a startled dog. Usofuki, with its blank expression, is often worn for the role of an animal or talking object. The Saru mask can represent a monkey (*saru*) or trickster animal such as a fox. HG

813 | **Usofuki**

KIMURA RYŪMIN, Japan, active mid- to late 19th century
wood
1 7/8 x 1 3/8 x 15/16 in. (4.8 x 3.5 x 2.3 cm)
M.91.250.380
incised: *Ryūmin saku* / "made by Ryūmin"

LITERATURE: Bushell, *Netsuke Masks*, fig. 171

See catalogue 812.

814 | **Saru**

KIMURA RYŪMIN, Japan, active mid- to late 19th century
wood
1 15/16 x 1 1/2 x 1 in. (4.9 x 3.8 x 2.5 cm)
M.91.250.378
incised: *Ryūmin saku* / "made by Ryūmin"

LITERATURE: Bushell, *Netsuke Masks*, fig. 172

See catalogue 812.

815 | **Kaminari**

KIMURA RYŪMIN, Japan, active mid- to late 19th century
wood
1 13/16 x 1 5/8 x 15/16 in. (4.6 x 4.2 x 2.3 cm)
M.91.250.375
incised: *Ryūmin saku* / "made by Ryūmin"

LITERATURE: Bushell, *Netsuke Masks*, fig. 175

The two final Ryūmin masks are supernatural beings, Kaminari and Tobi (Ko-Tengu) (CATS. 815–16). They may be worn in the roles of the god of thunder and a malevolent mountain goblin (*tengu*), respectively. Tobi also has a special function in noh, making it unique among other kyōgen characters. Tobi plays a discursive role during an intermission in noh, explicating some of the history or action that leads to the next section of the play. HG

816 | **Tobi (Ko-Tengu)**

KIMURA RYŪMIN, Japan, active mid- to late 19th century
wood
$1^{3}/_{4} \times 1^{1}/_{2} \times 1$ in. (4.4 x 3.8 x 2.5 cm)
M.91.250.379
incised: *Ryūmin saku* / "made by Ryūmin"

LITERATURE: Bushell, *Netsuke Masks*, fig. 176

See catalogue 815.

817 | **Fox Mask: Kitsune**

Japan, late 19th century
wood
$1^{5}/_{16} \times 1^{5}/_{16} \times 1^{1}/_{4}$ in. (3.4 x 3.3 x 3.1 cm)
AC1998.249.245

LITERATURE: AMICO, 2001–present; Bushell, *Netsuke Masks*, fig. 187

The fox mask is used in kyōgen to represent a fox that has transformed itself to its original form after being temporarily in human guise. The human form of the fox is portrayed with a Saru mask (CAT. 818). HG

818 | **Saru Mask**

Takehara Chikkō, Japan, active late 19th–mid-20th century
early 20th century
wood
1 1/8 x 1 7/16 x 7/8 in. (2.9 x 3.6 x 2.2 cm)
M.91.250.2
incised: *Chikkō saku* / "made by Chikkō"

LITERATURE: Bushell, *Netsuke Masks*, fig. 183

PROVENANCE: Ugo Alphonse Casal

The monkeylike Saru mask, carved here in a realistic style by Takehara Chikkō, could be used in monkey, fox, or *tanuki* roles for kyōgen. It was worn most famously in the role of an elderly fox taking the form of the priest Hakuzōsu in the play *Tsurigitsune* (Trapping of the fox). HG

819 | **Okina Mask**

Ōuchi Sōsui, Japan, 1911–1972
1929
wood with lacquer
1 1/2 x 1 1/8 x 11/16 in. (3.8 x 2.8 x 1.7 cm)
AC1998.249.228
incised: *Sōsui tō* / "carved by Sōsui"
ink on box lid: *Sōsui tō* / "carved by Sōsui"; *Shōwa tsuchi no to mi shōnen* / "New Year, 1929"
seal on box lid: *Sōsui*

LITERATURE: Bushell, *Netsuke Masks*, fig. 63; Bushell, "Questions & Answers" (1977), fig. 17, p. 46

Though he added color to heighten the realism of this mask, Ōuchi Sōsui was inventive with the eyebrows. He made them long and drooping rather than circular cotton patches worn high on the forehead, which were required for traditional Okina masks. In his netsuke, he uses wood to simulate the cord-hung jaw attachments of a performance mask. HG

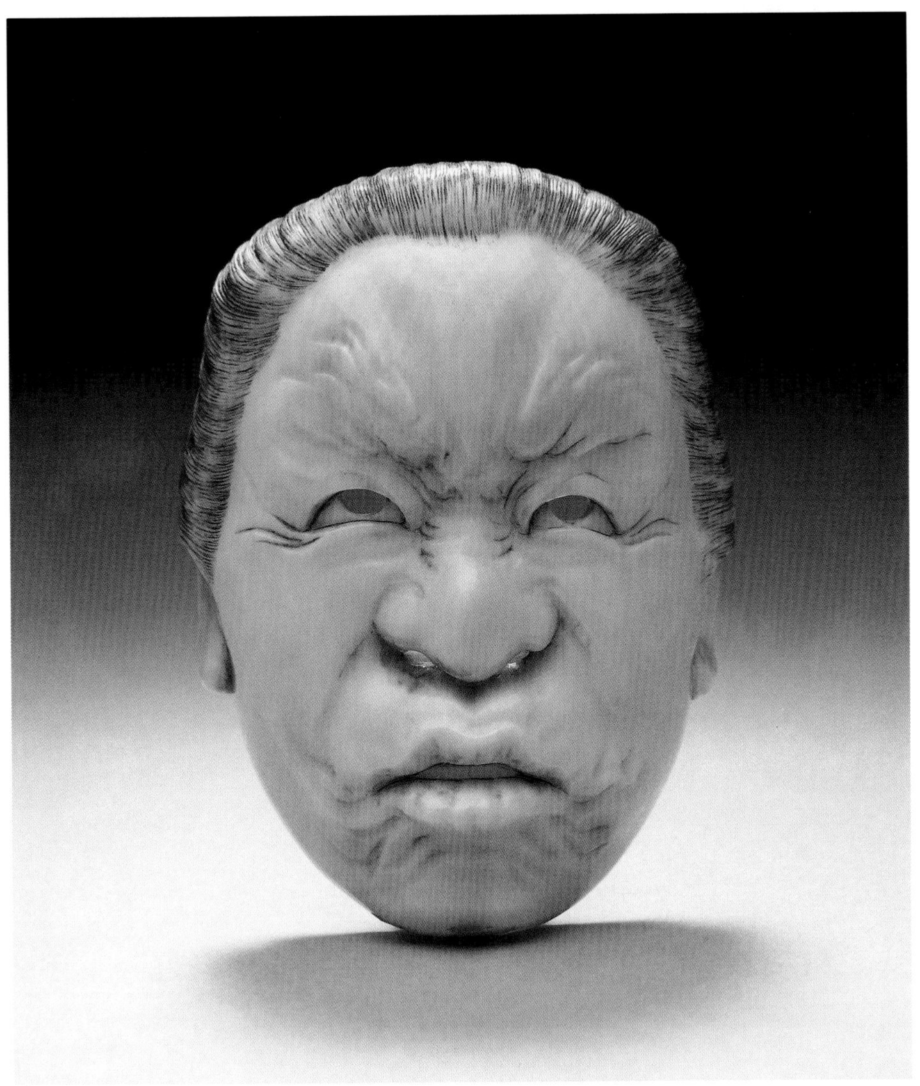

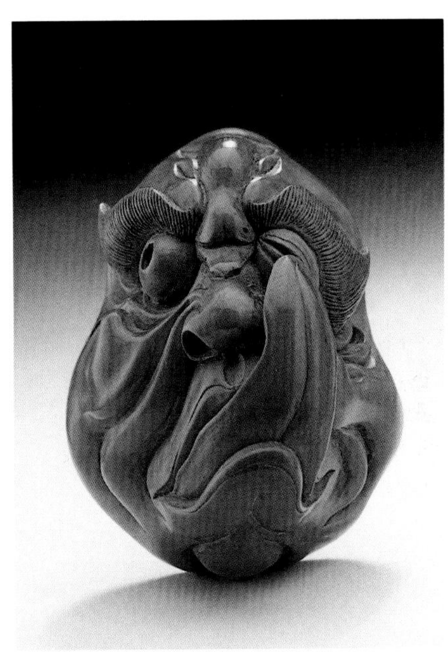

820 | **Mask Portrait of Old Woman**

Japan, late 19th–early 20th century
ivory with staining, sumi
1 15/16 x 1 1/2 x 1/2 in. (4.9 x 3.8 x 1.3 cm)
M.91.250.4

LITERATURE: AMICO, 2001–present; Bushell, *An Exhibition of Netsuke*, fig. 389, p. 26; Bushell, *Netsuke Familiar and Unfamiliar*, fig. 305, p. 145; Bushell, *Netsuke Masks*, fig. 289; Hill and Johnson, "The Raymond Bushell Netsuke Exhibition," fig. 389, p. 35

This may be intended to represent a specific face, perhaps the death mask of someone the carver knew. The care displayed in the details may hint at a familiar relationship. HG

821 | **Mask with Long Tongue**

Kokeisai Sanshō, Japan, 1871–1936
wood with inlay
2 1/8 x 1 5/8 x 1 1/4 in. (5.4 x 4.2 x 3.1 cm)
M.91.250.340
incised and stained on inlaid ivory plaque: *Sanshō*; kakihan

LITERATURE: Bushell, *Netsuke Masks*, fig. 330

Kokeisai Sanshō's characters are often profoundly exaggerated, and this set of masks (CATS. 821–25) epitomizes his fascination with the ludicrous. HG

822 | **Mask with Long Nose**

Kokeisai Sanshō, Japan, 1871–1936
wood
2 1/8 x 1 5/8 x 1 3/8 in. (5.4 x 4.2 x 3.5 cm)
M.91.250.341
incised and stained on inlaid ivory plaque:
Sanshō; kakihan

LITERATURE: Bushell, *Netsuke Familiar and Unfamiliar*, fig. 315, p. 147; Bushell, *Netsuke Masks*, fig. 327 and back of slipcase

See catalogue 821.

823 | **Comic Mask of Horned Demon**

Kokeisai Sanshō, Japan, 1871–1936
wood
2 3/16 x 1 5/8 x 1 1/4 in. (5.5 x 4.1 x 3.2 cm)
M.91.250.342
incised and stained on inlaid ivory plaque:
Sanshō; kakihan

LITERATURE: Bushell, *An Exhibition of Netsuke*, fig. 392, p. 71, and back cover; Bushell, *Netsuke Familiar and Unfamiliar*, fig. 314, p. 147; Bushell, *Netsuke Masks*, fig. 331; Hill and Johnson, "The Raymond Bushell Netsuke Exhibition," fig. 392, p. 29

See catalogue 821.

824 | **Exaggerated Usofuki Mask**

Kokeisai Sanshō, Japan, 1871–1936
wood
2 1/16 x 1 9/16 x 1 5/16 in. (5.2 x 4 x 3.4 cm)
M.91.250.343
incised and stained on inlaid ivory plaque:
Sanshō; kakihan

LITERATURE: Bushell, *Netsuke Masks*, fig. 329 and back of slipcase

See catalogue 821.

825 | **Comic Mask with Bulbous Nose**

Kokeisai Sanshō, Japan, 1871–1936
late 19th–early 20th century
wood with sumi
2 3/16 x 1 5/8 x 1 7/16 in. (5.5 x 4.1 x 3.7 cm)
M.91.250.344
incised and stained on inlaid ivory plaque: *Sanshō*; kakihan

LITERATURE: Bushell, *Netsuke Masks*, fig. 328

See catalogue 821.

827

826 | **Stylized Rakan Mask**

Illustrated on page 57
Ozaki Kokusai, Japan, 1835–circa 1892
stag antler with inlays
1 x 1 13/16 x 9/16 in. (2.5 x 2 x 1.5 cm)
AC1998.249.222
seal form, carved: *Koku*

LITERATURE: AMICO, 2001–present; Bushell, *Netsuke Familiar and Unfamiliar*, fig. 385, p. 159

On a button-sized piece of stag antler, Ozaki Kokusai has created an abstracted carving of the face of a *rakan* (a high-ranking disciple of the Buddha), complete with a hoop earring on an ear formed from a spiral design. HG

827 | **Rakan Mask**

Masatoshi (Nakamura Tokisada), Japan, 1915–2001
October 1978
ivory with light staining, sumi
2 1/8 x 1 13/16 x 1 1/8 in. (5.4 x 4.6 x 2.8 cm)
AC1998.249.213
incised and lightly stained: *Masatoshi tō* / "carved by Masatoshi"

LITERATURE: Bushell, *Masatoshi*, fig. 151, p. 28; Bushell, *Netsuke Masks*, fig. 326; Masatoshi, *The Art of Netsuke Carving*, fig. 151, p. 178

Masatoshi has used a mask format to create a portrait of a *rakan*. Heavy brows, elongated ears, bulging eyes, and an oversize nose convey his south- or central-Asian ancestry, while his twisting mouth indicates his eccentric character. HG

Inrō

An inrō, used for carrying small objects, is a tier or nest of small cases skillfully fitted into one another. It is suspended by a looped silk cord that passes through cord runners along its sides, then through a sliding bead (*ojime*), and then under the obi, where it is fastened to a netsuke that rests securely at the top of the sash. The ojime is moved up or down to allow the cases to be opened and closed. The inrō was worn almost exclusively by men, whose narrow sash neatly accommodated the ensemble. Women carried small objects by placing them in their roomy sleeves or tucking them into their wide obi.

The literal translation of *inrō* is "seal basket," suggesting that originally it was used to carry personal seals. In their earliest manifestation, inrō, which took a long and arduous time to make and were therefore expensive, were worn only by the daimyo and samurai. By the second half of the Edo period, the economy was flourishing and merchants and townspeople were becoming more affluent; anyone who could afford an inrō was allowed to wear it. Inrō were most popular during the 1700s and 1800s, when they were primarily used to hold medicines. During this period, inrō evolved from a purely functional object into a fashionable item, a form of jewelry for those denied personal adornment by the country's strict sumptuary laws. Well-to-do merchants frequently had inrō made to complement a high-quality kimono, for a special event, or simply to indicate their prosperity.

Historically, the inrō is about four hundred years old, roughly corresponding to the Edo period. Its precise origin is uncertain, but evidence, especially that recently provided by documents in the Tokyo National Museum, indicates that the portable inrō was definitely in use by 1600. The first inrō for personal wear specifically mentioned in the literature was owned by Toyotomi Hideyoshi (1536–1598), who gave it as a gift to a temple abbot around 1595. This inrō subsequently passed through

LEFT: *Inrō, ojime, and netsuke* (CAT. 833)

many hands. It was featured in the famous Red Cross Exhibition in 1915 and is now in the British Museum (Joly, *Legend in Japanese Art*, p. 72).

Inrō were made of wood, ivory, metal, woven reed, and pottery, but by far the largest number, and the most prized, were those made of lacquer. Families of lacquerers and their descendants practiced the art for generations, often using the same surname; for example, Kajikawa (CAT. 836), Koma (CAT. 833), or Somada (CAT. 835). Scrutiny of even a few lacquer inrō quickly reveals their beauty and decorative qualities, their astonishing range of color and shading, the enormous variety of subject matter depicted, and the precision with which the cases fit together so that the covering design maintains an uninterrupted flow.

The evolution of the inrō resulted in what has been called the finest miniature lacquer art ever known, a utilitarian object of exquisite beauty that was highly prized during the Edo period. The *tonkotsu* (CATS. 844–47), almost always made of wood, was used for carrying loose tobacco for pipe smokers. Like the inrō, it was worn suspended from the sash.

828 BACK

828 | **Inrō, ojime, and netsuke**

KIMURA JUKKYOKU, Japan, early to mid-18th century
inrō (*Shoki on Chinese Lion*): lacquer, mother-of-pearl inlays,
$2^{5}/_{8}$ x $2^{1}/_{4}$ x $^{7}/_{8}$ in. (6.5 x 5.7 x 2.2 cm)
ojime: mother-of-pearl, $^{1}/_{2}$ x $^{1}/_{2}$ in. (1.3 x 1.3 cm)
netsuke: narwhal tusk, $1^{7}/_{8}$ x $1^{5}/_{8}$ x 1 in. (4.7 x 4.1 x 2.4 cm)
AC1998.249.313
inrō, lacquered: *Kimura* or *Mokugai [?] Jukkyoku*; kakihan

LITERATURE: Bushell, *The Inrō Handbook*, fig. 46, p. 71

829 | **Inrō, ojime, and netsuke**

Also illustrated on page 28
Hara Yōyūsai, Japan, 1772–1845
inrō (*Monkeys in Mountain Cave*): lacquer, mixed metals,
2 3/16 x 2 7/16 x 15/16 in.
(5.6 x 6.2 x 2.3 cm)
ojime: coral, 1/2 x 9/16 in. (1.2 x 1.4 cm)
netsuke: wood, horn and ivory inlays,
1 13/16 x 1 3/4 x 1 5/16 in. (4.5 x 4.4 x 3.2 cm)
AC1998.249.307
inrō, lacquered: *Yōyūsai saku* / "made by Yōyūsai"
netsuke, incised in inlaid ivory plaque: *Gyokusō*
inlaid carved red lacquer: *Fuku*

LITERATURE: Bushell, *The Inrō Handbook*, fig. 53, p. 81

829 BACK

830 BACK

830 | **Inrō, ojime, and netsuke**

KANSHŌSAI, Japan, active late 18th–early 19th century
inrō (*Kanzan and Jitōkū*): lacquer, metal flecks,
3 3/8 x 1 7/8 x 1 in. (8.6 x 4.7 x 2.5 cm)
ojime: metal, 3/4 x 5/8 x 1/2 in. (1.9 x 1.6 x 1.3 cm)
netsuke: wood, 1 7/16 x 1 13/16 x 1 1/8 in. (3.6 x 4.5 x 2.9 cm)
AC1998.249.316
inrō, lacquered: *Shōshinhitsu Kanshōsai* or *Shōshin* [or *Naonobu*]; kakihan

831 | **Inrō, ojime, and netsuke**

Also illustrated on page 22
Japan, late 18th–early 19th century
inrō, saya type (*Maple Leaves on Fern Ground*): lacquer, metal flecks,
$1\frac{3}{4} \times 2\frac{3}{8} \times \frac{13}{16}$ in. (4.4 x 6.1 x 2 cm)
ojime: coral, $\frac{7}{16} \times \frac{1}{2}$ in. (1 x 1.1 cm)
netsuke, manjū type: ivory,
$\frac{11}{16} \times 1\frac{7}{16} \times \frac{15}{16}$ in. (1.7 x 3.5 x 2.2 cm)
AC1998.249.325

831 BACK

832 BACK

832 | **Inrō, ojime, and netsuke**

Sōshian, Japan, active late 18th–19th century
inrō (*Praying Mantis and Dragonfly in Grasses*): lacquer, metal flecks, 3 1/8 x 2 3/16 x 1 1/16 in. (7.9 x 5.4 x 2.6 cm)
ojime: agate, 1/2 x 9/16 in. (1.2 x 1.4 cm)
netsuke: ivory or stag antler, lacquered and stained, 1 x 1 9/16 x 1 in. (2.5 x 3.9 x 2.5 cm)
AC1998.249.324
inrō, lacquered: *Sōshian*
seal form, red lacquer: *Eigetsu*

833 | **Inrō, ojime, and netsuke**

Front illustrated on page 488
Koma Sadahide, Japan, active second half of the 18th–early 19th century
early 19th century
inrō (*Sparrows in Flight*): lacquer, metal flecks,
3 x 2 13/16 x 13/16 in. (7.6 x 7.1 x 2 cm)
ojime: ivory, metal, 3/4 x 3/4 in. (1.9 x 1.9 cm)
netsuke, manjū type: lacquer, 2 1/8 x 13/16 in. (5.3 x 2.1 cm)
AC1998.249.317
inrō, lacquered with gold flecks: *Koma Sadahide saku* / "made by Koma Sadahide"

833 BACK

834 | **Inrō, ojime, and netsuke**

Toshihide I, Japan, 1757–1833
early 19th century
inrō (*Boat with Autumn Moon and Reeds*): lacquer, metal flecks,
3 11/16 x 1 7/8 x 1 1/16 in. (9.4 x 4.8 x 2.7 cm)
ojime: coral, 7/16 x 5/8 in. (1.1 x 1.5 cm)
netsuke: wood, metal, 1 7/16 x 3 1/2 x 9/16 in. (3.6 x 8.9 x 1.3 cm)
AC1998.249.319
inrō, lacquered: *Toshihide*; red lacquer seal form: *Tōkei*
netsuke, carved in relief: *Minkō* [spurious]

834 BACK

835 BACK

835 | **Inrō, ojime, and netsuke**

SOMADA MITSUMASA, Japan, 1795–1856
inrō (*Daikoku Throwing Beans During New Year*): lacquer, mother-of-pearl inlays, 3 3/4 x 2 x 1 3/16 in. (9.5 x 5.1 x 3 cm)
ojime: water buffalo horn, 11/16 x 5/8 x 1/2 in. (1.7 x 1.5 x 1.3 cm)
netsuke: wood with vermilion and black lacquer, mother-of-pearl inlay, 1 1/16 x 1 3/16 x 7/8 in. (2.7 x 3 x 2.2 cm)
AC1998.249.323
inrō, lacquered: *Etchū Tōyama Somada Mitsumasa*; kakihan

836 BACK

836 | **Inrō, ojime, and netsuke**

Kajikawa School, Japan,
17th–19th century
19th century
inrō (*Two Heads of Actors*): lacquer, metal flecks, 2 7/8 x 2 9/16 x 1 1/16 in.
(7.2 x 6.4 x 2.7 cm)
ojime: carnelian, 1/2 x 9/16 in. (1.2 x 1.3 cm)
netsuke, kagamibuta type: *shakudō* disk, engraved, silver and copper *honzōgan*, bamboo bowl, 1 3/8 x 1 1/2 x 3/8 in.
(3.5 x 3.8 x 1 cm)
AC1998.249.308
inrō, lacquered: *Kajikawa saku* / "made by Kajikawa"; red lacquer seal, pot-shaped netsuke, inscribed: *Sharaku ga* / "after an image by Sharaku"

LITERATURE: Bushell, *The Inrō Handbook*, figs. 41 and 41a, p. 65

837 BACK

837 | **Inrō, ojime, and netsuke**

RYŪWA, Japan, active 19th century
inrō (*Pigeon Hawk on Pine Branch*): cherry bark with lacquer, metal flecks,
$3^1/_2$ x $1^7/_8$ x $^{11}/_{16}$ in.
(8.9 x 4.7 x 1.7 cm)
ojime: coral, $^5/_{16}$ x $^1/_2$ in. (0.8 x 1.2 cm)
netsuke: ivory, $^3/_4$ x $1^7/_8$ x $^3/_4$ in.
(1.9 x 4.7 x 1.8 cm)
AC1998.249.314
inrō, lacquered: *Ryūwa saku* / "made by Ryūwa"

LITERATURE: Bushell, *The Inrō Handbook*, fig. 73, p. 107

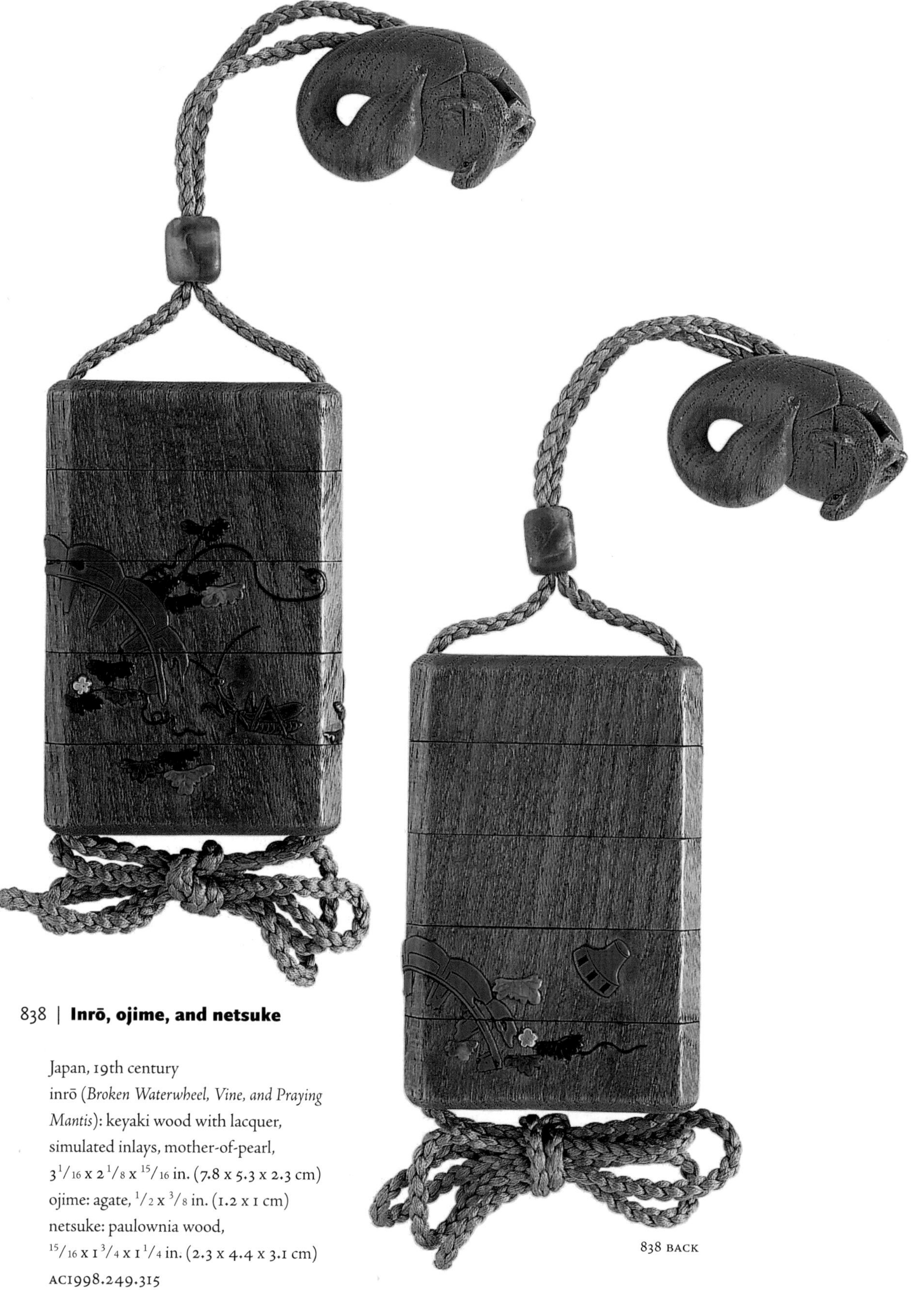

838 | **Inrō, ojime, and netsuke**

Japan, 19th century
inrō (*Broken Waterwheel, Vine, and Praying Mantis*): keyaki wood with lacquer, simulated inlays, mother-of-pearl, 3 1/16 x 2 1/8 x 15/16 in. (7.8 x 5.3 x 2.3 cm)
ojime: agate, 1/2 x 3/8 in. (1.2 x 1 cm)
netsuke: paulownia wood, 15/16 x 1 3/4 x 1 1/4 in. (2.3 x 4.4 x 3.1 cm)
AC1998.249.315

LITERATURE: Bushell, *The Inrō Handbook*, fig. 114, p. 153

838 BACK

839 back

839 | **Inrō, ojime, and netsuke**

Jitokusai, Japan, active 19th century
inrō (*Eight Views of Lake Biwa on Fans*):
lacquer, metal flecks, $3\,^{1}/_{4}$ x $2\,^{1}/_{16}$ x $^{13}/_{16}$ in.
(8.3 x 5.3 x 1.9 cm)
ojime: glass, $^{9}/_{16}$ x $^{5}/_{8}$ in. (1.3 x 1.5 cm)
netsuke: wood with lacquer, gold inlays,
1 x $1\,^{7}/_{8}$ x $^{9}/_{16}$ in. (2.4 x 4.8 x 1.3 cm)
AC1998.249.326
inrō, lacquered: *Jitokusai*

840 BACK

840 | **Inrō, ojime, and netsuke**

Attributed to Kansai III, Japan, died 1857

inrō (*Jurōjin under the Pleiades*): black lacquer, 4 1/4 x 1 15/16 x 11/16 in. (10.7 x 5 x 1.8 cm)

ojime: black hardstone or glass, 1/2 x 9/16 in. (1.2 x 1.4 cm)

netsuke, manjū type: ebony, 1 3/8 x 1 7/16 x 9/16 in. (3.4 x 3.5 x 1.4 cm)

AC1998.249.318

inrō, lacquered: *Kansai*; kakihan

netsuke, lacquered: *Kozan saku* / "made by Kozan"

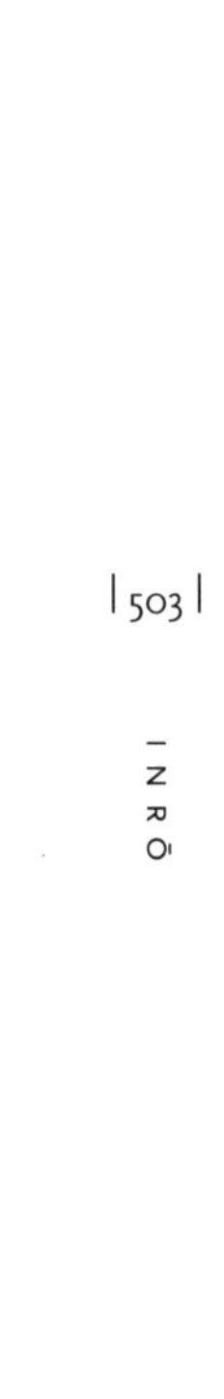

841 BACK

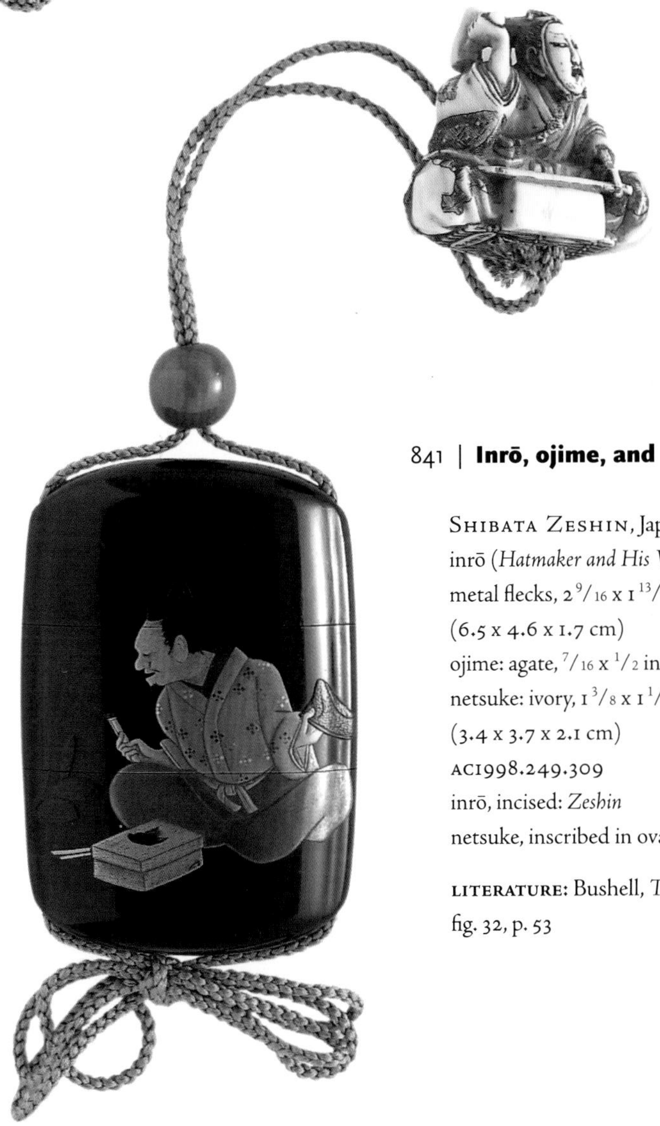

841 | Inrō, ojime, and netsuke

Shibata Zeshin, Japan, 1807–1891
inrō (*Hatmaker and His Wife*): lacquer, metal flecks, 2 9/16 x 1 13/16 x 11/16 in. (6.5 x 4.6 x 1.7 cm)
ojime: agate, 7/16 x 1/2 in. (1.1 x 1.2 cm)
netsuke: ivory, 1 3/8 x 1 1/2 x 7/8 in. (3.4 x 3.7 x 2.1 cm)
AC1998.249.309
inrō, incised: *Zeshin*
netsuke, inscribed in oval reserve: *Shōunsai*

LITERATURE: Bushell, *The Inrō Handbook*, fig. 32, p. 53

842 | Inrō, ojime, and netsuke

Nakayama Komin, Japan, 1808–1870
inrō (*Heron in Moonlight*): lacquer, metal flecks, 3 1/2 x 2 3/16 x 13/16 in.
(8.9 x 5.4 x 2 cm)
ojime: yellow glass, 3/8 x 9/16 in.
(1 x 1.4 cm)
netsuke: wood with lacquer, gold fitting, 1 3/4 x 1/2 in. (4.4 x 1.2 cm)
AC1998.249.322
inrō, lacquered: *Hokkyō Komin zō*

842 BACK

843 back

843 | **Inrō, ojime, and netsuke**

Ikeda Taishin, Japan, 1825–1903
inrō (*Rice and Barley with Bird Scare*):
lacquer, mother-of-pearl inlays,
lead or zinc, 2 9/16 x 2 3/8 x 5/8 in.
(6.4 x 6.1 x 1.5 cm)
ojime: coral, 7/16 x 5/8 in. (1.1 x 1.5 cm)
netsuke, manjū type: wood with lacquer,
1 3/4 x 11/16 in. (4.3 x 1.7 cm)
AC1998.249.321
inrō, lacquered: *Taishin*
netsuke, lacquered: *Kisensai*; kakihan

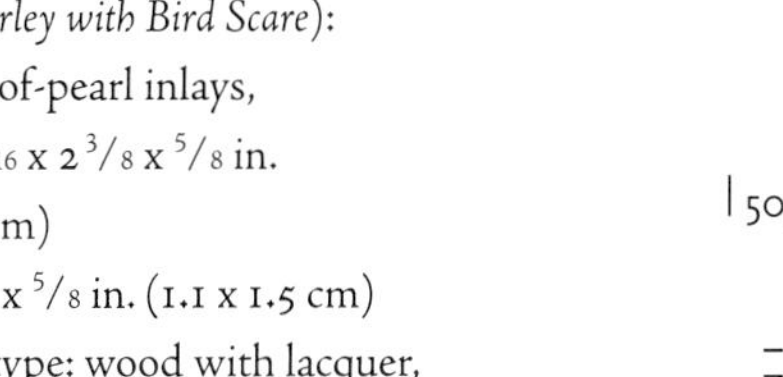

844 | **Tonkotsu, ojime, and netsuke**

Japan, 18th century
tonkotsu (*Kirin and Jurōjin*): cherry wood, $2\,^{3}/_{8}$ x $3\,^{5}/_{8}$ x $1\,^{1}/_{8}$ in. (6 x 9.1 x 2.7 cm)
ojime: stag antler, $^{5}/_{8}$ x $^{5}/_{8}$ in. (1.6 x 1.6 cm)
netsuke: ivory seal, $1\,^{1}/_{4}$ x 1 x $^{7}/_{8}$ in. (3.1 x 2.5 x 2.1 cm)
AC1998.249.310
ojime: [signature effaced]

LITERATURE: Bushell, *The Inrō Handbook*, fig. 108, p. 145

844 BACK

845 BACK

845 | **Tonkotsu, ojime, and netsuke**

MASAYOSHI, Japan, active early to mid-19th century
tonkotsu (*Chinese-style Landscape*): cherry wood, water buffalo horn loops, $3\,^{9}/_{16}$ x $2\,^{15}/_{16}$ x $1\,^{3}/_{4}$ in. (9 x 7.4 x 4.4 cm)
ojime: carved nut, $^{7}/_{8}$ x 1 x $^{5}/_{8}$ in. (2.1 x 2.5 x 1.6 cm)
netsuke: wood, $1\,^{13}/_{16}$ x $1\,^{9}/_{16}$ x $1\,^{1}/_{16}$ in. (4.6 x 4 x 2.6 cm)
AC1998.249.311
tonkotsu, inscribed: *Masayoshi* [or *Masami*]
netsuke, inscribed: *Ittan sanjin saku* / "made by Ittan"; kakihan

LITERATURE: Bushell, *The Inrō Handbook*, fig. 105, p. 142

846 BACK

846 | **Tonkotsu and netsuke**

Japan, mid- to late 19th century
tonkotsu (*Bat with "Kotobuki" Character*): stag antler, eyes inlaid with tortoiseshell, 3 3/16 x 3 x 1 5/16 in. (8.2 x 7.6 x 3.3 cm)
netsuke: stag antler, 1 5/8 x 13/16 x 15/16 in. (4 x 2 x 2.3 cm)
AC1998.249.320

847 BACK

847 | **Tonkotsu, ojime, and netsuke**

TOKEN, Japan, active 19th century
tonkotsu (*Maple Leaves*): paulownia wood, cloisonné inlay, bombe form [exterior]; *ki-urushi* (filtered raw lacquer) [interior]; 3 7/16 x 3 x 1 5/8 in. (8.8 x 7.4 x 4.1 cm)
ojime: agate, 7/8 x 15/16 in. (2.1 x 2.3 cm)
netsuke: gourd with gold lacquer, 2 7/16 x 1 3/16 in. (6.4 x 2.9 cm)
AC1998.249.312
inrō, lacquered: *Token* [or *Toshi*]; kakihan
netsuke, lacquered: [undecipherable]

LITERATURE: Bushell, *The Inrō Handbook*, fig. 59, p. 89

APPENDIX A

Signatures

Mokubei saku
Aoki Mokubei
青木 木米
CAT. 83

Bazan
Bazan
馬山
CAT. 466

MB
Birch, Michael
マイケル・バーチ
CAT. 639

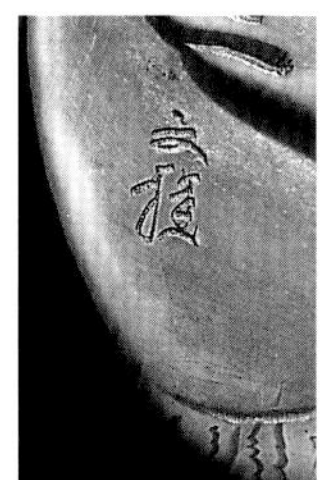

Bunga [or *Bunya*]
Bunga
文雅
CAT. 634

Chiku'unsai
Chiku'unsai
竹雲齋
CAT. 568

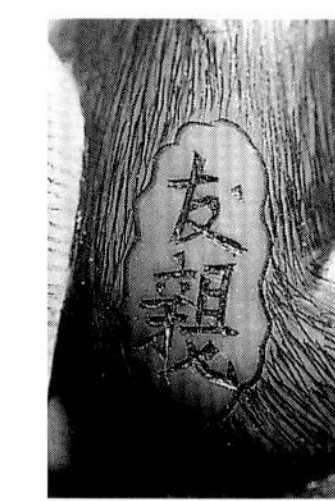

Tomochika
Chikuyōsai Tomochika
竹陽齋 友親
CAT. 267

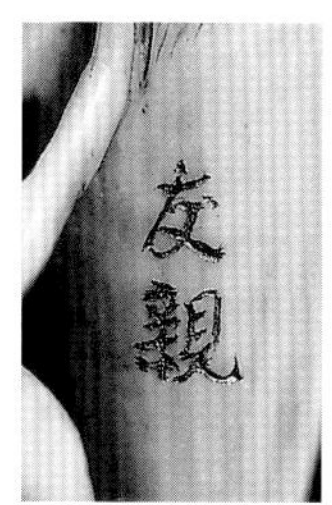

Tomochika
School of Chikuyōsai Tomochika
友親 派
CAT. 675

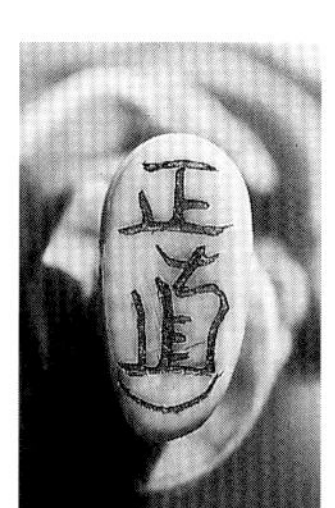

Masanao [added later]
Chingendō Hidemasa
珍元堂 秀正
CAT. 13

Hidemasa
Chingendō Hidemasa
珍元堂 秀正
CAT. 62

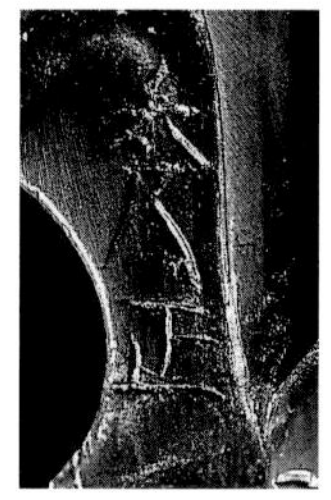

Hidemasa
Chingendō Hidemasa
珍元堂 秀正
CAT. 178

Hidemasa; kakihan
Chingendō Hidemasa
珍元堂 秀正
CAT. 277

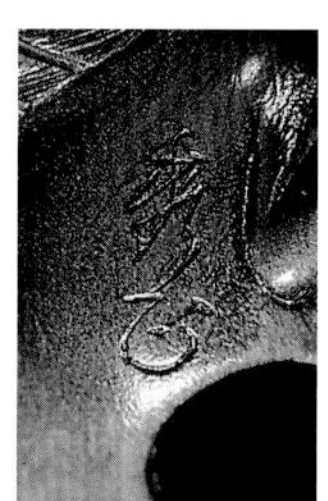

Hidemasa
Chingendō Hidemasa
珍元堂 秀正
CAT. 395

Hidemasa; kakihan
Chingendō Hidemasa
珍元堂 秀正
CAT. 524

Hidemasa
Chingendō Hidemasa
珍元堂 秀正
CAT. 554

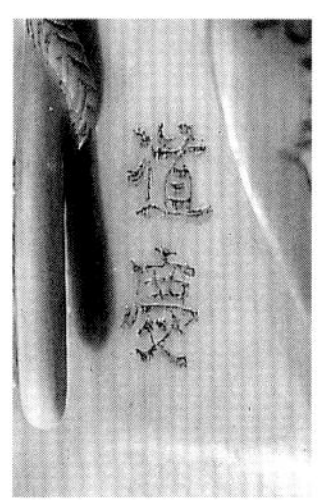

Dōkei
Dōkei
道慶
CAT. 545

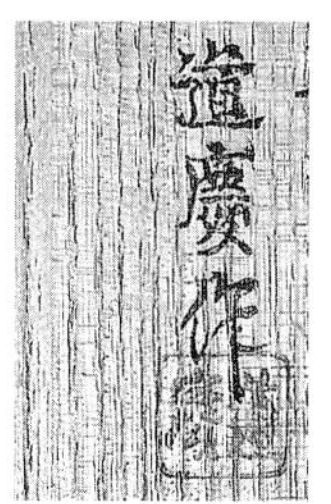

Dōkei saku; seal: *Dōkei*
Dōkei
道慶
CAT. 545 (box)

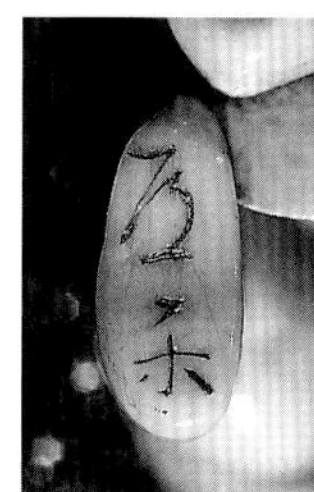

Dōraku
Dōraku (sai)
道楽 (齋)
CAT. 156

Dōraku
Dōraku (sai)
道楽 (齋)
CAT. 451

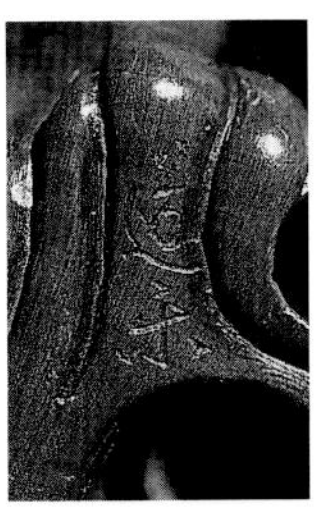

Dōraku
Dōraku (sai)
道楽（齋）
CAT. 651

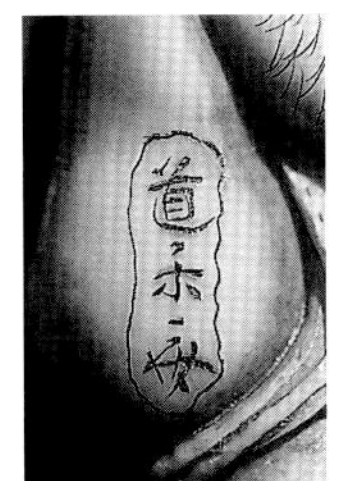

Dōrakusai
Dōraku (sai)
道楽（齋）
CAT. 652

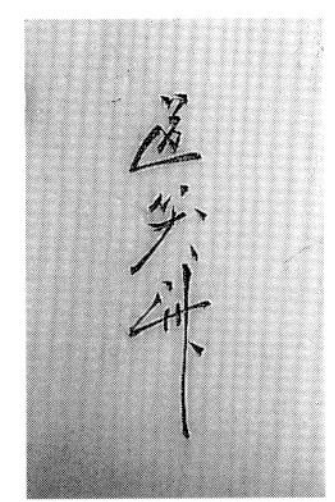

Dōshōsai
Dōshōsai
道笑齋
CAT. 261

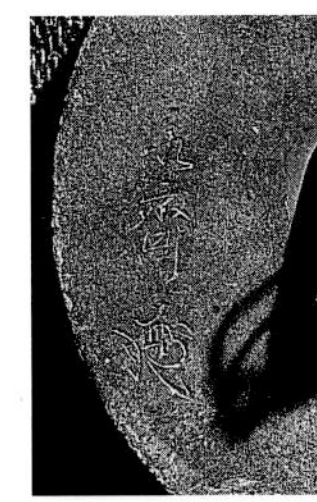

Eisai; kakihan
Eisai
永齋
CAT. 142

Hōmin
Fukumoto Hōmin
福本 法民
CAT. 572

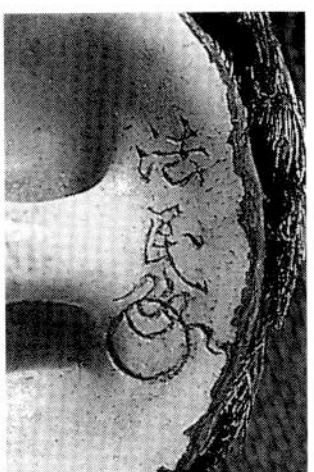

Hōmin; kakihan
Fukumoto Hōmin
福本 法民
CAT. 780

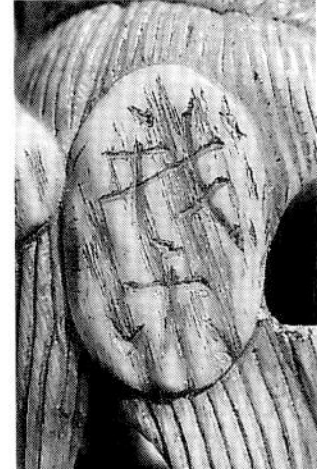

Garaku
Garaku
我楽
CAT. 18

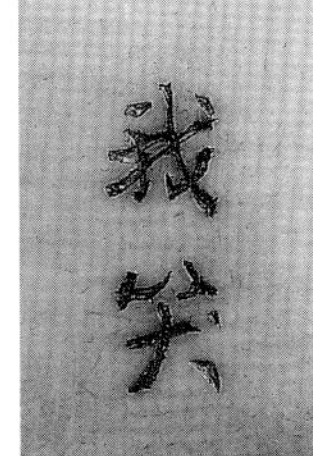

Gashō
Gashō
我笑
CAT. 659

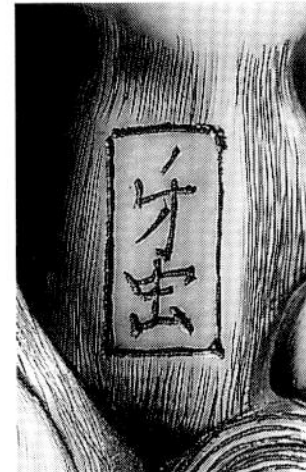

Gechū
Gechū
牙虫
CAT. 195

Gechū
Gechū
牙虫
CAT. 752

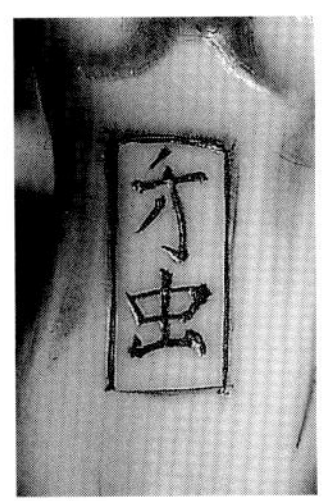

Gechū
Attributed to Gechū
伝 牙虫
CAT. 212

Minkoku
Genryōsai Minkoku I
元良斎 民谷（初代）
CAT. 498

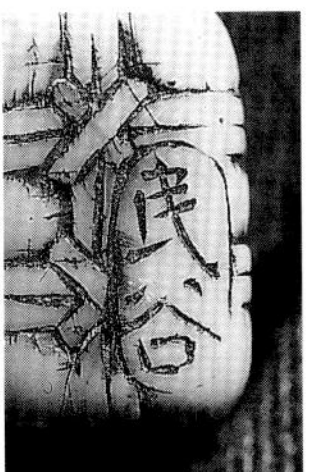

Minkoku
Genryōsai Minkoku I
元良斎 民谷（初代）
CAT. 509

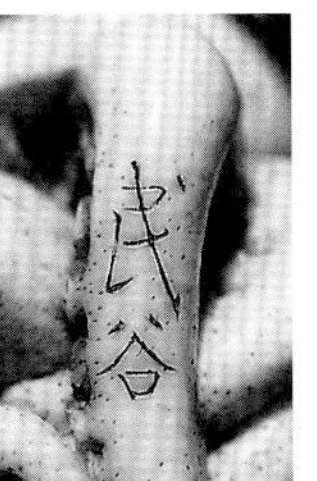

Minkoku
Genryōsai Minkoku II
元良斎 民谷（二代目）
CAT. 627

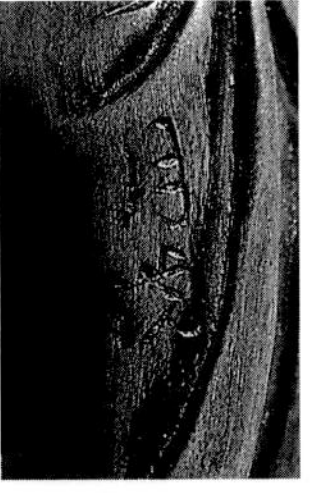

Gessen
Gessen
月洗
CAT. 646

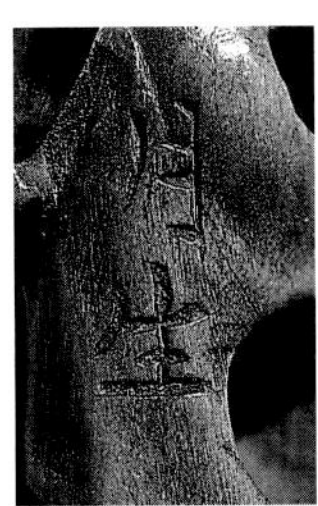

Gesshō
Gesshō (or Gessei)
月生
CAT. 27

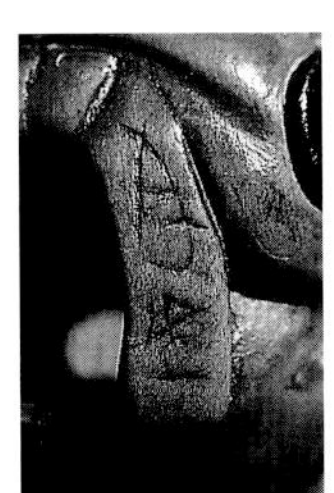

Gesshō [?] [partially effaced]
Gesshō (or Gessei)
月生
CAT. 565

Gotō Masayoshi
Gotō Masayoshi
後藤 正義
CAT. 493

Gyokurin
Gyokurin
玉林
CAT. 653

Hokkyō Gyokusensai; kakihan
Gyokusensai Tomochika
玉泉齋 友近
CAT. 731

Gyokuzan
Gyokuzan
玉山
CAT. 447

Ōju Gyokuzan saku
Gyokuzan
玉山
CAT. 189

seal forms: *Shūgetsu; Hōgen*
Hara Shūgetsu
(or Shūgetsu III)
原舟月
CAT. 412

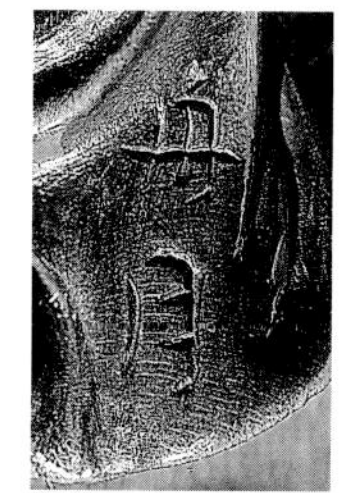
Shūgetsu
Hara Shūgetsu
(or Shūgetsu III)
原舟月
CAT. 617

Harumitsu
Harumitsu
春光
CAT. 401

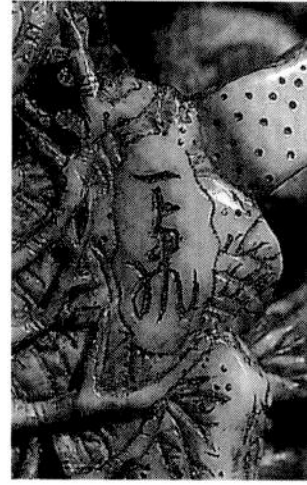
Ikko
Hasegawa Ikko
長谷川 一虎
CAT. 534

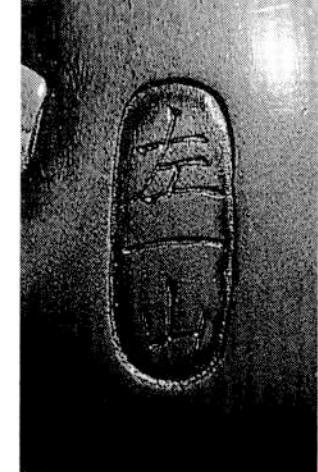
Hidari Issan
Hidari Issan
左 一山
CAT. 732

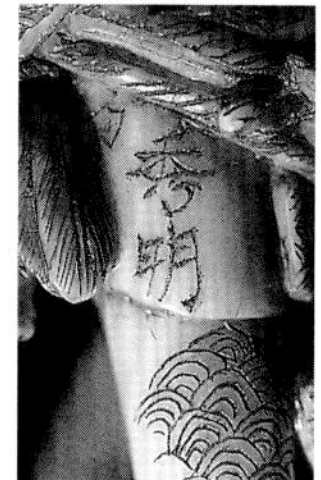
Hideaki (or *Shūmei*)
Hideaki (or Shūmei)
秀明
CAT. 35

Hideharu
Hideharu
秀晴
CAT. 461

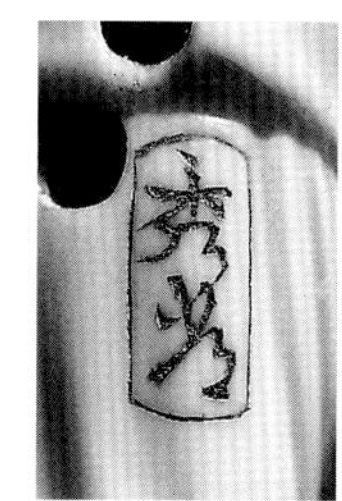
Hidetsune
Hidetsune
秀常
CAT. 116

Hisatoshi
Hisatoshi
寿利
CAT. 19

Hō
Hō
方
CAT. 735

Hōboku
Hōboku
宝北
CAT. 739

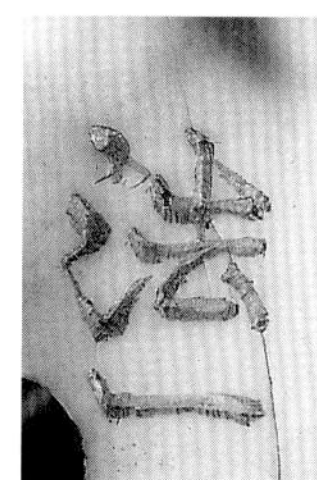
Hōichi
Hōichi
法一
CAT. 743

Sessai
Hokkyō Sessai
法橋 雪齋
CAT. 34

Sessai
Hokkyō Sessai
法橋 雪齋
CAT. 310

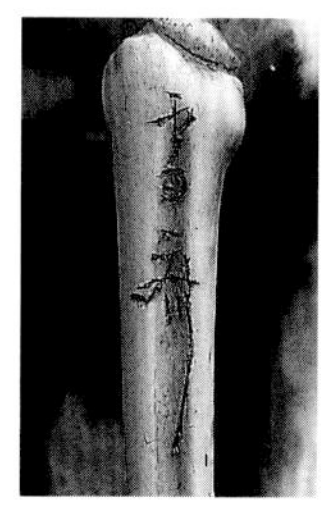
Sessai
Hokkyō Sessai
法橋 雪齋
CAT. 685

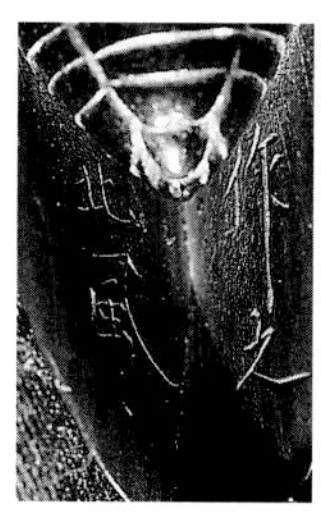
Hokufū saku nari
Hokufū
北風
CAT. 470

Itsuō tō
Hōkyūdō Itsumin
蓬丘堂 逸民
CAT. 655

Hōraku
Hōraku
宝楽
CAT. 366

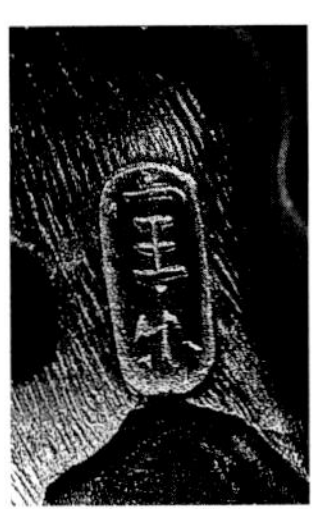

Hōraku
Hōraku
宝楽
CAT. 380

Masayuki
Hōshunsai Masayuki
宝春齋 正之
CAT. 551

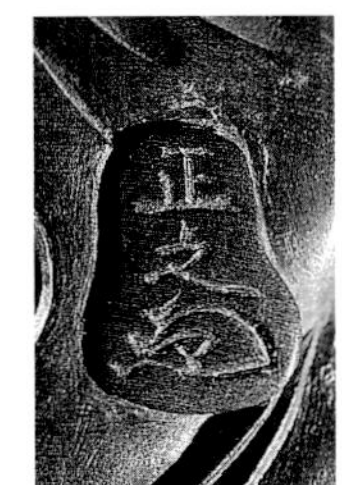

Masayuki; kakihan
Hōshunsai Masayuki
宝春齋 正之
CAT. 616

Hōshun [reads right, left, center]; kakihan
Hōshunsai Masayuki
宝春齋 正之
CAT. 658

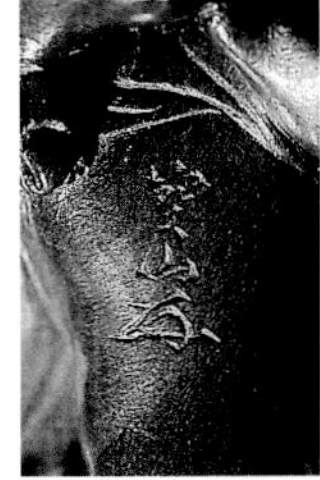

Hōzan; kakihan
Hōzan
宝山
CAT. 132

Ichigyoku
Ichigyoku
一玉
CAT. 496

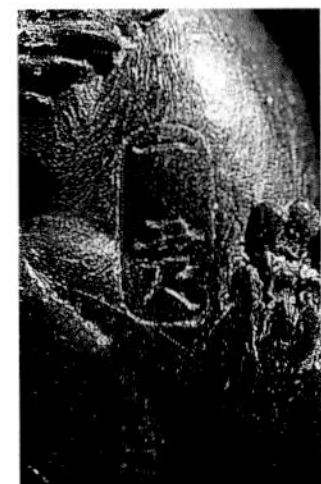

Ikkan
Ikkan
一貫
CAT. 265

Ikkan
Ikkan
一貫
CAT. 322

Seishinsai Ikkei
Ikkei Seishinsai
一渓 青岑齋
CAT. 376

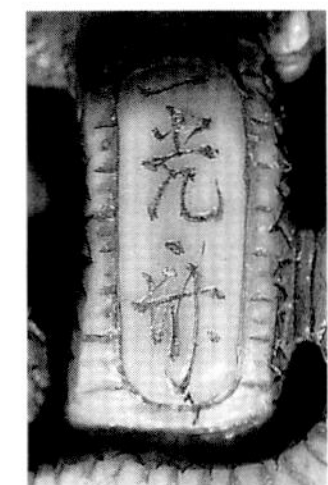

Ikkōsai
Ikkōsai (Saitō Itarō)
一光齋 (齋藤 伊太郎)
CAT. 303

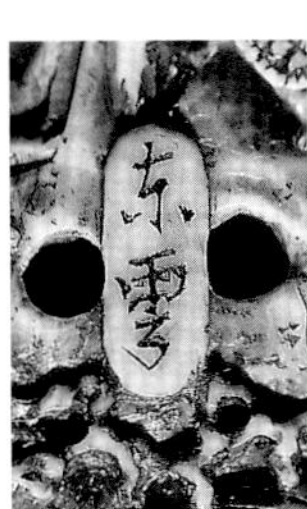

Tōun
Ikkōsai Tōun
一光齋 東雲
CAT. 138

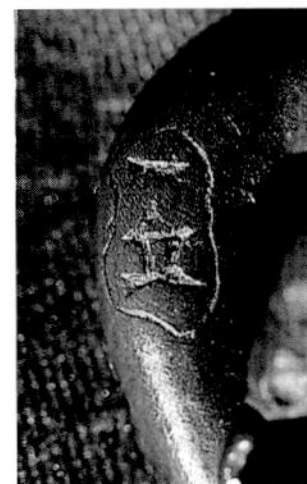

Ikkyū
Ikkyū
一丘
CAT. 448

Ichirō
Inada Ichirō
稲田 一郎
CAT. 635

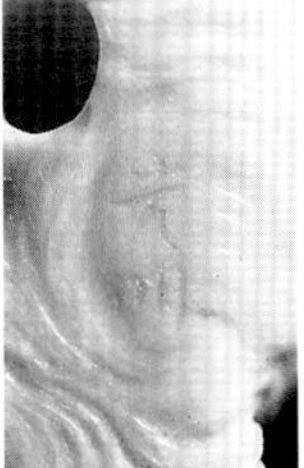

Kōmei
Ishikawa Kōmei
石川 光明
CAT. 330

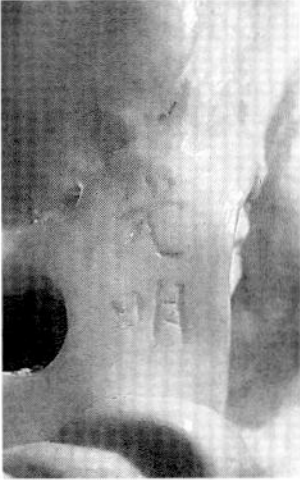

Kōmei
Ishikawa Kōmei
石川 光明
CAT. 595

seal form: *Ren*
Ishikawa Rensai
石川 蓮齋
CAT. 210

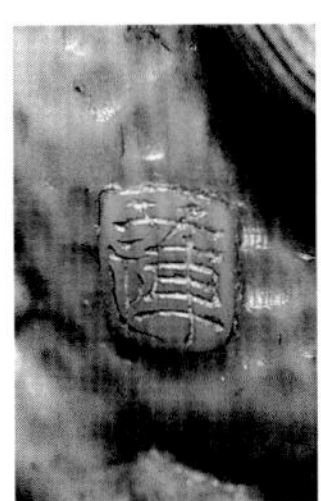

seal form: *Ren*
Ishikawa Rensai
石川 蓮齋
CAT. 211

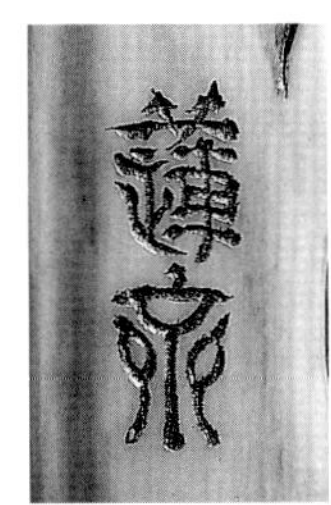

Rensai
Ishikawa Rensai
石川 蓮齋
CAT. 384

seal form: *Ren*
Ishikawa Rensai
石川 蓮齋
CAT. 389

seal form: *Ren*
Ishikawa Rensai
石川 蓮齋
CAT. 400

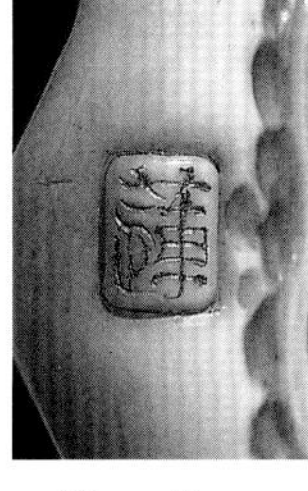

seal form: Ren
Ishikawa Rensai
石川 蓮齋
CAT. 425

Rensai
Ishikawa Rensai
石川 蓮齋
CAT. 704

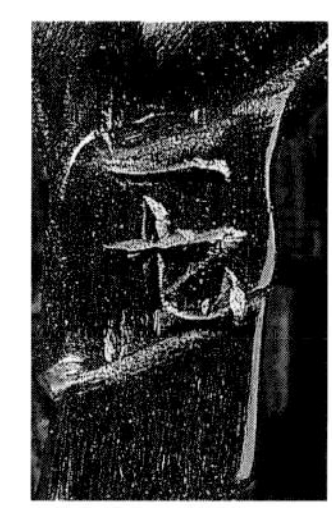

Isshin (or *Kazuya*)
Isshin (or Kazuya)
一也
CAT. 442

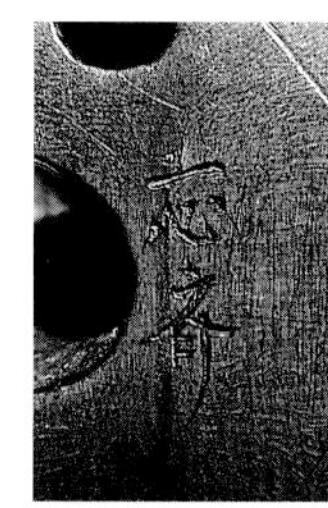

Isshinsai
Isshinsai Masanao
一心齋 正直
CAT. 117

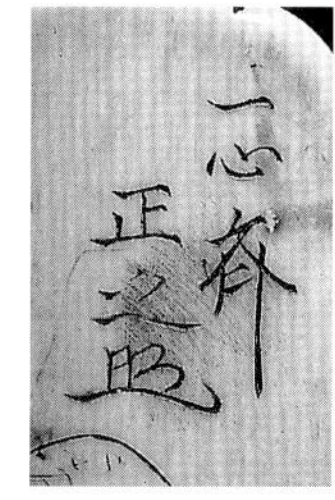

Isshinsai Masayuki; kakihan
Isshinsai Masayuki
一心齋 正之
CAT. 601

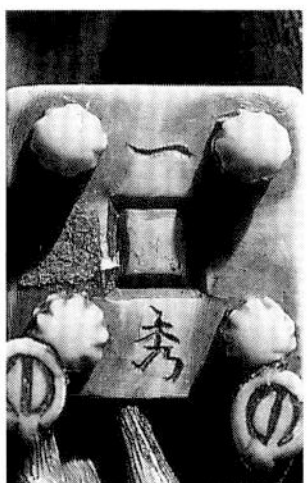

Isshū
Isshū
一秀
CAT. 527

Ittan; kakihan
Ittan
一旦
CAT. 268

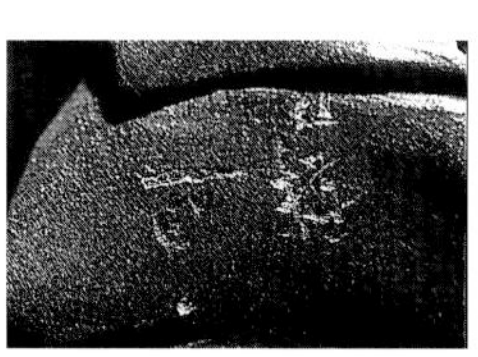

Ittan gi [?]
Ittan
一旦
CAT. 613

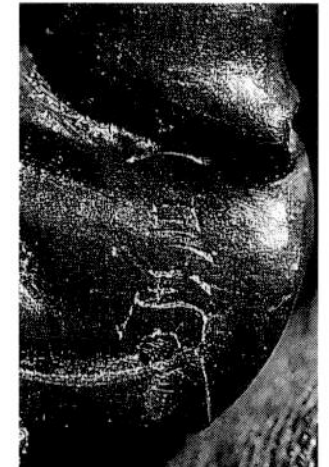

Ittan; kakihan
Ittan
一旦
CAT. 614

Ittan; kakihan
Ittan
一旦
CAT. 676

Ittokusai
Ittokusai
一得齋
CAT. 582

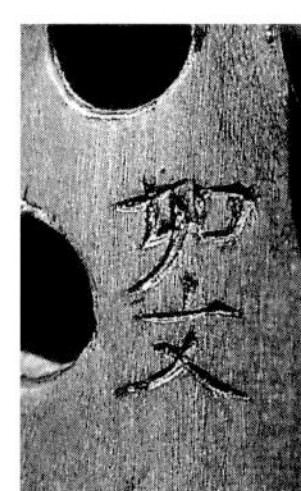

Jobun
Jobun
如文
CAT. 5

Jobun
Jobun
如文
CAT. 604

Jobun
Jobun
如文
CAT. 605

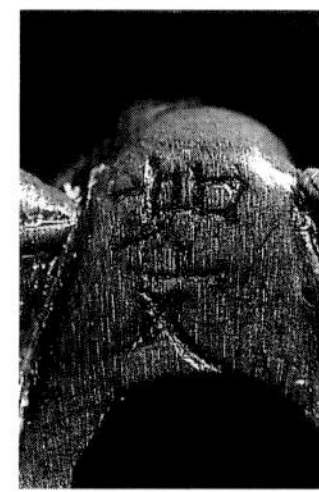

Jobun
Jobun
如文
CAT. 606

Jobun
Jobun
如文
CAT. 645

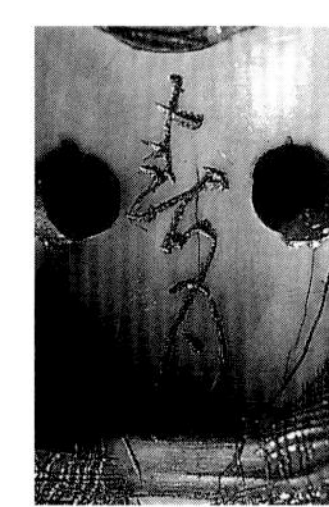

Jūgetsu
Jūgetsu
寿月
CAT. 165

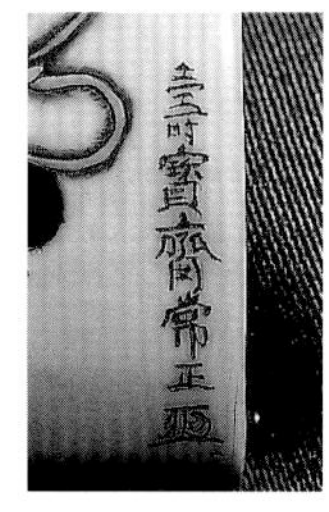

Juhōsai Tsunemasa; kakihan
Juhōsai Tsunemasa
壽宝齋 常政
CAT. 127

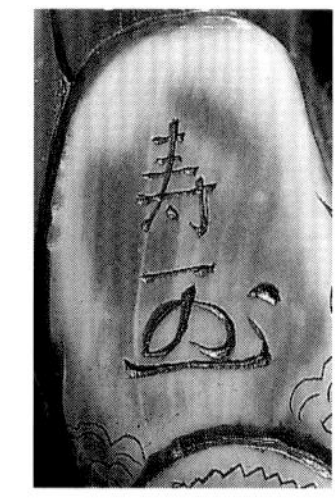

Ju; kakihan
Juichi (or Toshikazu)
寿一
CAT. 169

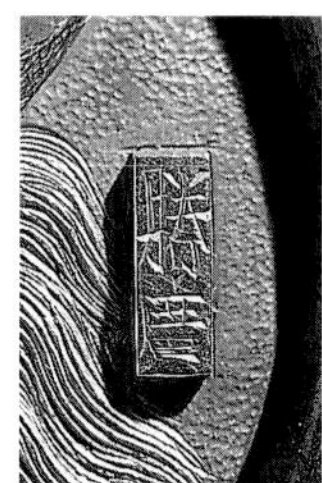

Katsuhiro
Kagawa Katsuhiro
香川 勝廣
CAT. 575

Kagetoshi
Kagetoshi
景利
CAT. 162

Kagetoshi
Kagetoshi
景利
CAT. 172

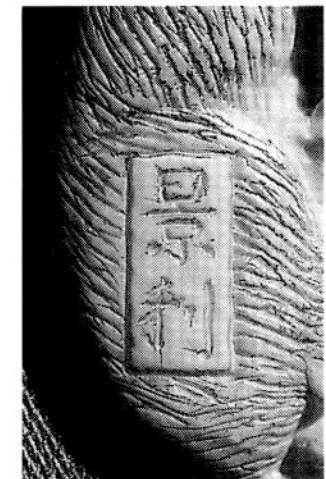
Kagetoshi
Kagetoshi
景利
CAT. 349

Kagetoshi
Kagetoshi
景利
CAT. 369

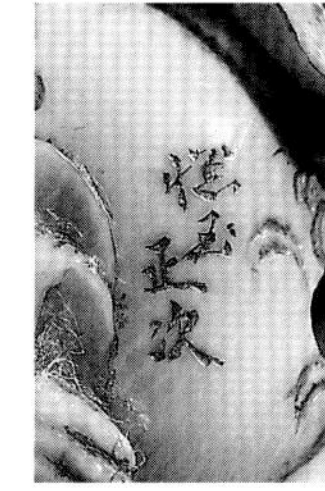
Kaigyoku Masatsugu
Kaigyokusai Masatsugu
懐玉斎 正次
懐玉堂
CAT. 55

Kaigyokusai Masatsugu
Kaigyokusai Masatsugu
懐玉斎 正次
懐玉堂
CAT. 75

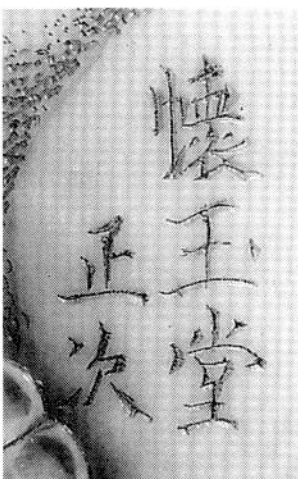
Kaigyokudō Masatsugu
Kaigyokusai Masatsugu
懐玉斎 正次
懐玉堂
CAT. 139

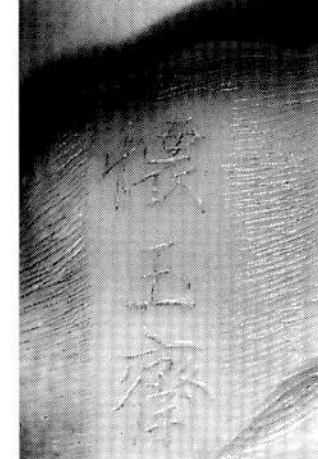
Kaigyokusai
Kaigyokusai Masatsugu
懐玉斎 正次
懐玉堂
CAT. 208

Kaigyokusai
Kaigyokusai Masatsugu
懐玉斎 正次
懐玉堂
CAT. 262

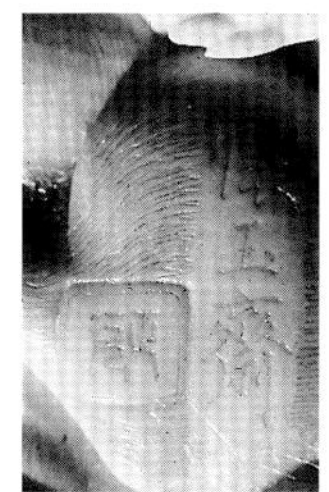
Kaigyokusai; seal form: *Masa*
Kaigyokusai Masatsugu
懐玉斎 正次
懐玉堂
CAT. 291

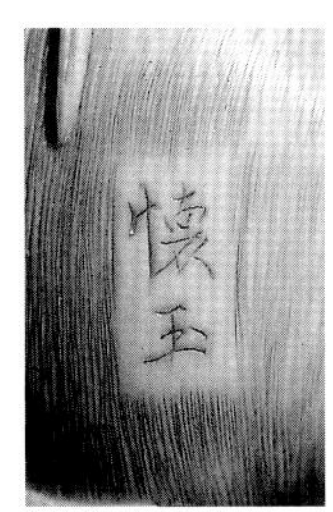
Kaigyoku
Kaigyokusai Masatsugu
懐玉斎 正次
懐玉堂
CAT. 344

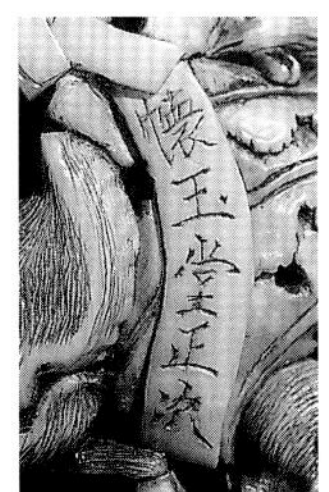
Kaigyokudō Masatsugu
Kaigyokusai Masatsugu
懐玉斎 正次
懐玉堂
CAT. 345

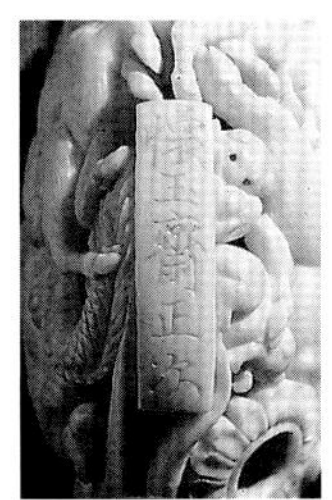
Kaigyokusai Masatsugu
Kaigyokusai Masatsugu
懐玉斎 正次
懐玉堂
CAT. 346

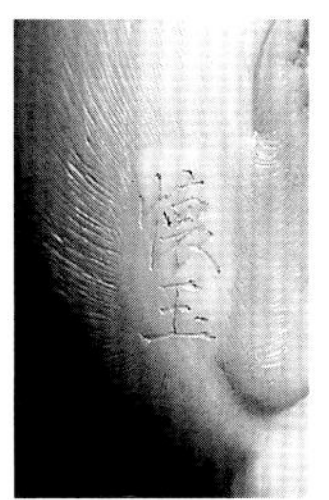
Kaigyoku
Kaigyokusai Masatsugu
懐玉斎 正次
懐玉堂
CAT. 358

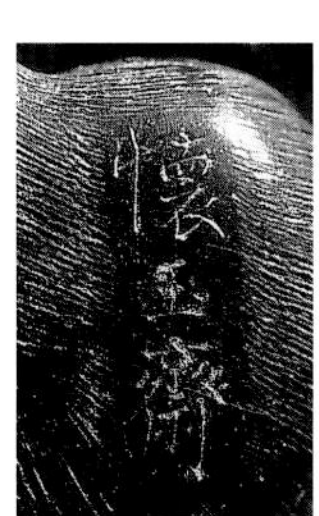
Kaigyokusai
Kaigyokusai Masatsugu
懐玉斎 正次
懐玉堂
CAT. 364

Kaigyokusai
Kaigyokusai Masatsugu
懐玉斎 正次
懐玉堂
CAT. 370

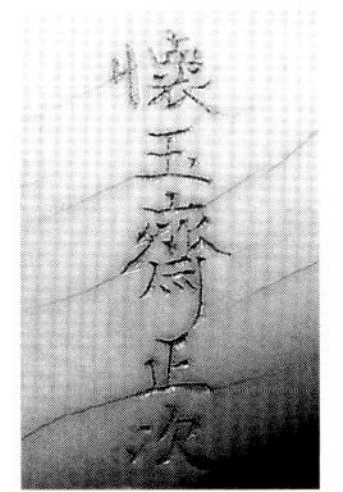
Kaigyokusai Masatsugu
Kaigyokusai Masatsugu
懐玉斎 正次
懐玉堂
CAT. 494

Kaigyokusai; seal form: *Masatsugu*
Kaigyokusai Masatsugu
懐玉斎 正次
懐玉堂
CAT. 495

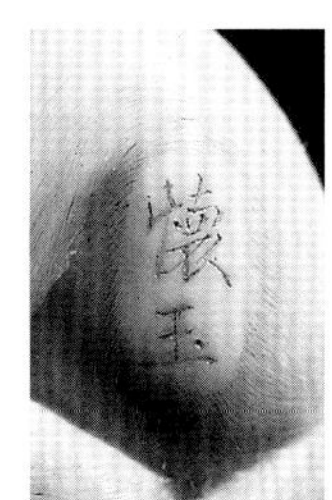
Kaigyoku
Kaigyokusai Masatsugu
懐玉斎 正次
懐玉堂
CAT. 560

Kaigyoku; seal form: *Masatsugu*
Kaigyokusai Masatsugu
懐玉斎 正次
懐玉堂
CAT. 561

Kaigyokudō Masatsugu
Attributed to Kaigyokusai Masatsugu
伝 懐玉齋 正次
懐玉堂
CAT. 209

Kaigyokusai
Attributed to Kaigyokusai Masatsugu
伝 懐玉齋 正次
懐玉堂
CAT. 711

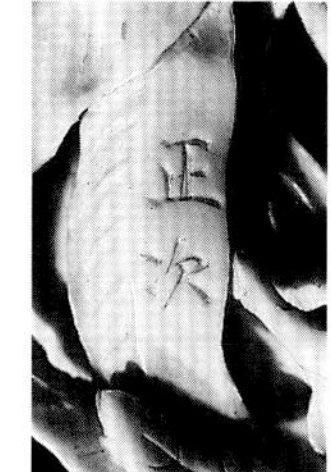

Masatsugu
School of Kaigyokusai
懐玉齋 派
CAT. 722

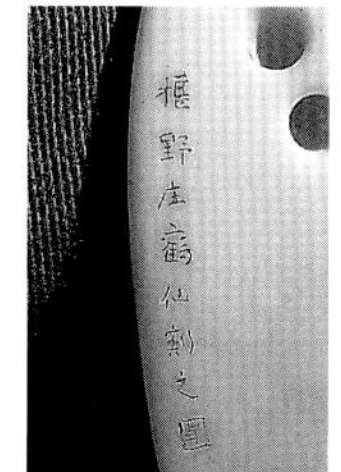

Uno [or Sawarano] sho Kakusen kore [o] kizamu; kakihan
Kakusen
鶴仙
CAT. 445

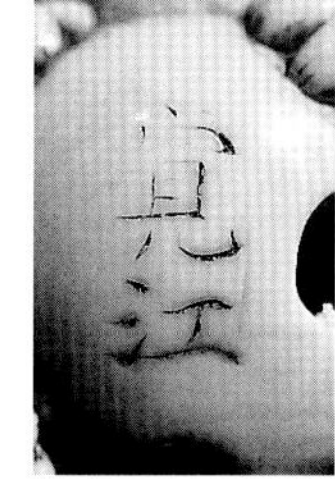

Kankō
Kankō
寛江
CAT. 213

Iwami Kanman tō; kakihan
Kanman
貫満
CAT. 302

Natsuo [in hiragana]
Attributed to Kanō Natsuo
伝加納 夏雄
CAT. 468

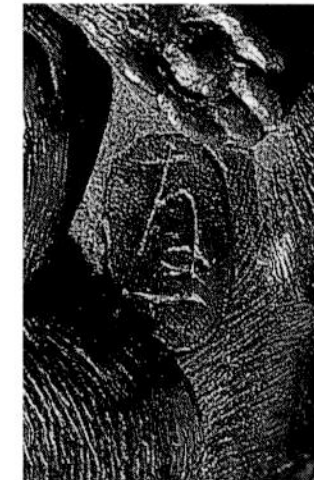

Tomokazu
Kano Tomokazu
加納 友一
CAT. 203

Tomokazu; kakihan
Kano Tomokazu
加納 友一
CAT. 295

Tomokazu
Kano Tomokazu
加納 友一
CAT. 316

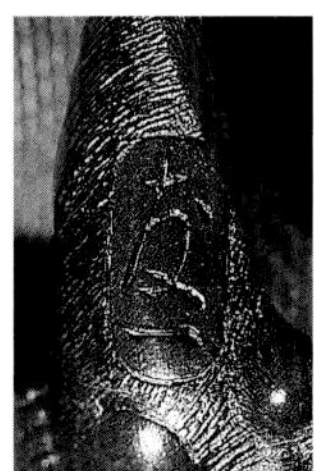

Tomokazu
Kano Tomokazu
加納 友一
CAT. 325

Tomokazu
Kano Tomokazu
加納 友一
CAT. 341

Tomokazu
Kano Tomokazu
加納 友一
CAT. 362

Tomokazu
Kano Tomokazu
加納 友一
CAT. 409

Mitsunaga; kakihan
School of Katsura Mitsunaga
桂 光長 派
CAT. 592

Katsuzan or *Kuzuyama*
Katsuzan or Kuzuyama
葛山
CAT. 89

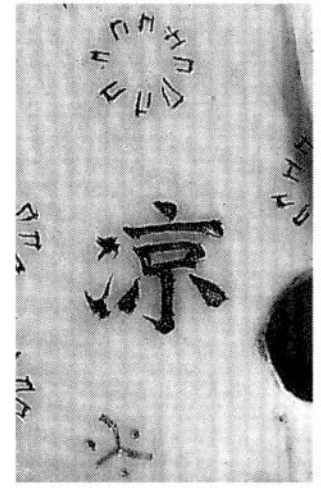

Ryō
Kawahara Ryō
河原 凉
CAT. 622

Ryō tō; seal: *Ryō*
Kawahara Ryō
河原 凉
CAT. 622 (box)

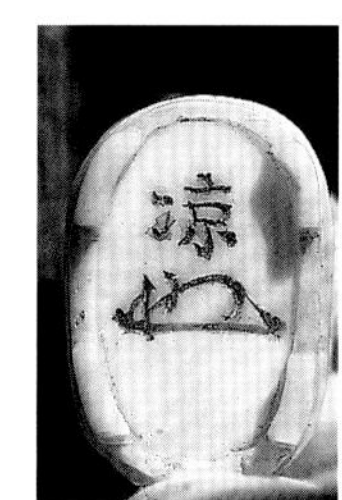

Ryō; kakihan
Kawahara Ryō
河原 凉
CAT. 623

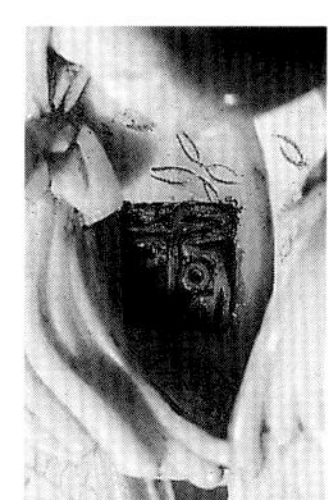

seal form: *Ryō [?]*
Kawahara Ryō
河原 凉
CAT. 642

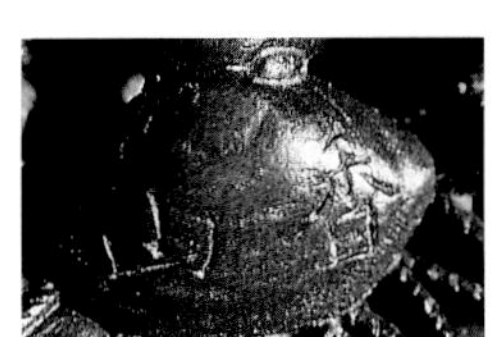

Kayama (or *Kōzan*)
Kayama (or Kōzan)
香山
CAT. 723

Kazushige
Kazushige
一重
CAT. 532

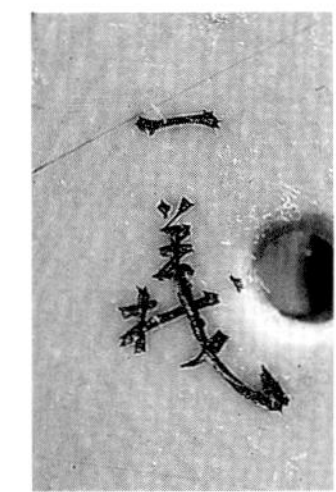

Kazuyoshi
Kazuyoshi
一義
CAT. 45

Keisai
Keisai
桂哉
CAT. 657

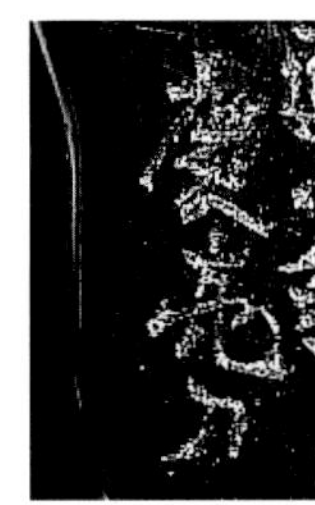

Keisuke tō
Keisuke
慶亮
CAT. 170

Kenya
Kenya
乾也
CAT. 181

Kenya
Kenya
乾也
CAT. 182

Tōbu domin Kenya tsukuru
Kenya
乾也
CAT. 182 (box)

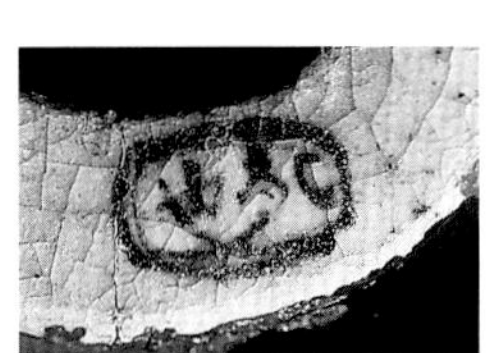

Kenya
Kenya
乾也
CAT. 730

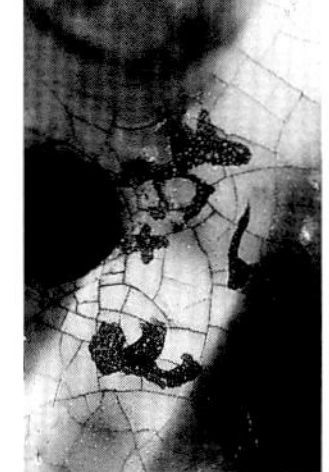

Kenzan
Follower of Kenzan
乾山派
CAT. 728

Kikugawa saku
Kikugawa Family
菊川派
CAT. 506

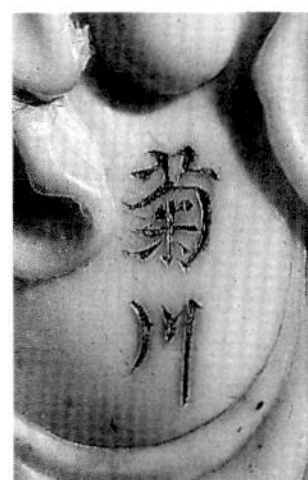

Kikugawa
Kikugawa Family
菊川派
CAT. 628

Ryūmin; kakihan
Kimura Ryūmin
木村 龍民
CAT. 14

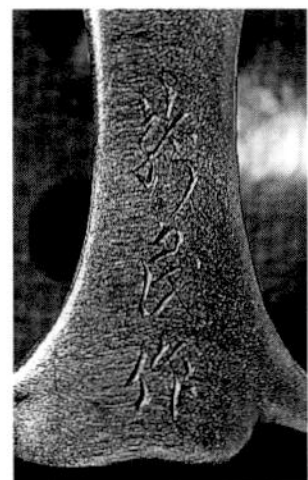

Ryūmin saku
Kimura Ryūmin
木村 龍民
CAT. 796

Kishōsai
Kishōsai
鬼笑齋
CAT. 660

Kiyokatsu
Kiyokatsu
清勝
CAT. 709

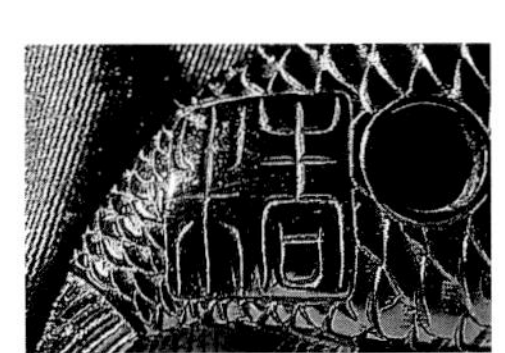

seal form: *Kiyoshi*
Kiyoshi
清
CAT. 437

Kōgetsusai; seal form: *Naomasa*
Kōgetsusai Naomasa
光月齋 直正
CAT. 559

Kokei
Kokei
虎渓
CAT. 219

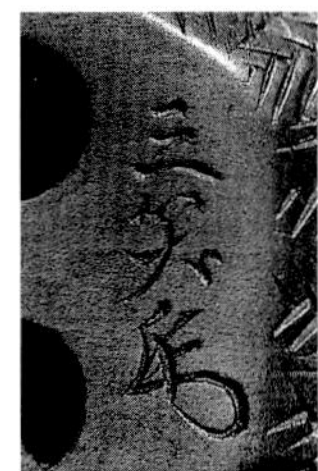

Sanshō; kakihan
Kokeisai Sanshō
虎渓齋 三笑
CAT. 590

Sanshō; kakihan
Kokeisai Sanshō
虎渓齋 三笑
CAT. 619

Sanshō; kakihan
Kokeisai Sanshō
虎渓齋 三笑
CAT. 620

Sanshō; kakihan
Kokeisai Sanshō
虎渓齋 三笑
CAT. 621

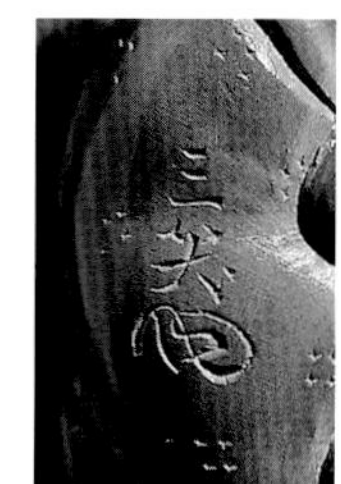

Sanshō; kakihan
Kokeisai Sanshō
虎渓齋 三笑
CAT. 663

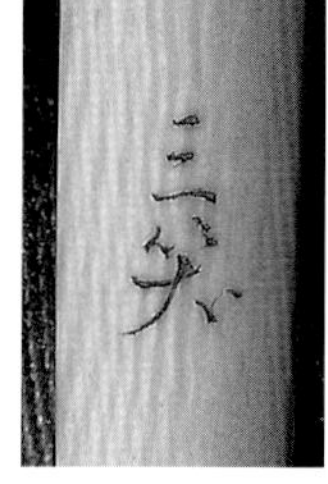

Sanshō
Kokeisai Sanshō
虎渓齋 三笑
CAT. 759

Kokeisai Sanshō saku kore;
seal: *Sanshō*
Kokeisai Sanshō
虎渓齋 三笑
CAT. 759 (box)

Sanshō; kakihan
Kokeisai Sanshō
虎渓齋 三笑
CAT. 821

Sanshō; kakihan
Kokeisai Sanshō
虎渓齋 三笑
CAT. 822

Sanshō; kakihan
Kokeisai Sanshō
虎渓齋 三笑
CAT. 823

Sanshō; kakihan
Kokeisai Sanshō
虎渓齋 三笑
CAT. 824

Sanshō; kakihan
Kokeisai Sanshō
虎渓齋 三笑
CAT. 825

Kōkoku; seal form: *Kōkoku*
Kōkoku
光谷
CAT. 242

Koma Bunsai
Koma Bunsai
古満 文哉
CAT. 576

Koma Bunsai
School of Koma Bunsai
古満 文哉 派
CAT. 573

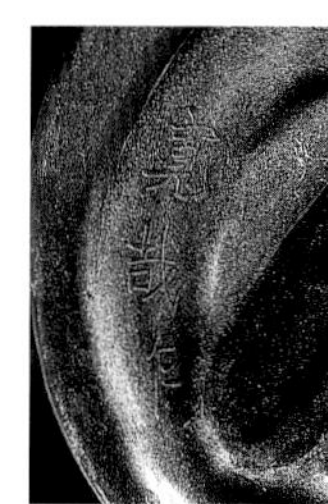

Kansai saku
Koma Kansai School
古満 寛哉 派
CAT. 184

Kōmin
Kōmin
光珉
CAT. 243

Kōryūsai
Kōryūsai (Naokazu or Naoichi)
光龍齋 直一
CAT. 528

Moritoshi; kakihan of crane
Kōsai Moritoshi
光齋 守寿
CAT. 512

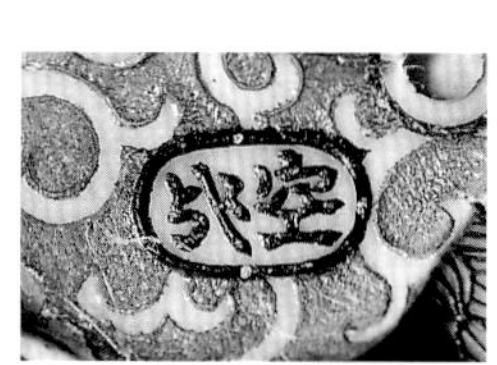

Kūya [reads left to right]
Kūya (Nakamura Shinzō)
空哉 (中村 慎三)
CAT. 91

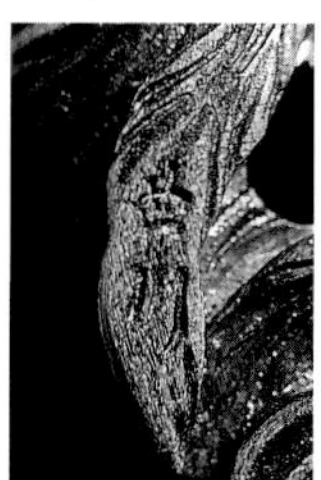

Kyokusen
Kyokusen
曲川
CAT. 161

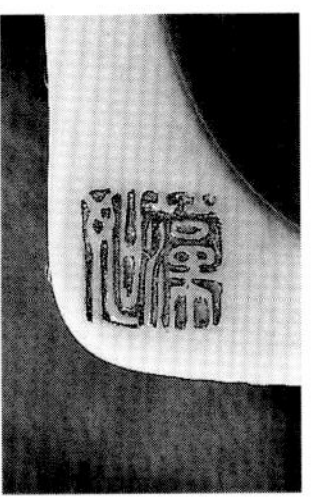
seal form: *Kyokusō*
Kyokusō
旭藻
CAT. 746

Masahide
Masahide
正秀
CAT. 279

Masakazu
Masakazu
正一
CAT. 233

Masanao
Masanao
正直
CAT. 335

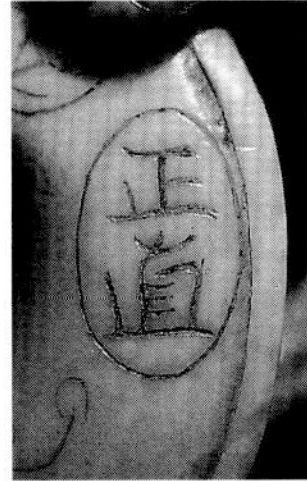
Masanao
Masanao
正直
CAT. 336

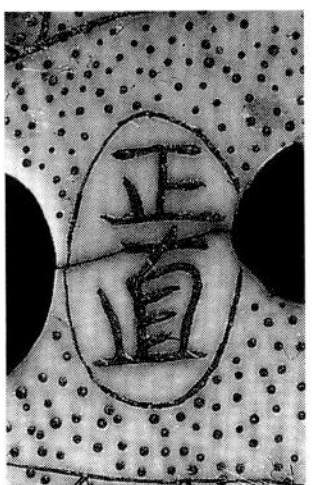
Masanao
Masanao
正直
CAT. 435

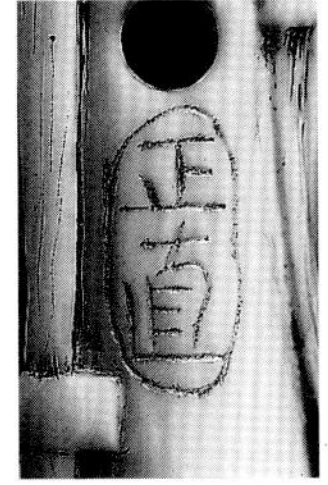
Masanao
School of Masanao
正直 派
CAT. 726

Masanao
Masanao II (Miyake)
正直二代目 (三宅)
CAT. 331

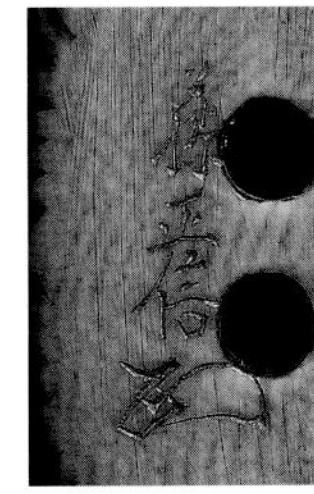
Fuji Masanobu; kakihan
Masanobu (Adachi Tomoshichi)
正信 (安達友七)
CAT. 374

Masatami tō
Masatami
正民
CAT. 548

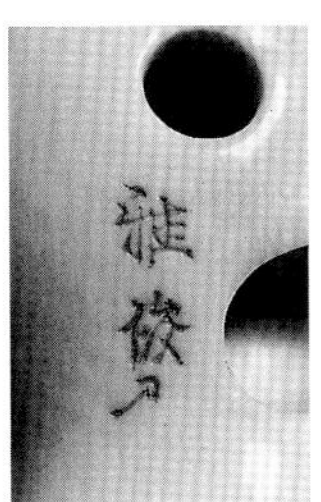
Masatoshi tō
Masatoshi
雅俊 (中村 時定)
CAT. 97

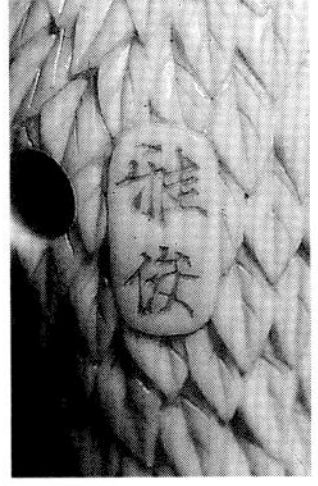
Masatoshi
Masatoshi
雅俊 (中村 時定)
CAT. 100

Masatoshi
Masatoshi
雅俊 (中村 時定)
CAT. 190

Masatoshi
Masatoshi
雅俊 (中村 時定)
CAT. 217

Masatoshi tō
Masatoshi
雅俊 (中村 時定)
CAT. 227

Saikaku Masatoshi tō
Masatoshi
雅俊 (中村 時定)
CAT. 228

Masatoshi
Masatoshi
雅俊 (中村 時定)
CAT. 229

Masatoshi tō
Masatoshi
雅俊 (中村 時定)
CAT. 230

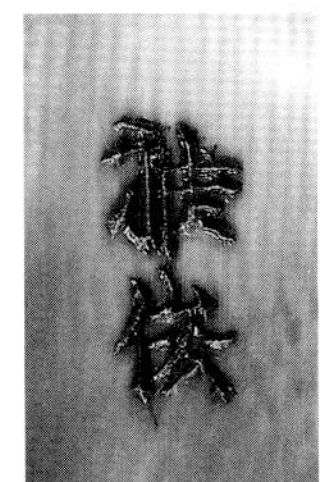
Masatoshi
Masatoshi
雅俊 (中村 時定)
CAT. 246

Masatoshi
Masatoshi
雅俊 (中村 時定)
CAT. 254

Masatoshi tō
Masatoshi
雅俊 (中村 時定)
CAT. 263

Masatoshi tō
Masatoshi
雅俊 (中村 時定)
CAT. 360

Masatoshi
Masatoshi
雅俊 (中村 時定)
CAT. 365

Tokisada
Masatoshi
雅俊 (中村 時定)
CAT. 403

Masatoshi; kakihan
Masatoshi
雅俊 (中村 時定)
CAT. 404

Masatoshi
Masatoshi
雅俊 (中村 時定)
CAT. 428

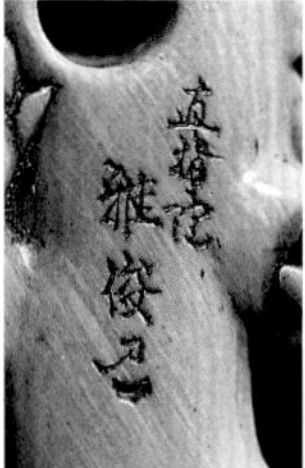

Jikishiin Masatoshi tō
Masatoshi
art name: Jikishiin
雅俊 (中村 時定)
CAT. 430

Masatoshi tō
Masatoshi
雅俊 (中村 時定)
CAT. 433

Masatoshi
Masatoshi
雅俊 (中村 時定)
CAT. 438

Jikishiin Masatoshi
Masatoshi
art name: Jikishiin
雅俊 (中村 時定)
CAT. 472

Masatoshi; kakihan
Masatoshi
雅俊 (中村 時定)
CAT. 492

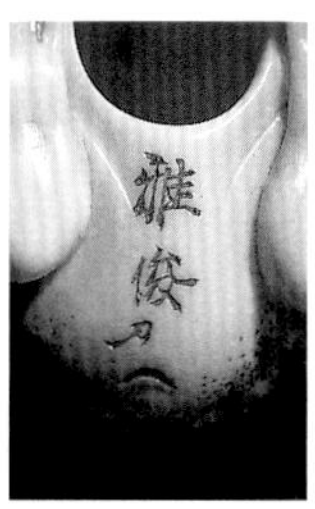

Masatoshi tō
Masatoshi
雅俊 (中村 時定)
CAT. 514

Masatoshi
Masatoshi
雅俊 (中村 時定)
CAT. 537

Isshunsai Masatoshi; kakihan;
seals: *Isshunsai*; *Masatoshi*
Masatoshi
雅俊 (中村 時定)
CAT. 537 (box)

Masatoshi
Masatoshi
雅俊 (中村 時定)
CAT. 546

Masatoshi
Masatoshi
雅俊 (中村 時定)
CAT. 552

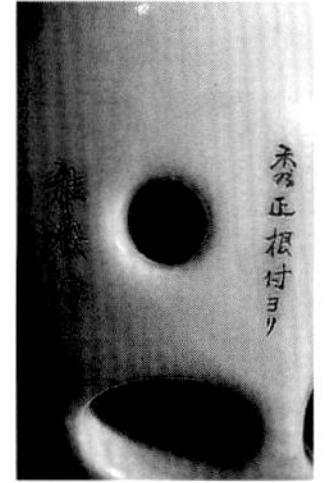

Hidemasa netsuke yori
Masatoshi sha
Masatoshi
雅俊 (中村 時定)
CAT. 555

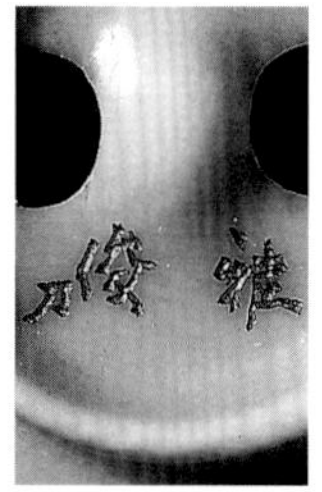

Masatoshi tō
Masatoshi
雅俊 (中村 時定)
CAT. 563

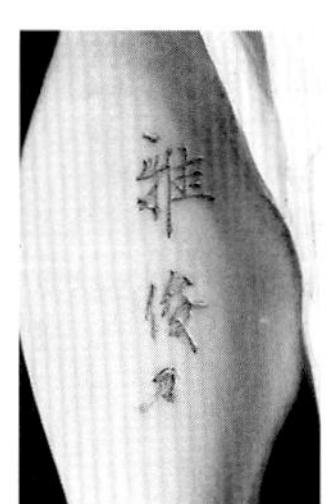

Masatoshi tō
Masatoshi
雅俊 (中村 時定)
CAT. 564

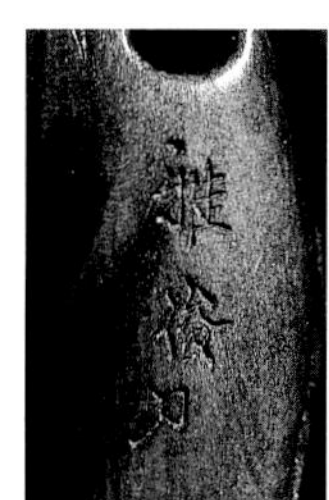

Masatoshi tō
Masatoshi
雅俊 (中村 時定)
CAT. 682

Masatoshi
Masatoshi
雅俊（中村 時定）
CAT. 725

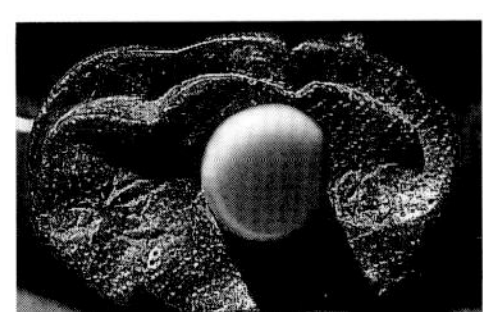

Tokisada tō
Masatoshi
雅俊（中村 時定）
CAT. 750

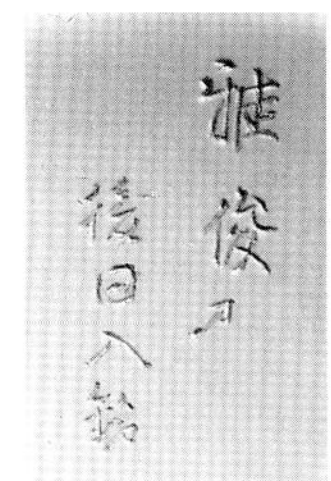

Masatoshi tō gojitsunyūmei
Masatoshi
雅俊（中村 時定）
CAT. 773

Masatoshi tō
Masatoshi
雅俊（中村 時定）
CAT. 827

Masatsugu
Masatsugu
正次
CAT. 244

Masatsugu
Masatsugu
正次
CAT. 465

Masayoshi
Masayoshi
正義
CAT. 258

Masayoshi
Masayoshi
正義
CAT. 319

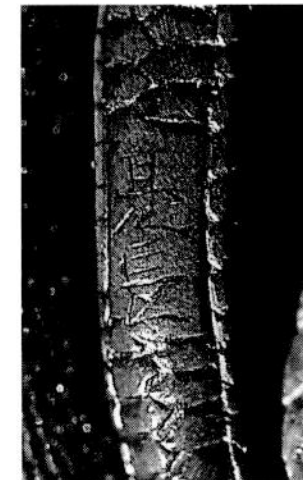

Sukenaga
Matsuda Sukenaga
松田 亮長
CAT. 309

Hida Sukenaga; kakihan
Matsuda Sukenaga
松田 亮長
CAT. 419

Sukenaga
Matsuda Sukenaga
松田 亮長
CAT. 420

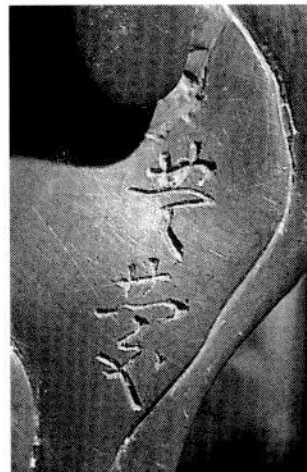

Hōkei
Matsuki Hōkei
松木 豊慶
CAT. 577

Otoman
Matsushita Otoman
松下 音満
CAT. 278

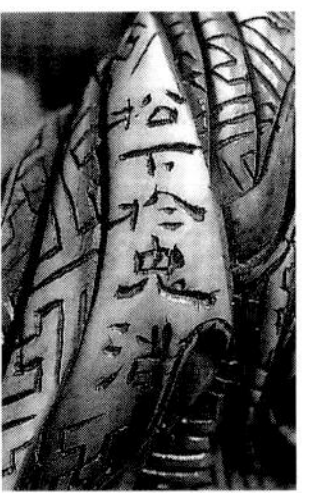

Matsushita Otoman
Matsushita Otoman
松下 音満
CAT. 530

Meikei
Meikei
明恵
CAT. 547

Hōjitsu
Meikeisai Hōjitsu
明奚齋 法實
CAT. 59

Meikeisai
Meikeisai Hōjitsu
明奚齋 法實
CAT. 589

Hōjitsu
Meikeisai Hōjitsu
明奚齋 法實
CAT. 656

Hagen
Meinertzhagen, Frederick M.
フレデリック・マイナーツハーゲン（羽玄）
CAT. 221

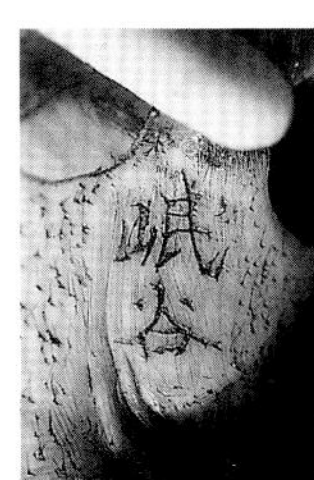

Minkoku
Minkoku II or Minkoku III
岷谷（二代目）or 民谷（三代目）
CAT. 567

Minkoku
Minkoku III
民谷（三代目）
CAT. 633

Mitsu; Kiyo
Mitsukiyo
光清
CAT. 306

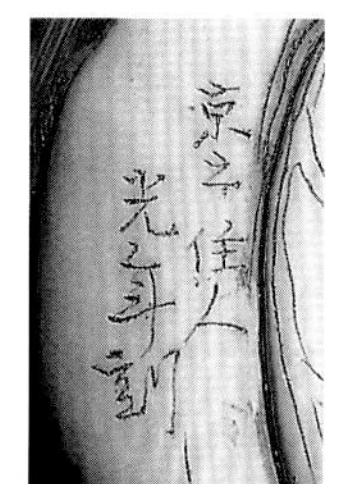

Kyō no junin Mitsutoshi koku
Mitsutoshi
光年
CAT. 368

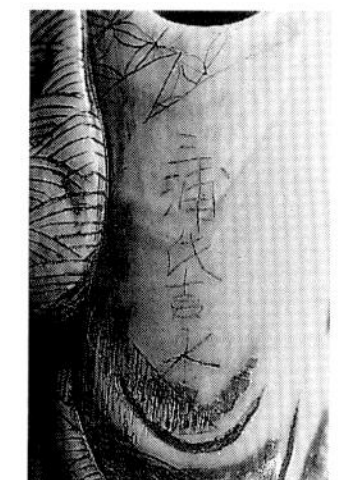

Miura shi Yoshinaga
Miura Yoshinaga
三浦　吉永
CAT. 157

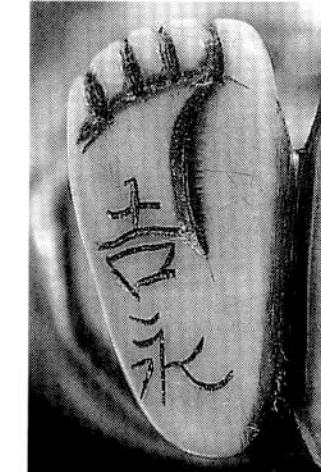

Yoshinaga
Miura Yoshinaga
三浦　吉永
CAT. 521

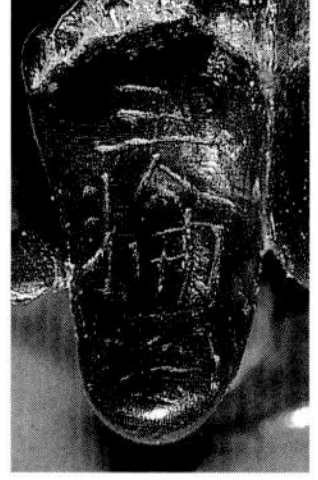

Miwa saku [?]
Miwa
三輪
CAT. 48

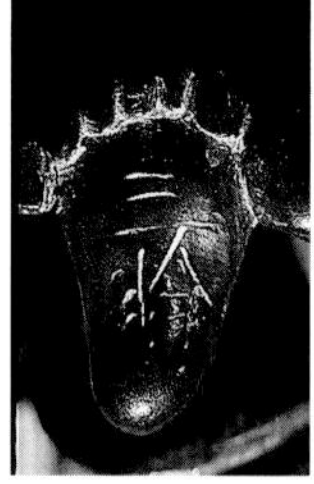

Miwa
School of Miwa
三輪派
CAT. 50

Miwa; kakihan
School of Miwa
三輪派
CAT. 51

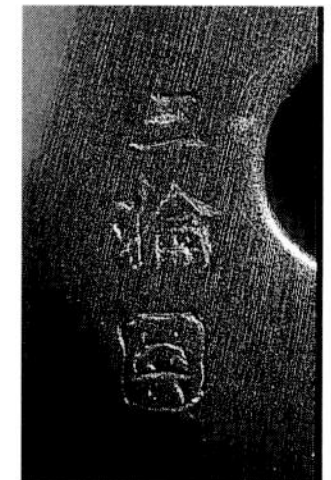

Miwa; kakihan
School of Miwa
三輪派
CAT. 130

Miwa
School of Miwa
三輪派
CAT. 131

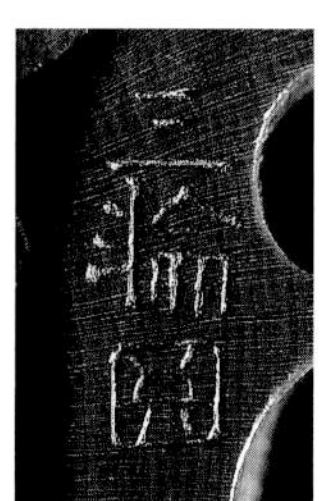

Miwa; kakihan
School of Miwa
三輪派
CAT. 618

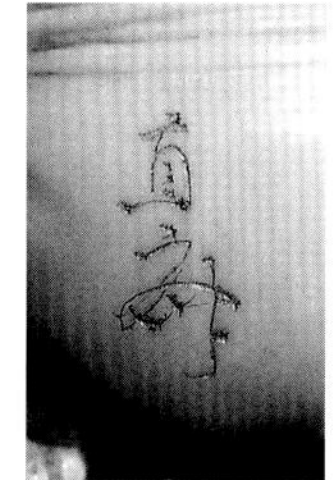

Chokusai
Miyagi Chokusai
(Masanosuke)
宮城　直齋（政之助）
CAT. 179

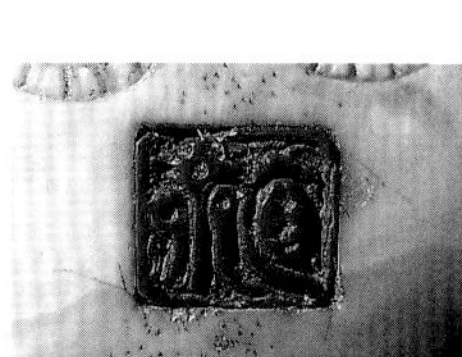

seal form: *Chokusai*
Miyagi Chokusai
(Masanosuke)
宮城　直齋（政之助）
CAT. 253

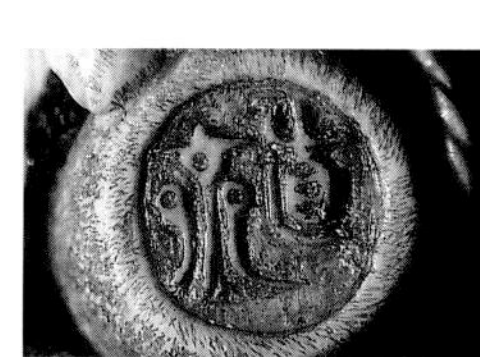

seal form: *Chokusai*
Miyagi Chokusai
(Masanosuke)
宮城　直齋（政之助）
CAT. 629

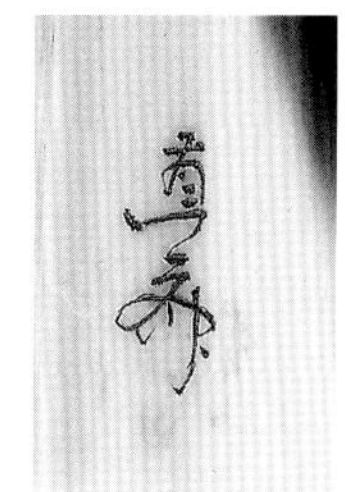

Chokusai
Miyagi Chokusai
(Masanosuke)
宮城　直齋（政之助）
CAT. 747

kakihan
Morikawa Toen
森川　杜園
CAT. 120

Toen
Morikawa Toen
森川　杜園
CAT. 536

To [?]; kakihan
Morikawa Toen
森川　杜園
CAT. 574

Murasada
Murasada
村定
CAT. 669

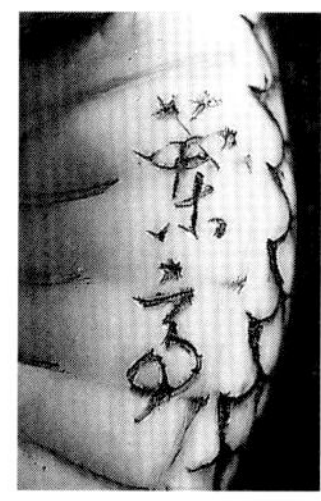

Rantei
Nagai Rantei
長井　蘭亭
CAT. 308

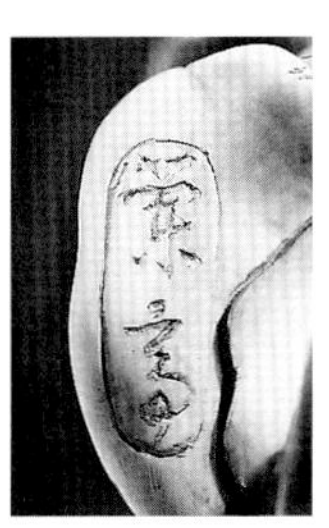
Rantei
School of Nagai Rantei
長井 蘭亭 派
CAT. 63

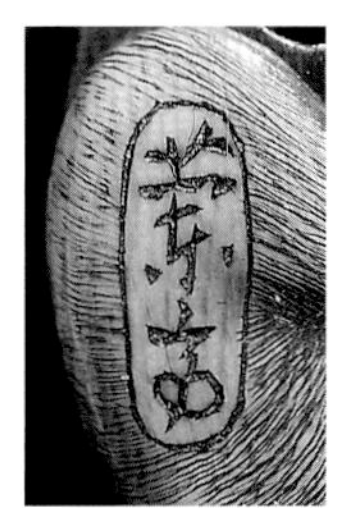
Rantei
School of Nagai Rantei
長井 蘭亭 派
CAT. 259

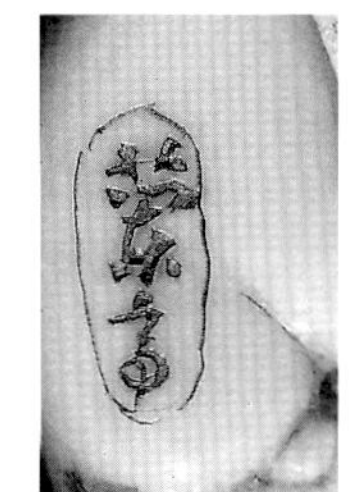
Rantei
School of Nagai Rantei
長井 蘭亭 派
CAT. 318

Rantei
School of Nagai Rantei
長井 蘭亭 派
CAT. 507

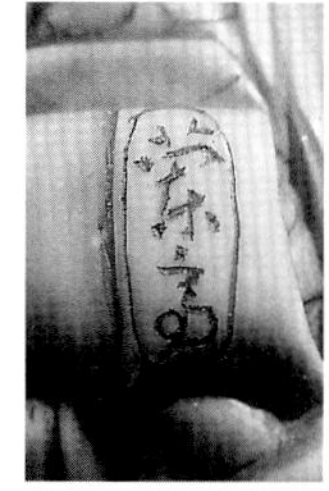
Rantei
School of Nagai Rantei
長井 蘭亭 派
CAT. 588

Nagami Iwao chōkoku
seals: *Ei; Naga*
Nagami Iwao
永見 巌
CAT. 464

Toyomasa
Naitō Toyomasa
内藤 豊昌
CAT. 52

Toyomasa
Naitō Toyomasa
内藤 豊昌
CAT. 247

Toyomasa
Naitō Toyomasa
内藤 豊昌
CAT. 248

Toyomasa
Naitō Toyomasa
内藤 豊昌
CAT. 276

Toyomasa
Naitō Toyomasa
内藤 豊昌
CAT. 280

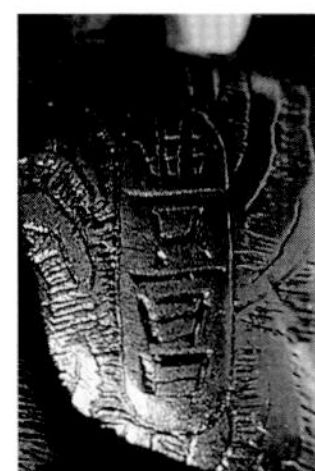
Toyomasa
Naitō Toyomasa
内藤 豊昌
CAT. 285

Toyomasa
Naitō Toyomasa
内藤 豊昌
CAT. 287

Toyomasa
Naitō Toyomasa
内藤 豊昌
CAT. 296

Toyomasa
Naitō Toyomasa
内藤 豊昌
CAT. 297

Toyomasa
Naitō Toyomasa
内藤 豊昌
CAT. 326

Toyomasa
Naitō Toyomasa
内藤 豊昌
CAT. 338

Toyomasa
Naitō Toyomasa
内藤 豊昌
CAT. 342

Toyomasa
Naitō Toyomasa
内藤 豊昌
CAT. 350

Toyomasa
Naitō Toyomasa
内藤 豊昌
CAT. 392

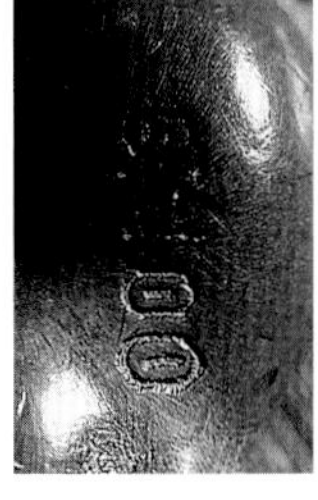
Toyomasa
Naitō Toyomasa
内藤 豊昌
CAT. 458

Toyomasa
Naitō Toyomasa
内藤 豊昌
CAT. 462

Toyomasa
Naitō Toyomasa
内藤 豊昌
CAT. 553

Toyomasa saku
Naitō Toyomasa
内藤 豊昌
CAT. 778

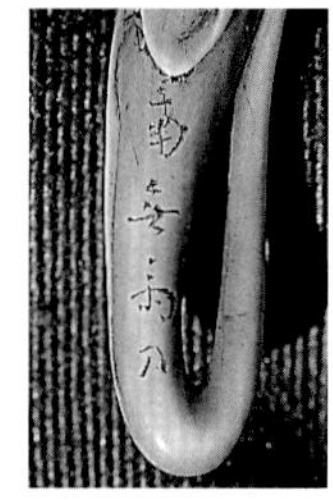
Nanmusai tō
Nanmusai
南無齋
CAT. 677

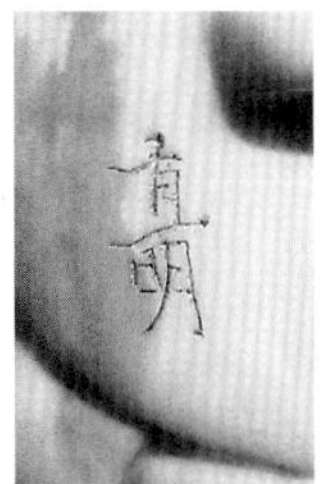
Naoaki
Naoaki
直明
CAT. 737

Ichiyūsai; seal form: *Naomitsu*
Naomitsu
art name: Ichiyūsai
直光
CAT. 523

Nisai tō
Nisai
二哉
CAT. 125

Nisai tō
Nisai
二哉
CAT. 423

Nisai tō
Nisai
二哉
CAT. 444

Nisai tō
Nisai
二哉
CAT. 489

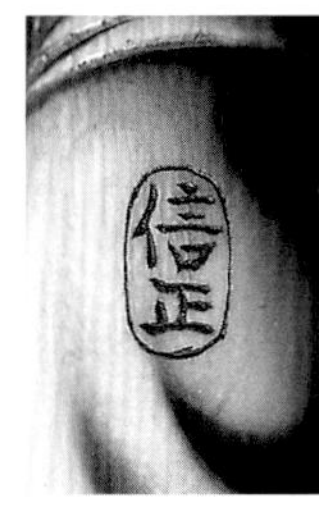
Nobumasa
Nobumasa
信正
CAT. 594

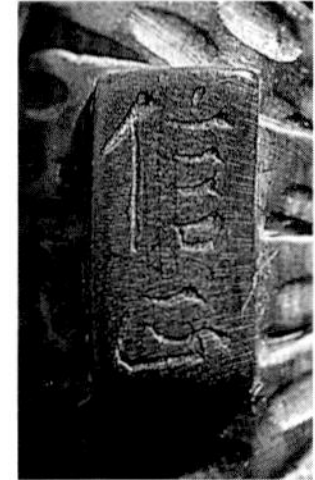
Nobumasa
Nobumasa
信正
CAT. 424

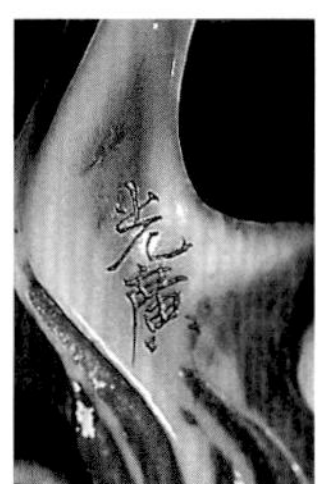
Mitsuhiro
Ōhara Mitsuhiro
大原 光廣
CAT. 168

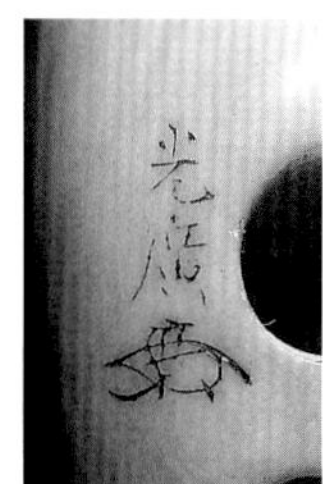
Mitsuhiro; kakihan
Ōhara Mitsuhiro
大原 光廣
CAT. 373

Mitsuhiro
Ōhara Mitsuhiro
大原 光廣
CAT. 388

Mitsuhiro; seal form: *Ōhara*
Ōhara Mitsuhiro
大原 光廣
CAT. 449

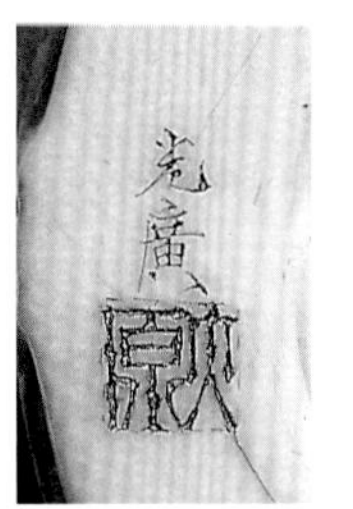
Mitsuhiro; seal form: *Ōhara*
Ōhara Mitsuhiro
大原 光廣
CAT. 476

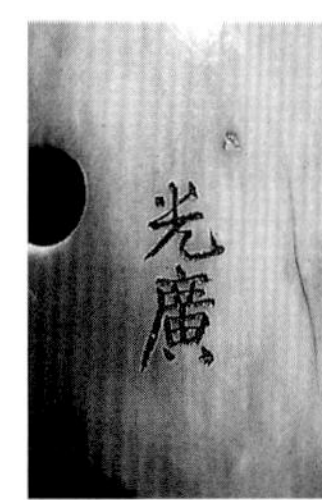
Mitsuhiro
Ōhara Mitsuhiro
大原 光廣
CAT. 488

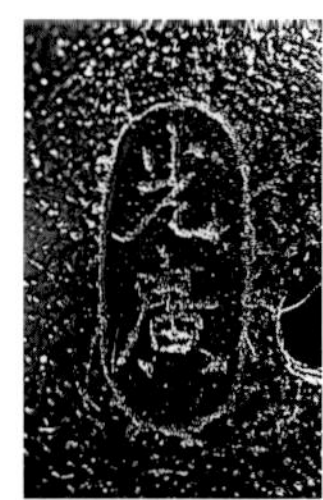
Mitsuhiro
Ōhara Mitsuhiro
大原 光廣
CAT. 558

Mitsuhiro; kakihan
Ōhara Mitsuhiro
大原 光廣
CAT. 587

Mitsuhiro
Ōhara Mitsuhiro
大原 光廣
CAT. 697

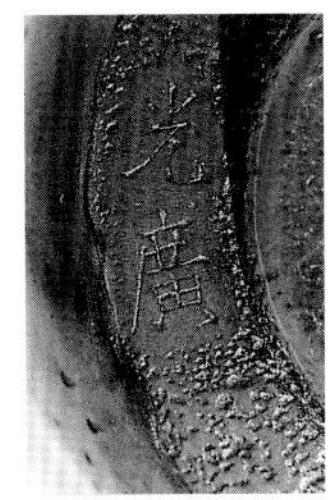

Mitsuhiro
Ōhara Mitsuhiro
大原 光廣
CAT. 706

Mitsuhiro; seal form: *Ōhara*
Ōhara Mitsuhiro
大原 光廣
CAT. 713

Mitsuhiro; seal form: *Ōhara*
Ōhara Mitsuhiro
大原 光廣
CAT. 714

Mitsuhiro
Ōhara Mitsuhiro
大原 光廣
CAT. 719

Mitsuhiro; seal form: *Ōhara*
Ōhara Mitsuhiro
大原 光廣
CAT. 720

Mitsuhiro saku
Ōhara Mitsuhiro
大原 光廣
CAT. 744

Mitsuhiro
After Ōhara Mitsuhiro
倣大原 光廣
CAT. 708

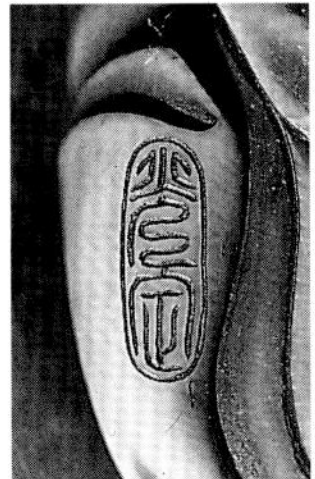

seal form: *Mitsusada*
Ōhara Mitsusada
大原 光定
CAT. 612

seal form: *Mitsusada*
Ōhara Mitsusada
大原 光定
CAT. 741

Okakoto
Okakoto
岡言
CAT. 298

Kahei
Ōmiya Kahei
近江屋 嘉兵衛
CAT. 749

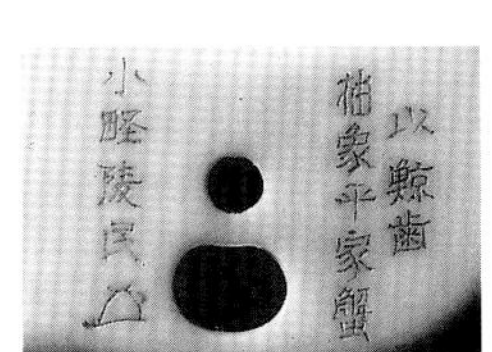

Ono Ryōmin; kakihan
Ono Ryōmin
小野 陵民
CAT. 446

Ono Ryōmin; kakihan
Ono Ryōmin
小野 陵民
CAT. 510

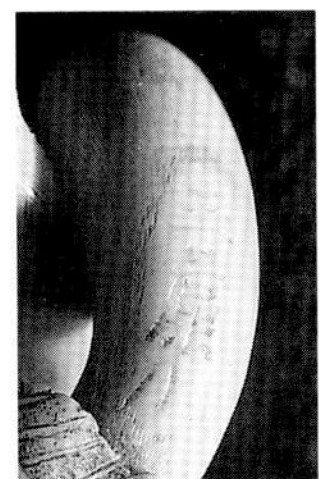

Gyokusō tō
Ōuchi Gyokusō
玉藻 (大内 治右衛門)
CAT. 238

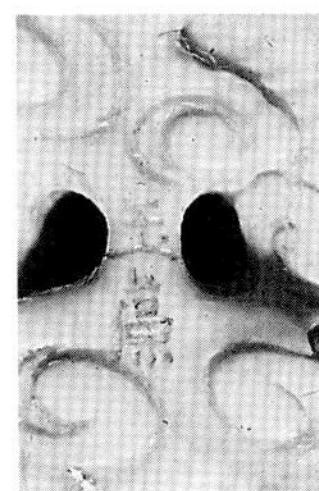

Gyokusō
Ōuchi Gyokusō
玉藻 (大内 治右衛門)
CAT. 543

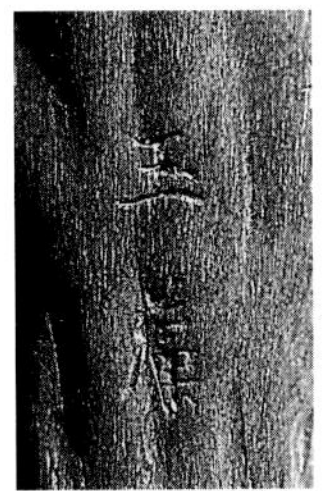

Gyokusō
Ōuchi Gyokusō
玉藻 (大内 治右衛門)
CAT. 631

Gyokusō
Ōuchi Gyokusō
玉藻 (大内 治右衛門)
CAT. 666

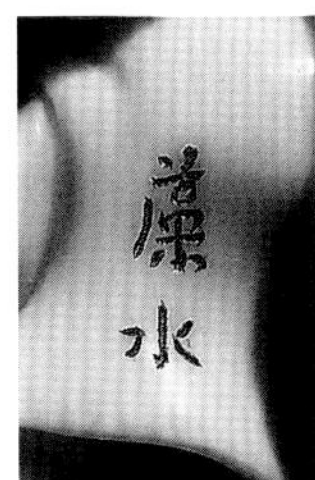

Sōsui
Ōuchi Sōsui
藻水 (大内 次郎)
CAT. 541

Sōsui
Ōuchi Sōsui
藻水 (大内 次郎)
CAT. 544

Ōuchi Sōsui koku
Ōuchi Sōsui
藻水 (大内 次郎)
CAT. 544 (box)

Sōsui
Ōuchi Sōsui
藻水 (大内 次郎)
CAT. 591

Sōsui
Ōuchi Sōsui
藻水 (大内 次郎)
CAT. 597

Sōsui
Ōuchi Sōsui
藻水 (大内 次郎)
CAT. 636

Sōsui saku; seal: *Sōsui*
Ōuchi Sōsui
藻水 (大内 次郎)
CAT. 636 (box)

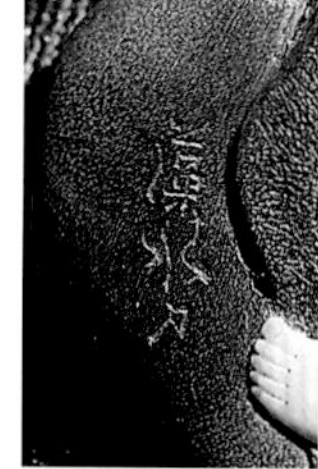

Sōsui tō
Ōuchi Sōsui
藻水 (大内 次郎)
CAT. 637

Sōsui saku; seal: *Sōsui*
Ōuchi Sōsui
藻水 (大内 次郎)
CAT. 637 (box)

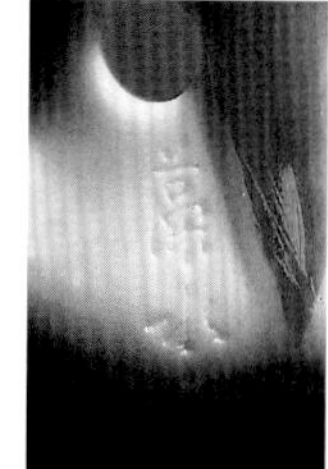

Sōsui
Ōuchi Sōsui
藻水 (大内 次郎)
CAT. 643

Sōsui
Ōuchi Sōsui
藻水 (大内 次郎)
CAT. 705

Sōsui
Ōuchi Sōsui
藻水 (大内 次郎)
CAT. 717

Sōsui saku; seal: *Sōsui*
Ōuchi Sōsui
藻水 (大内 次郎)
CAT. 717 (box)

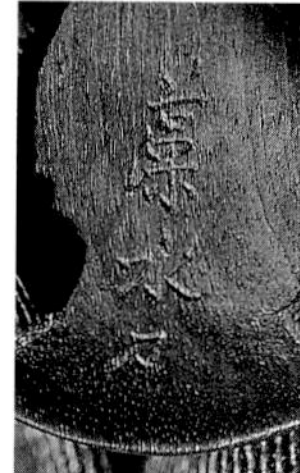

Sōsui tō
Ōuchi Sōsui
藻水 (大内 次郎)
CAT. 769

Taishō hi no e tora natsu, Sōsui;
seal: *Sōsui*
Ōuchi Sōsui
藻水 (大内 次郎)
CAT. 769 (box)

Sōsui tō
Ōuchi Sōsui
藻水 (大内 次郎)
CAT. 819

Sōsui tō; seal: *Sōsui*
Ōuchi Sōsui
藻水 (大内 次郎)
CAT. 819 (box)

Sekijōken; kakihan
Ōyama Motozane IV
art name: Sekijōken
泰山 元孚 (四代目)
石城軒
CAT. 245

Taizan Motozane; kakihan
Ōyama Motozane IV
泰山 元孚 (四代目)
石城軒
CAT. 538

seal form: *Koku*
Ozaki Kokusai
尾崎 谷齋
CAT. 249

seal form: *Koku*
Ozaki Kokusai
尾崎 谷齋
CAT. 328

seal form: *Seisai'in [?]* or *Tazai'in [?]*
Ozaki Kokusai
尾崎 谷齋
CAT. 329

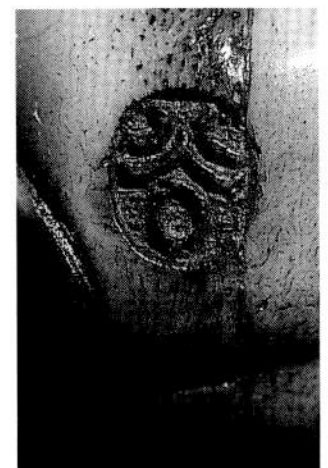

seal form: *Koku*
Ozaki Kokusai
尾崎 谷齋
CAT. 826

Shūraku; kakihan
Ozawa Shūraku
小沢 秀楽
CAT. 88

Shūraku; kakihan
Ozawa Shūraku
小沢 秀楽
CAT. 232

Shūraku; kakihan
Ozawa Shūraku
小沢 秀楽
CAT. 550

Shūraku; kakihan
Ozawa Shūraku
小沢 秀楽
CAT. 562

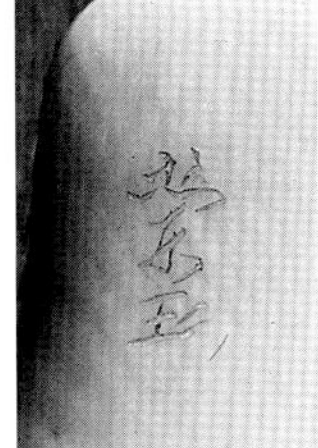

Rangyoku
Rangyoku
蘭玉
CAT. 393

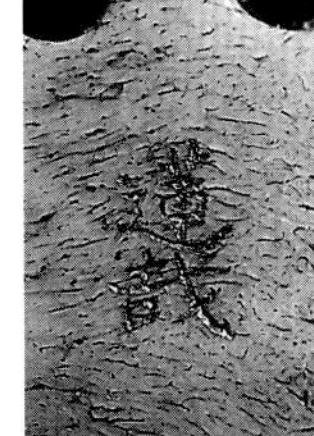

Rensai
Rensai
蓮哉
CAT. 252

Ryōichi
Ryōichi (or Yoshikazu)
良一
CAT. 410

Ryōkō
Ryōkō
良光
CAT. 292

Shūzan kokui Ryōmin utsusu
Ryōmin
凌民
CAT. 73

Ryōsai
Ryōsai
亮齋
CAT. 36

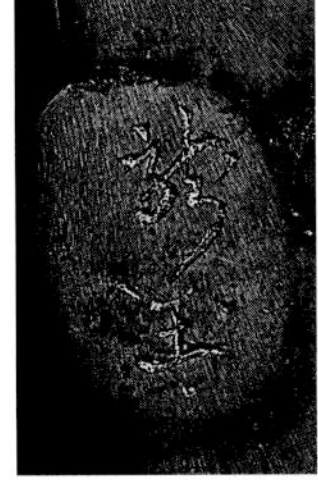

Ryūgyoku
Ryūgyoku
龍玉
CAT. 703

Ryūkei saku
Ryūkei I
龍珪（初代）
CAT. 24

Ryūkei; kakihan
Ryūkei I
龍珪（初代）
CAT. 28

Ryūkei
Ryūkei II
龍珪（二代目）
CAT. 648

Ryūkō
Ryūkō
隆光
CAT. 776

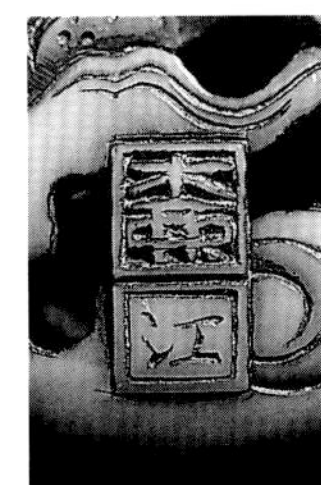

seal form: *Ryūkō*
Ryūkō
柳江
CAT. 304

Jugyoku; seal form: *no saku*
Ryūkōsai Jugyoku
龍光齋 寿玉
CAT. 415

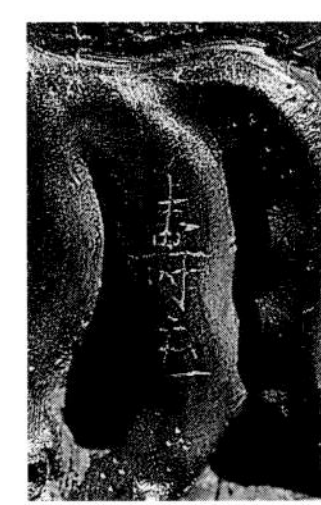

Jugyoku
Ryūkōsai Jugyoku
龍光齋 寿玉
CAT. 531

Jugyoku
Ryūkōsai Jugyoku
龍光齋 寿玉
CAT. 753

Jugyoku; seal form: *Jugyoku*
Ryūkōsai Jugyoku
龍光齋 寿玉
CAT. 754

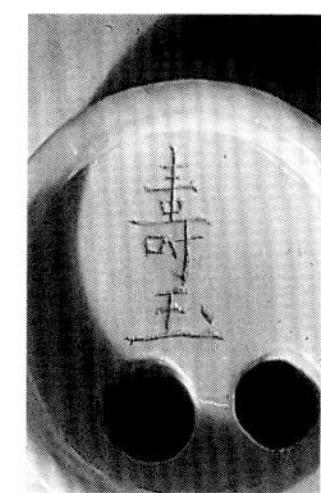

Jugyoku
Ryūkōsai Jugyoku II
龍光齋 寿玉 (二代目)
CAT. 260

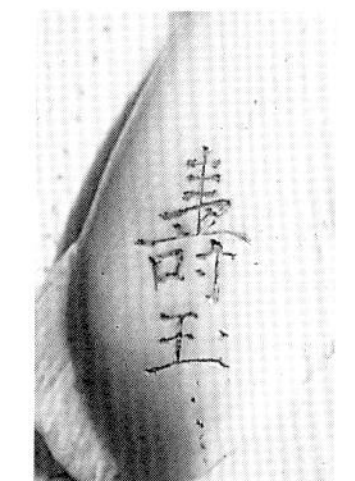

Jugyoku
Ryūkōsai Jugyoku II
龍光齋 寿玉 (二代目)
CAT. 721

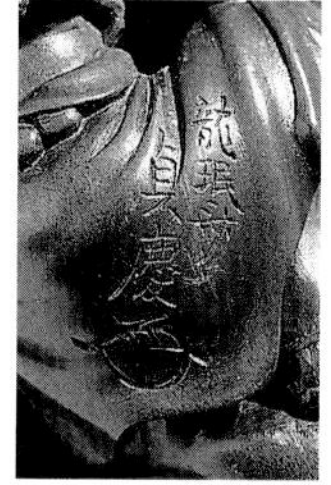

Ryūminsai Teikei; kakihan
Ryūminsai Teikei
龍珉齋 貞慶
CAT. 86

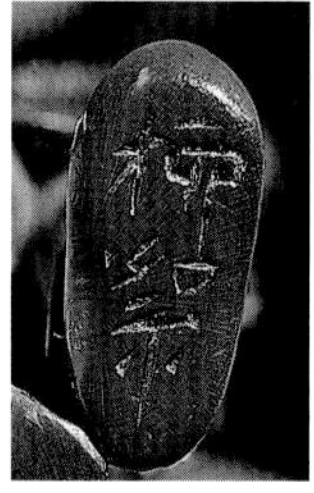

Ryūsai
Ryūsai
柳祭
CAT. 43

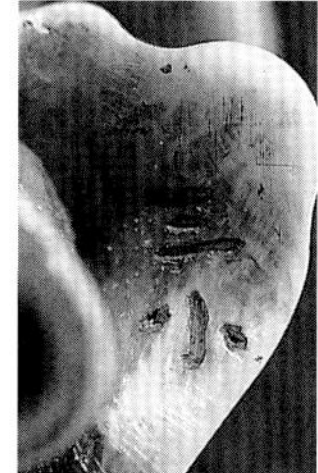

Sanko
Sanko
三小
CAT. 58

Sari
Sari
佐里
CAT. 436

Sasaki Tomiaki chōkoku; seal form: *Tomiaki*
Sasaki Tomiaki
佐々木 富明
CAT. 457

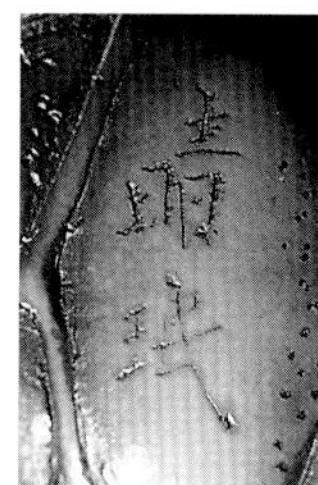

Seimin
Seimin
晴珉
CAT. 422

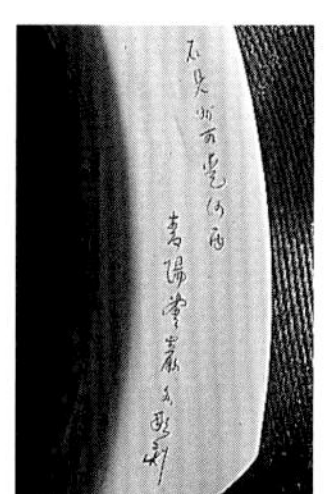

Iwami shū Kawaigawa nishi Seiyōdō Gansui chōkoku
Seiyōdō Gansui
青陽堂 巌水
CAT. 266

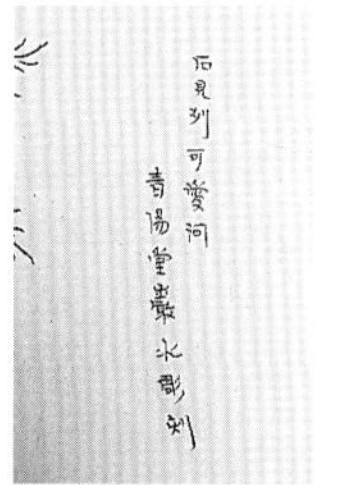

Iwami Kawaigawa Seiyōdō Gansui
Seiyōdō Gansui
青陽堂 巌水
CAT. 475

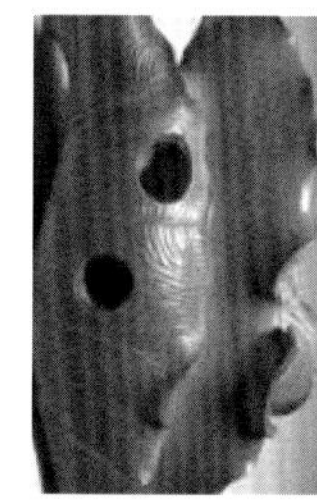

Seiyōdō Tomiharu ... chōkoku
Seiyōdō Tomiharu
青陽堂 富春
CAT. 413

Kawaigawa Seiyōdō Tomiharu kokuari
Seiyōdō Tomiharu
青陽堂 富春
CAT. 454

Nanajūnanasai Tomiharu chōkoku
Seiyōdō Tomiharu
青陽堂 富春
CAT. 455

Seiyōdō Tomiharu chōkoku
Seiyōdō Tomiharu
青陽堂 富春
CAT. 702

Nanajūroku Sekiran
Sekiran
石蘭
CAT. 281

Sekkō (or Yukimitsu)
Sekkō (or Yukimitsu)
雪光
CAT. 78

Zeshin
Shibata Zeshin
柴田 是真
CAT. 710

Shigemasa; kakihan
Shigemasa
重正
CAT. 417

Shigemasa; kakihan
Shigemasa
重正
CAT. 418

Shigemasa
Shigemasa
重正
CAT. 459

Mitsutoshi
Shinshinsai Mitsutoshi
神心齋 光利
CAT. 724

seal form: *Shō*
Shō (or Noboru)
昇
CAT. 664

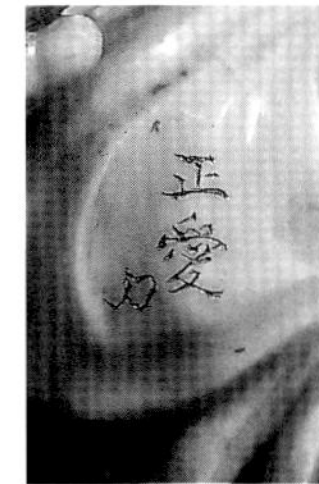

Shōai tō
Shōai
正愛
CAT. 615

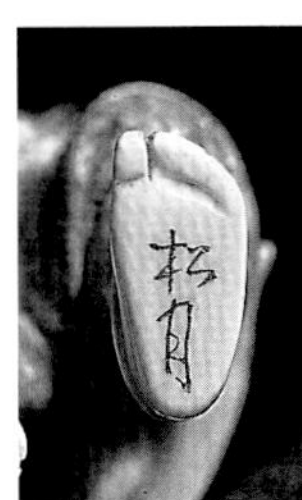

Shōgetsu
Shōgetsu
松月
CAT. 569

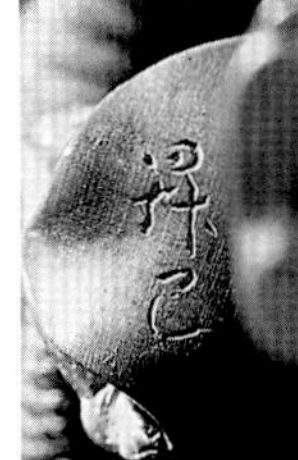

Shōko
Shōko (Nishino Shōtarō)
昇己 (西野昇太郎)
CAT. 80

Toyomasa shiki Hokusōjin Shōko koku; kakihan; seals: *Nishino; Shōko*
Shōko (Nishino Shōtarō)
昇己 (西野昇太郎)
CAT. 80 (box)

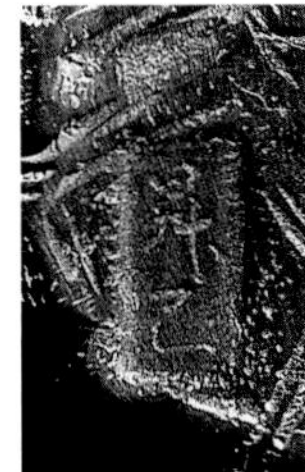

Shōko
Shōko (Nishino Shōtarō)
昇己 (西野昇太郎)
CAT. 93

Hokusōjin Shōko saku; seals: *Nishino; Shōko*
Shōko (Nishino Shōtarō)
昇己 (西野昇太郎)
CAT. 93 (box)

Shōko
Shōko (Nishino Shōtarō)
昇己 (西野昇太郎)
CAT. 94

Hokusōjin Shōko saku; kakihan; seals: *Nishino; Shōko*
Shōko (Nishino Shōtarō)
昇己 (西野昇太郎)
CAT. 94 (box)

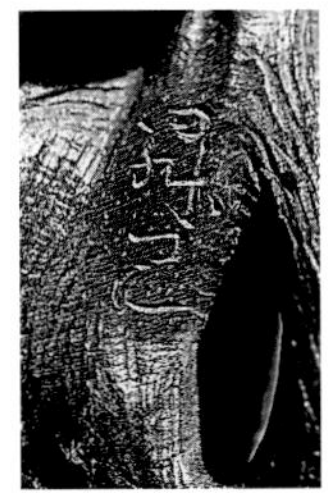

Shōko
Shōko (Nishino Shōtarō)
昇己 (西野昇太郎)
CAT. 224

Hokusōjin Shōko saku; seals: *Nishino; Shōko*
Shōko (Nishino Shōtarō)
昇己 (西野昇太郎)
CAT. 224 (box)

Shōko
Shōko (Nishino Shōtarō)
昇己 (西野昇太郎)
CAT. 225

Shōko
Shōko (Nishino Shōtarō)
昇己 (西野昇太郎)
CAT. 356

Hokusōjin Shōko saku and *Shōko;* seal: *Shōko*
Shōko (Nishino Shōtarō)
昇己 (西野昇太郎)
CAT. 356 (box)

Shōko
Shōko (Nishino Shōtarō)
昇己 (西野昇太郎)
CAT. 681

Hokusōjin Shōko saku; seals: *Nishino; Shōko*
Shōko (Nishino Shōtarō)
昇己 (西野昇太郎)
CAT. 681 (box)

Shōko
Shōko (Nishino Shōtarō)
昇己 (西野昇太郎)
CAT. 690

Hokusōjin Shōko saku; seals: *Nishino; Shōko*
Shōko (Nishino Shōtarō)
昇己 (西野昇太郎)
CAT. 690 (box)

Shōminsai
Shōminsai
松民齋
CAT. 542

Shōmosai
Shōmosai
松茂齋
CAT. 240

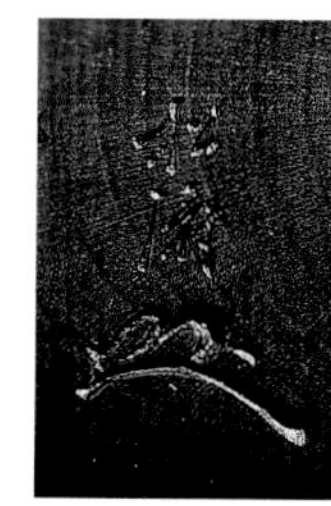

Shōtō; kakihan
Shōtō
松濤
CAT. 251

Shūchi [or *Shūji*]
Shūchi
秋治
CAT. 383

Anraku
Shūkōsai Anraku
周公齋 安樂
CAT. 119

Shūkōsai Anraku
Shūkōsai Anraku
周公齋 安樂
CAT. 174

Anraku
Shūkōsai Anraku
周公齋 安樂
CAT. 411

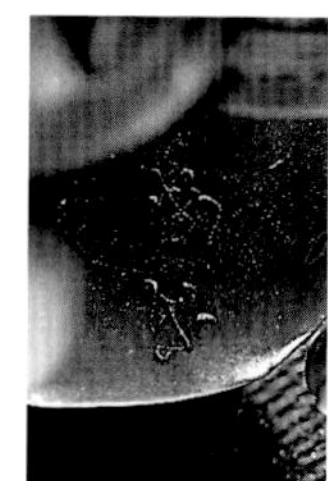

Anraku
Shūkōsai Anraku
周公齋 安樂
CAT. 508

Anraku
Shūkōsai Anraku
周公齋 安樂
CAT. 557

Seiyōdō Tomiharu otoko Shukutō chōkoku
Shukutō Atakanosuke
肅騰 阿多賀之助
CAT. 456

Shunkōsai
Shunkōsai Chōgetsu
春江齋 潮月
CAT. 526

Shunkōsai
Shunkōsai Chōgetsu
春江齋 潮月
CAT. 640

Shūōsai; seal form: *Masa; Fujimoto*
Shūōsai Hidemasa II
秀翁齋 秀正 (二代目)
CAT. 505

Shūōsai; kakihan;
seal form: *Fujimoto*
Shūōsai Hidemasa II
秀翁齋 秀正 (二代目)
CAT. 529

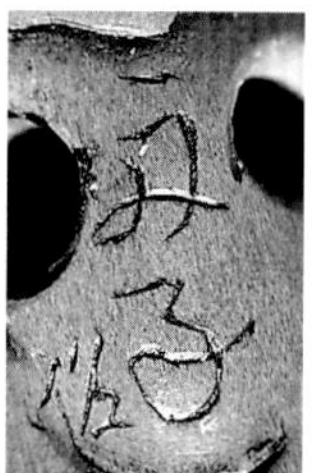

Shūshi; kakihan
Shūshi
舟子
CAT. 21

Shūzan
Shūzan
周山
CAT. 556

Shūzan
Shūzan
舟山
CAT. 305

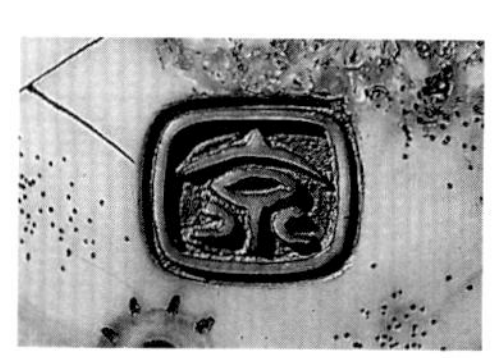

seal form: *Sō*
Sō
宗
CAT. 188

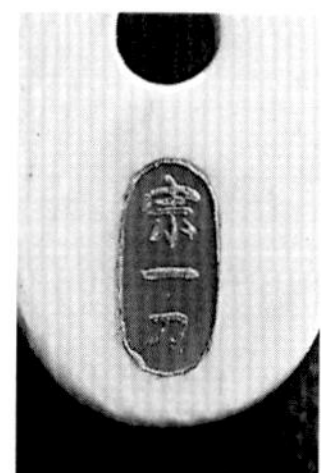

Sōichi tō
Sōichi
宗一
CAT. 355

Sōju tō
Sōju
藻壽
CAT. 226

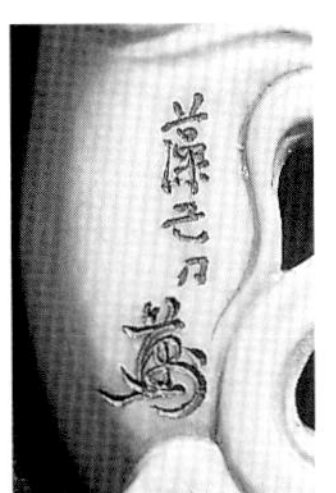
Sōko tō; kakihan
Sōko (Morita Kisaburō)
藻己（森田 喜三郎）
CAT. 126

Sōko
Sōko (Morita Kisaburō)
藻己（森田 喜三郎）
CAT. 133

Sōko tō; seal form: *Morita*
Sōko (Morita Kisaburō)
藻己（森田 喜三郎）
CAT. 134

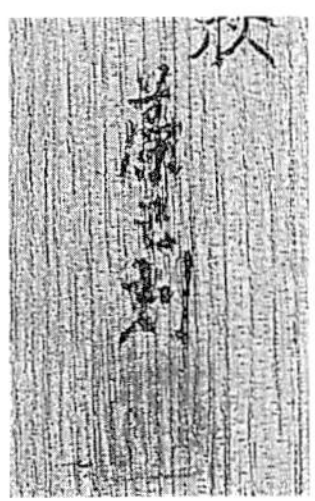
Sōko koku; seal: *Sōko*
Sōko (Morita Kisaburō)
藻己（森田 喜三郎）
CAT. 134 (box)

Sōko tō
Sōko (Morita Kisaburō)
藻己（森田 喜三郎）
CAT. 143

Sōko saku
Sōko (Morita Kisaburō)
藻己（森田 喜三郎）
CAT. 149

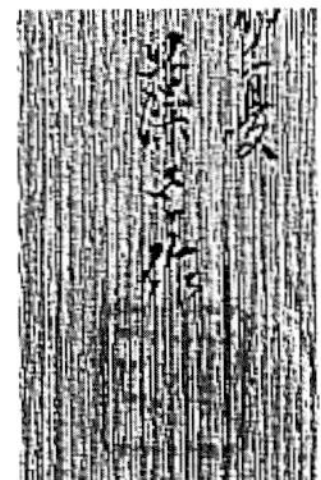
Sōko saku; seal: *Sōko*
Sōko (Morita Kisaburō)
藻己（森田 喜三郎）
CAT. 149 (box)

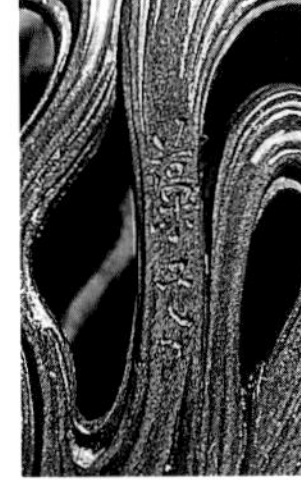
Sōko tō
Sōko (Morita Kisaburō)
藻己（森田 喜三郎）
CAT. 429

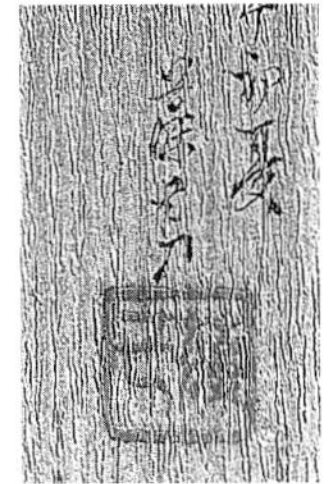
Sōko tō; seal: *Sōko*
Sōko (Morita Kisaburō)
藻己（森田 喜三郎）
CAT. 429 (box)

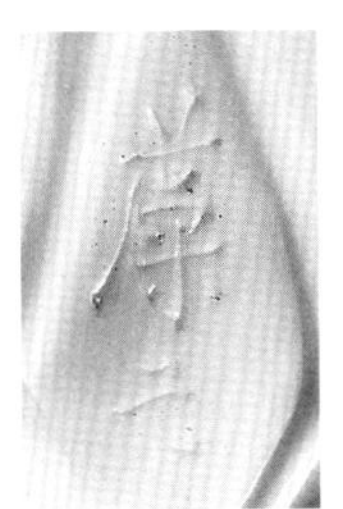
Sōko
Sōko (Morita Kisaburō)
藻己（森田 喜三郎）
CAT. 473

Sōko
Sōko (Morita Kisaburō)
藻己（森田 喜三郎）
CAT. 484

Sōko saku; seal: *Sōko*
Sōko (Morita Kisaburō)
藻己（森田 喜三郎）
CAT. 484 (box)

Sōko; seal form: *Sō*
Sōko (Morita Kisaburō)
藻己（森田 喜三郎）
CAT. 485

Sōko
Sōko (Morita Kisaburō)
藻己（森田 喜三郎）
CAT. 490

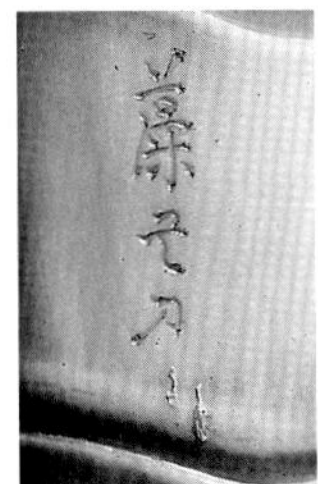
Sōko tō
Sōko (Morita Kisaburō)
藻己（森田 喜三郎）
CAT. 491

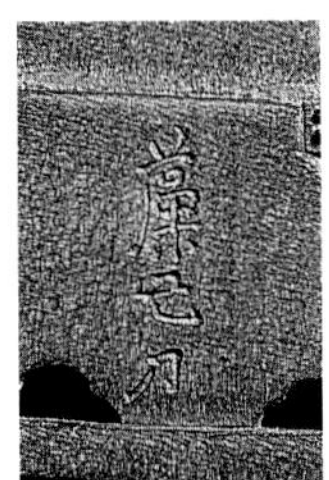
Sōko tō
Sōko (Morita Kisaburō)
藻己（森田 喜三郎）
CAT. 624

Sōko
Sōko (Morita Kisaburō)
藻己（森田 喜三郎）
CAT. 748

Sōko saku; seal: *Sōko*
Sōko (Morita Kisaburō)
藻己（森田 喜三郎）
CAT. 748 (box)

Sōko tō
Sōko (Morita Kisaburō)
藻己（森田 喜三郎）
CAT. 751

Sōko koku
Sōko (Morita Kisaburō)
藻己 (森田 喜三郎)
CAT. 755

Sōko
Sōko (Morita Kisaburō)
藻己 (森田 喜三郎)
CAT. 760

Sōko
Sōko (Morita Kisaburō)
藻己 (森田 喜三郎)
CAT. 761

Sōsai; kakihan
Sōsai
藻齋
CAT. 177

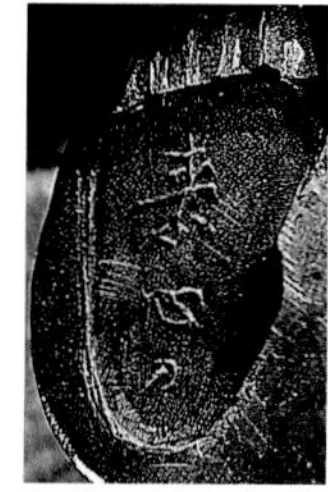

Soshin tō
Soshin
素心
CAT. 140

Sekishū
Sueyoshi Sekishū
末吉 石舟
CAT. 167

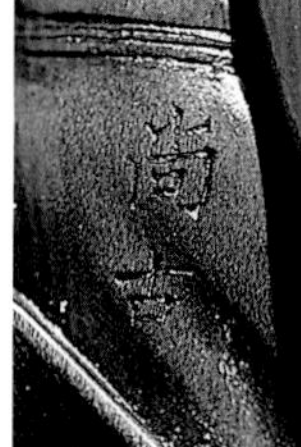

Shōko
Suganoya Shōko
菅谷 尚古
CAT. 600

Shōko
Suganoya Shōko
菅谷 尚古
CAT. 686

Sukenao
Sukenao
亮直
CAT. 321

Susumu
Susumu
進
CAT. 638

Masanao
Suzuki Masanao
鈴木 正直
CAT. 535

Masanao
Suzuki Masanao
鈴木 正直
CAT. 742

Tōkoku; seal form: *Bairyū*
Suzuki Tōkoku
鈴木 東谷
楳立
CAT. 121

Suzuki Tōkoku; seal: *Bairyū*
Suzuki Tōkoku
鈴木 東谷
楳立
CAT. 121 (box)

Tōkoku; seal form: *Bairyū*
Suzuki Tōkoku
鈴木 東谷
楳立
CAT. 122

seal forms: *Tōkoku* (red); *Bairyū* (gold)
Suzuki Tōkoku
鈴木 東谷
楳立
CAT. 381

Tōkoku Fūzui; seal form: *Bairyū*
Suzuki Tōkoku
鈴木 東谷
楳立
CAT. 679

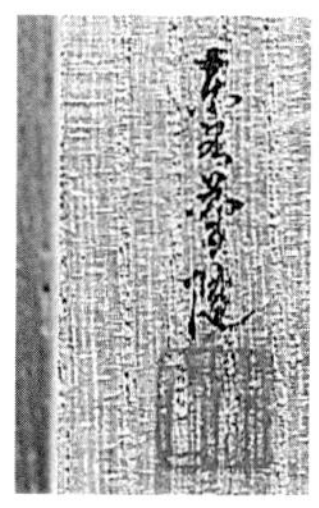

Tōkoku Fūzui; seal: *Bairyū*
Suzuki Tōkoku
鈴木 東谷
楳立
CAT. 679 (box)

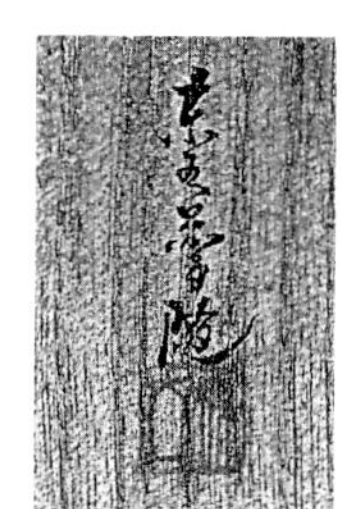

Tōkoku Fūzui; seal: *Bairyū*
Suzuki Tōkoku
鈴木 東谷
楳立
CAT. 700 (box)

Tōkoku; seal form: *Bairyū*
Suzuki Tōkoku
鈴木 東谷
楳立
CAT. 716

Tōkoku Fūzui; seal: *Bairyū*
Suzuki Tōkoku
鈴木 東谷
楳立
CAT. 716 (box)

Tadatoshi
Tadatoshi
定利
CAT. 204

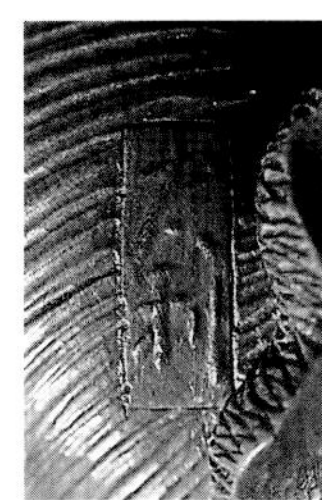

Tadatoshi
Tadatoshi
定利
CAT. 460

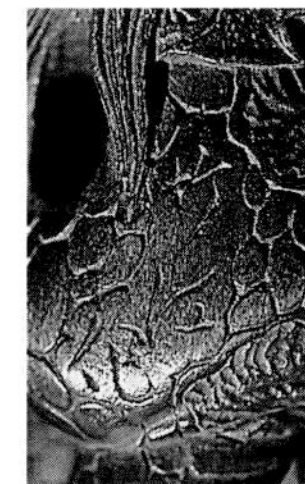

Chikkō
Takehara Chikkō
竹原 竹江
CAT. 596

Chikkō saku
Takehara Chikkō
竹原 竹江
CAT. 818

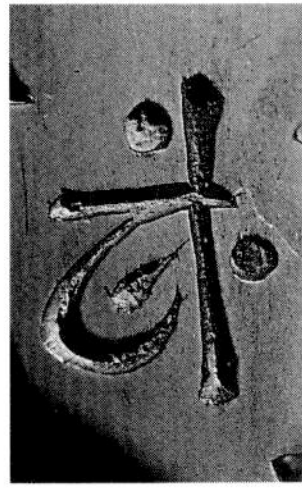

Takeshi [or *Bu*]
Takeshi
武
CAT. 678

Tomokazu [may have been added later]
Tamba School
丹波派
CAT. 205

Tametaka; kakihan
Tametaka
為隆
CAT. 12

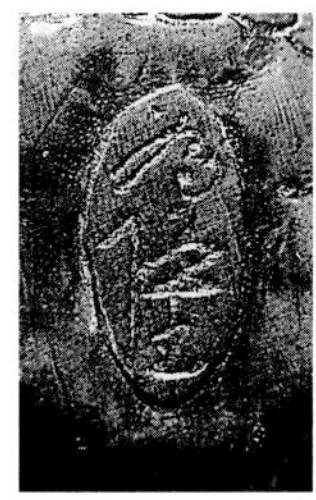

Tametaka
Tametaka
為隆
CAT. 192

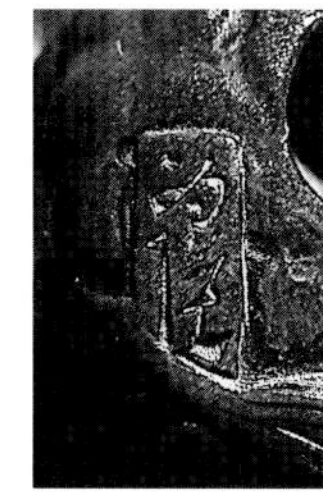

Tametaka
Tametaka
為隆
CAT. 193

Tametaka
Tametaka
為隆
CAT. 274

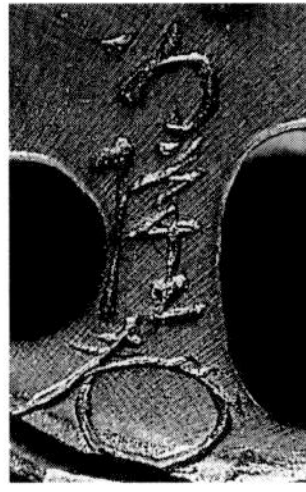

Tametaka; kakihan
Tametaka
為隆
CAT. 517

Tametaka; kakihan
Tametaka
為隆
CAT. 549

Minkō; kakihan
Tanaka Minkō
田中 岷江
CAT. 42

Minkō; kakihan
Tanaka Minkō
田中 岷江
CAT. 115

Minkō; kakihan
Tanaka Minkō
田中 岷江
CAT. 136

Tontoku Minkō; kakihan
Tanaka Minkō
art name: Tontoku Minkō
田中 岷江
CAT. 200

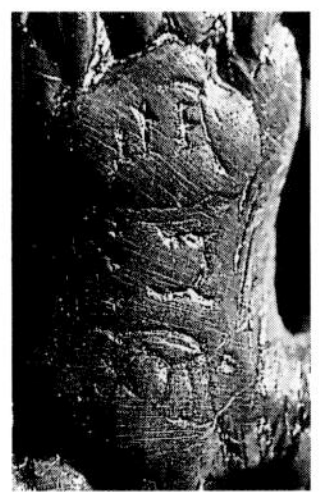

Minkō; kakihan
Tanaka Minkō
田中 岷江
CAT. 275

Minkō; kakihan
Tanaka Minkō
田中 岷江
CAT. 571

Tetsugen
Tetsugen (Kyūsai)
銕玄 (汲哉/鳩哉)
CAT. 79

Ikkyū tō
Tetsugen (Kyūsai)
art name: Ikkyū
銕玄（汲哉/鳩哉）
CAT. 153

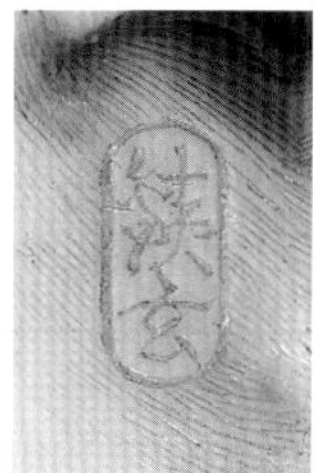
Tetsugen
Tetsugen (Kyūsai)
銕玄（汲哉/鳩哉）
CAT. 323

Tetsugen; seal: *Tetsugen*
Tetsugen (Kyūsai)
銕玄（汲哉/鳩哉）
CAT. 323 (box)

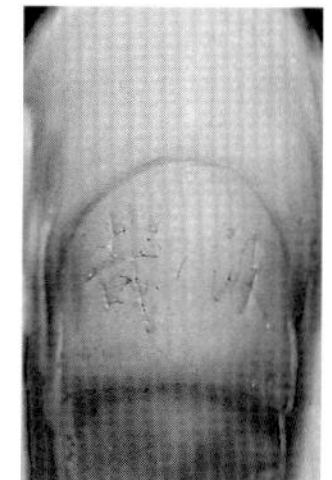
Kyūsai
Tetsugen (Kyūsai)
銕玄（汲哉/鳩哉）
CAT. 452

Kyūsai [o] kokusu kore
Tetsugen (Kyūsai)
銕玄（汲哉/鳩哉）
CAT. 452 (box)

Tetsugen saku; seal form: *Tetsu*
Tetsugen (Kyūsai)
銕玄（汲哉/鳩哉）
CAT. 471

Tetsugen; seal: *Tetsugen*
Tetsugen (Kyūsai)
銕玄（汲哉/鳩哉）
CAT. 471 (box)

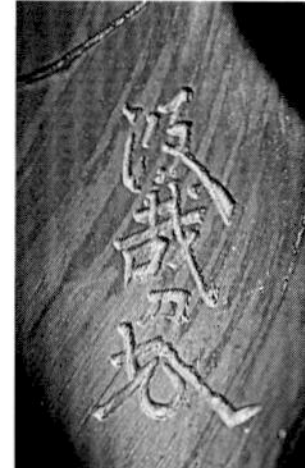
Kyūsai tō; kakihan
Tetsugen (Kyūsai)
銕玄（汲哉/鳩哉）
CAT. 474

Kyūsai kore o kizamu; seal: *Kyū*
Tetsugen (Kyūsai)
銕玄（汲哉/鳩哉）
CAT. 474 (box)

Tetsugen
Tetsugen (Kyūsai)
銕玄（汲哉/鳩哉）
CAT. 481

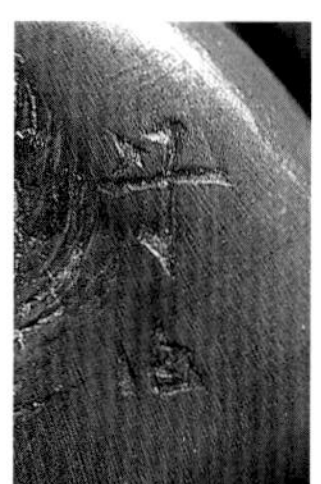
To (or Tō or Tan) saku
To (or Tan)
東
CAT. 237

Tōchinsai
Tōchinsai
唐珍齋
CAT. 585

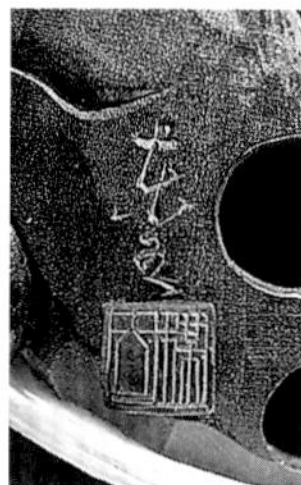
Tōkoku; seal form: *Bairyū*
Tōkoku I or Tōkoku II
東谷（初代目叉は二代目）
楳立
CAT. 123

Tōkoku Fūzui; seal: *Bairyū*
Tōkoku I or Tōkoku II
東谷（初代目叉は二代目）
楳立
CAT. 123 (box)

seal form: *Bairyū*
Tōkoku II or Tōkoku III
東谷（二代目叉は三代目）
楳立
CAT. 113

Tōkoku; seal form: *Bairyū*
Tōkoku II or Tōkoku III
東谷（二代目叉は三代目）
楳立
CAT. 124

Tōko; seal form: *Suzuki*
Tōkoku II or Tōkoku III
東谷（二代目叉は三代目）
楳立
CAT. 662

Tōmin
Tōmin
東岷
CAT. 256

Tomokazu
School of Tomokazu
友一 派
CAT. 288

Tomotada
Tomotada
友忠
CAT. 64

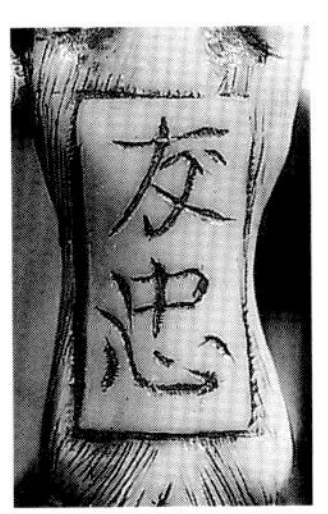

Tomotada
Tomotada
友忠
CAT. 196

Tomotada
Tomotada
友忠
CAT. 269

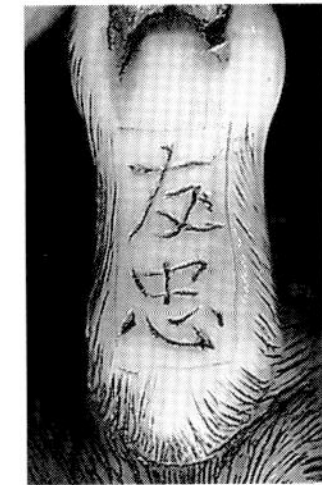

Tomotada
Tomotada
友忠
CAT. 272

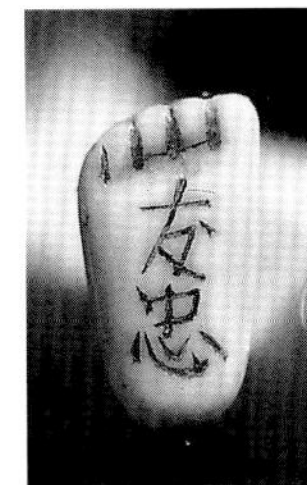

Tomotada
Tomotada
友忠
CAT. 583

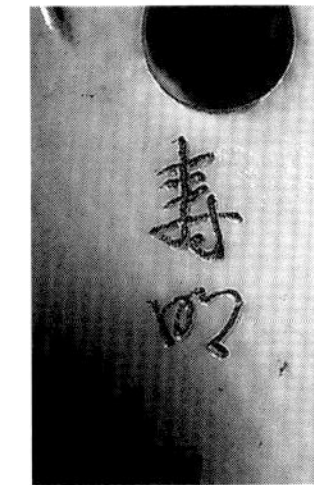

Toshiaki
Toshiaki
壽明
CAT. 434

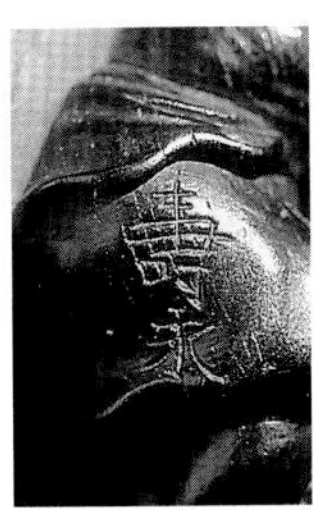

Toshinaga
Toshinaga
壽永
CAT. 30

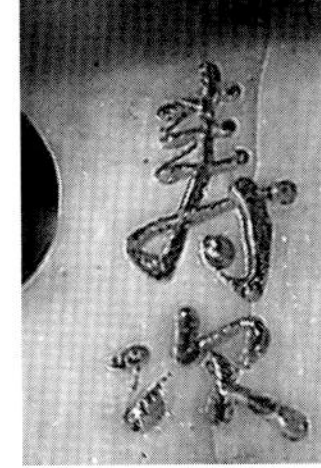

Toshitsugu
Toshitsugu
壽次
CAT. 758

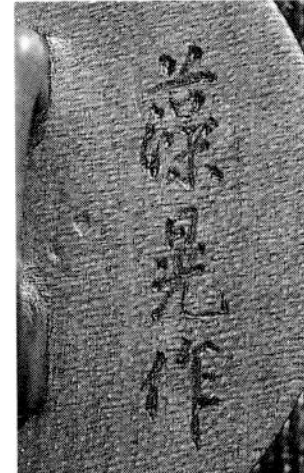

Sōkō saku
Toshiyama Sōkō
利山 藻晃
CAT. 593

Toyokazu
Toyokazu (Shūgasai)
豊一 (集雅齋)
CAT. 53

Toyokazu
Toyokazu (Shūgasai)
豊一 (集雅齋)
CAT. 235

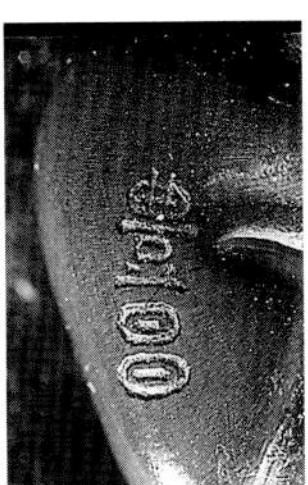

Toyomasa
Toyomasa II
豊昌 二代目
CAT. 270

Toyoyasu
Toyoyasu
豊容
CAT. 282

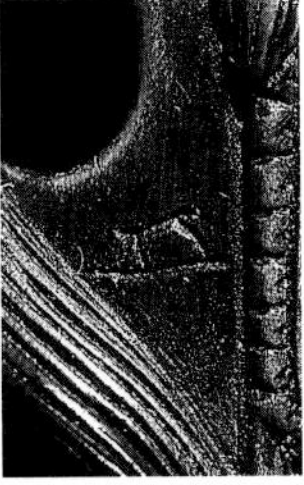

kakihan
Attributed to Tsuji
伝 辻
CAT. 44

Kyokusai
Tsukamoto Kyokusai
塚本 旭齋
CAT. 416

Kyokusai
Tsukamoto Kyokusai
塚本 旭齋
CAT. 480

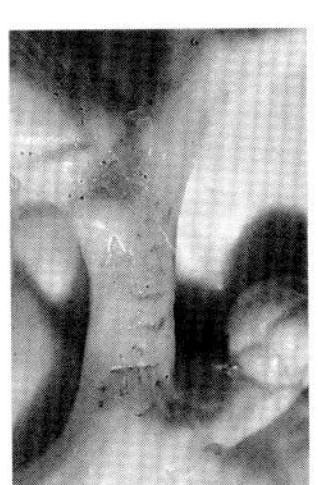

Kyokusai
Tsukamoto Kyokusai
塚本 旭齋
CAT. 482

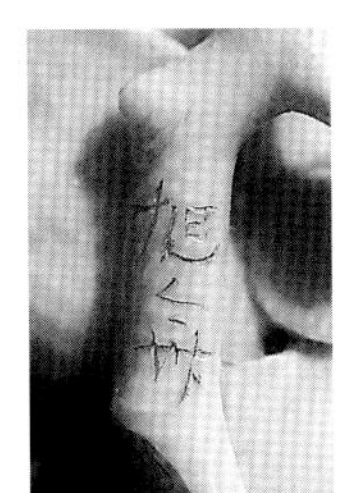

Kyokusai
Tsukamoto Kyokusai
塚本 旭齋
CAT. 483

Kyokusai
Tsukamoto Kyokusai
塚本 旭齋
CAT. 661

Kyokusai
Tsukamoto Kyokusai
塚本 旭齋
CAT. 745

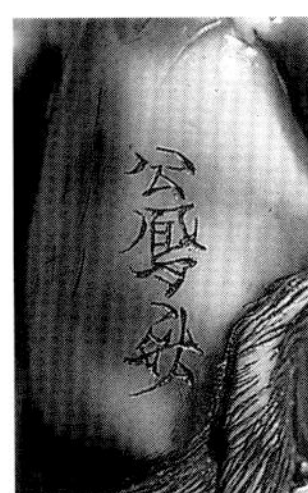

Kōhōsai
Ueda Kōhōsai
上田 公鳳齋
CAT. 141

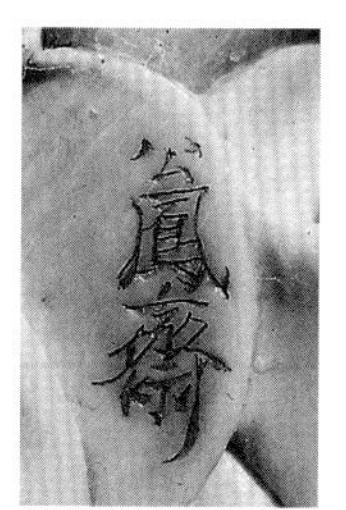

Kōhōsai
Ueda Kōhōsai
上田 公鳳齋
CAT. 540

Kōhōsai
Ueda Kōhōsai
上田 公鳳齋
CAT. 707

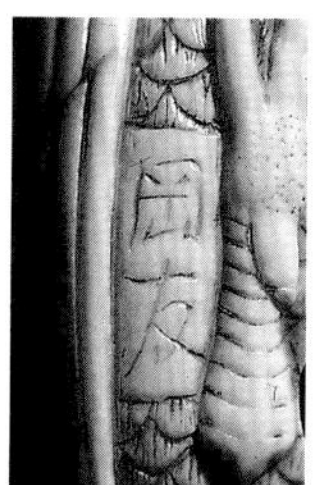

Okatomo
Yamaguchi Okatomo
山口 岡友
CAT. 332

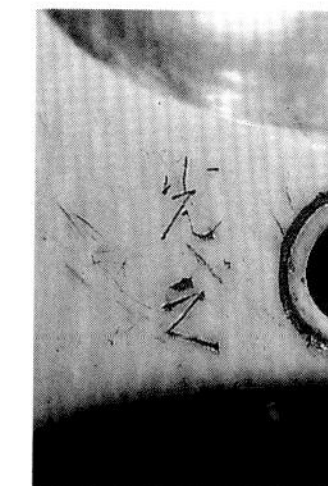

Mitsuyuki
Yamaji Mitsuyuki
山路 光之
CAT. 767

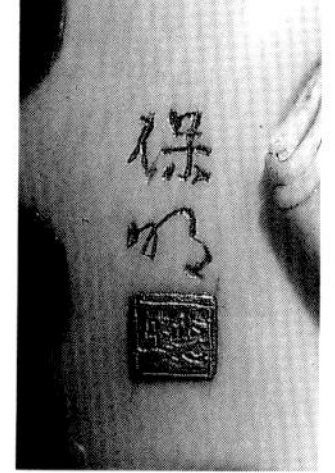

Yasuaki; seal form: *Kōdama*
Yasuaki
保明
CAT. 186

Yasumichi
Yasumichi
康道
CAT. 665

Yoshihide
Yoshihide
芳秀
CAT. 92

Yoshinaga
Yoshinaga
吉長
CAT. 340

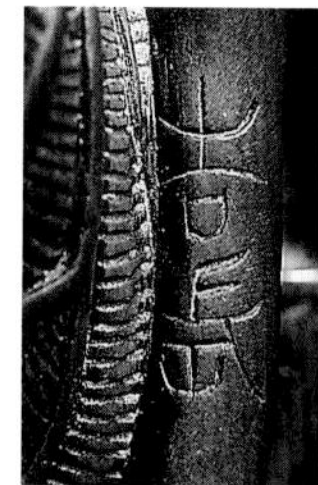

Yoshinaga
Yoshinaga
吉長
CAT. 406

Yoshinaga
Yoshinaga
吉長
CAT. 503

Yoshinobu koku
Yoshinobu
芳信
CAT. 250

Yūkoku
Yūkoku
幽谷
CAT. 630

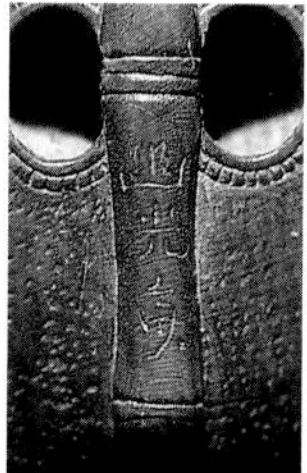

Yūkōsai
Yūkōsai
幽光齋
CAT. 90

Yūsō
Yūsō
遊藻
CAT. 765

Yūtoku
Yūtoku
有徳
CAT. 763

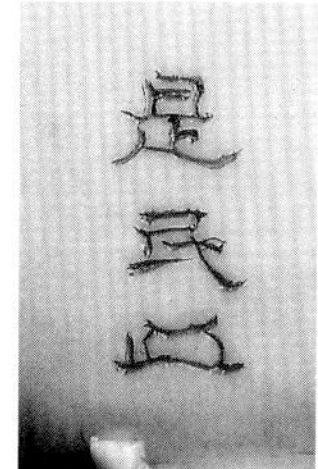

Zemin; kakihan
Zemin
是民
CAT. 599

Zōroku
Zōroku
蔵六
CAT. 399

Frog Figurine

China, Song dynasty, 10th–13th century
stone, turquoise inlays
$1^{5}/_{8}$ x $^{15}/_{16}$ x $^{11}/_{16}$ in. (4.1 x 2.4 x 1.8 cm)
AC1998.249.100

LITERATURE: Bushell, *An Exhibition of Netsuke*, fig. 362, p. 68; Bushell, "Questions & Answers" (1980b), p. 45

PROVENANCE: Natanael Wessen

Keris Handle

Indonesia, Java, 18th–19th century
stag antler
$2^{11}/_{16}$ x $1^{5}/_{16}$ x $1^{3}/_{16}$ in. (6.8 x 3.3 x 3 cm)
AC1998.249.268

APPENDIX B

Modified Netsuke

Found and retrofitted objects formed an important category of netsuke. The two works shown here, for example, were not by nature suited to function as netsuke: one is made of stone, which is rarely used in Japanese art; the other, of stag antler, is very heavy. During the eighteenth century, however, a fashion for exoticism made foreign-made objects an attractive source for adapted netsuke. The fetish-like Chinese frog, with its attractive patterns in the stone, would represent an aesthetic that was distinctly non-Japanese. A *keris* is a type of dagger, and this netsuke was modified from the dagger's handle, which was pierced to create the *himotōshi*. Covered with symmetrically arranged acanthus leaves, this handle was likewise outside Japanese experience.

APPENDIX C

Map of Japan

Modern Provinces (Ken)

(post 1889)

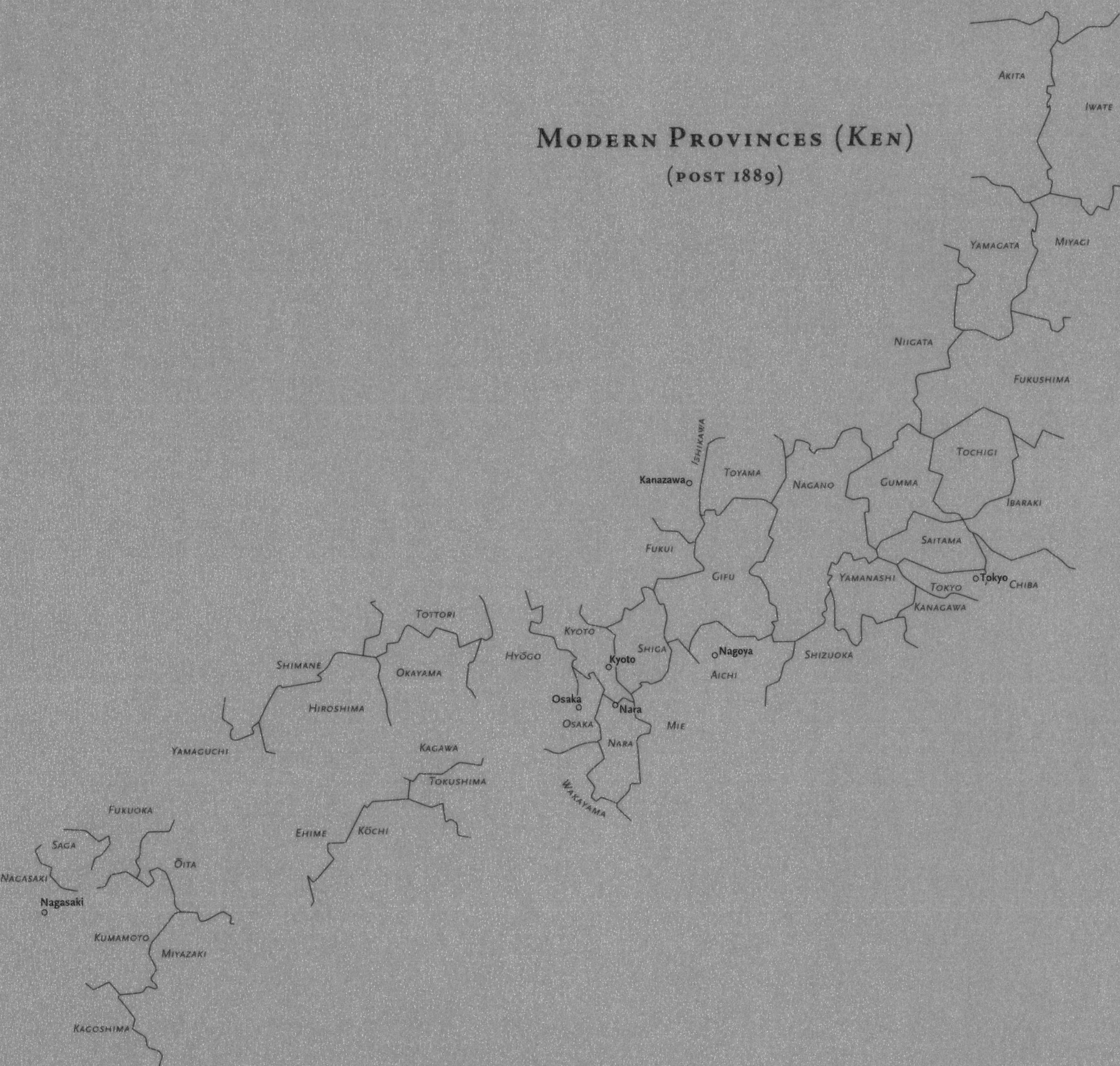

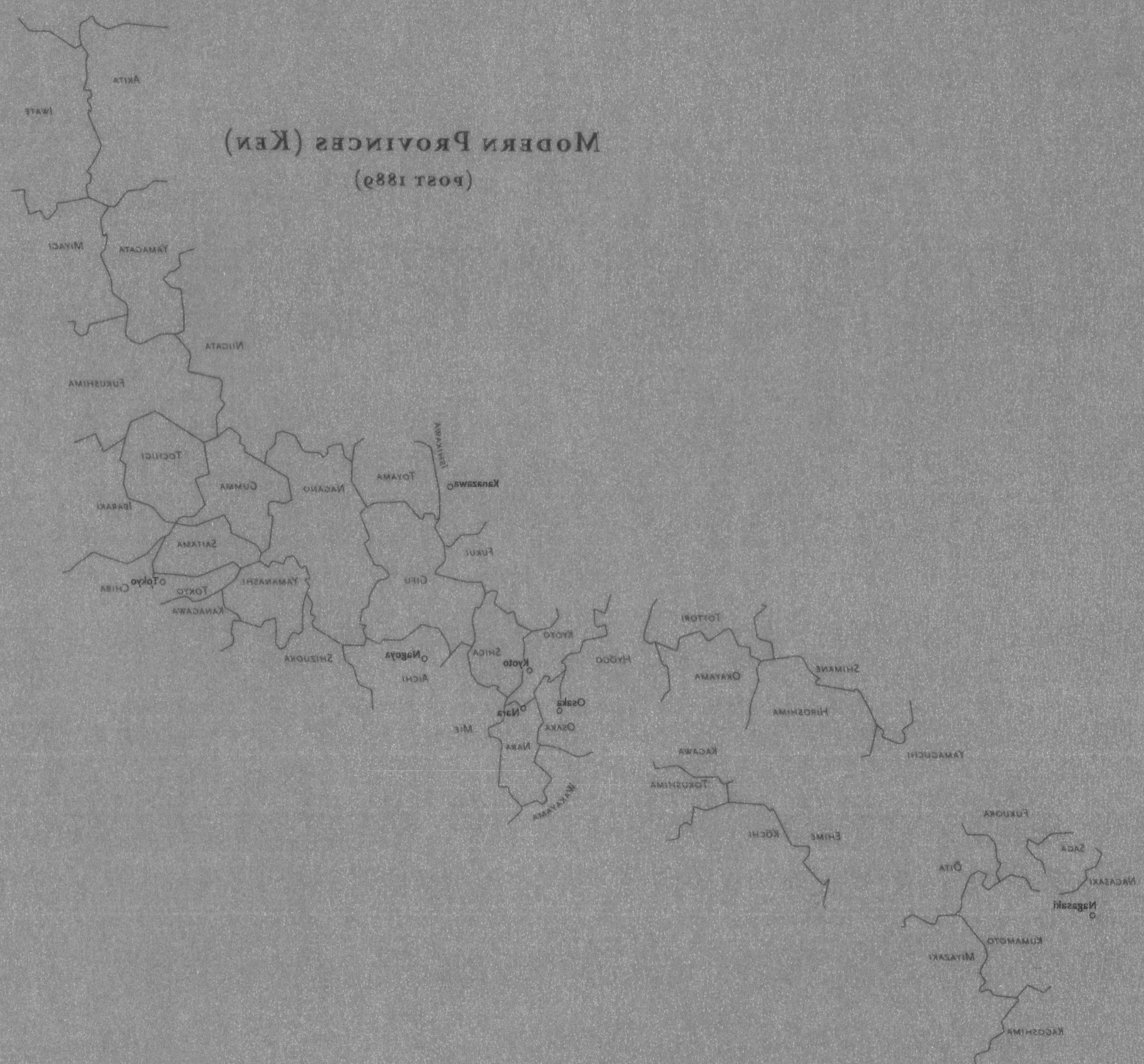

Ancient Provinces (Kuni)
(pre 1871)
Dejima: Japan's "Window to the World"
(ca. 1640s–1800s)
Nagasaki
Dejima
Nagasaki Bay
Hokkaidō
Honshū
Shikoku
Kyūshū
Sea of Japan
Pacific Ocean
Dewa
Mutsu
Sado
Echigo
Noto
Shimotsuke
Etchū
Shinano
Kōzuke
Kaga
Hida
Hitachi
Echizen
Musashi
Shimōsa
Edo
Mino
Kai
Mt. Fuji
Tango
Wakasa
Lake Biwa
Sagami
Kazusa
Hōki
Inaba
Tajima
Izumo
Tamba
Owari
Suruga
Mimasaka
Kyoto
Ōmi
Awa
Yamashiro
Mikawa
Harima
Settsu
Tōtōmi
Izu
Bingo
Bitchū
Bizen
Iga
Tōkaidō Road
Iwami
Kawachi
Tsushima
Aki
Awaji
Yamato
Nagato
Ise
Shima
Izumi
Itsukushima Shrine
Suō
Itsukushima
Sanuki
Iki
Awa
Hirado
Chikuzen
Buzen
Kii
Hizen
Iyo
Tosa
Chikugo
Bungo
Dejima
See Inset
Higo
Hyūga
Satsuma
North
Ōsumi
0
50 miles

Glossary

Netsuke examples that illustrate terms and concepts are in parentheses.

aji The patina an object acquires through generations of handling.

ama A female diver (CAT. 626).

anabori Deeply recessed "inside" carving (CAT. 374).

arashi A technique for roughening surfaces; used to simulate the appearance of textured materials such as leather and stone (CAT. 552).

bakemono A general term for monsters and goblins (CAT. 682).

baku A mythical beast of Chinese origin capable of eating anything, including nightmares (CAT. 213).

bijin A beautiful woman (CAT. 634).

bodhisattva (Skt) One who has attained the highest level of enlightenment before entering a Buddha state and is dedicated to guiding souls to paradise (CAT. 543).

bugaku A Shinto ritual dance performed for the imperial court; most popular during the Heian and Kamakura periods (CAT. 187).

daimyo A feudal lord who governed a large territory and oversaw an army of samurai to defend or expand it. In existence since the Muromachi period, the daimyo class was abolished in 1871. See also *samurai.*

Dejima (also Deshima) An artificial island off Nagasaki on which the Dutch were confined during Japan's self-imposed isolation (1639–1854).

dhoti (Hindi) A skirtlike garment worn by men in some parts of India (CAT. 87).

gagaku Japanese court music that accompanies *bugaku* or *kagura* performances (CAT. 188). See also *bugaku, kagura.*

haiku A traditional Japanese verse with a five-seven-five syllabic arrangement (CAT. 413).

himotōshi The openings or channels in a netsuke through which a cord is strung (CAT. 13, back view).

Hirado A Japanese fief renowned for the high quality of its porcelain (CAT. 175).

ibotarō A waxy secretion of the male larvae of an insect; used for polishing.

ibushi A staining technique in which the netsuke is fumigated with incense smoke.

ishime A carving technique in which the object's surface is covered with tiny gouges, giving it a rough, pitted appearance (CAT. 558).

ittōbori A carving technique that emphasizes use of a single knife (CAT. 120).

Iwami An ancient province, now part of Shimane prefecture; home to netsuke carvers who favored realistic renderings, often from boar tusk, of small reptiles and insects (CAT. 445).

kabuki A Japanese theatrical form combining drama, dance, and music, often elaborately staged (CAT. 514).

kagamibuta A type of netsuke, usually round and composed of a lid or disk, typically metal, and a bowl of ivory or wood (CAT. 538).

kagura Sacred dances performed to propitiate Shinto deities (CAT. 569).

kakihan A personal monogram derived from Japanese characters; inscribed by artists on works instead of or in addition to a signature.

kami Shinto deities; manifestations of the numinous force that resides in all of nature. Kami are honored at shrines with propitiatory offerings, dances, and rituals.

Kamigata An area comprising Kyoto, Nara, and Osaka that is a center for doll making, icon carving, and textile production.

kappa A creature from Japanese mythology that lurked in streams and ponds (CAT. 248).

katabori The most popular netsuke form; these figural netsuke are carved in the round.

kebori A hairline carving technique (CAT. 475).

kirin A mythical beast of Chinese origin with the body of a deer, the hooves of a horse, the tail of an ox, and the horn of a unicorn (CAT. 194).

kuchinashi A reddish yellow dye, also known as gamboge, made from the berries of the gardenia plant (CAT. 404).

kyōgen A form of comic theater, often performed with masks, that takes place between the acts of a noh play (CAT. 572).

makie A decorative lacquer technique in which gold, silver, or metallic powders are sprinkled on a wet lacquer ground (CAT. 184).

manjū A type of netsuke, either one or two pieces, of bunlike shape similar to the rice cake of the same name; if two pieces, they are fitted together with the cord passing through the holes in one half and strung through a ring inside (CAT. 476).

manzai A performance by two actors engaged in comic dialogue, usually performed at New Year's; also, the performers themselves (CAT. 586).

Maruyama School The atelier of Kyoto painter Maruyama Ōkyo (1733–1795); important for its influence on anatomical accuracy, naturalistic pose, and surface treatment in painting, prints, and netsuke.

Negoro A technique in which red lacquer is thinly applied over black lacquer, with layers rubbed away to expose the undercoat (CAT. 447).

netsukeshi A term meaning "netsuke carver" or "netsuke carvers."

nihonga A modern Japanese painting style combining Western concepts of space, light, and color with traditional Japanese brush techniques and materials.

nikawa A protein glue used to bind pigments; soft and easily abraded (CAT. 260).

noh An aristocratic form of traditional theatrical performance, usually involving masked actors (CAT. 574).

obi The sash or belt of a kimono.

obihasami A type of elongated netsuke, with hooked ends that grasp the upper and lower edges of the kimono sash (CAT. 328).

ojime A sliding bead through which the hanging cords pass; placed between the netsuke and the inrō, it allows the wearer to keep the inrō closed (CAT. 426).

okimono Decorative objects that function as sculpture, intended for placement in the *tokonoma* or on cabinet shelves (CAT. 91). See also *tokonoma*.

polychrome A term meaning "painted in many colors" (CAT. 17).

rakan (Skt: *arhat*) The most worthy five hundred disciples of the Buddha who received enlightenment during the Buddha's sermon at Vulture Peak (CAT. 83).

Raku ware A low-fired ceramic ware produced for the past fifteen generations by the Raku family in Kyoto (CAT. 707).

Rimpa School Artists working in various media, based on the styles of Hon'ami Kōetsu (1558–1637), Tawaraya Sōtatsu (?–1643?), and Ogata Kōrin (1658–1716) (CAT. 181).

rōnin A samurai who no longer has a master to serve (CAT. 668). See also *samurai*.

ryūsa A variation of a *manjū* netsuke, it is partially or entirely hollowed out, with the design executed by perforation; originated by the netsuke carver Ryūsa (CAT. 189). See also *manjū*.

sabiji A lacquer technique used to imitate the surface of old metal (CAT. 710).

sagemono A generic term for containers such as inrō and tobacco pouches that were suspended from the kimono sash by braided silk cords.

saku A word meaning "made by," often included with artist signatures.

samurai A term designating the class of warrior elite. See also *daimyo*, *rōnin*.

sashi A type of elongated netsuke, worn inserted between the sash and the kimono (CAT. 262).

Seiōbo (Ch: Xiwangmu; Queen Mother of the West) A central figure in the Daoist pantheon and the best-known female immortal (CAT. 57). The peach tree in her garden, located in the Western Paradise, sprouted fruit that granted immortality when eaten.

sennin A Daoist immortal (CAT. 79).

shamisen (also *samisen*) A Japanese three-stringed musical instrument (CAT. 601).

shibayama A technique of inlaying an object's surface with materials and semiprecious stones; perfected by Shibayama I (Ōnogi Senzō, fl. 1772–1780) (CAT. 478).

Shijō School The atelier of painter Goshun (1752–1811), a colleague of Maruyama Ōkyo, who like Ōkyo translated Western aesthetic principles, along with Japanese poetic lyricism, into his paintings. The Maruyama-Shijō School style influenced all Japanese painting by the 1850s.

shishi A Chinese lion; in Japanese mythology, believed to guard against evil (CAT. 195).

shokuin A limbless snakelike creature of Chinese legend (CAT. 137).

shōjō A mythical water spirit that loves sake (CAT. 260).

shosangin Silver nitrate; a chemical used to stain netsuke. Colors range from brown to purple to black (CAT. 430).

Shreger pattern An intersecting system of arches, unique to elephant ivory, that is visible in cross sections of the tusk (CAT. 702).

Shuihu zhuan (Ch; J: *Suikoden*; Tales of the water margin) Chinese novel; used as source material by netsuke artists (CAT. 509).

Sōken kishō (Strange and wonderful sword fittings, 1781) A book by Inaba Tsūryū, published in Osaka; devoted primarily to Japanese sword fittings, it also mentions fifty-seven netsuke artists.

Sō School A school founded by Miyazaki Josō (1855–1910); its most famous students were Sōko (Morita Kisaburō, 1879–1943) and Ōuchi Gyokusō (1879–1944), noted for their meticulous and realistic carving.

sumi Ink made of soot from burned wood or oil mixed with a binder and dried into a stick; a common stain for netsuke.

sutra A sacred Buddhist text (CAT. 91).

tanuki A viverrid, or small carnivorous mammal, that plays an important role in Japanese folklore; sometimes called a raccoon-dog (CAT. 237).

tensho An archaic writing style (CAT. 384).

tō A word meaning "carved by," often included with artist signatures.

Toba-e A style of satirical drawing traditionally attributed to Toba Sōjō (1053–1140) and seen in the *Chōjū giga* (Frolicking animal scrolls) (CAT. 641).

Tōkaidō Highway between Osaka, Kyoto, and Edo; one of five highways that enabled provincial netsuke carvers to have a steady customer base in urban areas.

tokonoma The alcove of a traditional Japanese house or tea house in which an art object or flowers are displayed.

Tokugawa regime Hereditary lineage of military leaders who ruled Japan from Edo during the years 1615 to 1868; also known as the Edo period.

tonkotsu A suspended container for carrying tobacco (CAT. 844).

tonoko A very fine polishing powder with an orange yellow color.

tsuge Boxwood; a slow-growing wood extolled by netsuke carvers for its fine grain and relative hardness, which make it well-suited for detail carving (CAT. 681).

tsuchiningyō Clay effigy dolls made in molds and sold at shrines and temples; when reproduced as netsuke, the mold seam is often evident (CAT. 741).

tsuishu A lacquer technique that originated in China and utilized a wood form under many layers of carved black, yellow, and vermilion lacquer (CAT. 729).

tsunoko A polishing powder made of burnt stag antler.

tsuzumi A double-ended drum typically used in noh drama (CAT. 7). See also *noh*.

ukibori A technique for raising surfaces in wood without relief carving; also called the "raised signature" technique (CAT. 407).

ukiyo-e Edo- and Meiji-period woodblock prints with subjects from the entertainment quarter or "floating world."

umimatsu A type of coral, usually black; also called "sea pine" (CAT. 30).

umoregi A type of partially fossilized wood (CAT. 455).

urushi Filtered raw lacquer made from sap from the *Rhus verniciflua* tree; used for binding, coating, and decorating objects that have a wood or hemp core (CAT. 725).

yashabushi (also *yashadama*, *yasha*) A dye extracted from the cones of a species of alder tree, and a common stain for ivory netsuke (CAT. 673).

yatate A portable container for writing implements and ink (CAT. 534).

Zen A form of Buddhism imported to Japan in the 1100s by Chinese Ch'an monks.

zōge Literally "elephant tusk." Only elephant tusk is considered true ivory; boar tusk, narwhal tusk, and teeth from large mammals are ivory-like materials.

Selected Bibliography

Addiss, Stephen, ed. *Japanese Ghosts and Demons: Art of the Supernatural*. New York: George Braziller, Inc., 1985.

Arakawa Hirokazu. *The Gō Collection of Netsuke, Tokyo National Museum*. Tokyo and New York: Kodansha International Ltd., 1983.

Art Museum Image Consortium (amico). Online collection of The amico Library; www.amico.org.

Atchley, Virginia G. "Kaigyokusai: An Appreciation." *Netsuke Kenkyūkai Study Journal* 12, no. 4 (1992), pp. 10–21.

———. "The Pavilion for Japanese Art in Los Angeles." *Netsuke Kenkyūkai Study Journal* 8, no. 4 (1988), pp. 18–25.

———. "The Tiger in Netsuke." *Journal of the International Netsuke Collectors Society* 1, no. 4 (1974), pp. 6–9.

Baer, N. S., and L. J. Majewski. *Ivory and Related Materials: An Annotated Bibliography*. New York: Institute of Fine Arts, 1971.

Baird, Merrily. *Symbols of Japan: Thematic Motifs in Art and Design*. New York: Rizzoli International Publications, Inc., 2001.

Barker, Richard, and Lawrence Smith. *Netsuke: The Miniature Sculpture of Japan*. London: British Museum, 1976.

Barnet, Peter, ed. *Images in Ivory: Precious Objects of the Gothic Age*. Detroit, Mich.: Detroit Institute of Arts, 1997.

Baten, Lea. *Japanese Dolls: The Image and the Motif*. Tokyo: Shufunotomo Co., Ltd., 1986.

Beckett, Wendy. *Sister Wendy's American Collection*. Edited by Toby Eady Associates. New York: HarperCollins Publishers, 2000.

Behrens, Walter Lionel. *Netsuke*. Vol. 1 of *W. L. Behrens Collection*, edited by Henri L. Joly. 1912. Reprint, New York: Paragon Book Reprint Corp., 1966.

Brinkley, F. (Frank). *Japan: Its History, Arts, and Literature*. Vol. 7. London: J. B. Millet Co., 1902.

British Museum. *Treasured Miniatures: Contemporary Netsuke*. Exh. cat. London: British Museum, 1994.

Bushell, Raymond. "Ceramic Netsuke." *Arts of Asia* 6, no. 2 (1976), pp. 25–31.

———. *Collectors' Netsuke*. New York: Walker/Weatherhill, 1971.

———. *An Exhibition of Netsuke from the Raymond Bushell Collection*. Tokyo: Mikimoto World Jewelers, 1979.

———. *The Inrō Handbook: Studies of Netsuke, Inrō, and Lacquer*. New York: Weatherhill, 1979.

———. *An Introduction to Netsuke*. Rutland, Vt.: Charles E. Tuttle Co., 1971.

———. *Masatoshi: Present-Day Master Netsuke Carver in the Tokugawa Tradition*. Tokyo: Mikimoto Pearl Co., 1982.

———. *Netsuke Familiar and Unfamiliar: New Principles for Collecting*. New York: Weatherhill, 1975.

———. *Netsuke Masks*. San Francisco: Kodansha International, Ltd., 1985.

———. "Netsuke: Miniature Sculptures." *PHP* (April 1976), pp. 34–41.

———. "Questions and Answers." *International Netsuke Society Journal* 16, no. 3 (1996), pp. 48–50.

———. "Questions and Answers." *Journal of the International Netsuke Collectors Society* 3, no. 4 (1976a), pp. 44–45, 48–51; 4, no. 1 (1976b), pp. 47–52; 4, no. 2 (1976c), pp. 46–52; 5, no. 3 (1977), pp. 42–48; 5, no. 4 (1978a), pp. 41–48; 6, no. 2 (1978b), pp. 6–7, 42–46; 6, no. 3 (1978c), pp. 12–18; 6, no. 10 (1978d), pp. 38–44; 8, no. 2 (1980a), pp. 38–44; 8, no. 3 (1980b), pp. 44–50; 8, no. 4 (1981), pp. 40–47; 3, no. 11 (1983) pp. 48–49.

———. "Questions and Answers." *Netsuke Kenkyūkai Study Journal* 8, no. 4 (1988), pp. 5–10; 11, no. 3 (1991), pp. 9–13; 13, no. 4 (1993), pp. 6–10.

———. "Shōko: An Untypical Netsuke Carver." *Arts of Asia* 13, no. 2 (1983), pp. 55–61.

———. "To Donate or Not to Donate." *Arts of Asia* 25, no. 1 (Jan.–Feb. 1995), pp. 127–39.

———. "Travels by Netsuke." *Arts of Asia* 14, no. 2 (1984), pp. 104–9.

———. *The Wonderful World of Netsuke*. Rutland, Vt.: Charles E. Tuttle Co., 1964.

Cammann, Schuyler Van Rensselaer. *Substance and Symbol in Chinese Toggles: Chinese Belt Toggles from the C. F. Bieber Collection*. Philadelphia: University of Pennsylvania Press, 1962.

Chappell, Sharen Thane. "Stylistic Developments in the Tokyo (Edo) School." *Journal of the International Netsuke Collectors Society* 11, no. 2 (1983), pp. 22–26.

Chinese Ivories from the Shang to the Qing. Exh. cat. London: Sotheby Publications, 1984.

Cholmondeley, L. B. "Some Information about Japanese Netsuke." *The Connoisseur* 39, no. 155 (July 1914), pp. 181–83.

Clunas, Craig. *Pictures and Visuality in Early Modern China*. Princeton: Princeton University Press, 1998.

Coaldrake, William H. *Architecture and Authority in Japan*. Nissan Institute/Routledge Japanese Studies Series. New York and London: Routledge, 1996.

Coullery, Marie-Thérèse, and Martin S. Newstead. *The Baur Collection*. Geneva, 1977.

Craft, Meg. "Decorative Arts." In *Caring for Your Collections*. Edited by Arthur W. Schultz. National Institute for the Conservation of Cultural Property, Harry N. Abrams, Inc., 1992.

Davey, Neil K. *Netsuke: A Comprehensive Study Based on the M. T. Hindson Collection*. Rev. ed. London: Philip Wilson Publishers Ltd., 1982.

Dee, Robert. "Toyomasa: Robert Dee's Visit to Tamba." *Journal of the International Netsuke Collectors Society* 11, no. 4 (1984), pp. 30–32.

Dillon, Ruth. "Philadelphians Display Netsuke." *Ikebana International* 15 (1964), pp. 16–19.

Dower, John W. *The Elements of Japanese Design: A Handbook of Family Crests, Heraldry and Symbolism*. New York: Weatherhill, 2000.

Earle, Joe. *Netsuke: Fantasy and Reality in Japanese Miniature Sculpture*. Boston: Museum of Fine Arts, Boston, 2001.

———. *The Robert S. Huthart Collection of Iwami Netsuke*. Hong Kong, 2000.

Edwards, Lisa A., and Margie M. Krebs. *Netsuke: The Collection of the Peabody Museum of Salem*. Salem, Mass.: Peabody Museum of Salem, 1980.

Espinosa, Edgard O'Neil, and Mary-Jacque Mann. *Identification Guide for Ivory and Ivory Substitutes*. 2d ed. Baltimore, Md.: World Wildlife Fund, 1992.

Falkove, Albert. "The Unique, the Extraordinary, and the Unusual." *Journal of the International Netsuke Collectors Society* 11, no. 3 (1983), pp. 26–27.

Fister, Patricia. "Tengu, the Mountain Goblin." In *Japanese Ghosts and Demons: Art of the Supernatural*. Edited by Stephen Addiss. New York: George Braziller, Inc., 1985.

Gerhart, Karen M. *The Eyes of Power: Art and Early Tokugawa Authority*. Honolulu: University of Hawaii Press, 1999.

Hall, John Whitney, ed. *Early Modern Japan*. Vol. 4 of *The Cambridge History of Japan*, edited by John Whitney Hall et al. New York: Cambridge University Press, 1991.

Harris, Victor. *Netsuke: The Hull Grundy Collection*. London: British Museum, 1987.

Hata Akira. "Naitō Toyomasa: A Carver Patronized by the Sasayama Clan." *Journal of the International Netsuke Collectors Society* 11, no. 4 (1984), pp. 32–39.

Hata Mitsuru. "Naitō Toyomasa: Han Artist of the Sasayama Domain." In *Netsuke no shizuku*. Tokyo: Nihon Netsuke Kenkyūkai, 2000.

Hickman, Money L., and Peter Fetchko. *Japan Day by Day: An Exhibition in Honor of Edward S. Morse*. Salem, Mass.: Peabody Museum of Salem, 1977.

Hill, Parry, and Johnny Johnson. "The Raymond Bushell Netsuke Exhibition." *Journal of the International Netsuke Collectors Society* 7, no. 3 (1979), pp. 28–36.

Hillier, Mary. "*Sessai Unkin zu fu* (Book of designs) by Sessai Unkin: A Famous Nineteenth-Century Netsuke Carver and His Work." *Oriental Art* 21, no. 3 (1975), pp. 252–58.

Hurtig, Bernard. "Collecting Legends." *Journal of the International Netsuke Collectors Society* 1, no. 1 (1973), pp. 14–18.

———. "Contemporary Netsuke." *Journal of the International Netsuke Collectors Society* 4, no. 1 (1976), pp. 18–28, 37–42.

———. "Kaigyokusai Masatsugu." *Journal of the International Netsuke Collectors Society* 1, no. 4 (1974), pp. 17–22.

———. "Masanao: The Kyoto Magician." *Journal of the International Netsuke Collectors Society* 11, no. 2 (1983), pp. 29–43.

———. *Masterpieces of Netsuke Art: One Thousand Favorites of Leading Collectors*. New York: Weatherhill, 1973.

———. *The Netsuke Hall of Fame's Record Breakers*. Honolulu: Bernard Hurtig's Orientwest, 1983.

———. "Shibata Zeshin." *Journal of the International Netsuke Collectors Society* 5, no. 1 (1977), pp. 24–30.

———. "The Tomotada Story." *Journal of the International Netsuke Collectors Society* 2, no. 2 (1974), pp. 19–25.

Joly, Henri L. *Legend in Japanese Art: A Description of Historical Episodes, Legendary Characters, Folk-lore Myths, Religious Symbolism, Illustrated in the Arts of Old Japan*. London: J. Lane, 1908.

Joly, Henri L., and Kumasaku Tomita. *Japanese Art and Handicraft: An Illustrated Record of the Loan Exhibition Held in Aid of the British Red Cross in October–November, 1915.* London: Yamanaka & Co., 1916.

Katsuhide Akabane. "Mitsuhiro and *Takarabukuro*." In Mitsuhiro, *Takarabukuro: A Netsuke Artist Notebook*, adapted by Charles Temple, translated by Misao Mikoshiba. Chicago: Art Media Resources, Ltd., 2001.

Kiej'e, Nikolas. *Japanese Grotesqueries.* Rutland, Vt.: Charles E. Tuttle Co., 1973.

Kinsey, Miriam. *Contemporary Netsuke.* Rutland, Vt.: Charles E. Tuttle Co., 1977.

———. *Living Masters of Netsuke.* Tokyo and New York: Kodansha International Ltd., 1985.

Kinsey, Robert, and Miriam Kinsey. *Contemporary Netsuke: Miniature Sculpture from Japan and Beyond.* Santa Ana, Calif.: The Bowers Museum of Cultural Art, 1997.

Kornicki, Peter. *The Book in Japan.* Honolulu: University of Hawaii Press, 2001.

Kvinnliga kimono och manilga knappar (Female kimono and male toggles). Exh. cat. Stockholm: Östasiatiska Museet, 1999.

Lazarnick, George. *Netsuke and Inro Artists, and How to Read Their Signatures.* 2 vols. Honolulu: Reed Publishers, 1981.

London Netsuke Committee. *Contrasting Styles: A Loan Exhibition of Netsuke and Kizeruzutsu from Private English Collections.* Exh. cat. London: Robert G. Sawers Publishing, 1980.

Masatoshi. *The Art of Netsuke Carving.* As told to Raymond Bushell. Tokyo and New York: Kodansha International Ltd., 1981.

Matienzo, L. J., and C. E. Snow. "The Chemical Effects of Hydrochloric Acid and Organic Solvents on the Surface of Ivory." *Studies in Conservation* 31 (1986), pp. 133–39.

Meinertzhagen, Frederick. *The Art of the Netsuke Carver.* London: Routledge and Kegan Paul, 1956.

———. *The Meinertzhagen Card Index on Netsuke in the Archives of the British Museum*, Parts A and B. Edited by George Lazarnick. New York: Alan R. Liss, Inc., 1986.

Michener, James A., ed. *The Hokusai Sketchbooks.* Tokyo: Charles E. Tuttle Co., 1958.

Mikoshiba, Misao, and Raymond Bushell. "Netsuke and the *Sōken kishō*." *Arts of Asia, Hong Kong* 10, no. 6 (1980), pp. 103–17.

Mitsuhiro. *Takarabukuro: A Netsuke Artist Notebook.* Adapted by Charles Temple. Translated by Misao Mikoshiba. Chicago: Art Media Resources, Ltd., 2001.

Morse, Peter. "Tokuno's Description of Japanese Printmaking." In *Essays on Japanese Art Presented to Jack Hillier.* Edited by Matthi Forrer. Somerset, England: Robert G. Sawers Publishing, 1982.

Moss, Paul. *Zodiac Beasts and Distant Cousins: Japanese Netsuke for Connoisseurs.* London: Sydney L. Moss Ltd., 1993.

Nishiyama Matsunosuke. *Edo Culture: Daily Life and Diversions in Urban Japan, 1600–1868.* Honolulu: University of Hawaii Press, 1997.

O'Brien, Mary Louise. *Netsuke: A Guide for Collectors.* Rutland, Vt.: Charles E. Tuttle Co., 1981.

Okada, Barbra Teri. *Netsuke: Masterpieces from the Metropolitan Museum of Art.* New York: Harry N. Abrams, Inc., 1982.

Okada, Barbra Teri, and Mary Gardner Neill. *Real and Imaginary Beings: The Netsuke Collection of Joseph and Edith Kurstin.* New Haven: Yale University Art Gallery, 1980.

Phillips, Phoebe, ed. *The Collectors' Encyclopedia of Antiques.* New York: Crown Publishers, Inc., 1973.

Rasmussen, Jens Salen. "Discussion of the Iwami School." *Journal of the International Netsuke Collectors Society* 2, no. 1 (1974), pp. 20–26.

Ritchie, Carson I. A. *Bone and Horn Carving.* London: A. S. Barnes and Co., Inc., 1975.

———. *Ivory Carving.* London: Arthur Barker Ltd., 1969.

———. *Modern Ivory Carving.* London: A. S. Barnes and Co., Inc., 1972.

Ross, Doran H., ed. *Elephant: The Animal and Its Ivory in African Culture.* Los Angeles: Fowler Museum of Cultural History, University of California, Los Angeles, 1992.

Sandfield, Norman L. *The Ultimate Netsuke Bibliography: An Annotated Guide to Miniature Japanese Carvings.* Chicago: Art Media Resources, Ltd., 1999.

Screech, Timon. *Sex and the Floating World: Erotic Images in Japan, 1700–1820.* Honolulu: University of Hawaii Press, 1999.

———. *The Shogun's Painted Culture: Fear and Creativity in the Japanese States, 1760–1829.* Envisioning Asia. London: Reaktion Books, 2000.

———. *The Western Scientific Gaze and Popular Imagery in Later Edo Japan: The Lens within the Heart.* Cambridge, England: Cambridge University Press, 1996.

Shimatani Yoichi. "Red Robe Kokusai." Edited and translated by Nori Watanabe. *International Netsuke Society Journal* 19, no. 2 (summer 1999).

Snow, Carol E., and Terry Drayman Weisser. "The Examination and Treatment of Ivory and Related Materials." *Adhesives and Consolidants* (1984), pp. 141–45.

Stratos, Milton. The Netsuke Carvings of Jobun." *International Netsuke Society Journal* 22, no. 1 (spring 2002), pp. 14–27.

Tadashi Naito. "Genmatsu Minsho no kometsuke (I)." *Nihon bijutsu kogei* 173 (March 1953).

Tardy. *Les ivories: Évolution décorative du 1er siècle a nos jours*. 2 vols. Paris, 1977.

Trower, Harry Seymour. *Catalogue of the H. Seymour Trower Collection of Japanese Art*. Edited by Henri L. Joly. 1913. Reprint, Hollywood, Florida: Kurstin-Schneider, 1975.

Ueda Reikichi. *The Netsuke Handbook of Ueda Reikichi*. Adapted from the Japanese by Raymond Bushell. Rutland, Vt.: Charles E. Tuttle Co., 1961.

Vaparis, Contantine N. "Caveat Viator: Advice to Travelers in the Edo Period." *Monumenta Nipponica* 44, no. 4 (winter 1999).

Watanabe Masanori. "Thoughts on Early Netsuke in Relation to *Kokon meiga mitate zumo*." *International Netsuke Society Journal* 18, no. 4 (winter 1998).

Welch, Matthew, and Sharen Thane Chappell. *Netsuke: The Japanese Art of Miniature Carving*. Minneapolis: Minneapolis Institute of Arts; Chicago: Paragon Press, 1999.

Williams, C.A.S. *Chinese Symbolism and Art Motifs*. Edison, New Jersey: Castle Books, 1974.

Woodhouse, Charles Platten. *Ivories: A History and Guide*. London: David & Charles, 1976.

Wrangham, E. A. *The Index of Inrō Artists*. Edited by Joe Earle. Alnwick, England: Harehope Publications, 1995.

Index

Note: Italic page numbers refer to illustrations.